C. P. WELLS
Chairman, Department of Mathematics
Michigan State University
ADVISORY EDITOR TO DODD, MEAD & COMPANY

INTRODUCTORY MATHEMATICS

INTRODUCTORY MATHEMATICS

Seymour Hayden

Clark University

DODD, MEAD & COMPANY

New York   Toronto   1967

To Charles T. Bumer
In Memoriam

Tables A-1 and A-2 are reprinted from *Fundamentals of Mathematics* by Moses Richardson by permission of The Macmillan Company. © Moses Richardson 1958.

Library of Congress Catalog Card Number: 67-16220
Printed in the United States of America

editor's introduction

The trend in writing and publishing mathematics textbooks continues unabated at all levels. Likewise the trend toward excellence in textbooks continues although by no means uniformly. The present book on Introductory Mathematics in my opinion is an example of one of those which has achieved a mark of excellence. The author firmly believes that one can write with mathematical rigor and yet in a manner which beginning college students or even advanced high school students can understand and appreciate. He has succeeded admirably in this goal.

There are and always will be those who will argue the logical development of the mathematics in a book of this kind. It is here that the author must take his stand and trace the development and structure of the book on the maturity of the students he has in mind as well as on his own experience as a teacher. This book will be for many students their first introduction to rigorous mathematics and to the nature of a mathematical proof. It will be a welcome replacement for the more traditional books in college algebra and for other introductory texts in mathematics. It will play an important role in mathematics education programs for both elementary and secondary school teachers.

The book begins with the basic notions of sets and operations on sets. It continues with the development of the real numbers, their algebraic properties and some computational aspects, followed by a discussion of ordering of real numbers, inequalities, and absolute values. A strong point of this part of the book is the treatment of mathematical induction. The last part of the book takes up some of the more traditional topics of introductory mathematics. In this the author considers polynomial, exponential, logarithmic, and trigonometric functions as well as a brief treatment of analytic geometry.

C. P. WELLS

preface

At the present time, curricula throughout the country are being revised. It is my experience that more and more departments on the junior and senior high school level are being asked to convert to a "modern" curriculum. Indeed, the term "modern mathematics" is now familiar to most teachers, students, and parents.

Why does one want to change a curriculum?

Of course one reason is that one would like to have a mathematical curriculum reflect the scientific and cultural needs of the present and hopefully the foreseeable future era.

But a second reason is to make available, where possible and relevant, the understanding which has been obtained through the achievements of the mathematical community throughout the history of mathematics. In this connection it may happen that recent innovations can make advanced mathematics of a past era accessible to the present elementary curriculum. For it is well known, though often neglected, that simplicity and depth need not be incompatible.

Certainly in the past we have seen the mathematical research of one era find its way into the elementary curriculum of another. For example, the coordinate system in analytic geometry introduced by Descartes in the seventeenth century is certainly familiar and has been for some time to secondary school students. Indeed, the secondary school student is also aware of complex numbers and rational and irrational numbers. The problem in recent times has been that mathematical (and other) research, for example in the last one hundred years, has made such enormous strides that it has been difficult to organize and assimilate the appropriate changes in the elementary curriculum reflecting the deeper insights achieved.

Professor Edward G. Begle and his School Mathematics Study Group (SMSG) have been among the leaders in helping to overcome these difficulties. Based on intensive discussions, members of the School Mathematics Study Group have written textbooks designed to stimulate further discussion and writing by other mathematicians and educators. These textbooks have in fact been used in many schools.

But contrary to the spirit of the SMSG texts, many authors and teachers have concentrated on the new concepts and vocabulary of modern mathematics. They have lost sight of its relation to the mathematical problems and ideas it helps to expose, and to the consequent power afforded the student in both understanding and problem-solving. This has led to valid criticism of the teaching of the "new mathematics," and to lamenting the inadequate preparation of teachers.

It is my hope that this book will prove useful in improving the preparation of mathematics teachers. As it concerns topics drawn from the precalculus curriculum, it will also serve college students who wish another chance to obtain the background for further study in mathematics, since no specific prerequisites are needed. In fact it is designed to provide a *working* background, and at least half of the text is devoted to illustrative examples and exercises. Indeed a student familiar with the material of this text will have more than enough background to begin the study of calculus. I believe that this book will serve the interests of general education courses. For in exposing the topics of this text, some of the major ideas of mathematics have been brought in, and historical comments have been added to reveal the changing and living nature of our subject. Finally I have found that mathematics majors and even graduate students have shown an interest in reading this text.

In order to provide a view of the elementary curriculum within a single volume, it was necessary to omit a number of topics. Nevertheless a glance at the table of contents will indicate that considerable ground is covered. Probability and statistical inference are not covered. A discussion of Euclidean geometry in the plane is included, but not a complete axiomatic treatment. A serious omission, if this book were used for a student's first exposure to mathematics, is the applications of mathematics to other disciplines. The one exception is the inclusion of elementary "maximum-minimum" type problems so as to have an example of at least one application. It goes without saying that applications of mathematics to other disciplines are extremely relevant to the elementary curriculum. Vector methods and matrices are not included, nor is a discussion of logic.

This book is not written for the student or teacher who regards a method of teaching as successful if it provides a specific rule for each particular class of problems arising in a given course. This approach serves neither the spirit nor the substance of mathematics. Nor does this approach contribute to the educational process in which a student increases his power to work effectively on his own. On the contrary, such an approach fosters an ever-increasing resistance within the student to his development of a method of study which by its nature is self-generating in its multiplication of technical and imaginative resources. It leads to the situation between student and professor, or reader and author, which Gerald Moore expresses (in the *Unashamed Accompanist*) as occurring between the singer and the accompanist: the singer pulls the song one way, the accompanist another, and together they pull it apart.

The study of mathematics requires personal involvement. It is not a conglomeration of rote formulas for every occasion. It is something different for each of its students. And a program of study must be devised to bring each individual to his own view and appreciation of its design. The concept of a definitive view of mathematics, as with all great disciplines of art and scholarship, can be held only by those who remain on formal terms with it. A flexible and inquiring approach to mathematics will lead one to an ever-changing but increasing personal attachment to it. I hope that this book will at least help its readers to initiate such a study of mathematics.

This book would never have been written had it not been for the late Professor Charles T. Bumer. For after I had given a course in the National Science Foundation Institute for High School and Junior College teachers at Clark University in the summer of 1959, of which Professor Bumer was the Director, Professor Bumer suggested that we collaborate in writing a textbook. The first part was to be my project, and based upon the lectures delivered in the above course. From this background, Dr. Bumer had planned to develop chapters on probability and statistical inference.

Unfortunately, before Dr. Bumer could undertake his part of this project, he became suddenly ill in 1960 and died. As a result, the plan of this book has been revised, and in particular the subjects of probability and statistical inference are not considered.

Nevertheless, although Dr. Bumer's pen may not have explicitly reached these pages, his influence as a teacher, mathematician, and human being will always be reflected in my work at its best. The students of Clark University have often noted the privilege they felt it was to have come into the path of this great teacher. I have shared this privilege many times, and feel the deepest gratitude.

I wish to express my gratitude also to the many people who contributed their advice and encouragement during the writing and in the preliminary use of this textbook. Among these are Professors Charles P. Wells, Edward G. Begle, Daniel Gorenstein, Henry Frandsen, John F. Kennison; also while graduate students at Clark University are Mrs. Anna Sia, Elwood Ede, Allan Ephraim, Thomas Cramton, Robert Perry, Richard Montgomery; as an undergraduate, Miss Margaret Taft; and Mrs. Margaret C. Jaquith, Secretary of the Department of Mathematics.

I am furthermore indebted to the teachers attending my lectures in the National Science Foundation programs in 1959 and in 1966. It was because of the favorable response of the participants in 1959 that the writing of this book was undertaken. The enthusiastic response of the participants in 1966 was extremely gratifying, and I was pleased to learn of the relevance the material in this book had to an understanding of many of the topics in the present mathematics curriculum of the junior and senior high school.

At Clark University, preliminary versions of this text have been used for a year course on the freshman level from 1959 to 1966. Many of the revisions from the earliest version to the final one are a result of the experience obtained in these classes. Both the favorable and unfavorable comments during these years were of great value, and I am grateful to the students in these classes for the inspiration I received during my attempts to improve various parts of the text.

In conclusion I wish to express my appreciation to Dodd, Mead and Company for the assistance and cooperation I have received throughout this project, and in particular to Mrs. Genia Graves, Managing Editor, College Department; Mr. Edward F. Webster, Assistant Director, College Department; and to Mr. William Oman, Vice President.

SEYMOUR HAYDEN

contents

Part I
BASIC CONCEPTS

The reader of this book will probably have had some background in arithmetic from his elementary-school training, and varying degrees of experience with secondary-school mathematics. Nevertheless, we shall formally assume only a knowledge of how to add and how to multiply two natural numbers. (The natural numbers are the numbers 1, 2, 3, 4, ...) Even addition and multiplication will be fully developed in what follows, but to allow the student to develop technical skills sooner, we make use of the addition and multiplication tables for natural numbers before we expose their logical development. An exception to this statement of prerequisites is made, however, in Part I of the text, where, for the purposes of illustrative examples only, we assume the student knows how to subtract and divide two natural numbers.

The reason that we can assume such limited prerequisites is that we shall develop arithmetic and algebra, and the transition from the former to the latter, in systems other than the familiar number systems. In so doing, we shall at the same time provide the background and training upon which we shall draw to unfold the arithmetic and algebra of the real-number system in Part II.

To clarify the rules of arithmetic or algebra, it seems best to consider these ideas in systems of numbers which are new to the student. One will get a better idea of what is involved in learning an addition table, for example, by considering a table which he has not seen before. By comparing the logical reasoning involved in the rules of arithmetic and algebra in various systems, one will be able to acquire a sharper insight into these rules for the more familiar number systems.

Thus in place of the set of natural numbers and the binary operation of addition, we consider many other sets of objects, as well as other binary operations. We discuss equations in these systems, and proceed from a most primitive arithmetic approach to solving equations to a more sophisticated and more powerful algebraic one. We are then in a position, at the very outset of Part II, to develop the algebra of the real-number system.

This approach has the further advantage that it develops methods and ideas and training which are important for the consideration of many mathematical systems, other than the classical ones of real and complex numbers, systems which today have become important both in applications and in the development of mathematics itself. Although we do not intend to emphasize this applicability to other systems, it is our hope that the mathematical maturity one will acquire through his study of this text will bring his study of such systems more easily within reach, if desired.

It is not the intention of this text to forsake the "classical" curriculum. On the contrary, the approach here has been taken primarily to provide a unified and logical treatment of such a curriculum. We are still interested in the development and/or acquisition of classical skills, but they should be based upon a secure understanding. Indeed, such understanding should lead to the improvement and extension of such skills.

Numerous exercises are included to encourage the greatest amount of activity from the student. Such activity is necessary for a successful reading of this text. The safest criterion for the success of a lecturer or writer is how much and how effectively he has stimulated the student to work on his own. At any rate, the presentation to follow is based on this conviction.

chapter i

SETS

In this chapter we establish a vocabulary that will be used throughout the text. In this connection, the idea of a *set* is a very useful one, as is the concept of *subsets of a set*. The language of sets may be used throughout all branches of mathematics, so it is important to establish what one can say about all sets. After discussing sets and subsets in Sections 1 and 2, we prove statements concerning sets in Section 3. In Section 4 we elaborate further how sets can be formed. In particular, we consider the power set of a given set, which is the set of all subsets of the given set; and also the Cartesian product of sets.

1. The Language of Sets

1.1 What Is a Set?

In the study of mathematics, one encounters collections of objects of various kinds. For example, one considers the points on a line, or in a plane; or the planes (or spheres) of space; or the natural numbers 1, 2, 3, . . . ; or the equations of "first degree." We shall call any such collection of objects a *set*.

The introduction of the idea of a set turns out to be a very useful one, as we shall see. To give a preliminary illustration, consider the statement: "3 can be written as a product of two numbers in precisely two ways: $3 = 3 \cdot 1$ and $3 = 1 \cdot 3$." The correctness of this statement depends upon the *set* of numbers being considered. In the *set of natural numbers*, this is correct. But if one considers the *set of integers* (i.e., the numbers 0, 1, −1, 2, −2, . . .), it is incorrect, as $3 = (-1)(-3)$ also. In the set of fractions, $3 = \frac{9}{2} \cdot \frac{2}{3}$.

One clarifies this situation by referring to the set being considered. That is, *"In the set of natural numbers, 3 can be written as a product of two numbers in precisely two ways."*

Similarly, every two distinct nonparallel lines intersect in a point if one is considering the set of lines in some plane, but not if one is considering the set of lines in space.

A set, which is what we said we would call any collection of objects, is a very general concept, and need not consist only of points, or lines, or numbers, or equations. Consider the following examples.

Example 1. The set of cities in the United States.
Example 2. The set of people in France who can read English.

Example 3. The set of seats in a given theater.
Example 4. The set of students attending a given university.
Example 5. The set of newspaper publishers in the world.

Of course, one also has the following:

Example 6. The set of natural numbers.
Example 7. The set of lines in a plane.
Example 8. The set of odd natural numbers.
Example 9. The set of planes in space.

Clearly, one can go on and on.

1.2   Notation

As we shall be considering many sets in the sequel, it is convenient to consider first some of the things which can be said about all such sets. To this end, we establish some vocabulary and notation.

The members of a set will be called *elements* of the set. Thus an element of the set of cities in the United States is Atlanta; another element is Chicago. Again, 3 is an element of the set of natural numbers (or also of the set of odd natural numbers).

In a given discussion of particular sets, instead of continually describing each of the sets—such as "the set of cities in the United States"; "the set of natural numbers"; "the set of odd natural numbers"—it is sometimes more convenient to use symbols, such as letters, to denote each set. For example, in this discussion we can let

A = the set of cities in the United States
B = the set of natural numbers
C = the set of odd natural numbers

Then we could say Atlanta is an element of A; Chicago is an element of A; 3 is an element of B; 3 is an element of C.

Another method used for specifying a set is to give a complete list of its elements. In this method of designation we use braces to enclose the elements of the set. Thus

A = {Atlanta, Chicago, Dallas, Providence, Mt. Holly, Ames, . . . , Worcester}
B = {1, 2, 3, . . .}
C = {1, 3, 5, 7, . . .}

Other examples are

D = {1, 2, 3, 5}
E = {1, 2, 3, 4, 5, 6, 7, 8, 9, 10}
F = {3, 6, 9, 12, . . .}
G = {3, 6, 9, 12}
H = {#, b, x}

In sets *D, E, G,* and *H* we gave a complete listing of the elements which were included. In set *A* we could have given such a listing but, to save time and space, omitted all but seven of its elements. The three dots appearing after 'Ames' and before 'Worcester' indicate there are a *finite* number of elements omitted. This is in contrast to sets *B, C,* and *F.* Here the three dots indicate the listing is to go on indefinitely. In these cases, there is no last element listed; in set *A* such a last element was given, namely, Worcester.

In set *D,* there are precisely four elements, namely, 1, 2, 3, and 5. We could also write $D = \{3, 1, 2, 5\}$, since this again consists of the elements 3, 1, 2, 5. Thus $\{1, 2, 3, 5\}$ and $\{3, 1, 2, 5\}$ are the same sets; that is, they consist of the same elements.

Each member of a set is said to be *an element of* (or to *belong to*) the set. The phrase "is an element of" arises often enough to warrant abbreviation, and we shall use 'ϵ' in place of this phrase.[1] Thus, 'Dallas is an element of *A*' will be written 'Dallas ϵ *A*.' Similarly, Chicago ϵ *A*, 3 ϵ *B*, 3 ϵ *C*, 5 ϵ *D*, 9 ϵ *E*, 21 ϵ *F*, 6 ϵ *G*, # ϵ *H*.

1.3   The Null Set

We have seen examples of sets having an infinite number of elements (for example, *B, C, F* above, or the set of points in a plane). Also some have a finite number of elements: *D* has 4, *E* has 10. It will also be useful to consider a set with no elements. This set can be described in many ways. For example, "the set of points common to two distinct parallel lines in the plane" has no elements. The set of three-year-olds enrolled in a university (probably) has no elements. We shall consider each a description of the same set—*the set with no elements.*

The set consisting of no elements will be called the *empty set* or the *null set,* and will be denoted by '$\emptyset$.' Thus,

$\emptyset$ = the set of points common to two distinct parallel lines in the plane

Also,

$\emptyset$ = the set of three-year-olds attending a university

We have said (Section 1.2) that, if *S* is a set and *s* is an element of *S*, we shall write

$$s \epsilon S$$

If *t* is not an element of *S*, we shall write [2]

$$t \notin S$$

---

[1] ϵ is the Greek lower-case epsilon.

[2] That is, if "ϵ" means "is a member of," then "$\notin$" means "is not a member of." Similarly if "=" means "is equal to," then "$\neq$" means "is not equal to." Or if "$\equiv$" means "is congruent to," then "$\not\equiv$" means "is not congruent to," etc.

Thus, in the examples of Section 1.2, Massachusetts $\notin A$, $-1 \notin B$, $2 \notin C$, $6 \notin D$, $\frac{1}{2} \notin D$, $121 \notin E$, $8 \notin F$, $5 \notin G$, California $\notin G$.

Exercises

1. Let $L = \{2, 4, 6, 9\}$.
   (a) Is $2 \in L$ (i.e., is 2 an element of L)?
   (b) Is it correct to say that $3 \notin L$?
   (c) If $M = \{5, 7\}$, what is the set of elements common to L and M?
   (d) If $S = \{2, 4, 10, 13, 19\}$, what is the set of elements common to L and S? to M and S?
2. Let A, B, C, D, E, F, G, H refer to the sets of Section 1.2.
   (a) Let $c \in C$ (i.e., let c be any element of C). Does it follow that $c \in B$?
   (b) Which of the following are true?
       (i) $2 \notin A$.
       (ii) $2 \notin B$.
       (iii) $2 \in C$.
       (iv) $2 \in D$.
       (v) $2 \notin E$.
       (vi) $2 \in F$.
       (vii) If $a \in G$, then $a \in F$.
       (viii) If $a \in F$, then $a \in G$.
       (ix) $\# \in H$.
       (x) The set of elements in common with D and F is $\{3\}$.
       (xi) The set of elements in common with C and E is $\{1, 3, 5, 7, 9\}$.
       (xii) The set of elements in common with B and D is $\{1, 2, 3\}$.

2. The Subsets of a Set

2.1 Definition and Examples

Let $S = \{2, 3, 8\}$ and $T = \{1, 2, 3, 4, 7, 8, 10\}$. We observe that every element of S is also an element of T. Thus $2 \in S$ and also $2 \in T$; similarly, $3 \in S$ and $3 \in T$; $8 \in S$ and $8 \in T$. We can therefore say that, if a is any element of S (that is, $a \in S$), then a is also an element of T (that is, $a \in T$). For if $a \in S$, then a must be either 2, or 3, or 8, each of which is an element of T.

In such a case, that is, when every element of S is an element of T, we shall call S a *subset* of T. We shall state this formally.

Definition 1. If S and T are sets, we say S is a *subset* of T if every element of S is also an element of T.

Example 10. The set of odd natural numbers is a subset of the set of natural numbers.
Example 11. Let T be the set of states in the United States, and S the set of New England states. Then S is a subset of T.

Example 12. Let K be the set of points in a given plane, and L the set of points on a given line in that plane. Then L is a subset of K. That is, every point of the line is also a point of the plane.

Example 13. If K is as in Example 12, and L is the set of points on a given circle in the plane, then again L is a subset of K.

Example 14. K as above. If L is the set of points on any given curve in the plane, then L is a subset of K.

Example 15. If C is the set of undergraduates at a given college, and D is the set of freshmen, then D is a subset of C.

Example 16. If V is the set of members of the U.S. Congress (both Houses), and U the set of U.S. Senators, then U is a subset of V. The set U is usually referred to as "The Senate."

Example 17. $\{\#, b\}$ is a subset of $\{\#, b, ϵ\}$.

Example 18. $\{\#, b, ϵ\}$ is a subset of $\{\#, b, ϵ\}$.

Note in this last example that we are saying that the set $\{\#, b, ϵ\}$ is a subset of itself. This is consistent with Definition 1 and is the case where S and T (cf. Definition 1) are the same sets (i.e., consist of the same elements). Hence, if $s \in S$, certainly $s \in T$. This is quite general:

If S is any set, then S is a subset of S

2.2   The Null Set as a Subset

To show that a set A is *not* a subset of a set B (i.e., to show "A is a subset of B" is false), it is sufficient to find *one* element of A which is not an element of B. For example, if $A = \{2, 3, 4, 5\}$ and $B = \{1, 3, 4, 5, 6\}$, then A is not a subset of B, because $2 \in A$, but $2 \notin B$.

Similarly, to show that "$\varnothing$ is a subset of B" is false, one must find an element of $\varnothing$ which is not an element of B. But $\varnothing$ is empty, so no such element can exist. Hence "$\varnothing$ is a subset of B" is true. Because in this argument, B could have been any set, we may state:

$\varnothing$ is a subset of every set

Example 19. What are all the subsets of $\{1, 2\}$?
  Answer: $\varnothing$, $\{1\}$, $\{2\}$, $\{1, 2\}$. Thus there are four subsets of $\{1, 2\}$.

Example 20. What are all the subsets of $\{1\}$?
  Answer: There are two: $\varnothing$, $\{1\}$.

Example 21. What are all the subsets of $\{a, b, c\}$?
  Answer: There are eight: $\varnothing$, $\{a\}$, $\{b\}$, $\{c\}$, $\{a, b\}$, $\{a, c\}$, $\{b, c\}$, $\{a, b, c\}$.

Example 22. What are all the subsets of $\varnothing$?
  Answer: There is one: $\varnothing$.

Example 23. Give examples of finite and infinite subsets of the set of natural numbers. (Recall that the set of natural numbers is $\{1, 2, 3, \ldots\}$.)
  Answer: Some finite subsets are $\{1\}$, $\{1, 101, 153, 2014\}$. We shall also regard $\varnothing$ as a finite subset of every set. Some infinite subsets are $\{1, 3, 5, 7, \ldots\}$, $\{2, 4, 6, 8, \ldots\}$, $\{1, 2, 3, 4, \ldots\}$, $\{4, 8, 12, 16, \ldots\}$.

Exercises

3. Let $A = \{1, 2, 3, 4\}$.
   (a) List the subsets of A which have more than two elements.
   (b) List the subsets of A having exactly two elements.
   (c) List the subsets of A having at most two elements.
   (d) Is $\varnothing$ an element of A?
   (e) Does $A \in A$?
   (f) Is A a subset of A?
   (g) Does $1 \in A$?
4. Let $B = \{1, 2, a, 5, \alpha, x, U, -3\}$.
   (a) List the subsets of B having exactly 1 element.
   (b) List the subsets of B having exactly 2 elements.
   (c) List the subsets of B having exactly 6 elements.
   (d) List the subsets of B having exactly 7 elements.
   (e) List the subsets of B having at least 7 elements.
   (f) List the subsets of B having more than 7 elements.
   (g) List the subsets of B having at most 1 element.
   (h) List the subsets of B having less than 2 elements.
   (i) List the subsets of B having less than 1 element.
   (j) How many subsets of B have exactly 3 elements?
5. Suppose C is a committee consisting of five people, say, $C = \{$Mr. Cole, Mrs. Herz, Miss Smith, Mr. Gauss, Mr. Bach$\}$. Regard "committee" as another name for "set of people."
   (a) List the subcommittees consisting of exactly 2 members.
   (b) How many subcommittees can one form of at most 2 members?
   (c) What is the total number of subcommittees one can form?
   (d) How many subcommittees can one form having more than 1 member?
6. Let $Q = \{0, 1, 2\}$ and $P = \{1, 2, 3\}$.
   (a) List all subsets of Q with 1 element; 2 elements; 3 elements.
   (b) List the subsets of P with 1 element; 2 elements; 3 elements.
   (c) List all subsets in (a) and (b) that consist only of elements common to P and Q.

3. Relations between Subsets of a Set

3.1   The Relation $A \subseteq B$; $B \supseteq A$

Let A and B be sets. If A is a subset of B, we shall write $A \subseteq B$. Thus $\{1, 3\} \subseteq \{1, 2, 3\}$. Also $\varnothing \subseteq \{2, a\}$. Other examples are:

$$\{1\} \subseteq \{1\}$$
$$\{1\} \subseteq \{1, 2\}$$
$$\{\text{Mr. Cole, Mrs. Herz}\} \subseteq \{\text{Mr. Cole, Mrs. Herz, Mr. Bach}\}$$

From remarks in Sections 2.1 and 2.2, if A is any set, we have $A \subseteq A$ and $\varnothing \subseteq A$.

Another notation used for "A is a subset of B" is $B \supseteq A$. In writing $A \subseteq B$, one often says: *A is contained in B*; in writing $B \supseteq A$ one often says: *B contains A*. However, all these mean precisely the same thing, and are all in current use. We summarize these many ways of expressing this relation between A and B:

1. A is a subset of B.
2. A is contained in B.
3. B contains A.
4. $A \subseteq B$.
5. $B \supseteq A$.
6. Every element of A is an element of B.

Example 24. Suppose $A = \{2, 3\}$, $B = \{1\}$, $C = \{1, 2, 3, 4\}$, $D = \{1, 3, 4\}$. Then we have $A \subseteq C$, $D \supseteq B$, $C \supseteq D$, $B \subseteq C$. We also have $A \nsubseteq B$ (that is, A is not a subset of B), $B \nsubseteq A$, $C \nsubseteq D$, $D \nsupseteq A$.

3.2 The Relation $A \subset B$; $B \supset A$

One has occasion to consider all the subsets of a set, excluding the set itself. These are called the *proper subsets* of the set. Thus if $A = \{1, 2\}$, the subsets of A are $\varnothing$, $\{1\}$, $\{2\}$, $\{1, 2\}$; the proper subsets of A are $\varnothing$, $\{1\}$, $\{2\}$.

Definition 2. We say A is a *proper subset* of B if (a) A is a subset of B and (b) $A \neq B$. We shall write $A \subset B$ or also $B \supset A$ to mean A is a proper subset of B. Thus $A \subset B$ or $B \supset A$ means (a) $A \subseteq B$ (also $B \supseteq A$) and (b) $A \neq B$.

Example 25. List the proper subsets of $\{c\}$.
  Answer: $\varnothing$.
Example 26. List the proper subsets of $\varnothing$.
  Answer: There are none.
Example 27. If a set T has 3 elements, there are 8 subsets of T and 7 proper subsets of T.
Example 28. Let A, B, C, D be as in Example 24. Then

$$A \nsubseteq A, \qquad D \nsupseteq D, \qquad A \subset C, \qquad D \supset B$$

Example 29. $\{2, 4, 6, \ldots\} \subset \{1, 2, 3, \ldots\}$. That is, the set of even natural numbers is a proper subset of the set of natural numbers.
Example 30. If A is a set such that $\varnothing \subset A$, what can be said about A?
  Answer: A is nonempty, that is, A has at least one element.

Exercises

7. Let $F = \{4, 8\}$. Find all the subsets of F. Which of these are proper subsets of F?
8. Given $A = \{a, b, c\}$ and $B = \{b, c\}$. Fill in the blanks with the appropriate symbols (ϵ, $\subset$, $\supset$).
  (a) a ___ A.   (d) B ___ A.
  (b) $\{a\}$ ___ A.   (e) c ___ B.
  (c) A ___ B.   (f) $\varnothing$ ___ A.

9. Let $L = \{0, a, g\}$, $M = \{0, a, H\}$, $N = \{0, H\}$, $\mathcal{O} = \{0, H, g, a, x\}$. State whether the following are true or false:

(a) $L \subset M$.   (g) $0 \in \varnothing$.

(b) $N \subseteq M$.   (h) $\{0\}$ is a subset of L, M, N, and $\mathcal{O}$.

(c) $M \supset N$.   (i) 0 is an element of L, M, and $\mathcal{O}$.

(d) $N \in \mathcal{O}$.   (j) $L \not\subseteq M$.

(e) $\varnothing \subset N$.   (k) $M \supset \mathcal{O}$.

(f) $\varnothing \supset \varnothing$.   (l) $u \notin \varnothing$.

10. Let A be the set of natural numbers, B the set of even natural numbers, C the set of odd natural numbers.

(a) List 3 subsets of C which have 1 element; list 2 subsets of B which have 3 elements.

(b) List 2 subsets of A which are also subsets of B.

(c) Construct a proper subset K of A which has 4 elements, such that B has a nonempty subset which is a proper subset of K, and C also has a non-empty subset which is a proper subset of K.

3.3   Consequences of Definitions 1 and 2

In Section 1.2 we said we would consider some things which can be stated about all sets. With the vocabulary and notation we have given above, we are ready to prove the following:

Let A, B, C be any three sets:

(1) $A \subseteq A$ and $\varnothing \subseteq A$.

(2) If $A = B$, then $A \subseteq B$ and $B \subseteq A$.

(3) If $A \subseteq B$ and $B \subseteq A$, then $A = B$.

(4) If $A \subseteq B$ and $B \subseteq C$, then $A \subseteq C$.

(5) If $A \subset B$, then $A \subseteq B$.

(6) If $A \subset B$, then $A \neq B$.

(7) If $A \subset B$, there exists an element of B which is not an element of A (i.e., there exists $b \in B$ such that $b \notin A$).

(8) If $A \subset B$ and $B \subseteq C$, then $A \subset C$.

(9) If $A \subseteq B$ and $B \subset C$, then $A \subset C$.

(10) If $A \subset B$ and $B \subset C$, then $A \subset C$.

The argument showing that A is a subset of A has been given in Section 2.1. That $\varnothing \subseteq A$ was discussed in Section 2.2. Thus (1) has been established.

If $A = B$, then $A \subseteq B$ and $B \subseteq A$ are simply restatements of "$A \subseteq A$" [that is, (2) is merely a restatement of "$A \subseteq A$"].

We now turn to the proofs of (3) through (10).

Proof of (3): We are told that $A \subseteq B$ and $B \subseteq A$. We must show that $A = B$, i.e., that A and B consist of the same elements. Now every element of A is an element of B, by Definition 1, since $A \subseteq B$. Can B have any elements other than the ones which are in A? The answer is no, since, if $b \in B$, then $b \in A$ by Definition 1 (since $B \subseteq A$).

Hence A and B consist of the same elements, and $A = B$.

Proof of (4): We are given $A \subseteq B$ and $B \subseteq C$. We must show $A \subseteq C$; that is, we must show (according to Definition 1) that, if $a \in A$, then $a \in C$. (If $A = \emptyset$, then A is a subset of C since we have already seen that the null set is a subset of every set.) Thus, suppose $a \in A$. Then since $A \subseteq B$, by Definition 1 we have $a \in B$. But now, since $B \subseteq C$ and $a \in B$, again by Definition 1, we see that $a \in C$. Therefore, we have shown that, if $a \in A$, then $a \in C$.

Hence $A \subseteq C$.

Proof of (5): Suppose $A \subset B$. Then by Definition 2, $A \subseteq B$ *and* $A \neq B$. In particular, $A \subseteq B$.

Proof of (6): Similar to (5).

Proof of (7): We are given $A \subset B$. We wish to show that it cannot happen that *every* element of B is an element of A.

Suppose, to the contrary, that it were true that every element of B is an element of A. Then we would have $B \subseteq A$. But, since $A \subset B$, we have by (5) that $A \subseteq B$. Thus $A \subseteq B$ and $B \subseteq A$, which would mean, by (3), that $A = B$. But this contradicts the fact that $A \neq B$. (For since $A \subset B$, we see that $A \neq B$.)

We must conclude that not every element of B is an element of A, which proves (7).

The proofs of (8), (9), and (10) are left as exercises (cf. Exercises 11 and 12).

3.4 Remarks on Statements in Section 3.3

We call attention to the fact that in (2) we have

Given: $A = B$
To prove: $A \subseteq B$ and $B \subseteq A$

In (3) we have

Given: $A \subseteq B$ and $B \subseteq A$
To prove: $A = B$

Of course, in both cases we are given that A and B are sets. But what we are interested in observing here is that what is given and what has to be proved in (2) is exactly reversed in (3). In such an instance, we call one statement the *converse* of the other. Thus we could have written (2) and (3) together as follows:

Let A and B be sets. If $A = B$, then $A \subseteq B$ and $B \subseteq A$; and conversely.

Or, if we wished to emphasize the statement of the converse, we would say

Let A and B be sets. If $A = B$, then $A \subseteq B$ and $B \subseteq A$; conversely, if $A \subseteq B$ and $B \subseteq A$, then $A = B$.

Another example of a statement in which the converse is true is

If Tom is married to Ellen, then Ellen is married to Tom.

The converse is

If Ellen is married to Tom, then Tom is married to Ellen.

The above statement and converse may be combined as follows:

If Tom is married to Ellen, then Ellen is married to Tom; and conversely.

An alternative method frequently used to express the fact that a statement and its converse both hold is by means of the phrase "if and only if." Thus we say

$A = B$ *if and only if* $A \subseteq B$ and $B \subseteq A$.
Tom is married to Ellen *if and only if* Ellen is married to Tom.
2 is less than a *if and only if* a is greater than 2.

All these are instances in which a statement and its converse are both correct. However, this is not always the case. For consider the statement

If a is a natural number less than 4, then a is a natural number less than 9.

This statement is correct. But its converse is incorrect. The latter would say

If a is a natural number less than 9, then a is a natural number less than 4.

This is false, since 7 is less than 9 but 7 is not less than 4.
The converse of (5) would be:

If $A \subseteq B$, then $A \subset B$.

This is not true. The converse of (6) is false, as are the converses of (7), (8), (9), and (10). For example, the converse of (10) would be

If $A \subset C$, then $A \subset B$ and $B \subset C$.

To show this is false, we must reveal one instance in which it is false. Let

A = the set of residents of Florida
B = the set of residents of California
C = the set of residents of the United States

Then $A \subset C$, but $A \not\subset B$.

3.5   Definitions

A definition, in mathematics, introduces new terminology which is completely interchangeable with the old. Thus, according to Definition 1, "S is a subset of T" can be used interchangeably with "every element of S is an element of T." Although in Definition 1 we say "S is a subset of T *if* every element of S is an element of T," a definition nevertheless is always understood to be *if and only if*. Thus Definition 2 is understood to mean that A is a proper subset of B *if and only if* A is a subset of B and $A \neq B$.

Exercises

11. Let A, B, C be sets. Prove that, if $A \subset B$ and $B \subseteq C$, then $A \subset C$. (*Hint:* By Definition 2, one must show $A \subseteq C$ and $A \neq C$. Prove these separately.)

12. Let A, B, C be sets. Prove the following:
   (a) If $A \subseteq B$ and $B \subset C$, then $A \subset C$.
   (b) If $A \subset B$ and $B \subset C$, then $A \subset C$.

13. Let A, B, C, D be sets. Prove: If $A \subseteq B$, $B \subseteq C$, $C \subseteq D$, then $A \subseteq D$. (*Hint:* One can pattern the proof after that of (4). But it is easier to apply (4) twice.)

14. Let A, B, C, D be sets. Prove: If $A \subseteq B$, $B \subset C$, $C \subseteq D$, then $A \subset D$.

15. State and prove two of the remaining cases suggested by Exercises 13 and 14.

16. Extend Exercise 13 to five sets.

17. In the following, state whether each statement is true or false. If it is true, prove it. If it is false, prove that it is false by giving a specific example. Capital letters refer to sets.
   (a) If $A \subset B$ and $B \not\subseteq C$, then $A \not\subseteq C$.
   (b) If $a \in A$ and $A \subset F$, then $a \in F$.
   (c) $D \subseteq G$ and $E \supseteq G$ if and only if $D \neq G$ or $E \neq G$.
   (d) If $S \subset T$, then $S \neq T$; and conversely.
   (e) If $A \not\subseteq B$ and $B \subset C$, then $A \not\subseteq C$.
   (f) If $A \not\supseteq B$ and $B \not\supseteq C$, then $A \not\supseteq C$.
   (g) If $A \subseteq B$ and $B \subset C$, then there exists an element $c \in C$ such that $c \notin A$.

18. Give five examples of statements which are true but whose converses are false.

19. Give five examples of statements which are true and whose converses are also true.

20. Give five examples of statements which are false but whose converses are true.

21. State the converses of statements (6) to (9) given at the beginning of Section 3.3.

4. Construction of New Sets from Given Ones

4.1 The Power Set of a Set

We have said that a set is a collection of elements (for example, the set of points in a plane, or the set of lines in a plane, or the set of points on a line). Here we have an example of a set consisting of elements which themselves are sets. That is, if A is the set of lines in a plane, then the elements of A (the lines) are themselves sets, namely of points.

It frequently occurs that one considers sets, some or all of whose elements are themselves sets. If we begin with a set such as $A = \{a, b\}$, we may consider the set consisting of all the subsets of A. For example, if a and b were people, one may wish to consider the set of all possible committees one can form from these two people. They are

$$\varnothing, \{a\}, \{b\}, \{a, b\}$$

Hence the set of all subsets of A is

$$\{\varnothing, \{a\}, \{b\}, \{a, b\}\}$$

We shall denote this set by $[A]$.

Definition 3. If S is any set, then $[S]$ will denote the set consisting of all the subsets of S. We shall call $[S]$ the *power set* of S.

Example 31. If $S = \{a\}$, then $[S] = \{\varnothing, \{a\}\}$.
Example 32. If $S = \{1, 2\}$, then $[S] = \{\varnothing, \{1\}, \{2\}, \{1, 2\}\}$.
Example 33. If $T = \{a, b, c\}$, then $[T] = \{\varnothing, \{a\}, \{b\}, \{c\}, \{a, b\}, \{a, c\}, \{b, c\}, \{a, b, c\}\}$.
Example 34. $[\varnothing] = \{\varnothing\}$, since the only subset of $\varnothing$ is $\varnothing$, so that $\varnothing$ is an element of $[\varnothing]$.

In general, we can say that $C \in [S]$ means that C is a subset of S. That is, $C \in [S]$ if and only if $C \subseteq S$.

Exercises

22. Let $A = \{a, b, c\}$; state whether the following statements are true or false:
(a) $a \in \{a\}$.   (c) $\varnothing \subset A$.   (e) $A \in [A]$.
(b) $\varnothing \in [A]$.   (d) $A \subseteq [A]$.
23. Given $A = \{a, b, c\}$ and $B = \{b, c\}$. Fill in the blanks with the appropriate symbols ($\in$, $\subset$, $\supset$):
(a) $\{a\}$ ____ $[A]$.   (c) $[A]$ ____ $[B]$.
(b) $\{\{a, b\}, \{a\}\}$ ____ $[A]$.   (d) $\{\varnothing, \{b, c\}\}$ ____ $[B]$.
24. Given $S = \{\alpha, \beta\}$. Find $[S]$.
25. The same as Exercise 24, with $S = \{\lambda, \rho, \sigma\}$.
26. Let $A = \{1\}$.
(a) Find $[A]$.
(b) Find $[[A]]$, that is, the power set of the power set of A.
27. (a) Find $[\varnothing]$.   (c) Find $[\{\varnothing\}]$.
(b) Find $[[\varnothing]]$.   (d) Find $[[\{a\}]]$.
28. If $A = \{a, b, c\}$, list three *subsets* of $[A]$.
29. Let A and B be sets. Prove that, if $A \subseteq B$, then $[A] \subseteq [B]$; and conversely.

4.2 The Cartesian Product of Sets

Let A be a set of 10 teams in a given baseball league. Say $A = \{1, 2, 3, 4, 5, 6, 7, 8, 9, 10\}$. In making up a schedule of games to be played, one considers subsets of A consisting of two elements. For example, $\{1, 4\}$, $\{2, 3\}$, $\{5, 10\}$, $\{6, 8\}$, $\{7, 9\}$ could represent the teams playing one another on a given day.

However, one must also specify which should be the "home" team, and which the "visiting" team. Thus one would like to specify the pair 1 and 4, in that order, to mean, say, that 1 visits 4. Then 4 and 1 would mean 4 visits 1.

This is an example of a situation in which we would like to consider a pair of elements a and b taken from a set *in that order*. We shall refer to such a pair of objects (that is, where the order makes a difference) as an *ordered pair* and denote it by '(a, b).' Thus $(2, 3)$ is the pair 2 followed by 3. Note that $(2, 3) \neq (3, 2)$. However, in recalling our set notation, we see that $\{2, 3\} = \{3, 2\}$. For '$\{2, 3\}$' and '$\{3, 2\}$' both designate the set whose elements are 2 and 3.

Power sets offer one method of constructing new sets from given ones. Another method is to consider the set of all ordered pairs of a given set. Thus if $A = \{1, 2\}$, the set of all ordered pairs of A is the set

$$\{(1, 1), (1, 2), (2, 1), (2, 2)\}$$

This set, then, has four elements.

Again, if $B = \{u, v, w\}$, the set of all ordered pairs of B is the set

$$\{(u, u), (u, v), (u, w), (v, u), (v, v), (v, w), (w, u), (w, v), (w, w)\}$$

We shall write '$A \times A$' to designate the set of all ordered pairs of A, and one says "A cross A" for this set.

If C is the set of natural numbers, some elements of $C \times C$ are $(1, 5)$, $(102, 65)$, $(3, 1007)$, $(6, 6)$, $(5, 1)$.

If D is the set of odd natural numbers, some elements of $D \times D$ are $(1, 5)$, $(7, 501)$, $(109, 109)$, $(23, 33)$, $(33, 23)$.

A more general idea is that of constructing the set of all ordered pairs using two sets, say S and T. If one begins with two sets S and T, one can consider the set of all ordered pairs (s, t), where $s \in S$ and $t \in T$. For example, if $S = \{1, 2\}$ and $T = \{a, b, c\}$, then the set of all ordered pairs from S and T, denoted by '$S \times T$,' is

$$S \times T = \{(1, a), (1, b), (1, c), (2, a), (2, b), (2, c)\}$$

The set $S \times T$ is called the *Cartesian product* of S and T. The set $A \times A$ is a special case, where the two sets involved are the same. We say that $A \times A$ is the Cartesian product of A with itself.

Beginning with three sets, say S, T, and U, we could define the Cartesian product of S, T, and U: Namely $S \times T \times U$ is the set of all ordered triples (s, t, u) for which $s \in S$, $t \in T$, $u \in U$. Then $A \times A \times A$ is the special case where the three sets involved are equal. Similarly, we could define $S \times T \times U \times V$ and $A \times A \times A \times A$.

If $H = \{a, b\}$, we have

$$H \times H \times H$$

$$= \{(a, a, a), (a, a, b), (a, b, a), (a, b, b), (b, a, a), (b, a, b), (b, b, a), (b, b, b)\}$$

If $R = \{1\}$, $S = \{1, a\}$, $T = \{2\}$, then

$$R \times S \times T = \{(1, 1, 2), (1, a, 2)\}$$

We can make a graphical interpretation of the Cartesian product of two sets as follows. If A and B are sets, represent the elements of A as points on a horizontal line, and of B as points on a vertical line. For example, if $A = \{1, 3, 6\}$ and $B = \{\alpha, \gamma\}$, we would have Fig. 1.1. Let us call the

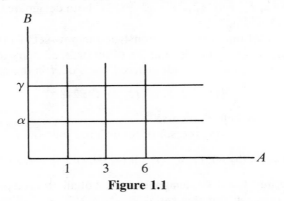

Figure 1.1

horizontal line beginning at α an α-horizontal, and at γ, a γ-horizontal. Similarly, the vertical lines beginning at 1, 3, 6 are the 1-vertical, 3-vertical, 6-vertical, respectively. Then the point at which the 1-vertical and α-horizontal intersect will represent the element $(1, \alpha)$ of $A \times B$. Similarly, $(6, \gamma)$, for example, is represented by the point at which the 6-vertical and γ-horizontal intersect. Thus we have Fig. 1.2.

As another example, let $S = \{1, 2, 3, 4\}$. Then the graphical representation of $S \times S$ is as in Fig. 1.3.

To graph $A \times B \times C$, we would need a line for C perpendicular to the plane of the lines for A and B. The elements of $A \times B \times C$ would then be represented by points in space.

To graph $A \times B \times C \times D$ would then become physically impossible (by this method—which is only one of numerous methods of giving pictorial representations of sets). However, one derives a great deal of intuition on Cartesian products of four or more sets by considering corresponding situations for two (or three) sets.

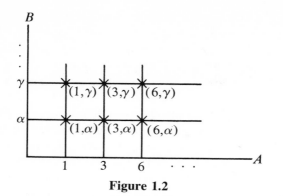

Figure 1.2

If we took S to be the set of natural numbers, we would have to imagine the graphical representation of $S \times S$, and could only give an indication of what it looks like. An extension of Fig. 1.3, for example, might be such an indication.

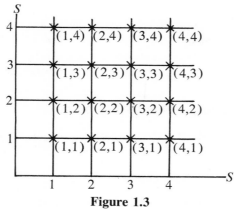

Figure 1.3

Exercises

30. Let $T = \{0, 1\}$.
   (a) Construct $[T]$.
   (b) List the subsets of T.
   (c) List the proper subsets of T.
   (d) List the proper subsets of $[T]$.
   (e) Construct $T \times T$.
   (f) Construct $T \times T \times T$.
   (g) Graph $T \times T$.
31. Let $A = \{1, 2, 3\}$ and $B = \{2, 3, 5, 6\}$.
   (a) Graph $A \times B$.
   (b) Give two subsets of $A \times B$ having five elements.
32. If $X = \{a, b\}$ and $Y = \{c\}$, find $[X \times Y]$.
33. If A is a set with m elements, B a set with n elements, and C a set with r elements, how many elements does the set $A \times B \times C$ have?

chapter ii

BINARY OPERATIONS ON A SET

Our first experience with numbers is usually in counting. We ask for two pennies, or three cookies, etc. With experience, we learn to "count" larger sets of objects, and eventually discover that we can count up to larger and larger numbers, perhaps indefinitely. The numbers used in counting are called *natural numbers,* or *whole numbers.* As we have stated in Chapter 1, the set of natural numbers is the set {1, 2, 3, 4, . . .}.

The arithmetic of natural numbers begins when one considers, for example, the idea that two pennies and three more pennies would give five pennies. Eventually, this leads to the concept of adding two natural numbers: $2 + 3 = 5$. Our early training then begins with learning addition tables of natural numbers.

The set of natural numbers is an example of a set, and addition is an example of what we shall call a *binary operation on a set.* We have seen in Chapter 1 the generality of the concept of a set. In this chapter we shall see the generality of the concept of binary operation on a set.

1. Examples of Binary Operations on a Set

We shall first indicate the meaning of a binary operation on a set by means of examples.

Example 1. Consider the set of natural numbers, that is, the set {1, 2, 3, 4, . . .}. An example of a binary operation on this set is the operation + (plus). Thus, if we take any two elements of our set, say 5 and 9, and apply the binary operation to these elements, we get a third element, in this case 14. One could write $+(5, 9) = 14$ to mean that $+$ applied to 5 and 9 is 14, but it is more customary to write $5 + 9 = 14$ for this.

We could tabulate the results of the binary operation $+$ on this set as follows:

$$1 + 1 = 2 \qquad 2 + 1 = 3 \qquad 3 + 1 = 4 \qquad \cdots$$
$$1 + 2 = 3 \qquad 2 + 2 = 4 \qquad \cdot$$
$$1 + 3 = 4 \qquad 2 + 3 = 5 \qquad \cdot$$
$$\cdot \qquad\qquad \cdot$$
$$\cdot \qquad\qquad \cdot$$
$$\cdot \qquad\qquad \cdot$$

The dots indicate that the tabulation continues indefinitely.

A second method for listing the above information, and one which will be emphasized, is the use of a table such as Table 2.1 for the binary operation + on the set of natural numbers. In this example, to find 2 + 4, one finds 2 in the left (outside) column and 4 on the top (outside) row; then

Table 2.1

+	1	2	3	④	·	·	·
1	2	3	4	5	·	·	·
②	3	4	5	⑥	·	·	·
3	4	5	6	7	·	·	·
4	5	6	7	8	·	·	·
·	·	·	·	·	·	·	·
·	·	·	·	·	·	·	·
·	·	·	·	·	·	·	·

the answer is the element in the same row as the 2 and the same column as the 4. That is, $2 + 4 = 6$.

Observe that we distinguish which of the two elements is to be considered "first" in applying the binary operation. The first element is always indicated in the outside left column; the second element is in the outside top row. It is important which comes first and which second, as will be seen in our next example.

Example 2. Again consider the set of natural numbers, this time with the binary operation − (minus). Thus − applied to 9 and 5 is 4; to 5 and 9 is −4 (that is, $9 − 5 = 4$ and $5 − 9 = −4$). Here it is clear that the results of the binary operation on two numbers depend on the order in which they are considered.

In this example, − applied to two elements of our set yields a third element *which may or may not be in our set,* as 4 is in our set but −4 is not. Table 2.2 corresponds to this set and this binary operation.

Table 2.2

−	1	2	3	4	·	·	·
1	0	−1	−2	−3	·	·	·
2	1	0	−1	−2	·	·	·
3	2	1	0	−1	·	·	·
4	3	2	1	0	·	·	·
·	·	·	·	·	·	·	·
·	·	·	·	·	·	·	·
·	·	·	·	·	·	·	·

Example 3. The set of natural numbers under · (i.e., with the binary operation

multiplication [1]) is another example of a set on which a binary operation is defined (Table 2.3). Thus $3 \cdot 2 = 6$, $4 \cdot 1 = 4$, $2 \cdot 3 = 6$, etc.

Table 2.3

·	1	2	3	4	·	·	·
1	1	2	3	4	·	·	·
2	2	4	6	8	·	·	·
3	3	6	9	12	·	·	·
4	4	8	12	16	·	·	·
·	·	·	·	·	·	·	·
·	·	·	·	·	·	·	·
·	·	·	·	·	·	·	·

Example 4. A further example is the set of natural numbers under ÷ (division), as in Table 2.4.

Table 2.4

÷	1	2	3	4	·	·	·
1	1	$\frac{1}{2}$	$\frac{1}{3}$	$\frac{1}{4}$	·	·	·
2	2	1	$\frac{2}{3}$	$\frac{1}{2}$	·	·	·
3	3	$\frac{3}{2}$	1	$\frac{3}{4}$	·	·	·
4	4	2	$\frac{4}{3}$	1	·	·	·
·	·	·	·	·	·	·	·
·	·	·	·	·	·	·	·
·	·	·	·	·	·	·	·

In Examples 1 through 4 we have considered the set of natural numbers, but in each case with a different binary operation defined on it. We now consider other sets.

Example 5. Take the set $\{1, 3, 5, 7, \ldots\}$, that is, the set of odd natural numbers. Let + be the binary operation.

Example 6. Set: $\{1, 3, 5, 7, \ldots\}$. Binary operation: ·

Example 7. Set: $\{2, 4, 6, 8, \ldots\}$, that is, the set of even natural numbers. Binary operation: +

Example 8. Set: $\{2, 4, 6, 8, \ldots\}$. Binary operation: ·

Example 9. Set: $\{1, 3, 6, 8\}$, that is, the set whose elements are 1, 3, 6, and 8. Binary operation: +

[1] By convention, we always use "·" for multiplication.

In this example, unlike the preceding, the table can be written out completely (Table 2.5).

Table 2.5

+	1	3	6	8
1	2	4	7	9
3	4	6	9	11
6	7	9	12	14
8	9	11	14	16

Example 10. Set: {5}, that is, the set whose only element is 5.
   Binary operation: −
   Table:

−	5
5	0

In this example, the only elements to which we can apply − are 5 and 5. Thus $5 - 5 = 0$ is the only rule of "subtraction" one has to know on this set to know the rules of subtraction completely.

Example 11. Set: {1, 2, 3, 4, 5, 6, 7}.
   Binary operation: ·
Example 12. Set: {1, 2, 3, 4, 5, 6, 7}.
   Binary operation: ÷

2. Binary Operation on a Set

2.1 Definition of "Binary Operation on a Set"

Before giving further examples, let us formulate what we mean when we say a set has a binary operation defined on it. In each of the above examples, we begin with a set of objects, and then give a rule which is to be applied to any pair of objects from our set. In applying this rule, it may make a difference which object of a pair is regarded first, and which second. For instance, in Example 2 the rule applied to 9 and 4 is 5, but the rule applied to 4 and 9 is −5.

Thus, a binary operation defined on a set of objects is a rule which assigns to every pair of elements a and b taken from the set in that order, a unique third object. (The "third object" need not necessarily be different from a or from b, nor need it necessarily be an element of the original set.) We may define a binary operation on a set, then, as follows:

Definition 1. A *binary operation on a set A* is a rule which assigns to every ordered pair (a, b) taken from the set (i.e., to every element of $A \times A$) a unique third object.

2.2   Analysis of the Definition of a Binary Operation

We may think of a binary operation on a set as being a machine, as in Fig. 2.1.

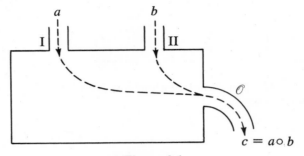

Figure 2.1

We take objects a and b from our set and put a into the pipe labeled I, b into the pipe labeled II. The machine then works away at these objects, and from the output pipe $\mathcal{O}$ is dropped an object c. If we denote the binary operation by the symbol '$\circ$', for c we shall also write $a \circ b$. That is, $a \circ b = c$.

If we put b in pipe I, and a in pipe II, the output may not be c. That is, $a \circ b$ and $b \circ a$ need not be the same.

Furthermore, we have to be allowed to put any element from our set in pipe I, and any element from our set in pipe II, in order that this machine be a binary operation for our set. It follows from this that subtraction, as defined in early grade school, would not be a binary operation on the set of natural numbers. In grade school the idea of subtraction was, say, that from 8 objects one takes away 3 objects and is left with 5 objects, so that $8 - 3 = 5$. Thus $a - b$ had meaning, there, only in the cases where a was greater than b. But this would mean that the machine could not take 3 in pipe I and 21 in pipe II, for example, since 3 is not greater than 21. Presumably, it would break down if someone tried it. But to have a binary operation on the set of natural numbers, we must be able to place *any* natural number (or in general, *any* element of the set in question) in either pipe, and obtain an "answer" from the output pipe $\mathcal{O}$. Table 2.2, on the other hand, shows $-$ used as a binary operation on the set of natural numbers.

We use the word *unique* to indicate that '$a \circ b$' does not designate more than one object. That is, if $2 + 4$ is 6, it is not true that $2 + 4$ is also 7 (unless $6 = 7$).

In machine terms, *whenever* two specific objects are dropped into the machine in the same order, the same third object is produced at $\mathcal{O}$ consistently.

However, observe that a binary operation applied to two different pairs of objects may yield the same result, as in Example 5, where $1 + 5 = 6$ and $3 + 3 = 6$.

Exercises

1. Given a set $\{1, 2, 3, 4\}$ and a binary operation $\circ$ defined by the table

$\circ$	1	2	3	4
1	1	2	3	4
2	2	3	4	1
3	3	1	5	2
4	4	1	2	7

(a) Does $3 \circ 3$ belong to the set? Does $2 \circ 2$ belong to the set?

(b) Does $2 \circ 3 = 3 \circ 2$? Does $4 \circ 3 = 3 \circ 4$?

(c) Is $(3, 5)$ an ordered pair of this set?

(d) How many ordered pairs does this set have?

(e) Does the table assign a unique third object to each of these?

(f) What is the "third object" assigned to $(2, 1)$; to $(1, 1)$; to $(4, 2)$; to $(2, 4)$? (*Note:* $3 \circ 2 = 4 \circ 2$, and yet $3 \neq 4$. Hence the "cancellation law" does not hold in this particular case.)

2. Construct the table for the binary operation and set of Example 11.

3. Construct the table for the binary operation and set of Example 12.

4. Consider the set $\{0, 1, 2\}$ with operation $\circ$ defined by the following:

$$0 \circ 1 = 2 \qquad 1 \circ 2 = 2$$
$$1 \circ 1 = 3 \qquad 0 \circ 1 = 3$$
$$2 \circ 1 = 0 \qquad 2 \circ 0 = 1$$

Is $\circ$ a binary operation on this set? Justify your answer. (This means to indicate reasons for your answer: If the answer is yes, indicate how $\circ$ fulfills *all* requirements of Definition 1; if your answer is no, it is only necessary to find *one* failure of $\circ$ to meet a condition of Definition 1.)

3. Further Examples of Binary Operations on Sets

It is not necessary to confine our sets to being sets of numbers, or our binary operations to being $+$, $-$, $\cdot$, or $\div$. We can consider any set of objects, and make up any rule at all which assigns to every ordered pair from our set a unique third object. Indeed, as in Exercise 1, we can even use the table as a way of expressing the rule, since the table reveals completely which element is to be assigned to any ordered pair from the set.

Example 13. Set: $\{a, b, c, d\}$.

Binary operation: To the ordered pair (s, t) of the set is assigned the element t.

The description of the binary operation means that the binary operation assigns to each ordered pair of elements the second element of that pair. We also could have written: "If s and t are any elements of $\{a, b, c, d\}$, then $s \circ t = t$."

In this example, $a \circ c = c$, $c \circ c = c$, $a \circ d = d$, $d \circ a = a$, etc. Observe that $a \circ d \neq d \circ a$.

From the description of the binary operation given above, we can construct Table 2.6.

Table 2.6

$\circ$	a	b	c	d
a	a	b	c	d
b	a	b	c	d
c	a	b	c	d
d	a	b	c	d

Instead of making up different symbols for different binary operations — such as $\circ$, $*$, b, $\diamond$, $\#$ — we shall use $\circ$ repeatedly in the examples to follow. Indeed, in Examples 1 and 5, we used '+' both times, even though these are different binary operations. In Example 1 it is defined on the set of natural numbers, in 5 on the set of odd natural numbers.

Example 14. Set: $\{a, b, c, d\}$.

Binary operation: Table 2.7.

Table 2.7

$\circ$	a	b	c	$\textcircled{d}$
a	a	b	c	d
$\textcircled{b}$	c	b	c	$\textcircled{a}$
c	d	a	b	c
d	a	c	d	e

To find $b \circ d$, look at b on the left and d at the top. Then $b \circ d$ is found to the right of b and below d, that is, in the second row and the fourth column of the table. One sees that $b \circ d = a$. Also $a \circ b = b$, $d \circ c = d$, $d \circ b = c$, etc.

Observe that there are 16 ordered pairs of this set; hence there are 16 entries in the table, one corresponding to each ordered pair.

Example 15. Set: The set of natural numbers.

Binary operation: $a \circ b$ is the larger of a or b when $a \neq b$; $a \circ a$ is a.

Thus $3 \circ 5 = 5$, $4 \circ 4 = 4$, $5 \circ 3 = 5$, etc. One often writes max $\{a, b\}$ for this binary operation:

$$\text{max } \{3, 5\} = 5, \qquad \text{max } \{4, 4\} = 4, \qquad \text{max } \{5, 3\} = 5, \qquad \text{etc.}$$

Example 16. Set: The set of natural numbers.

Binary operation: If $a \neq b$, $a \circ b$ is a or b, whichever is smaller; also $a \circ a = a$ for all natural numbers a.

Thus $3 \circ 15 = 3$, $15 \circ 3 = 3$, $8 \circ 8 = 8$, etc. One often writes min $\{a, b\}$ for this binary operation:

$$\text{min } \{3, 15\} = 3, \qquad \text{min } \{15, 3\} = 3, \qquad \text{min } \{8, 8\} = 8, \qquad \text{etc.}$$

Example 17. Set: $\{0, 1, 2, 3, 4, 5, 6\}$.

Binary operation: $a \circ b$ is the remainder one obtains upon dividing $a + b$ by 7.

Thus, $3 \circ 6 = 2$, since $3 + 6$ divided by 7 leaves a remainder of 2. Similarly $2 \circ 3 = 5$, $2 \circ 4 = 6$, $2 \circ 5 = 0$, $2 \circ 6 = 1$, etc.

From the above description of this binary operation, we can construct Table 2.8.

Table 2.8

$\circ$	0	1	2	3	4	5	6
0	0	1	2	3	4	5	6
1	1	2	3	4	5	6	0
2	2	3	4	5	6	0	1
3	3	4	5	6	0	1	2
4	4	5	6	0	1	2	3
5	5	6	0	1	2	3	4
6	6	0	1	2	3	4	5

Exercises

5. Given the set $\{1, 2, 3\}$, construct tables describing the following binary operations on this set:
   (a) To each ordered pair (x, y) is assigned the number 5 (that is, $x \circ y = 5$ for all elements x and y in $\{1, 2, 3\}$).
   (b) $x \circ y$ means $x + y$.
   (c) $x \circ y$ means max $\{x, y\}$.
6. Given the set $\{2, 4, 6, 8\}$ and the binary operation which assigns to every or-

dered pair (s, t) the number $(s + t)/2$, construct the table describing this binary operation.

7. Given the set $\{0, 1, 2, 3\}$. $a \circ b$ means the remainder obtained upon dividing $a + b$ by 4. Construct the table describing this binary operation.

8. Consider the set $A \times B$, where A is the set $\{2, 4\}$ and B the set $\{1, 3, 5\}$. If (a, b) and (c, d) are elements of $A \times B$, let $*$ be the binary operation defined by

$$(a, b) * (c, d) = (ac, b - d)$$

Construct the table.

4. Binary Operations Defined on $[S]$

4.1   The Binary Operation of Intersection on $[S]$

For S a set, we showed in Chapter 1 how one can form a new set $[S]$ consisting of the subsets of S. Thus, $A \in [S]$ means that $A \subseteq S$. $[S]$ was called the power set of S.

Our next example of a binary operation will be defined on the power set of a set.

Example 18. Set: $[S]$ where $S = \{a, b, c\}$.
   Binary operation: If G and H are subsets of S (hence elements of $[S]$), $G \circ H = K$ will mean that K is the subset of S (or element of $[S]$, therefore) consisting of the elements which are in *both* the given sets G and H.

The set on which we are defining this binary operation is $\{\varnothing, \{a\}, \{b\}, \{c\}, \{a, b\}, \{a, c\}, \{b, c\}, \{a, b, c\}\} = [S]$. To find $\{a, b\} \circ \{b, c\}$, for example, we are to look for the elements appearing in both $\{a, b\}$ and $\{b, c\}$. The only such element is b. Hence the set consisting of b, i.e., $\{b\}$, is the result

$$\{a, b\} \circ \{b, c\} = \{b\}$$

Similarly, $\{a\} \circ \{a, c\} = \{a\}$, since a is the only element of S which is in both $\{a\}$ and $\{a, c\}$.

Other examples follow:

$$\{a\} \circ \{b, c\} = \varnothing$$
$$\{a, b, c\} \circ \{b, c\} = \{b, c\}$$
$$\{b\} \circ \{c\} = \varnothing$$
$$\{a, b\} \circ \varnothing = \varnothing$$
$$\{c\} \circ \{c\} = \{c\}$$

It is customary to use the symbol '$\cap$' for this binary operation. Thus, we write $\{a, b\} \cap \{b, c\} = \{b\}$, and say "$\{a, b\}$ *cap* (or *intersected with*, or *intersect*) $\{b, c\}$ is equal to $\{b\}$," or "the *intersection* of $\{a, b\}$ and $\{b, c\}$ is $\{b\}$." Similarly,

$\{a\} \cap \{a, c\} = \{a\}$
$\{a, b, c\}$ cap $\{b, c\}$ is $\{b, c\}$; i.e., $\{a, b, c\} \cap \{b, c\} = \{b, c\}$
$\{a, b\}$ intersected with $\{a, c\}$ is $\{a\}$; i.e., $\{a, b\} \cap \{a, c\} = \{a\}$

We indicate, partially, the table for this set and binary operation as Table 2.9; the student is invited (Exercise 10a) to complete the table.

Table 2.9

$\cap$	$\varnothing$	$\{a\}$	$\{b\}$	$\{c\}$	$\{a, b\}$	$\{a, c\}$	$\{b, c\}$	$\{a, b, c\}$
$\varnothing$	$\varnothing$	$\varnothing$	$\varnothing$	$\varnothing$	$\varnothing$	$\varnothing$	$\varnothing$	$\varnothing$
$\{a\}$	$\varnothing$	$\{a\}$	$\varnothing$	$\varnothing$	$\{a\}$	$\{a\}$	$\varnothing$	$\{a\}$
$\{b\}$					$\{b\}$	$\varnothing$	$\{b\}$	$\{b\}$
$\{c\}$						$\{c\}$	$\{c\}$	
$\{a, b\}$						$\{a\}$	$\{b\}$	
$\{a, c\}$						$\{a, c\}$	$\{c\}$	
$\{b, c\}$								
$\{a, b, c\}$								

Although we defined $\cap$ on $[S]$ above in the case where $S = \{a, b, c\}$, it is clear that if T is any other set, one could define the binary operation of intersection on $[T]$. One again uses the notation '$\cap$' for this operation. Thus, if M and N are elements of $[T]$, then $M \cap N$ is the subset of T consisting of the elements of T common to both M and N. The subset $M \cap N$ of T is then called the *intersection* of M and N (or also M cap N, or M intersect N).

According to our definition of $M \cap N$, we see that $t \in M \cap N$ if and only if $t \in M$ and $t \in N$.

Example 19. Set: $[T]$, where T is the set of points in a plane.
    Binary operation: $\cap$

Of course, in this example, it would be impossible to construct a complete table. One can only indicate the results for sample elements. For example, assume T is the set of points in the plane of the page, and let A and B be the sets of points on the circumference and interior of the two intersecting circles in Fig. 2.2, respectively. Thus, $A \in [T]$ and $B \in [T]$.

Then $A \cap B$ is the set of points common to A and to B, which is the shaded portion.

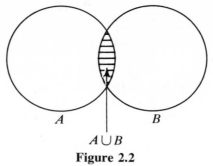

$$A \cup B$$

Figure 2.2

4.2   *The Binary Operation of Union on* [S]

Example 20. Set: [S], where $S = \{a, b, c\}$.

Binary operation: If G and H are subsets of S, $G \circ H = K$ shall mean that K is the subset of S consisting of the elements which are either in G or in H.[2] Another way to phrase this is to say that K is the subset of S consisting of the elements which are in at least one of the subsets G and H.

Thus, $\{a, b\} \circ \{b, c\} = \{a, b, c\}$, since $a \in \{a, b\}$, $b \in \{a, b\}$ (and also $b \in \{b, c\}$, and $c \in \{b, c\}$).

Similarly, $\{a, b\} \circ \{b\} = \{a, b\}$; $\{a\} \circ \varnothing = \{a\}$; $\{a\} \circ \{b\} = \{a, b\}$; etc.

It is customary to use the symbol '$\cup$' for this binary operation. Thus we write $\{a, b\} \cup \{b, c\} = \{a, b, c\}$, and say "$\{a, b\}$ *cup* (or *union*) $\{b, c\}$ is equal to $\{a, b, c\}$." One also says "the *union* of $\{a, b\}$ and $\{b, c\}$ is $\{a, b, c\}$."

Similarly $\{a\} \cup \{c\} = \{a, c\}$; $\varnothing \cup \varnothing = \varnothing$; $\{a\} \cup \{a, b, c\} = \{a, b, c\}$; $\{b\} \cup \varnothing = \{b\}$; etc.

As with intersection, one can define the binary operation of union on [T] for any set T. One again uses the notation '$\cup$' for this operation.

According to our definition of $M \cup N$ for M and N subsets of T, an element $t \in M \cup N$ if and only if $t \in M$ or $t \in N$.

Example 21. Set: [T], where T is the set of points in a plane (say the plane of this page)

Binary operation: $\cup$

Let A and B be the circles in Fig. 2.3, as in Example 19.
Then $A \cup B$ is the shaded portion.

---

[2] When we use the word "or" in a sentence of the type "this *or* that," we shall always assume that the phrase "or both" is understood. If we do not wish this additional phrase to be understood, we will say explicitly, "this or that but not both."

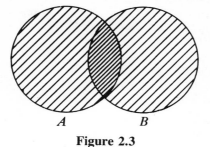

Figure 2.3

Exercises

9. Let $A = \{a, b, c\}$, $B = \{b, c, d\}$; answer whether the following statements are true or false:

(a) $\{a, b\} \cup \{a\} = \{a\}$.   (f) $c \in A \cap B$.

(b) $\{a, b\} \cap \{a\} = \{b\}$.   (g) $A \cap B = \{b, c\}$.

(c) $\{a\} \subseteq A \cup B$.

(d) $d \in A \cap B$.

(e) $a \in \{a\} \cap B$.

10. (a) Construct the table for the set and binary operation given in Example 18.

   (b) The same for Example 20.

11. Given $S = \{1, 2\}$.

   (a) Find $[S]$.

   (b) Construct the table describing the binary operation *union* on the set $[S]$.

   (c) Construct the table describing the binary operation *intersection* on the set $[S]$.

12. Same as Exercise 11 with $S = \{3, 4, 5\}$.

13. Given $Y = \{2, 3\}$.

   (a) Find $Y \times Y$.

   (b) Graph $Y \times Y$.

   (c) Construct the table of the binary operation on $Y \times Y$ defined by $(a, b) \circ (c, d) = (a \cdot d, b \cdot c)$. [For example, $(2, 2) \circ (2, 3) = (6, 4)$.]

14. Same as (13) with $Y = \{1, 2, 3\}$.

15. Suppose A and B are sets, and $A \cup B = \{1, 2, 3\}$ and $A \cap B = \{2\}$.

   (a) What is the largest number of elements that A can have and what are they?

   (b) What is the least number of elements that A can have and what are they?

   (c) If A has two elements, how many elements must B have? Give an example.

16. Let

$$X = \{1, 2, 3, 4, 5, 6\}$$
$$A = \{1, 2, 3\}$$
$$B = \{2, 3, 5, 6\}$$
$$C = \{2, 4, 6\}$$

Find:
(a) $A \cup B.$ (e) $A \cap C.$
(b) $C \cup A.$ (f) $A \cap X.$
(c) $B \cup B.$ (g) $X \cup X.$
(d) $A \cap A.$ (h) $X \cup \emptyset.$

17. Let $X = \{a, b, c, d, e\}$, $A \subseteq X$, $B \subseteq X$. If $A = \{a, b\}$, $A \cap B = \{a\}$, and $A \cup B = X$, what is B?

chapter iii

EQUATIONS IN A SET

One of the classical mathematical problems is the determination of solutions of equations. For example, one may wish to find a natural number—call it α—such that $(\alpha \cdot \alpha) + (2 \cdot \alpha) = 3$. If one tries 1, he will see that this is such a number: $(1 \cdot 1) + (2 \cdot 1) = 3$. Trying 2, 3, and 4, he will see that none of these works. This is a primitive approach to the problem—trying each number in turn—but one which reveals clearly what one is searching for in finding a solution of an equation.

In the above equation, if one tries -3 for α, he also obtains a solution; but -3 is not a natural number. Thus, in determining solutions of equations, it is important to know in what set one is working.

We shall in this chapter, therefore, consider the problem of solving equations in sets with binary operation(s) defined on them. For this, we first must consider the meaning of *equality*, of *variable*, and of *equation* in a set. We then take up equations in one and more variables. The method for solving such equations considered at this time is essentially the one referred to above.[1]

1. Equality

1.1 Elements and Names of Elements

In our preceding discussions, we have often made the statement that something is equal to something else. For example, $7 + 3 = 10$, or also $6 + 4 = 8 + 2$, or we could also say $10 = 10$, and so on. What we mean by the statement $7 + 3 = 10$ is that $7 + 3$ and 10 are the same natural numbers, or also that '7 + 3' and '10' are names for the same natural number.

We see a need, here, to distinguish between the ideas of (1) a natural number, and (2) a name for a natural number. For example, a person may be named 'Mary.' When you say: "Mary, are you there?" you are probably referring to a person rather than to the four-letter word 'Mary.' On the other hand, if someone walks up to her and asks her what her name is, it would be of no interest if she pointed to herself. Rather, he really wants to know the *name* of this person: 'Mary.'

When we use single quotation marks around a word, we shall always be

---

[1] It is, of course, impossible to try out every element of an infinite set. Thus, in the set of natural numbers, we make greater use of one's background in adding, subtracting, multiplying, and dividing.

referring to the word itself, that is, to the *name* of the object it represents. Thus 'Mary' is a four-letter word, but Mary is a person. Similarly 3 is a natural number, but '3' is the name of a natural number.

Thus $6 + 4 = 8 + 2$ states that $6 + 4$ and $8 + 2$ are the same natural numbers; it also says that '$6 + 4$' and '$8 + 2$' are names, in this case different names, for the same natural number.

A binary operation on a set, besides being a certain type of rule, may be thought of as introducing new names for elements. For example, suppose we consider the natural numbers as named by the symbols: '1,' '2,' '3,' etc. Now defining the binary operation $+$ on this set introduces the new name '$1 + 2$' for the natural number named by '3.' Another name for 3 is '$2 + 1$.' Similarly, defining the binary operation $-$ on this set introduces the new name '$1 - 3$' for -2. (One observes that in this case the element -2 is not in the original set.)

Again, suppose $A = \{a, b, c, d\}$. Then we have four elements in A, namely a, b, c, and d. The name of a is 'a'; of b is 'b'; of c is 'c'; and of d is 'd.' Now let $\circ$ be the binary operation on A defined by Table 3.1.

Table 3.1

$\circ$	a	b	c	d
a	a	H	g	c
b	d	a	b	b
c	α	5	$\#$	$\diamondsuit$
d	π	e	a	d

Then some names for the element a are

$$\text{'}a\text{,' '}a \circ a\text{,' '}b \circ b\text{,' '}d \circ c\text{'}$$

Some names for b are

$$\text{'}b \circ c\text{,' '}b \circ d\text{,' '}b\text{'}$$

Similarly $a \circ d = c$, or '$a \circ d$' and 'c' are names of c; also '$c \circ a$' and 'α' are names for α.

1.2   The Use of Parentheses

In the statement $7 + 3 = 10$, one may wish to replace '3' by '$2 + 1$' as a name for 3. In this case, we employ parentheses [2] around '$2 + 1$' to

---

[2] In addition to using parentheses, we shall also use brackets, [   ], and braces, {   }. (See Exercises 2, 5, and 6.) The brackets can usually be distinguished from power set notation, and the braces from set notation, by the context.

indicate that the sum is treated as a single element. Thus $7 + (2 + 1)$ is another way of writing $7 + 3$. Similarly $7 - (3 + 1)$ means $7 - 4$; $3 \cdot (5 - 3)$ means $3 \cdot 2$; $(3 + 2) - (4 - 2)$ means $5 - 2$; etc.

The symbol '$3 + 2 + 4$' has no meaning, since $+$ is a binary operation and can handle only two elements at a time. However, '$(3 + 2) + 4$' and '$3 + (2 + 4)$' are both legitimate expressions, for $5 + 4$ and $3 + 6$, respectively.

It happens in this particular instance that $(3 + 2) + 4 = 3 + (2 + 4)$, so the manner of grouping these three elements does not matter. But $(3 - 2) - 4 \neq 3 - (2 - 4)$, and in general two different ways of grouping elements may yield different results. In Example 14 of Chapter 2, $b \circ (a \circ c) = b \circ (c) = c$. But $(b \circ a) \circ c = (c) \circ c = b$; hence $b \circ (a \circ c) \neq (b \circ a) \circ c$.

Expressions can be more complicated, as in $8 + (3 + (1 + 2))$. This means 8 is added to the number in the outer set of parentheses, that is, to $(3 + (1 + 2))$. But $3 + (1 + 2)$ is $3 + 3$ or 6. So 8 is added to 6, which is 14. This may be written out formally as follows: [3]

$$8 + (3 + (1 + 2)) = 8 + (3 + 3)$$
$$= 8 + 6$$
$$= 14$$

We may consider sets on which two binary operations are defined, in which case parentheses are useful in clarifying the meaning of complicated expressions. For example, the binary operations $+$ and $\cdot$ are defined on the set of natural numbers. Then

$$\{[8 \cdot (3 + 5)] + 2\} \cdot (6 + 4)$$

is the product of *two* natural numbers, namely $[8 \cdot (3 + 5)] + 2$ and $6 + 4$. The first number is the sum of $8 \cdot (3 + 5)$ and 2, the second is the sum of 6 and 4. Then $8 \cdot (3 + 5)$ can be broken down further, and the result may be written

$$\{[8 \cdot (3 + 5)] + 2\} \cdot (6 + 4) = \{[8 \cdot 8] + 2\} \cdot 10$$
$$= \{64 + 2\} \cdot 10$$
$$= 66 \cdot 10$$
$$= 660$$

It is important that the signs designating binary operations always appear between only two elements of the set. Even when they did not in your earlier work, as in

$$7 + 3 + 5 + 6$$

[3] The left side of the first equal sign, i.e., '$8 + (3 + (1 + 2))$,' is assumed to appear on the left sides of the second and third equal signs. Thus the concluding line is $8 + (3 + (1 + 2)) = 14$.

you really thought of this as $[(7 + 3) + 5] + 6$; for in adding these figures, you probably said to yourself: "$7 + 3$ is 10 and 5 is 15 and 6 is 21."

1.3   Restrictions on the Use of Equality

The notion of equality as we are using it is one which has meaning in a particular mathematical system, and does not apply to elements coming from different systems. If in a given discussion we are considering the set of lines in a plane, we may call a particular *line* by the name '*a*.' However, in another discussion we may be considering the points on the circumference of a circle, and we may also call a particular *point* by the name '*a*.'

Although in a particular system, we do not give the same name to different elements, in different systems this may well occur. Thus we may consider the system of Example 13 of Chapter 2, which involves a set $\{a, b, c, d\}$ and a binary operation $\circ$. In Example 14 we considered a set $\{a, b, c, d\}$ whose elements may or may not be the same as the ones in Example 13, and another binary operation $\circ$. In Example 13, $c \circ b = b$; whereas in Example 14, $c \circ b \neq b$.

If one wished to consider a system involving the set $\{a, b, c, d\}$ and both the binary operations of Examples 13 and 14, then he would have to use different notations for these binary operations. If we retained '$\circ$' for Example 13, we could use '$*$' for 14. Then $c \circ b = b$, and $c * b = a$.

A similar situation arises in the study of the set of natural numbers. One may wish to consider the system consisting of the set of natural numbers, together with the binary operations, say, of addition and multiplication. Then one must use different names for these binary operations, such as '$+$' and '$\cdot$'. Otherwise, one would be calling different numbers by the same name.

In discussing equality of sets, the understanding is that we are considering a large enough set of elements, say S, so that all the sets appearing in the discussion are subsets of S. Then to say two sets are equal means that they are the same elements of $[S]$. Thus $B \cup B = B$ means that '$B \cup B$' and 'B' are names for the same element of $[S]$.

Exercises

1. Compute the following:
   (a) $(6 + 3) + 2$.   (c) $(6 - 3) - 2$.
   (b) $6 + (3 + 2)$.   (d) $6 - (3 - 2)$.
2. Compute $\{[(2 + 4) \cdot 3] + 2\} \cdot [1 + (3 \cdot 3)]$.
3. Let $\circ$ be the binary operation on the set $\{1, 2, 3\}$ defined by the table

○	1	2	3
1	1	2	3
2	2	3	2
3	3	1	2

Compute the following:

(a) $2 \circ (3 \circ 2)$.

(b) $(2 \circ 3) \circ 2$.

(c) $[(2 \circ 3) \circ 2] \circ (3 \circ 2)$.

4. Let ○ be the binary operation on the set $\{1, 2, 3\}$ defined by the table

○	1	2	3
1	1	2	3
2	2	3	2
3	3	2	4

Compute the following:

(a) $(2 \circ 3) \circ 2$.   (c) $(2 \circ 3) \circ 3$.

(b) $2 \circ (3 \circ 2)$.   (d) $2 \circ (3 \circ 3)$.

5. Consider the set $\{a, b, c, d\}$ on which the binary operations ○ and ∗ are defined by the following tables:

○	a	b	c	d
a	a	b	c	d
b	b	c	d	a
c	c	d	a	b
d	d	a	b	c

∗	a	b	c	d
a	a	a	a	a
b	b	b	b	b
c	c	c	c	c
d	d	d	d	d

Compute:

(a) $a \circ b, a * b, (c \circ c) * b, c \circ (c * b)$.

(b) $d * [a * (b * c)]$.

(c) $[(c \circ d) \circ b] * [(b * a) \circ c]$.

6. Given the sets $A = \{a, b, c\}, B = \{b, c, d\}, C = \{a, d\}$, compute:

(a) $(A \cup B) \cup C, (A \cap B) \cap C, (A \cup B) \cap C, A \cup (B \cap C)$.

(b) $(A \cap B) \cup (B \cap C), (B \cap C) \cup (A \cap C), (A \cup B) \cup (B \cup C)$.

(c) $\{[(B \cap C) \cup A] \cap B\} \cap C$.

2. Equations

2.1 Equations Having No Variables

An equation in a set X is a statement asserting that two elements of the set are in fact identical; that is, that one element of the set is equal to the other element of the set. Or it may also be regarded as a statement that two names designate the same element of the set. The statement itself may be either true or false.

For example, the following are equations in the set of natural numbers:

$$3 + 2 = 4 + 1$$
$$5 + 2 = 4 + 3$$
$$2 + 4 = 4 + 2$$
$$3 + 5 = 7 + 5$$
$$8 + 8 = 4 \cdot 11$$
$$9 + 3 = 12$$
$$4 \cdot 2 = 8 \cdot 1$$
$$4 \cdot 3 = [(6 \cdot (2 + 5)] - 30$$
$$5 \cdot 3 = 3 \cdot 5$$
$$6 = 7$$

Some of the above are true statements, and others false. But nevertheless, each asserts that one natural number is identical with another natural number, and hence each is an equation in the set of natural numbers.

2.2 Variables

Instead of making a statement about a particular natural number, one may wish to refer to more than one natural number or even any natural number. For example, one may wish to consider all equations of the type

$$2 \cdot (\ \ ) = 6$$

where any natural number may appear in the parentheses. Thus he is considering the statements:

$$2 \cdot 1 = 6$$
$$2 \cdot 2 = 6$$
$$2 \cdot 3 = 6$$
$$2 \cdot 4 = 6 \qquad \text{etc.}$$

In this case only one of the equations is true. The parentheses indicate the place where natural numbers are to be substituted. It is customary to use a letter as a symbol for this "place-holder," and write

$$2 \cdot x = 6$$

and then to specify the set from which elements are drawn to replace x. Thus $2 \cdot x = 6$ is not a statement, but, so to speak, a form which many statements have. Meaningful statements occur upon replacement of 'x' by symbols designating elements of the set in question.

More generally, *x is a variable over a set A* means x is a place-holder for which elements of A may be substituted to make statements. Although we are at present interested in variables appearing in equations, variables may be used in statements other than those concerning equality, as we shall see in Chapter 7.

2.3   Equations in One Variable; Solution Sets

In the above illustration we call $2 \cdot x = 6$ an equation in one variable over the set of natural numbers. Here we used the symbol 'x' to designate the *variable* or *place-holder;* the symbols '2' and '6,' on the other hand, designate specific elements. We shall call 2 and 6 *constants* as opposed to x, which is a *variable.*

In Section 2.1 we considered equations in which no variables appeared. Such an equation was an assertion that two expressions are names for the same element. An equation in one variable x over a set A represents a *collection* of such assertions, one for each replacement of x by an element of the given set A.

The subset of the set A whose elements, upon replacement for the variable — say x — yield correct assertions, is called the *solution set* (of the equation). Thus in the equation $2 \cdot x = 6$ over the set of natural numbers, $\{3\}$ is the solution set. The elements of the solution set are called *solutions.* Hence 3 is a solution of $2 \cdot x = 6$ over N.

If in $2 \cdot x = 6$, x is a variable over the set of even natural numbers, then the solution set is $\varnothing$, i.e., the null set, since *no* even natural number, when substituted for the variable, yields a correct assertion.

In Example 14 of Chapter 2, we considered the set $\{a, b, c, d\}$, with binary operation $\circ$ defined by Table 3.2. Let $x \circ x = x$ be an equation in

Table 3.2

$\circ$	a	b	c	d
a	a	b	c	d
b	c	b	c	a
c	d	a	b	c
d	a	c	d	e

the variable x over $\{a, b, c, d\}$. From the table we see that $\{a, b\}$ is the solution set; i.e., $a \circ a = a$ and $b \circ b = b$ are both correct assertions; but $c \circ c = c$ and $d \circ d = d$ are false statements, so that c and d are not solutions.

Let p be a variable over the set of natural numbers. Consider the equation $p + 2 = 2 + p$. The solution set is the entire set of natural numbers, since when p is replaced by any natural number, the statement obtained is true.

All these are examples of equations in one variable over a set X.

Definition 1. Let S be the solution set of an equation in one variable over a set X. (Thus, $S \subseteq X$.) If $S = X$, the equation is called an *identity;* if S is a proper subset of X, the equation is said to be *conditional*.

Thus in the above examples:

$2 \cdot x = 6$ is conditional over the set of natural numbers
$2 \cdot x = 6$ is conditional over the even natural numbers
$x \circ x = x$ is conditional over the set of Example 14
$p + 2 = 2 + p$ is an identity over the set of natural numbers

Definition 2. To *solve an equation* shall mean to find its solution set.

Example 1. Let $X = \{2, 4, 7, a, b\}$, and $\circ$ the binary operation on X defined by Table 3.3. Solve the equation $x \circ 7 = a \circ x$, where x is a variable over X.

Table 3.3

$\circ$	2	4	7	a	b
2	2	4	7	a	b
4	4	8	10	9	a
7	7	6	a	c	r
a	a	4	2	7	2
b	b	7	a	y	π

Solution: (i) Replace x by 2. On the left we obtain $2 \circ 7$ or 7; on the right $a \circ 2$ or a. Hence 2 is not a solution.

(ii) Replace x by 4. We obtain $4 \circ 7 = a \circ 4$, or $10 = 4$. As we shall assume the table does not introduce new names for elements of our set, so that $10 \neq 4$, we see that 4 is not a solution.

(iii) Replace x by 7. We obtain $7 \circ 7 = a \circ 7$, or $a = 2$. Hence 7 is not a solution.

(iv) Replace x by a. We obtain $a \circ 7 = a \circ a$, or $2 = 7$. Hence a is not a solution.

(v) Replace x by b. We obtain $b \circ 7 = a \circ b$, or $a = 2$. Hence b is not a solution.

It follows that $\emptyset$ is the solution set.

Example 2. Let X and $\circ$ be as in Example 1. Solve the equation $x \circ 2 = 2 \circ x$ in the variable x over X.

Solution: We consider the five cases as in Example 1.

(i) $2 \circ 2 = 2 \circ 2$. Hence 2 is a solution.

(ii) $4 \circ 2 = 2 \circ 4$ or $4 = 4$. Hence 4 is a solution.

(iii) $7 \circ 2 = 2 \circ 7$ or $7 = 7$. Hence 7 is a solution.

(iv) $a \circ 2 = 2 \circ a$ or $a = a$. Hence a is a solution.

(v) $b \circ 2 = 2 \circ b$ or $b = b$. Hence b is a solution.

The solution set is therefore X, and the equation $x \circ 2 = 2 \circ x$ is an identity (over X).

Example 3. Let X and $\circ$ be as above. Solve the equation $x \circ 4 = 4 \circ x$.

Solution: Upon following the procedures in Examples 1 and 2, the solution set is seen to be $\{2, 4\}$.

2.4   Equations in More Than One Variable

We may also have equations in more than one variable. For example, consider the equation in the variables a, b over the set of natural numbers: $a + b = 3$. In this case, solutions will be pairs of natural numbers. If we try 1 for a and 1 for b, the equation becomes $1 + 1 = 3$, which is false. Trying 1 for a and 2 for b, we get $1 + 2 = 3$, which is correct.

The problem is best handled by considering as solutions ordered pairs of natural numbers. If we arrange the variables in a specific order, say (a, b), and if A denotes the set of natural numbers, then the solutions are elements of $A \times A$, and the solution set is a subset of $A \times A$.

We observed above that $(1, 1)$ is not a solution of $a + b = 3$, but $(1, 2)$ is a solution. In each case, the first element of the ordered pair is substituted for the variable which has been designated as "first" (in this case a), and the second element is substituted for the second variable. Further trial shows the complete solution set is $\{(1, 2), (2, 1)\}$.

If we represent $A \times A$ graphically, we may indicate the solution set by circling the appropriate points (Fig. 3.1).

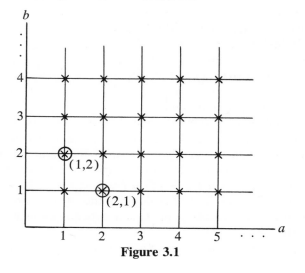

Figure 3.1

Note that in this representation of the solution set, we label the first horizontal line 'a,' the first vertical line 'b.' This indicates the order of the variables. We shall call these lines, respectively, the a-axis and b-axis.

As a further example, the equation $j - k = 2$ in two variables j and k (in that order) over the set of natural numbers has a solution set $\{(3, 1), (4, 2), (5, 3), \ldots\}$.

Graphically, we obtain Fig. 3.2.

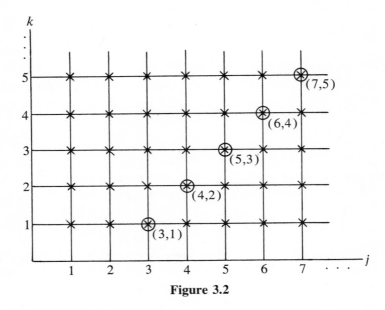

Figure 3.2

Similarly, if we have an equation in three variables, a, b, c, over a set X, then the solution set will be a subset of $X \times X \times X$, and its elements (the solutions of the equation) will be ordered triples.

The definitions of *identity* and *conditional equation* may be extended to equations involving more than one variable. For example, an equation in two variables over a set X is said to be an *identity* if its solution set is $X \times X$. Otherwise (i.e., if its solution set is a proper subset of $X \times X$), it is said to be *conditional*.

Letters, as well as other symbols, may denote constants. For example, '7' denotes the natural number 7. But we can also let t be a constant in the natural numbers. Then if x is a variable over the natural numbers, the equation $x + t = 5$ is an equation in one variable, with solution set $\{4\}$ if $t = 1$, $\{3\}$ if $t = 2$, $\{2\}$ if $t = 3$, $\{1\}$ if $t = 4$. If $t \neq 1, 2, 3, 4$, then the solution set is $\varnothing$. In any case, if A denotes the set of natural numbers, then the solution set is a subset of A, and depends upon which natural number t represents.

On the other hand, if both x and t are variables over A, in that order, the solution set is a subset of $A \times A$, and in fact is $\{(4, 1), (3, 2), (2, 3), (1, 4)\}$.

2.5   An Example

We consider an example of an equation in a set, where the set has three binary operations defined on it.

Thus, let $M = \{1, 2, 3\}$, and let $+$, $-$, and $\circ$ be binary operations defined on M according to Tables 3.4.

Tables 3.4

+	1	2	3
1	3	t	1
2	g	3	1
3	1	2	2

−	1	2	3
1	2	2	α
2	R	1	2
3	3	1	g

$\circ$	1	2	3
1	1	1	g
2	t	1	π
3	1	1	α

Problem: Solve the equation $(x - x) + y = x \circ (y + y)$, where x and y are variables over M.

Solution: We regard the order of the variables as x followed by y. To solve this equation, we must replace (x, y) by each element of $M \times M$. As there are nine elements of $M \times M$, we have nine cases to consider.

(1) *Replace (x, y) by $(1, 1)$.*

We obtain: $(1 - 1) + 1 = 1 \circ (1 + 1)$
$$2 + 1 = 1 \circ 3$$
$$g = g$$

Hence $(1, 1)$ *is* a solution.

(2) *We next consider $(1, 2)$.*
$$(1 - 1) + 2 = 1 \circ (2 + 2)$$
$$2 + 2 = 1 \circ 3$$
$$3 = g$$

Hence $(1, 2)$ *is not* a solution.

(3) *$(1, 3)$*
$$(1 - 1) + 3 = 1 \circ (3 + 3)$$
$$2 + 3 = 1 \circ 2$$
$$1 = 1$$

Hence $(1, 3)$ *is* a solution.

(4) *$(2, 1)$*
$$(2 - 2) + 1 = 2 \circ (1 + 1)$$
$$1 + 1 = 2 \circ 3$$
$$3 = \pi$$

Hence $(2, 1)$ *is not* a solution.

(5) *$(2, 2)$*
$$(2 - 2) + 2 = 2 \circ (2 + 2)$$
$$1 + 2 = 2 \circ 3$$
$$t = \pi$$

Hence (2, 2) *is not* a solution.

(6) *(2, 3)*

$$(2 - 2) + 3 = 2 \circ (3 + 3)$$
$$1 + 3 = 2 \circ 2$$
$$1 = 1$$

Hence (2, 3) *is* a solution.

(7) *(3, 1)*

$$(3 - 3) + 1 = 3 \circ (1 + 1)$$
$$g + 1 = 3 \circ 3$$

Here we see that the left-hand side is undefined, since + is a binary operation on M, and $g \notin M$. Thus, replacing (x, y) by (3, 1) produces a meaningless (and hence not a true) statement. Thus (3, 1) *is not* a solution.

(8) and (9) *(3, 2) and (3, 3) are not* solutions. The reasoning is as in (7).

The solution set is, therefore,

$$\{(1, 1), (1, 3), (2, 3)\}$$

Graphically, we obtain Fig. 3.3.

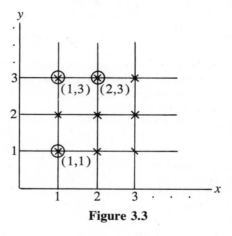

Figure 3.3

2.6   *Further Examples*

Consider the equation $x + (y - y) = 5$, where x and y are variables over the natural numbers. (Unless otherwise specified, we assume the order of the variables is according to their appearance in the alphabet.) The solution set is, clearly,

$$\{(5, 1), (5, 2), (5, 3), (5, 4), \ldots\}$$

One sees that an ordered pair is in the solution set as long as the first number is 5. The second number can be any natural number. In such a case one often writes the equation as

$$x = 5$$

and specifies this to be an equation in two variables x and y. In this case, (a, b) is a solution if upon substituting a wherever x appears and b wherever y appears, one obtains a correct statement.

As a further illustration, consider the equation

$$x + y = 2$$

where this is to be regarded as an equation in three variables, say, x, y, and z over the natural numbers. The solution set is then

$$\{(1, 1, 1), (1, 1, 2), (1, 1, 3), \ldots\}$$

On the other hand, regarded as an equation in two variables, the solution set is

$$\{(1, 1)\}$$

Exercises

7. If x is a variable over the set of natural numbers, find the solution sets of the following equations. State whether the equations are identities, or conditional.
   (a) $x + 3 = 5$. (e) $x + 1 = 100$.
   (b) $2 + x = x + 2$. (f) $2 \cdot x = 5$.
   (c) $x - 3 = 5$. (g) $5 - x = 10$.
   (d) $x + 1 = 4$.

8. Same as Exercise 7, but with x a variable over the set $\{1, 2, 3\}$. (The binary operations $+$ and $\cdot$ defined as they were for the set of natural numbers.)

9. Same as Exercise 7, but with x a variable over the set of even natural numbers.

10. Let t be a variable over the set $\{a, b, c\}$, and $\circ$ a binary operation defined by the table

$\circ$	a	b	c
a	c	a	b
b	a	b	c
c	b	c	a

Solve the following equations:
   (a) $t \circ a = b$. (d) $t \circ b = b \circ t$.
   (b) $a \circ t = b$. (e) $t \circ (b \circ c) = a \circ a$.
   (c) $t \circ (a \circ b) = a \circ b$.

Which of the above are identities, and which conditional equations?

11. If X is a variable over the set $[\{a, b, c, d\}]$ (observe this is the *power set* of $\{a, b, c, d\}$), solve the following equations:
   (a) $X \cup \{a, b, c\} = \{a, b, c, d\}$.
   (b) $\{a, b, c, d\} \cap X = \{a, b\}$.
   (c) $\{a, b\} \cap X = \varnothing$.
   (d) $(\{a, b, c\} \cap \{a, b\}) \cup X = \{a, b, c, d\} \cap \{a, b, c\}$.
   (e) $(X \cup \{a, b\}) \cap \{b, c, d\} = \{b, c\}$.

(f) $X \cup \{b, c\} = X \cap \{b, c, d\}$.

12. If x and y are variables over the set of natural numbers, find the solution sets of the following equations, and indicate the solution sets graphically:
    (a) $(2 \cdot x) + y = 5$.
    (b) $x + y = 1$.
    (c) $x \cdot y = 2$.

13. Same as Exercise 12, but with x and y variables over $\{0, 1, 2\}$, with the binary operations defined by

+	0	1	2
0	0	1	2
1	1	2	3
2	2	3	4

·	0	1	2
0	0	0	0
1	0	1	2
2	0	2	4

14. If x and y are variables over $\{1, 2, 3\}$ with binary operation $\circ$ defined by the table on the right, solve the following equations
    (i) as equations in two variables;
    (ii) as equations in three variables.
    (iii) Indicate the solutions of (i) graphically.

    (a) $x \circ y = 3$.
    (b) $y \circ y = 3$.
    (c) $2 \circ x = y$.
    (d) $2 \circ y = x$.
    (e) $2 \circ y = y$.
    (f) $x \circ 3 = 3 \circ y$.
    (g) $x \circ x = x$.

$\circ$	1	2	3
1	1	2	3
2	2	3	1
3	3	1	2

15. Given the set $\{a, b, c\}$ with binary operation $\circ$ defined by the table, find the solution set of the equation $x \circ a = c$
    (a) when considered as an equation in one variable (x);
    (b) when considered as an equation in two variables (x, y);
    (c) when considered as an equation in three variables (x, y, z).

$\circ$	a	b	c
a	b	c	a
b	c	a	b
c	a	b	c

16. Given that x and y are variables over the set of natural numbers, find the solution set of $(3 \cdot x) + y = 7$
    (a) when considered as an equation in two variables;
    (b) when considered as an equation in three variables.

chapter iv

TRANSITION FROM ARITHMETIC TO ALGEBRA

Up to now, we considered sets, sets with binary operations, and equations over these sets involving the given binary operations. The approach we took to solving equations was, essentially, to try each element of the set. This is what we refer to as the *arithmetic* approach. In this chapter we discuss the transition from this to the *algebraic* approach. This latter approach involves determining general rules which hold for some or all elements of the given set. Using such rules, one can often pass from a given equation to a simpler one having the same solution set. Solving this simpler equation, therefore, solves the original one.

We then turn to a discussion of some of the rules which arise in various systems. In particular we discuss sets with binary operations in which we have the following (defined and elaborated in Section 3):
- (a) Closure.
- (b) Associativity.
- (c) Commutativity.
- (d) An identity.
- (e) Elements having inverses.
- (f) Distributive law.

1. Algebraic Methods

1.1 Algebraic Methods in Learning Tables

In first learning the addition table for the natural numbers, when you saw $5 + 3$ you would try to memorize that the answer was 8. The answer was also 8 for $3 + 5$. It perhaps occurred to you that it was foolish to memorize the answer for $5 + 3$ and also $3 + 5$, since changing the order never changed the answer. In our language, you were making use of the fact that the equation

$$x + y = y + x$$

is an identity in the variables x and y over the natural numbers. As a result, in learning the addition table for the natural numbers from 1 to 6, for example, it was enough to learn the part indicated in Table 4.1. To find $3 + 5$, you look up $5 + 3$ and find the answer 8. Thus $3 + 5 = 8$ also. Observing the above identity was one of your early glimpses into the algebra of natural numbers under addition.

47

Table 4.1

+	1	2	3	4	5	6
1	2					
2	3	4				
3	4	5	6			
4	5	6	7	8		
5	6	7	8	9	10	
6	7	8	9	10	11	12

Let us follow the transition from arithmetic to algebra in another example. Consider the set $\{a, b, c, d\}$ with binary operation $\circ$ as defined by Table 4.2. If this were a table you were given to memorize as a child,

Table 4.2

$\circ$	a	b	c	d
a	a	b	c	d
b	b	a	f	f
c	c	e	a	f
d	d	e	e	a

you might make up cards, each separate card containing three entries, such as b, d, and f, where this would mean $b \circ d = f$. In the usual designation of grade school, we might see

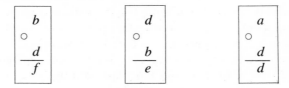

We would need 16 such cards. This is the arithmetic of the set $\{a, b, c, d\}$ with respect to $\circ$.

But now we may observe some more general rules, rules which apply to more than two specific elements of our set with respect to $\circ$.

> For example, note that in the first column of the table, a, b, c, and d appear in that order. This means that $x \circ a = x$ is an identity in the variable x. So is $a \circ x = x$. Thus $a \circ b = b$, $c \circ a = c$, $a \circ a = a$, etc.; that is, when a, b, c, or d is

combined with a on the left or right, we obtain a, b, c, and d, respectively.

Note also that $x \circ x = a$ is an identity.

These rules take care of 10 of the 16 cards.

One might wish to remember that $x \circ b = e$ has the solution set $\{c, d\}$, and $b \circ x = f$ the solution set $\{c, d\}$. This takes care of 4 more cards, leaving $c \circ d = f$ and $d \circ c = e$.

Even if one did not have the language of "identities" and "equations," one would eventually come upon many of these rules through experience, and use them as memory-saving devices. Indeed, in learning the addition and multiplication tables for natural numbers, one need only learn them for the numbers from 1 to 9, and then learn the methods for handling larger numbers in terms of these. Much of the reasoning behind these methods, as we shall see in Part II, lies in the algebraic rules which hold for addition and multiplication of natural numbers. For the present, however, we turn to another use of algebraic rules — solving equations.

1.2 Algebraic Methods in Solving Equations

Up to now in solving equations over a set, we used an arithmetic approach. That is, we replaced the variables by each element of the set, and checked to see whether the resulting statement was a correct one. As a review of this approach, let us consider the set $\{a, b, c, d\}$ with binary operation $\circ$ defined by Table 4.2 of Section 1.1 and the equation in one variable over this set:

$$x \circ x = c \circ x \qquad (1)$$

Replacing x by a, we obtain $a \circ a = c \circ a$, or (using the table) $a = c$. This statement is false (since a and c are assumed distinct). Hence a is not a solution.

Similarly, substituting b yields the statement $a = e$; c yields $a = a$; d yields $a = f$.

Hence the solution set of equation (1) is $\{c\}$.

On the other hand, if we were able to observe in advance that $x \circ x = a$ is an identity in the variable x over this set, then we would be able to see that any solution of (1) is also a solution of

$$a = c \circ x \qquad (2)$$

and conversely.

For if t is any element of $\{a, b, c, d\}$ (so that $t = a$, or $t = b$, or $t = c$, or $t = d$), then upon replacing x by t, (1) becomes

$$t \circ t = c \circ t \qquad (3)$$

and (2) becomes

$$a = c \circ t \tag{4}$$

But $t \circ t = a$ no matter which element t is (as $x \circ x = a$ is an identity). Hence the left side of (3) is a, and (3) and (4) are seen to be the same statements.

Thus to solve (1), it is sufficient to solve (2), since (1) and (2) have the same solution sets. But (2) is easily solved by arithmetic (i.e., from the table), since the only element satisfying $a = c \circ x$ is c, as is easily seen by looking at the third row of the table.

Hence the solution set is $\{c\}$.

One may feel that the arithmetic approach is easier than the algebraic one. But the power of the algebraic method becomes more dramatic when the set under consideration contains a large number of elements. Moreover, once an identity is seen, it may be used to solve numerous equations.

As a second illustration, consider the set $\{0, 1, 2, 3, \ldots\}$ consisting of 0 and the natural numbers, with binary operations $+$ and $-$. If y is a variable over this set, the equation

$$6 + (y - y) = (3 + 2) + y \tag{5}$$

has the same solution set as

$$6 = 5 + y \tag{6}$$

For regardless of the element which replaces y, the left-hand side of the statement is always 6, since we have the identity $z - z = 0$, where z is a variable over the above set. The addition table allows us to write $3 + 2$ as 5, again without altering the statement.

Hence the solution set of (5) is the same as that of (6). From (6), we easily see that the solution set is $\{1\}$.

As a third illustration, we consider the set and binary operation of Example 17, Chapter 2. The set $X = \{0, 1, 2, 3, 4, 5, 6\}$ has binary operation $\circ$, where '$a \circ b$' designates the *remainder* obtained by dividing $a + b$ by 7. We consider the equation

$$(3 \circ m) \circ 2 = m \circ (m \circ 1) \tag{7}$$

where m is a variable over X.

Certainly one method of finding the solution set would be to consider every element of X, replace m by this element, and compute from the table both sides of the given equation to determine whether or not a true statement resulted. This is what we have referred to as the *arithmetic* approach.

For example, if one tries the element 0, the left side of the equation becomes

$$(3 \circ 0) \circ 2, \text{ or } 3 \circ 2, \text{ or } 5$$

the right side

$$0 \circ (0 \circ 1), \text{ or } 0 \circ 1, \text{ or } 1$$

Hence 0 is not a solution of (7).

Employing this procedure in turn for 1, 2, 3, 4, 5, 6, we see that only 4 yields a correct statement, so that the solution set is $\{4\}$.

Suppose one knew in this system, however, that for every $a, b, c \in X$ the following rules held:

(i) $(a \circ b) \circ c = a \circ (b \circ c)$;
(ii) $a \circ b = b \circ a$;
(iii) $a \circ b = a \circ c$ if and only if $b = c$.

[The third rule means that in the table for this set and binary operation, no element appears in any row more than once. (Why?)]

To solve (7), we observe that each of the following equations in the variable m have the same solution set. The reason, in each case, is given to the right of the given equation. (Explanatory remarks are given below.)

(a) $(3 \circ m) \circ 2 = m \circ (m \circ 1)$
(b) $(m \circ 3) \circ 2 = m \circ (m \circ 1)$ Rule (ii)
(c) $m \circ (3 \circ 2) = m \circ (m \circ 1)$ Rule (i)
(d) $m \circ 5 = m \circ (m \circ 1)$ Arithmetic
(e) $5 = m \circ 1$ Rule (iii)

The solution set is then seen to be $\{4\}$ by arithmetic (i.e., by looking at the table).

Remarks: Note that the only difference between line (a) and line (b) is that '$3 \circ m$' appears on the left side of (a), and '$m \circ 3$' on the left side of (b). Since $3 \circ m = m \circ 3$ is an identity in m by rule (ii), replacing m by any element of X in line (a) yields precisely the same results as replacing m in line (b). This is why we write that the equation (b) has the same solution set as the equation (a) by rule (ii).

Similarly the left side of (c) yields the same results as the left side of (b) upon replacing m by any element of X. For by rule (i), $(m \circ 3) \circ 2 = m \circ (3 \circ 2)$ is an identity in m.

In passing from line (c) to line (d), we replace '$3 \circ 2$' by '5.' These designate the same element by the table, so that we list the reason as "arithmetic."

Finally, rule (iii) shows that $m \circ 5 = m \circ (m \circ 1)$ has the same solution set as $5 = m \circ 1$.

Our method here (as in the previous examples) was to use rules which held for all elements of X in order to determine an equation simpler than the one with which we started, and having the same solution set. This latter equation could then be solved by inspection. We shall refer to this approach as the *algebraic* method of solving equations.

Definition 1. Two equations are said to be *equivalent* if they have the same solution set.

Thus, the method of this section has been to determine an equation *equivalent* with the original one, from which the solution set could be seen by inspection. This was accomplished by algebraic methods; which is to say that we made use of rules which held, in this case, for all elements of X, as well as making use of arithmetic. The more such rules we can find for a set X, the more powerful our tools would be in solving equations by the algebraic approach.

2. Examples

2.1   Example 1

Let $X = \{a, b, c, d\}$ with binary operation defined by Table 4.3. Sup-

Table 4.3

$\circ$	a	b	c	d
a	a	b	c	d
b	b	a	d	c
c	c	d	a	b
d	d	c	b	a

pose we knew the following rules held for X with respect to $\circ$:

(1) $x \circ x = a$ is an identity in the variable x over X (i.e., $r \circ r = a$ for all $r \in X$).

(2) $x \circ y = y \circ x$ is an identity in the variables x and y over X (i.e., $r \circ s = s \circ r$ for all $r, s \in X$).

(3) $(x \circ y) \circ z = x \circ (y \circ z)$ is an identity in the variables x, y, z over X (i.e., $(r \circ s) \circ t = r \circ (s \circ t)$ for all $r, s, t \in X$).

Then, as in the preceding section, we can solve equations algebraically. We place in each succeeding line an *equivalent* equation together with the reason showing why it is an equivalent equation:

$(x \circ a) \circ x = (x \circ d) \circ (a \circ c)$
$(x \circ a) \circ x = (x \circ d) \circ c$ Arithmetic (i.e., from the table)
$(a \circ x) \circ x = (x \circ d) \circ c$ Rule 2
$a \circ (x \circ x) = x \circ (d \circ c)$ Rule 3
$a \circ a = x \circ (d \circ c)$ Rule 1
$a = x \circ b$ Arithmetic
Solution set: $\{b\}$ Arithmetic

2.2 Example 2

Consider the set $Y = \{a, b, c, d, e, f\}$ with binary operation defined by Table 4.4. We have boxed off the elements a, b, c, and d and the

Table 4.4

$\circ$	a	b	c	d	e	f
a	a	b	c	d	f	e
b	b	a	d	c	g	e
c	c	d	a	b	e	f
d	d	c	b	a	f	g
e	b	c	d	e	f	g
f	d	e	f	g	a	b

rows and columns they determine to call attention to the fact that this part of the table is identical with the table for the preceding example. Observe that $X \subset Y$.

Suppose we now wish to solve the equation

$$(x \circ a) \circ x = (x \circ d) \circ (a \circ c)$$

of Example 1, where now x is to be regarded as a variable over Y. Rules (1), (2), and (3) become correct for our present system Y under $\circ$ providing that we restrict the variables x, y, and z to the subset X of Y, where $X = \{a, b, c, d\}$. Thus our work of Example 1 is valid as regards the elements a, b, c, and d. That is, among the elements a, b, c, and d only b is a solution of the equation under consideration. Unfortunately, the rules of X do not extend to Y, but to complete the problem one may apply arithmetic to see whether e and f are solutions:

(i) Replacing x by e in the above equation vields

$$(e \circ a) \circ e = (e \circ d) \circ (a \circ c)$$
$$b \circ e = e \circ c$$
$$g = d$$

Hence e is not a solution.

(ii) Replacing x by f in the equation yields

$$(f \circ a) \circ f = (f \circ d) \circ (a \circ c)$$
$$d \circ f = g \circ c$$

and since $g \circ c$ is undefined ($g \notin Y$), f is not a solution.

In this case, it therefore happens that no new solutions of the equation are introduced.

2.3 Summary

The method of solving an equation in this last example has been to determine an equation equivalent with the original one over a subset X of the set Y under consideration, from which the part of the solution set which is in X could be seen by inspection. We then applied arithmetic methods to the remaining elements. If one is to have a manageable algebra, one should seek rules over sufficiently large subsets X of a set Y so that the exceptional elements which are treated arithmetically are few in number.

Exercises

1. Let $X = \{a, b, c, d\}$, and $\circ$ be defined as in Section 1.1.
   (a) If q is a variable over X, solve $q \circ q = a \circ q$ arithmetically.
   (b) Solve $q \circ q = a \circ q$ algebraically.
   (c) If x and y are variables over X, solve $x \circ a = y$ arithmetically.
   (d) Solve $x \circ a = y$ algebraically.
   (e) If x is a variable over X, and y a constant (i.e., a "fixed" element of the set), solve $x \circ a = y$.
   (f) If t is a variable over X, solve $(t \circ d) \circ b = t \circ (d \circ b)$.
2. Determine as many *algebraic* rules as you can for the following systems:
   (a) Example 2.13 (that is, Example 13 of Chapter 2).
   (b) Example 2.18.
   (c) Example 2.19.
3. Let $X = \{a, b, c, d\}$, and $\circ$ be defined as in the example of Section 2.1.
   (a) If x is a variable over X, solve $x \circ (c \circ x) = (b \circ x) \circ c$ algebraically. Check your answers arithmetically (i.e., substitute your solutions for x to ascertain that true statements result).
   (b) Find the solution set of (a) if regarded as an equation in two variables (x, y).
   (c) If x and y are variables over X, solve the following algebraically:
       (i) $b \circ (x \circ c) = y \circ (c \circ y)$
       (ii) $(x \circ b) \circ (c \circ d) = (y \circ a) \circ c$.
   Check your answers arithmetically.
4. Let $Y = \{a, b, c, d, e, f\}$, and $\circ$ be defined as in Section 2.2.
   Answer (a), (b), (c) of Exercise 3, replacing X by Y throughout.
   (d) If x is a variable over Y, solve $(x \circ x) \circ a = x \circ (x \circ b)$.

3. Classification of Binary Operations

One's earliest experience with algebraic rules is ordinarily in the set of natural numbers. As previously stated, one soon learns that $a + b = b + a$ and $a \cdot b = b \cdot a$ for any two natural numbers a and b. That is, the binary operations $+$ and $\cdot$ yield the same result when applied to (a, b) as they do when applied to (b, a). The binary operation $-$ (or $\div$) does not have this property. This is an illustration of classifying binary operations according to whether they do or do not have a given property.

In this section we classify binary operations with respect to certain properties. We select these particular ones because of their importance in the study of the real-number system (in Part II). But it happens that they are also important in the study of many other mathematical systems.

3.1   The Law of Closure

We have seen various examples of a set X with a binary operation, say $\circ$. In some cases, if $a, b \in X$, then $a \circ b$ also was in X; in others this was not the case.

In Example 2.1, where we had $X = \{1, 2, \ldots\}$ and binary operation $+$, for all $a, b \in X$ we also had $a + b \in X$. In Example 2.2, however, for $X = \{1, 2, \ldots\}$ and binary operation $-$, it was not always true that $a - b \in X$. For example, $9 - 5 = 4 \in X$; but $5 - 9 = -4 \notin X$.

Definition 2. Given a set X on which a binary operation $\circ$ is defined. If $a \circ b \in X$ for all $a, b \in X$, then X is said to be *closed* with respect to $\circ$ [or also the law of *closure* is said to hold in X (with respect to $\circ$)].

Thus, the set of natural numbers is closed with respect to $+$, but is not closed under $-$. Again, the set of natural numbers is closed under $\cdot$, but not under $\div$.

The set of odd natural numbers is not closed under $+$, but closure holds with respect to $\cdot$. The set of even natural numbers is closed under $+$ and $\cdot$. The set $\{1, 3, 6, 8\}$ of Example 2.9 is not closed under $+$, since $8 + 8$, for example, is not an element of the set. Neither is the set of Example 2.10 under the given binary operation.

A set X will be closed under $\circ$ if and only if all elements appearing in the table of the binary operation on X are elements of X.

3.2   *The Associative Law*

When we apply a binary operation $\circ$ to three elements of a set, we can handle only two at a time, and we have observed that it may make a difference which way the three are "grouped" in pairs.

For example, $(7 - 4) - 1 = 3 - 1 = 2;\ 7 - (4 - 1) = 7 - 3 = 4.$

Hence $(7 - 4) - 1 \neq 7 - (4 - 1)$. However, $(7 + 4) + 1 = 7 + (4 + 1)$.

> In the table of Section 2.2, $e \circ (a \circ c) = e \circ c = d$ and $(e \circ a) \circ c = b \circ c = d$; hence $e \circ (a \circ c) = (e \circ a) \circ c$; i.e., the two groupings (for the elements in a fixed *order*) yield the same result. However, $(a \circ e) \circ c = f \circ c = f$ and $a \circ (e \circ c) = a \circ d = d$, so $(a \circ e) \circ c \neq a \circ (e \circ c)$; i.e., the two groupings yield *different* results. Similarly, $(e \circ c) \circ e = d \circ e \neq f$ and $e \circ (c \circ e) = e \circ e = f$, so $(e \circ c) \circ e = e \circ (c \circ e)$. But $(e \circ a) \circ f = b \circ f = e$ and $e \circ (a \circ f) = e \circ e = f$, so $(e \circ a) \circ f \neq e \circ (a \circ f)$.

> $(e \circ b) \circ e = c \circ e = e$ and $e \circ (b \circ e) = e \circ g$, but g is not an element of the set, so $e \circ g$ is *undefined*, and consequently $e \neq e \circ g$; i.e., $(e \circ b) \circ e \neq e \circ (b \circ e)$. However, g *is* a valid object, even though the binary operation cannot be applied to it. Thus $(e \circ a) \circ e = b \circ e = g$ and $e \circ (a \circ e) = e \circ f = g$, so $(e \circ a) \circ e = e \circ (a \circ e)$, since g *itself* is *not* undefined.

> Observe that $(e \circ d) \circ e = e \circ e = f$ and $e \circ (d \circ e) = e \circ f = g$, so $(e \circ d) \circ e \neq e \circ (d \circ e)$. But this is because f and g are distinct elements, *not* because g is not in the set. $(f \circ d) \circ f = g \circ f$ and $f \circ (d \circ f) = f \circ g$, so $(f \circ d) \circ f \neq f \circ (d \circ f)$, since both $g \circ f$ and $f \circ g$ are undefined. This would be the case even if $f \circ x = x \circ f$ were an identity in Y, for g could not replace x (i.e., g is not a solution of this identity) since $g \notin Y$.

> Beware apparently "obvious" cases: although $(f \circ f) \circ f = b \circ f = e$ and $f \circ (f \circ f) = f \circ b = e$, so $(f \circ f) \circ f = f \circ (f \circ f)$, observe $(e \circ e) \circ e = f \circ e = a$ and $e \circ (e \circ e) = e \circ f = g$, so $(e \circ e) \circ e \neq e \circ (e \circ e)$.

Definition 3. If for all $a,b,c \in X$, $(a \circ b) \circ c = a \circ (b \circ c)$, then $\circ$ is said to be *associative*, or the associative law is said to hold.

Another way to express associativity is to say that $(x \circ y) \circ z = x \circ (y \circ z)$ is an identity in the three variables x, y, z over X.

We say an ordered triple (u, v, w) is associative under $\circ$ if $(u \circ v) \circ w = u \circ (v \circ w)$. Hence the binary operation $\circ$ is associative *if and only if* every ordered triple of $X \times X \times X$ is associative. Thus, in order to prove associativity, one must show that *every* ordered triple is associative. However, if a set is *not* associative, one can prove this by exhibiting *one* ordered triple which is not associative.

If closure does not hold, then automatically the associative law does not hold, since there will be some $m,n \in X$ such that $m \circ n \notin X$. Hence for any $p \in X, p \circ (m \circ n)$ is undefined. However, a set may be closed and yet *not* be associative; e.g., Example 14 of Chapter 2: (c, b, c), among others, is not associative.

Associativity holds in the natural numbers under $+$, and also under $\cdot$; however, we do not possess the tools to prove this now. The natural numbers are *not* associative under $-$ or $\div$; to prove this, observe they are not closed under $-$ or $\div$.

3.3   The Commutative Law

Definition 4. If $a \circ b = b \circ a$ for all $a,b \in X$, then $\circ$ is said to be *commutative*. (Also the *commutative law* is said to hold.)

Alternatively: X is commutative under $\circ$ if $x \circ y = y \circ x$ is an identity in the two variables x and y over X.

The set of natural numbers is commutative under $+$ but not under $-$. The set X of Section 2.1 is commutative under $\circ$, but the set Y of Section 2.2 is not commutative.

From looking at the table of a binary operation, one cannot tell by inspection whether or not the associative law holds (unless closure fails). But the commutative law can be seen easily. Consider the form of Table 4.5. We placed asterisks where the elements $a \circ a$, $b \circ b$, $c \circ c$, $d \circ d, \ldots$ would appear. Then the table is "symmetric" about the line through these asterisks. (This line is called the *diagonal* of the table.) That is, whatever appears on one side of the diagonal appears at the same distance on the other side. Note, for example, where $d \circ a$ and $a \circ d$ would appear.

Thus to learn such a table (cf. Section 1.1), one would have to learn what appears on and below the diagonal, or on and above the diagonal. The other side of the diagonal would be a mirror image.

Observe that associativity and commutativity are independent. That is, there are systems satisfying each without satisfying the other; there are also systems satisfying both, and some satisfying neither.

Table 4.5

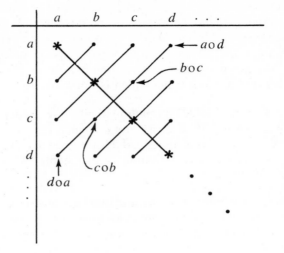

The set of natural numbers under $+$ satisfies both the commutative law and the associative law.

The same set under $-$ satisfies neither the associative nor the commutative laws.

The set $\{0, 1, 2\}$ of Exercise 13, Chapter 3, is commutative under $+$, but not associative (since it is not closed).

Table 4.6 defines a binary operation $*$ such that the set is associative but not commutative.

Table 4.6

$*$	a	b
a	a	a
b	b	b

3.4   Existence of an Identity

In Definition 5 below, we define the meaning of the term *identity* (in a set with binary operation). We have already used the word *identity*, however, with reference to an *equation* in a set whose solution set is the entire set. These uses of the word *identity* are unrelated, and the meaning is generally clear from the context. In the alternative form of the definition below, 'identity' appears in quotation marks when the previous meaning is intended.

Definition 5. Let X be a set with binary operation $\circ$. An element $c \in X$ is said to be an *identity* of X with respect to $\circ$, if $a \circ c = c \circ a = a$ for all $a \in X$.

Alternatively, we may phrase Definition 5 as follows: An element $c \in X$ is said to be an *identity* of X with respect to $\circ$ if $x \circ c = x$ and $c \circ x = x$ are both "identities" in the variable x over X.

> The student has probably already seen examples of sets having an identity with respect to a binary operation. Namely, if $W = \{0, 1, 2, 3, \ldots\}$, then an identity of W with respect to $+$ is 0; an identity of W with respect to $\cdot$ is 1. For if a is any element of W,
>
> $$a + 0 = a \qquad \text{and} \qquad 0 + a = a$$
>
> and similarly
>
> $$a \cdot 1 = a \qquad \text{and} \qquad 1 \cdot a = a$$

Note that the question of which element (if any) of a set is an identity depends upon the binary operation on that set being considered.

> Thus 0 is an identity of W with respect to addition, but not with respect to multiplication. Similarly, 1 is an identity of W with respect to multiplication, but not with respect to addition.

We now consider other examples of sets with binary operations, and consider which elements of these sets, if any, are identities:

> In the set of even natural numbers, there is no identity under $+$ or under $-$, under $\cdot$, or under $\div$.
>
> The set $\{0, 2, 4, \ldots\}$ has 0 as an identity under $+$, but none under $\cdot$.
>
> The set of natural numbers has no identity under $+$, but 1 is an identity under $\cdot$.
>
> In the set $\{a, b, c, d\}$ with binary operation given as in Example 13 of Chapter 2, there is no identity.

If $\{0, 1, 2\}$ has binary operation given by Table 4.7, then 1 is an identity.

Table 4.7

∘	0	1	2
0	7	0	g
1	0	1	2
2	H	2	π

One can see from the table of a set with binary operation which elements are identities. For if t is an identity, then $a \circ t = a$, $b \circ t = b$, $c \circ t = c, \ldots$. The table would look as indicated in Table 4.8. That is, the column under t would reproduce the column on the left outside in the same order.

Table 4.8

∘	a	b	c	·	·	·	t	·	·	·
a							a			
b							b			
c							c			
·							·			
·							·			
·							·			

Similarly, we would have the result given in Table 4.9. Thus, in the set

Table 4.9

∘	a	b	c	·	·	·
a						
b						
c						
·						
·						
·						
t	a	b	c	·	·	·
·						
·						
·						

of natural numbers under ·, we have Table 4.10.

Table 4.10

·	1	2	3	·	·	·
1	1	2	3	·	·	·
2	2					
3	3					
·	·					
·	·					
·	·					

The column under the top outside 1 reproduces the left outside column. The row to the right of the left outside 1 reproduces the top outside row. It follows that 1 is an identity (under ·).

The student will find it instructive to attempt to construct a set having more than one identity (with respect to a binary operation). He will soon see this is impossible, since one can show that a set X with binary operation ○ can have no more than one identity.

For suppose e and f are identities. Then $e \circ x = x = x \circ e$ and $f \circ x = x = x \circ f$ are "identities" in x. Replace x by f in the first and x by e in the second of these "identities." One obtains

$$e \circ f = f = f \circ e$$
$$f \circ e = e = e \circ f$$

In particular, $e \circ f = f$ and $e \circ f = e$, so that $e = f$.

3.5 Elements Having Inverses

Definition 6. Let X be a set with binary operation ○, and suppose X has an identity e (which is therefore the only identity) with respect to ○. If $a \in X$, then any element $b \in X$ such that $a \circ b = b \circ a = e$ is called an *inverse* of a (with respect to ○). If at least one such inverse of a exists in X, we say a has an inverse (with respect to ○).

Thus, to say that a has an inverse means that the equations

$$x \circ a = e$$
$$a \circ x = e$$

have a common solution.

It is clear that if b is an inverse of a, then a is an inverse of b, and conversely.

Thus the set of integers, $\{\ldots, -3, -2, -1, 0, 1, 2, 3, \ldots\}$ has an identity, namely 0, under $+$. An inverse of 2 under $+$

is -2 since $2 + (-2) = (-2) + 2 = 0$. It follows that 2 is an inverse of -2 under $+$. Also 0 is an inverse of 0 under $+$.

In the same set under multiplication, 1 is the identity. There is no inverse of 2, nor of -2 or 0. The inverse of -1 is -1 [since $(-1) \cdot (-1) = 1$, as we shall see in Part II], and the inverse of 1 is 1, since $1 \cdot 1 = 1$.

(If one considered the set of fractions, then 2 would have the inverse $1/2$ under multiplication; $2/3$ would have the inverse $3/2$, etc.)

Observe that before considering inverses of elements, one must have an *identity* of the set. However, we do not speak of inverses of a set. Rather we speak of an inverse of some particular element in the set.

Let $A = \{a, b, c, d\}$ have binary operation $\circ$ (Table 4.11). We look for

Table 4.11

$\circ$	a	b	c	d
a	c	a	b	b
b	a	b	c	d
c	b	c	a	a
d	b	d	b	b

an identity of A under $\circ$. Looking at the columns of the table, only the second repeats the outside left column. Further investigation shows that b is an identity under $\circ$.

The possible inverses of a can be found by looking in the row of a. Thus b appears under c and d so that c and d are possible inverses of a. For $a \circ c = b$, and $a \circ d = b$.

Since $c \circ a = b$, c is an inverse of a. The same is true for d, since $d \circ a = b$.

So a has two inverses, c and d.

Similarly: b has inverse b.

$\qquad$ c has inverse a.

$\qquad$ d has inverses a and d.

If X is the set of the example in Section 2.1, then a is the identity, and every element has an inverse, namely itself. For $a \circ a = b \circ b = c \circ c = d \circ d = a$.

3.6 The Distributive Law

Definition 7. Let X be a set on which binary operations $\circ$ and $*$ are defined. We shall say that the *left distributive law* of $\circ$ with respect to $*$ holds on X if $x \circ (y * z) = (x \circ y) * (x \circ z)$ is an identity in the variables x, y, and z over X. The *right distributive law* holds if $(x * y) \circ z = (x \circ z) * (y \circ z)$ is an identity in the variables x, y, and z over X. If both right and left distributive laws hold, we say X satisfies the *distributive law* (of $\circ$ with respect to $*$).

The set of natural numbers satisfies the distributive law of multiplication with respect to addition: namely, $a \cdot (b + c) = (a \cdot b) + (a \cdot c)$ and also $(a + b) \cdot c = (a \cdot c) + (b \cdot c)$ for all natural numbers a, b, and c.

However, the distributive law for $+$ with respect to $\cdot$ does *not* hold. To prove this, as with associativity, we must exhibit an ordered triple for which the distributive law in question fails. One such in this case is $(3, 2, 1)$, since $3 + (2 \cdot 1) = 3 + 2 = 5$ and $(3 + 2) \cdot (3 + 1) = 5 \cdot 4 = 20$, hence $3 + (2 \cdot 1) \neq (3 + 2) \cdot (3 + 1)$. To prove that a distributive law holds in a set, one must check each ordered triple, as with associativity.

3.7 Examples

Example 3. Let $X = \{1, 2, 3\}$, with binary operation $-$, be defined by Table 4.12.

Table 4.12

$-$	1	2	3
1	3	2	1
2	1	3	2
3	2	1	3

Observe that under $-$
(A) $x - x = 3$ is an identity in one variable.
(B) $x - 3 = x$ is an identity in one variable.

Problem: Referring in each step by letter (i.e., A or B) to the above rules or to arithmetic, find the solution set of $(y - 3) - y = \{[(1 - 2) - (2 - 1)] - (2 - 2)\} - y$, where y is a variable over X.

Solution:

$y - y = \{[(1 - 2) - (2 - 1)] - (2 - 2)\} - y$	(B)
$3 = \{[(1 - 2) - (2 - 1)] - (2 - 2)\} - y$	(A)
$3 = \{[2 - 1] - 3\} - y$	Arithmetic
$3 = \{1 - 3\} - y$	Arithmetic
$3 = 1 - y$	Arithmetic or (B)
Solution set is $\{1\}$	Arithmetic

Example 4. Suppose $X = \{a, b, c\}$ is a set with binary operation $\circ$ in which the following hold:

(1) Law of closure.   (4) c is an identity.
(2) Associative law.   (5) a is an inverse of b.
(3) Commutative law.

Fill in Table 4.13, justifying *each* entry on the basis of the rules above:

Table 4.13

$\circ$	a	b	c
a			
b			
c			

Solution: By (4), we can fill in the c row and c column (Table 4.14). By (5), $b \circ a =$

Table 4.14

$\circ$	a	b	c
a			a
b			b
c	a	b	c

$c = a \circ b$ (Table 4.15). The remaining spaces are to be filled in with either

Table 4.15

	a	b	c
a		c	a
b	c		b
c	a	b	c

a, b, or c, by (1).

We wish to find $a \circ a$ and $b \circ b$. The only law that will help is the associative law (2). We are already assured that no matter what we fill in for $a \circ a$ or $b \circ b$, the commutative law will hold. Hence, $a \circ (a \circ a) = (a \circ a) \circ a$ will hold no matter what we use for $a \circ a$. Let us try $(a \circ a) \circ b = a \circ (a \circ b)$, which must hold by (2).

Then $(a \circ a) \circ b = a \circ c$, since $a \circ b = c$.

$$(a \circ a) \circ b = a \qquad \text{since } a \circ c = a \qquad (*)$$

Either $a \circ a = a$, $a \circ a = b$, or $a \circ a = c$.

(1) Suppose $a \circ a = a$. We obtain from (*) $a \circ b = a$ and this contradicts the fact that $a \circ b = c$. Hence $a \circ a \neq a$.

(2) Suppose $a \circ a = b$. We obtain from (*) $b \circ b = a$. As we do not yet know what $b \circ b$ is, this is possible.

(3) Suppose $a \circ a = c$. We obtain from (*) $c \circ b = a$ or $b = a$ (since $c \circ b = b$). This is not so; hence $a \circ a \neq c$.

Hence we conclude $a \circ a = b$, which in turn leads to $b \circ b = a$ (Table 4.16).

Table 4.16

$\circ$	a	b	c
a	b	c	a
b	c	a	b
c	a	b	c

Thus, if rules (1) to (5) are to hold, the above binary operation (defined by the table) is the only one possible. It is clear that (1), (3), (4), and (5) do in fact hold, but to be sure that (2) holds, one must check that all ordered triples are associative.

Exercises

5. In the following X is a set with binary operation $\circ$. Which of the following are necessarily true?
   (a) If $\circ$ is associative, then X is closed with respect to $\circ$.
   (b) If $\circ$ is commutative, then X is closed with respect to $\circ$.
   (c) If X is closed with respect to $\circ$, then $\circ$ is associative.
   (d) If $a \circ a = a$ for all $a \in X$, then X must have an identity.

6. Let $X = \{a, 1, 2, b, \pi\}$ be a set with binary operation $\circ$ defined by the table

$\circ$	a	1	2	b	π
a	b	a	π	a	2
1	a	b	a	1	π
2	π	b	π	2	a
b	a	1	2	b	π
π	2	π	1	π	a

   (a) Is X closed?
   (b) Is $\circ$ commutative?
   (c) Which element is the identity of X?
   (d) Which elements have inverses?
   (e) Prove that $\circ$ is not associative.

7. Given $\{a, b\}$ with a binary operation $\circ$ defined by the table

$\circ$	a	b
a	a	b
b	b	c

   (a) Is $\{a, b\}$ closed with respect to $\circ$?
   (b) Does the associative law hold?
   (c) Does the commutative law hold?
   (d) Find the inverses of each element, if they exist.

8. Given $\{a, b, c\}$ with a binary operation $\circ$ partially defined by the table

$\circ$	a	b	c
a	a		c
b	c	b	a
c	c	a	c

(a) If $\{a, b, c\}$ is closed with respect to $\circ$, which elements could fill the blank?

(b) If the commutative law holds, which elements could fill the blank?

9. Given $\{d, e, f\}$ with a binary operation $\circ$ partially defined by the table

$\circ$	d	e	f
d	d	e	f
e	e		d
f	f	d	e

(a) If $\{d, e, f\}$ is closed with respect to $\circ$, which elements could fill the blank?

(b) If the commutative law holds, which elements could fill the blank?

(c) If the associative law holds, which elements could fill the blank?

10. Given $X = \{a, b, c\}$ with the binary operation $\circ$, it is known that X satisfies the associative and commutative laws with respect to $\circ$. With this information, complete the following table (show clearly how you arrive at your answers):

$\circ$	a	b	c
a	a	b	
b		c	a
c	c		

11. Given $S = \{1, 2, 3, 4\}$ with binary operation $\circ$ defined by $a \circ b = \max \{a, b\}$ for all $a, b \in S$.

(a) Is S closed with respect to $\circ$?

(b) Is $\circ$ commutative?

(c) Is $\circ$ associative?

(d) Find the inverses of each element, if they exist.

12. Given $\{a, b, c, d\}$ with a binary operation $\circ$ defined by the table

$\circ$	a	b	c	d
a	a	b	a	e
b	d	d	b	d
c	a	b	c	d
d	c	c	d	c

(a) What is the identity of $\{a, b, c, d\}$ with respect to $\circ$?

(b) Which elements have inverses?

13. Given $\{a, b, c, d\}$ with a binary operation $\circ$ defined by the table

$\circ$	a	b	c	d
a	a	b	c	d
b	c	d	a	b
c	a	a	b	c
d	a	b	c	d

(a) Is there an identity element?
(b) Which elements, if any, have inverses?

14. Same as Exercise 11 but $a \circ b$ shall mean min $\{a, b\}$.
15. Given $S = \{\{a\}, \{b\}, \{a, b\}\}$, binary operation is *union*.
(a) Is S closed with respect to the binary operation?
(b) Does the associative law hold?
(c) Does the commutative law hold?
(d) List the identity, if any.
(e) Find the inverses of each element of S, if they exist.
16. Same as Exercise 15, but binary operation is *intersection*.
17. Same as Exercise 15, but $S = [\{1, 2\}]$.
18. Same as Exercise 17, but binary operation is *intersection*.
19. Given $X = \{a, b, c\}$ with a binary operation $\circ$ such that X is closed, the commutative and associative laws hold, c is an identity, and $a \circ a = b, b \circ a = c$; construct the table which describes this binary operation. (Show clearly how you arrive at all your entries.)
20. Given $X = \{a, b, c, d\}$ with a binary operation $\circ$ defined on X such that X is closed, the associative and commutative laws hold, a is an identity in X, and each element of X has an inverse, namely itself. Construct the table which describes this binary operation. (Show clearly how you arrive at all your entries.)

4. Concluding Remarks

In Part I, which we have essentially concluded with the last section, we have introduced arithmetic and algebra in sets quite different from the usual number system that one is familiar with in reading temperatures or speedometers or house numbers or grade-point averages. Now algebra, not to mention arithmetic, is a very old subject. The solutions of some types of equations were already known to the Babylonians by 2000 B.C. A papyrus of about 1950 B.C. reveals a knowledge of some algebra by the Egyptians. The Egyptians even had symbols for "plus" and "minus," for "equals" and for an "unknown." [1] The actual signs '+' and '−' seem to have been introduced by the Germans in about the fifteenth century. Cajori, in his *History of Mathematics* states that "the arithmetic of John

[1] Cf. Howard Eves, *An Introduction to the History of Mathematics*, Holt, New York, 1953.

Widmann, printed A.D. 1489 in Leipzig, is the earliest book in which the + and − symbols have been found." [2]

But it was in the early nineteenth century that the structure of algebra was first seriously considered. This is seen in the work in 1830 of George Peacock (1791–1858); and D. F. Gregory (1813–1844) wrote a paper in 1840 bringing out clearly the commutative and distributive laws. But the "liberation of algebra" [3] takes place with William Rowan Hamilton (1805–1865) and Hermann Grassmann (1809–1877). Hamilton, motivated by physical applications, constructed a consistent algebraic system (called *quaternions*) in which the commutative law did not hold. This was in 1843. Grassmann considered systems of much greater generality than Hamilton. Indeed his work was expressed in such generality and embedded in such philosophical discourse as to seriously dampen its influence. E. T. Bell writes, [4] "This was one of the greater tragedies of mathematics."

The algebra of sets with respect to the operations of union and intersection was first included in the work of George Boole (1815–1864). This was in connection with his work in mathematical logic. The theory of sets as it currently appears in the deeper investigations into the foundations of mathematics was initiated by Georg Cantor (1845–1918).

The strides in mathematics in the last hundred years have been enormous. The *Mathematical Reviews*, published monthly by the American Mathematical Society, contain brief abstracts of the research published in the various mathematical journals. In the October 1961 edition, for example, the section on algebra contains some 16 pages devoted to about 80 research publications. At a conference at Dartmouth College (November 3–4, 1961) entitled *New Directions in Mathematics*, [5] Professor Irving Kaplansky predicted that the 1984 volume of *Mathematical Reviews* will devote about 600 pages to algebra. As he noted in his talk, attempts at predictions of this type in the past have "turned out to be ludicrously conservative."

In preparation, we now turn to Part II.

---

[2] Florian Cajori, *A History of Mathematics*, p. 150, Macmillan, New York, 1894.

[3] Cf. E. T. Bell, *Development of Mathematics*, p. 182, McGraw-Hill, New York, 1940; and also H. Eves and C. K. Newsom, *An Introduction to the Foundations and Fundamental Concepts of Mathematics*, p. 133, Holt, New York, 1965.

[4] *Ibid.*, p. 183.

[5] Dartmouth College Mathematics Conference 1961, *New Directions in Mathematics*, R. W. Ritchie, Ed., p. 133, Prentice-Hall, Englewood Cliffs, N.J., 1963.

Part II
THE REAL NUMBERS

In Section 1.1 of Chapter 3 we drew a distinction between the concept of a natural number and the name of the natural number, although no attempt was made to state clearly exactly what a natural number was. If '7' is the name of an object 7, what is this object 7? Something is told about the natural number 7 by the use of 7 as an adjective; we speak of 7 books, 7 apples, 7 students, 7 years, 7 inches, and we think of these collections as having something in common, described perhaps as their *sevenness*. But when we write $7 + 4 = 11$, we are stating something about the natural numbers 7, 4, and 11 themselves.

When measuring lengths, moreover, one discovers that natural numbers are inadequate for the task. Numbers like $\frac{1}{2}, \frac{2}{3}$, and $\frac{1}{8}$ arise, fractions whose numerators and denominators are natural numbers. The union of the set of natural numbers and the set of fractions does not suffice to measure every length. For, if one tries to measure the length of the hypotenuse of a right triangle whose sides are each 1 inch in length, one finds that the hypotenuse of the right triangle is a inches long, where a is a number such that $a \cdot a = 2$. Later we shall see that there is no fraction of the form p/q, where p and q are natural numbers, for which $p/q \cdot p/q = 2$. Indeed, we shall find that there are many numbers used to designate lengths which cannot be written as a quotient p/q of natural numbers. Thus in addition to the natural numbers we now have fractions (defined in terms of natural numbers) and still other numbers used for measuring lengths.

There are still other numbers used, if one has other applications in mind. For the length of a point, there is the number 0. And if one is measuring distances on a line from a fixed point on that line, and uses 'a' to designate the number representing a length in one direction, he may use '$\bar{a}$' to designate the number representing the same length in the other direction. He may then think of $a + \bar{a}$ as applying to the result of going first a units in the one direction, and then a units in the other. Thus for him, $a + \bar{a} = 0$. Indeed, the set of all numbers used in this particular application is called the *set of real numbers*, or the *real-number system*, and any element of this set is called a *real number*.

But here we are talking about real numbers, or about how real numbers are used, and have yet to say what a real number is — or even what a natural number is. And yet we can continue to discuss these numbers —

such as asserting that the set of natural numbers is a proper subset of the set of real numbers, and so on. Our aim in Part II shall be to undertake a study of the real-number system. It would seem that we should first, therefore, define clearly what a real number is.

A similar problem arises in geometry. There one makes statements concerning points and lines. For example: "Through every two distinct points passes one and only one line." But although this represents a statement of a relationship between points and lines, this is not a statement of what a point is or what a line is.

Actually one is aware that when one draws dots for points, he may then with sufficiently fine equipment draw more than one line through two dots. But he is convinced, in some ideal sense, that only one line passes through two points. It is here that he is passing from an application to a "mathematical model" which he feels fits the application. Thus he invents (ideal) lines and (ideal) points which he assumes to satisfy certain specified relations. From these assumptions (called *axioms* or *postulates*) concerning points and lines, he derives many consequences. It is not important what the words 'line' and 'point' designate. They remain undefined, and the derivation of consequences depend only upon the axioms which the undefined terms (called *primitives*) satisfy. (They depend also on the logical reasoning one uses.)

A mathematical system (primitives, axioms, and derivable consequences through a system of logical reasoning) may have many realizations. Thus one may think of a line as something one draws with a straightedge, a point as a dot. Another realization, however, would be to regard as points people a, b, c and as lines committees $A = \{a, b\}$, $B = \{b, c\}$, and $C = \{a, c\}$. If one feels that with this interpretation of point and line the axiom that through every two distinct points passes one and only one line is satisfied, then he would be able to apply every derivable consequence where the same interpretation for point and line is made. So we see that a mathematical system may be a mathematical model for more than one realization. We thereby gain in one development results which may then be applied to many situations.

We have said that a study of a mathematical system arises from a realization of this system. At another level of abstraction, it very often happens that the realization is itself another mathematical system. That is, a set of postulates may in turn be applied to many other mathematical systems. (Of course it is conceivable that one may study a mathematical system without any realization in mind. However, this is not ordinarily done.)

Thus we shall not define what a real number is. Rather we shall assume the existence of a set R of elements (called real numbers) satisfying certain postulates. One arrives at these postulates by a consideration of one or more of the realizations. For example, we shall assume there is a binary operation + defined on the set of real numbers. As a motivation for the postulates assumed for this binary operation, one can think of the realization of measuring distances on a line from a fixed point on that line, as mentioned above. We shall also assume that there is a binary operation · defined on the set of real numbers which is commutative; i.e., $a \cdot b = b \cdot a$ for all $a, b \in R$. As motivation for this, we think of the area of a rectangle:

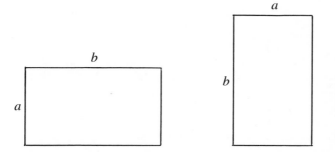

The area should be the same whether we consider $a \cdot b$ or $b \cdot a$. Similarly, a consideration of volume yields $(a \cdot b) \cdot c = a \cdot (b \cdot c)$. The applications, however, indicate these latter rules for the numbers used to designate length, but how about 0 and the numbers $\bar{a}$, $\bar{b}$, etc., indicating direction? Here we would like to assume the same rules hold for these elements so as to obtain a manageable algebra. This is a second consideration in the selection of postulates.

The question then arises as to whether a set of postulates is consistent. That is, they are inconsistent if they are incompatible with each other, or with any theorem, or if any theorems are incompatible. Thus, it would be a happier situation if one could begin with a system one feels he knows better (such as the natural numbers), and develop the real numbers and their properties from these. Although this is possible, it is probably best deferred until one has obtained a somewhat greater mathematical maturity. In our development, we list postulates for the real numbers, and all consequences are derived from these. There are many sets of postulates which one can use, and we select one of these.

chapter v

ALGEBRAIC PROPERTIES OF REAL NUMBERS

In this chapter we list some of the postulates for the real-number system. All the theorems we derive, then, will be based only on this partial list of postulates. It follows, therefore, that to any other mathematical system satisfying these postulates, one may also apply these derivable theorems. All mathematical systems satisfying the postulates of this chapter (i.e., those labeled below as A1, A2, A3, A4, A5, M1, M2, M3, M4, M5, D, and B) are called *fields*. Thus the first assumption we make concerning the set of real numbers is that it is a field.

At first, all proofs given are formal. The method of proof presented here is designed to reveal how every step of a proof is used in reaching a conclusion. Rather than discuss this procedure beforehand, we expose it by example, with remarks following the early proofs of theorems to explain their essential aspects. In Section 4 we turn to informal proofs.

Many of the theorems appear as exercises, and in the proof of any theorem or exercise, we allow ourselves to use any previous theorem or exercise. Even if the student omits some of the exercises, therefore, he should read the statements of them.

One of the interesting results which will emerge from the development set forth in this chapter is that the hundreds of algebraic manipulative rules for real numbers to which the student may have been exposed are all deducible from the above handful of postulates. And as we have pointed out above, these rules also hold for *any field*.

And this development provides the student the further pleasure of gaining experience in proving theorems. At a later stage in his development, he may wish to investigate the nature of a proof and of logical reasoning. There is no better preparation for this study than the serious practice of constructing proofs.

It is further hoped that the logical unfolding of the algebra of fields will allow the student to obtain a comprehension and clarification of algebraic rules which may have appeared to him to be arbitrary and unrelated in his previous work.

It is possible that some may desire to resort to rules which they learned by rote in their earlier experience with algebra. Why worry about *why* you are doing something, so long as you know *how*, would be the idea. It is a well-known phenomenon that there often exists in all of us a resistance to thinking and to new ideas. With all due sympathy, we shall take the point of view here that it is our function to resist such resistance. It will be seen, we believe, that the improvement one will observe in his old manipulative techniques, the new manipulative techniques he will acquire, the comprehension and clarification he will gain, and the new insights to which he will be led will be fitting reward for his (hopefully) sincere labors in this subject.

1. Algebraic Postulates for the Real Numbers

1.1   The Postulates Listed

We shall assume the existence of a set R, whose elements we shall call *real numbers*, on which two binary operations, $+$ and $\cdot$, are defined, called *addition* and *multiplication*, respectively, under which R satisfies the following conditions or postulates:

A1 R is closed under addition.
A2   Addition is associative.
A3   Addition is commutative.
A4   There is an additive identity 0 in R such that

$$a + 0 = 0 + a = a \qquad \text{for all } a \in R$$

(We shall call this additive identity "zero.")

A5   For each element a in R, there is an additive inverse b in R such that

$$a + b = b + a = 0$$

M1 R is closed under multiplication.
M2   Multiplication is associative.
M3   Multiplication is commutative.
M4   There is a multiplicative identity 1 in R such that

$$a \cdot 1 = 1 \cdot a = a \qquad \text{for all } a \in R$$

(We shall call this multiplicative identity "one.")

M5   For each element $a \neq 0$ in R, there is a multiplicative inverse b in R such that

$$a \cdot b = b \cdot a = 1$$

D   For all $a,b,c \in R$, the distributive laws hold:

$$a \cdot (b + c) = a \cdot b + a \cdot c \,^{1}$$
$$(b + c) \cdot a = b \cdot a + c \cdot a$$

B   The element zero (0) is different from the element one (1).

---

[1] $a \cdot b + a \cdot c$ means $(a \cdot b) + (a \cdot c)$. We adopt the convention when omitting parentheses in such situations that the multiplication is performed first, then the addition.

(Note that postulate B implies that there are at least two distinct elements in the set R.)

This is not the full set of postulates we shall assume for the set of real numbers, and in the remaining chapters of Part II we shall introduce further postulates for the set of real numbers. But in this chapter, we shall use only the above. Any set with two binary operations, say $+$ and $\cdot$, satisfying the above is called a *field*.

1.2   Remarks Concerning the Postulates

1. The A postulates are analogous to the M postulates, except for A5 and M5. In A5, *every element* of R has an additive inverse. In M5, *every element distinct from* 0 has a multiplicative inverse. We shall be able to deduce later, in fact, that 0 does not have a multiplicative inverse. For the present, all we are told is that 0 may or may not have a multiplicative inverse.

2. In D it would have been sufficient to postulate the left distributive law; one could then deduce the right distributive law (cf. Section 1.3).

1.3   An Example of a Proof

As an example, we prove remark 2 of Section 1.2; that is, we show how we could replace D by the left distributive law, and prove as a consequence the right distributive law.

Thus, we wish to prove, on the basis of our postulates—except that D is to be regarded as the left distributive law—the following theorem:

If $a,b,c \in R$, then $(b + c) \cdot a = b \cdot a + c \cdot a$.

We shall give the proof first, and then analyze it below.

Proof: (1) $a,b,c \in R$ (1) Hypothesis
         (2) $b + c \in R$ (2) A1, step 1
         (3) $(b + c) \cdot a = a \cdot (b + c)$ (3) Steps 1, 2; M3
         (4) $= a \cdot b + a \cdot c$ (4) Steps 1, 3; left distributive law
         (5) $= b \cdot a + c \cdot a$ (5) Steps 1, 4; M3

Analysis of the Proof

(a) We are *given* that $a,b,c \in R$ and we are *to prove* $(b + c) \cdot a = b \cdot a + c \cdot a$. The statements given are called the *hypothesis;* what is to be proved is called the *conclusion*.

(b) The steps of the proof are given in the left column, their reasons in the right.

(c) The basic idea of the proof is to apply the commutative law of multiplication (M3) to $b + c$ and a, in order to get a on the left of $b + c$. Then we can apply the modified postulate (D)—the left distributive law—to obtain the desired result. Thus the basic part of the argument appears in steps 3, 4, and 5.

(d) To apply M3, we must be sure the elements to which we apply it are in R. We have seen examples of a set X with binary operation $\circ$, where if $b,c \in X$, it may happen that $b \circ c \notin X$. This is why we need step 2, which tells us that $b + c \in R$, and step 1, which tells us that $a \in R$. Knowing a and $b + c$ are elements of R, we may then apply M3 to $b + c$ and a. The reason column for step 3 there-fore refers to steps 1 and 2, M3.

(e) To see that $b + c \in R$, we applied A1 to b and c. We use step 1 to show that $b,c \in R$, so that A1 can be applied.

(f) In steps 4 and 5, the left side of the '=' is assumed to read as in the left side of step 3.

(g) To derive step 4, one applies the left distributive law to the right side of step 3. We need step 1 to see that $a,b,c \in R$. For the left distributive law of addi-tion with respect to multiplication in R states: *If $a,b,c \in R$, then $a \cdot (b + c) = a \cdot b + a \cdot c$.* Thus step 4 repeats step 3, but replaces '$a \cdot (b + c)$' by another name for the same element, namely '$a \cdot b + a \cdot c$' (this is why step 3 is listed as a reason for step 4).

(h) In step 5, we copy step 4, except that for the element $a \cdot b$ we use the name '$b \cdot a$' and for $a \cdot c$ the name '$c \cdot a$.' This is by M3. Again to apply M3, we must know $a,b,c \in R$ — which is step 1.

(i) On any given line, there is only one reason given in addition to possible reference to previous steps. Thus we do not go directly (at this time) from step 3 to step 5 and list both the left distributive law and M3 as reasons. This helps to demonstrate precisely how each reason is being applied.

(j) The conclusion is the last step of the proof.

1.4   A Second Example

We now assume our postulates as stated in Section 1.1. We prove the following theorem:

If $a,b,c,d \in R$, then $(a + b)c + d \in R$ [2]

Proof: (1) $a,b,c,d \in R$ (1) Hyp.
        (2) $a + b \in R$ (2) A1, step 1
        (3) $(a + b)c \in R$ (3) Steps 1, 2; M1
        (4) $(a + b)c + d \in R$ (4) Steps 1, 3; A1

Analysis of the Proof

(a) In step 2, we use step 1 to see that $a,b \in R$; then A1 may be applied to a and b.

(b) In step 3, we use step 2 to see that $a + b \in R$ and step 1 to see that $c \in R$. Then we may apply M1 to $a + b$ and c.

(c) In step 4, we use step 3 to see that $(a + b)c \in R$ and step 1 to see that $d \in R$. We may then apply A1 to $(a + b)c$ and d.

1.5   Conventions

1. Because we have the law of closure under addition and under multi-plication, there is no danger of obtaining an element outside of R by applying $+$ and $\cdot$ any finite number of times. Although this sweeping state-

[2] We shall often omit the dot used for multiplication. Thus $(a + b)c + d$ means $[(a + b) \cdot c] + d$.

ment requires proof (which we shall have the machinery to give only in a later chapter), in any particular case that arises one can give an argument such as in the example of Section 1.4. For notational simplification, therefore, we shall omit steps such as steps 1 and 2 of the example of Section 1.3.

2. In the reason column, we shall usually omit reference to the preceding step. Thus if in a proof, one is using step 5 to obtain step 6, we shall not always record this fact in the reason column. But the use of step 4, or 3, etc., to obtain step 6 will be so recorded. If recording the previous step makes the argument easier to follow, we shall do so.

Thus, the proof given in the example of Section 1.3 would read:

(1) $(b + c)a = a(b + c)$ (1) M3
(2) $\quad\quad\quad = ab + ac$ (2) D (meaning, here, the left distributive law)
(3) $\quad\quad\quad = ba + ca$ (3) M3

3. If $a,b,c \in R$ and $a = b$, then $a + c = b + c$, and $ac = bc$. The reason for this is that 'a' and 'b' are names of the same element, according to the meaning of equality. Hence adding a and c or adding b and c is doing precisely the same thing. Since $+$ is a binary operation, one must always obtain a *unique* result. Hence $a + c = b + c$.

Therefore, the reason which will be given for such a statement is: "$a = b$; $+$ is a binary operation." Of course, if "$a = b$" is the previous statement of the proof, in accordance with step 2 we shall omit reference to it.

Similar remarks apply to $ac = bc$.

4. On any given line, the reason column should contain only one reason (such as: hypothesis; or M2; or Definition 3; or Theorem 8) in addition to possible reference to previous steps.

Exercises

1. Let $S = \{0, 1\}$, and let $+$ and $\cdot$ be binary operations on S defined by the following tables:

+	0	1
0	0	1
1	1	0

$\cdot$	0	1
0	0	0
1	0	1

Show that S is a field.

2. Let $T = \{0, 1, 2\}$, and $+$ and $\cdot$ be binary operations defined by

+	0	1	2
0	0	1	2
1	1	2	0
2	2	0	1

$\cdot$	0	1	2
0	0	0	0
1	0	1	2
2	0	2	1

Show that T is a field.

3. Suppose $W = \{0, 1\}$, and $+$ and $\cdot$ are defined partially by

+	0	1
0	0	
1	1	

$\cdot$	0	1
0		
1	0	1

In how many ways can you fill in the remaining entries if W is to be a field? Justify your answer.

4. (a) If postulate A4 were to read: "There is an element 0 in R such that $a + 0 = a$ for all $a \in R$," prove that 0 is an additive identity.
   [*Hint:* The statements of a proof would be: (1) $a + 0 = a$ for all $a \in R$; (2) $0 + a = a$ for all $a \in R$.]
   (b) If postulate M5 were to read: "For each element $a \neq 0$, there is an element b in R such that $b \cdot a = 1$," prove that b is a multiplicative inverse of a.

2. Theorems on Addition

2.1   Introduction

We now formally begin the development of the algebraic properties of real numbers. If one thinks, however, of 'R' as designating any field, then this entire chapter would apply to this interpretation of R.

In the reason column for a proof of any particular theorem, we shall use the following: postulates; preceding theorems, exercises, or definitions; steps of the proof previous to the one being stated. Of course, we shall observe the conventions of Section 1.5.

Throughout Section 2 only consequences of postulates A1, A2, A3, A4, and A5 are considered.

We shall use a different number for each theorem and exercise for purposes of easier reference. Thus, since we have had four exercises in this chapter, we call our first theorem Theorem 5.

2.2   Cancellation Laws for Addition

Theorem 5. If $a,b,c \in R$, then $a + b = a + c$ if and only if $b = c$.

Proof: As this is an abbreviation for two statements, we prove each separately:
(α) If $a,b,c \in R$ and $b = c$, then $a + b = a + c$.

(1) $\quad b = c$	(1) Hyp.
(2) $a + b = a + c$	(2) + is a binary operation

(β) If $a,b,c \in R$ and $a + b = a + c$, then $b = c$.

(1) There exists $d \in R$ such that $d + a = 0$	(1) A5
(2) $\quad a + b = a + c$	(2) Hyp.
(3) $d + (a + b) = d + (a + c)$	(3) + is a binary operation
(4) $(d + a) + b = (d + a) + c$	(4) A2
(5) $\quad 0 + b = 0 + c$	(5) Step 1 (applied to step 4)
(6) $\quad\quad b = c$	(6) A4

Theorem 6. If $a,b,c \in R$, then $b + a = c + a$ if and only if $b = c$.

Proof: (α) We first prove: If $a,b,c \in R$ and $b = c$, then $b + a = c + a$.

(1) $\quad b = c$	(1) Hyp.
(2) $b + a = c + a$	(2) + is a binary operation

(β) We next prove: If $a,b,c \in R$ and $b + a = c + a$, then $b = c$.

(1) $b + a = c + a$	(1) Hyp.
(2) $a + b = a + c$	(2) A3
(3) $\quad b = c$	(3) Th. 5

Remarks:

1. In part β we could have imitated the proof of Theorem 5. The proof given is shorter, and utilizes the *results* of previous work.

2. We are applying part β of Theorem 5 in step 3. The hypothesis of that part was: $a,b,c \in R$ and $a + b = a + c$. By convention, we need not state in the proof that $a,b,c \in R$; but we must have $a + b = a + c$ as a previous statement in order to be able to apply the conclusion of Theorem 5. This was given in step 2.

Exercise

7. Prove the following theorems, using any of the field postulates, and any of the preceding theorems (which up to this point are Theorem 5 and Theorem 6).
   (a) If $a,b,c \in R$ and $a + b = c + a$, then $b = c$; and conversely.
   (b) If $a,b,c,d \in R$, then $a = d$ if and only if $a + (b + c) = c + (b + d)$.

2.3   *Uniqueness of Additive Identity, Inverses*

We have seen in Section 3, Chapter 4, that if an identity exists, it is unique. In order to make the theorems in this chapter self-contained, we repeat the proof here. In this proof 0 and $0'$ play the roles of e and f in the argument given in Chapter 4.

Theorem 8. If $0'$ is an additive identity of R, then $0' = 0$.

Proof: (1) $0' + 0 = 0$ (1) ($0'$ is an additive identity by) hyp.
     (2) $0' + 0 = 0'$ (2) (0 is an additive identity by) A4
     (3) $0 = 0'$ (3) Steps 1, 2

Remark: It is clearer, in this proof, if we indicate step 2 as a reason for step 3. Thus step 1 states '0' is a name for $0' + 0$, and step 2 states '$0'$' is also a name for $0' + 0$. Since they name the same element, we obtain that $0 = 0'$.

Theorem 9. If $r,s,t \in R$, $r + s = 0$ and $r + t = 0$, then $s = t$. (This proves that the additive inverse of any element is unique.)

Proof: (1) $r + s = 0$ (1)
         $r + t = 0$
     (2) $r + s = r + t$ (2) Step 1
     (3) $s = t$ (3)

Exercises

10. Complete the reasoning in the proof of Theorem 9.
11. Prove: If $a \in R$ and $b + a = b$ for all $b \in R$, then $a = 0$.
12. Prove: If $u,v,w \in R$ and u is an additive inverse of both v and w, then $v = w$.

Now A5 tells us that if $a \in R$, there exists an additive inverse b (in R) of a; that is, $a + b = b + a = 0$. But Theorem 9 states that there is at most one such additive inverse of a. Thus the additive inverse of a in R is unique.

Definition 1. If $a \in R$, the unique additive inverse of a in R shall be designated by '$-a$.'[3]

Thus $-a$ is the unique element in R such that

$$a + (-a) = (-a) + a = 0$$

Note that in even stating Definition 1, we are implicitly using A5 and Theorem 9. Thus, when giving Definition 1 as a reason, we shall assume that this includes A5 and Theorem 9 if either is needed.

[3] One often uses $+a$ to mean a. This is convenient for abbreviating $\{a, -a\}$ to $\{\pm a\}$.

Exercises

13. In Exercise 1, we saw that the addition table for S satisfies A1, A2, A3, A4, and A5. Hence the theorems and definitions of this section apply to that system.

(a) Which of the elements of $S = \{0, 1\}$ is -0?

(b) -1?

14. Let T be as in Exercise 2. State which of the elements of $T = \{0, 1, 2\}$ is $-0; -1; -2$.

15. Let $S = \{0, a, b, c\}$, and $+$ be defined by the following table:

+	0	a	b	c
0	0	a	b	c
a	a	0	c	b
b	b	c	0	a
c	c	b	a	0

(a) Show that S under $+$ satisfies A1, A2, A3, A4, and A5.

(b) State which of the elements of S is $-0; -a; -b; -c$.

(c) State which of the elements of S is $c + (-b)$; $(-c) + b$; $(-a) + (-b)$; $-(a+b)$.

Theorem 16. $-0 = 0$.

Proof: (1) $0 + 0 = 0$ (1) A4

(2) $0 = -0$ (2) Def. 1

Remarks: (a) Since 0 is the additive identity of R, $0 + a = a$ for all $a \in R$. Hence in particular with $a = 0$, $0 + 0 = 0$ (cf. step 1).

(b) According to step 1, 0 is an additive inverse of 0. But Definition 1 labels the *unique additive inverse* of 0 by '-0.' Hence '-0' is another name for 0.

Theorem 17. If $a \in R$, then $-(-a) = a$.

Proof: (1) $(-a) + a = 0$ (1) Def. 1

(2) $a = -(-a)$ (2) Step 1, Def. 1

Remarks: The proof is similar to that of Theorem 16. Thus in step 1 we use Definition 1 to observe that $(-a) + a = 0$. But according to Definition 1, the unique element which yields 0 when added to $-a$ is $-(-a)$. By step 1, a is such an element. Hence Definition 1 applied to step 1 yields $a = -(-a)$.

Exercises

18. Below is an alternative proof of Theorem 16. Fill in the reason column.

(1) $0 + 0 = 0$

(2) $0 + (-0) = 0$
(3) $0 + 0 = 0 + (-0)$
(4) $0 = -0$

19. Below is an alternative proof of Theorem 17. Fill in the reason column.

(1) $(-a) + a = 0$
(2) $(-a) + [-(-a)] = 0$
(3) $(-a) + [-(-a)] = (-a) + a$
(4) $-(-a) = a$

2.4   Subtraction

Definition 2. If $a,b \in R$, then $a - b$ shall mean $a + (-b)$; i.e., $a - b = a + (-b)$.

Thus by $a - b$ we mean the sum of a and the additive inverse of b.

Note we are giving a second meaning to the "minus" sign '$-$.' Our first meaning assigned the minus sign to each $a \in R$ to designate the unique additive inverse of a. The second use of the minus sign is applied to every ordered pair (a,b) with $a,b \in R$. Namely,

$$a - b = a + (-b)$$

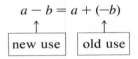

new use   old use

Although it might be clearer if two different symbols were used, the standard notation throughout the mathematical literature is as given above. There can be no confusion if one remembers that the first use of $-$ applies to a single element; the second use to an ordered pair of elements, thus making $-$ a binary operation on R in this latter case. This binary operation is usually called "subtraction."

Since a and $-b$ are in R if a and b are, it follows from A1 that $a + (-b) \in R$, so that $a - b \in R$. Hence we shall now assume that any finite number of applications of $+$, $\cdot$, and $-$ to elements of R leads to elements of R (cf. Section 1.5, convention 1).

Theorem 20. If $a \in R$, then $a - 0 = a$.

Proof: (1) $a - 0 = a + (-0)$ (1) Def. 2
      (2) $= a + 0$ (2) Th. 16
      (3) $= a$ (3) A4

Remark: In step 2 we rewrote step 1 replacing '0' for '-0,' since Theorem 16 tells us that $-0 = 0$.

Exercises

21. Prove: If $a \in R$, then $a - a = 0$.

22. Prove: If $a \in R$, then $0 - a = -a$.

23. Fill in the following table for Exercise 1:

$-$	0	1
0		
1		

24. (a) Fill in the following table for Exercise 2:

$-$	0	1	2
0			
1			
2			

(b) Write out a similar table for Exercise 15.

25. Prove: If $a \in R$, then $-a - 0 = -a$. [$-a - 0$ means $(-a) - 0$].

26. Prove: If $a,b \in R$, then $-a = -b$ if and only if $a = b$.

27. Prove: If $a,b \in R$, then $a - (-b) = a + b$.

2.5 *Generalizations of A2 and A3*

Up to now we have a meaning for the sum of only *two* elements in R. We give, in the following definition, a meaning for the sum of three elements of R.

Definition 3. If $a,b,c \in R$,

$$a + b + c = (a + b) + c \quad \text{(and also by A2)}$$
$$= a + (b + c)$$

Also,

$$a + b - c = a + b + (-c)$$
$$a - b + c = a + (-b) + c$$
$$-a + b - c = (-a) + b + (-c) \qquad \text{etc.}$$

Theorem 28. If $a,b,c,d \in R$,

(1) $(a + b + c) + d = (a + b) + (c + d)$

(2) $(a + b + c) + d = a + (b + c + d)$

Proof of Theorem 28 (1): (1) $(a + b + c) + d = [(a + b) + c] + d$ (1) Def. 3

         (2) $= (a + b) + (c + d)$ (2) A2

Remark: We applied A2 to the three elements $a + b$, c, and d.

Exercise

29. Prove Theorem 28 (2).

> **Definition 4.** If $a,b,c,d \in R$,
>
> $$a + b + c + d = (a + b + c) + d \quad \text{[and therefore also by Th. 28 (1)]}$$
> $$= (a + b) + (c + d) \quad \text{[and by Th. 28 (2)]}$$
> $$= a + (b + c + d)$$

Similarly,

$$a + b + c - d = a + b + c + (-d) \qquad \text{etc.}$$

It is clear how one would define $a + b + c + d + e$, and $a + b + c + d + e + f$, etc., and what theorems he should prove to show that it doesn't matter how he inserts parentheses. It is important, however, that when inserting or removing parentheses, all terms be separated *only* by $+$ signs.

Exercises

30. (a) If $a,b,c,d,e \in R$, how would one define $a + b + c + d + e$?
  (b) What theorems should one prove to show that it does not matter how one inserts parentheses?
  (c) Prove two of the theorems of part b.
31. Answer the same questions as in Exercise 30 for $a + b + c + d + e + f$.
32. (a) If $a,b,c \in R$, prove $a + b + c = b + a + c$.
  (b) If $a,b,c \in R$, prove $a + b + c = a + c + b$.
  (c) If $a,b,c \in R$, prove $a + b + c = b + c + a$ etc.
  (*Remark:* Exercise 32 tells us that rearranging a, b, c in any order under $+$ yields the same real number. This might be regarded as a commutative law for three terms.)
33. State and prove similar theorems as in Exercise 32 for the sum of four terms. (This would be the commutative law for four terms.)

2.6   Solutions of Equations over R

The following important theorem shows that the equation $a + x = b$ has a *unique* solution in R, where $a,b \in R$ and x is a variable over R.

Theorem 34. If $a,b \in R$ and x is a variable over R, then the solution set of the equation $a + x = b$ (hence also of $x + a = b$) is $\{b - a\}$. This theorem actually has two parts:

  (1) $b - a$ is a solution of $a + x = b$.
  (2) $b - a$ is the *only* solution of $a + x = b$; that is, if c is any solution of $a + x = b$, then $c = b - a$.

Proof of Theorem 34 (1): We show that $a + (b - a) = b$.

(1) $a + (b - a) = a + [b + (-a)]$		(1) Def. 2
(2) $= a + b + (-a)$		(2) Def. 3
(3) $= a + (-a) + b$		(3) Ex. 32
(4) $= [a + (-a)] + b$		(4) Def. 3
(5) $= 0 + b$		(5) Def. 1
(6) $= b$		(6) A4

Proof of Theorem 34 (2): We show that if $a + c = b$, then $c = b - a$.

(1) $a + c = b$		(1) Hyp.
(2) $a + (b - a) = b$		(2) Th. 34 (1) [4]
(3) $a + c = a + (b - a)$		(3) Steps 1, 2
(4) $c = b - a$		(4) Th. 5

Exercises

35. Prove (for $a \in R$, x a variable over R):
  (a) The solution set of $x + a = 0$ is $\{-a\}$.
     (*Hint:* One could imitate the proof of Theorem 34. We give the statements of an alternative proof:
     (1) The solution set of $x + a = 0$ is $\{0 - a\}$.
     (2) The solution set of $x + a = 0$ is $\{-a\}$.)
  (b) The solution set of $x - a = 0$ is $\{a\}$.
36. Solve the following equations, where u is a variable over R and $l, j, k \in R$:
  (a) $u + j + k = 0$.   (c) $u - (k - l)(j - k) = 0$.
  (b) $jk - l + u = k$.   (d) $j - u = k$.

The following theorem is useful in solving certain equations (cf. Exercise 39).

Theorem 37. Let $a, b, c, d \in R$. Then $a - b = c - d$ if and only if $a + d = b + c$.

This must be considered as two theorems, to be proved separately:

  (1) If $a - b = c - d$, then $a + d = b + c$.
  (2) If $a + d = b + c$, then $a - b = c - d$.

Proof of Theorem 37 (1):

(1) $a - b = c - d$		(1) Hyp.
(2) $(a - b) + (b + d) = (c - d) + (b + d)$		(2) Th. 5 (step 1) [Or: "+ is a binary operation"]
(3) $[a + (-b)] + (b + d)$ $= [c + (-d)] + (b + d)$		(3) Def. 2

[4] Having proved Theorem 34 (1), we may now regard it as a "previous theorem."

(4) $a + (-b) + b + d = c + (-d) + b + d$ (4) Def. 4
(5) $(-b) + b + a + d = (-d) + d + b + c$ (5) Ex. 33
(6) $[(-b) + b] + (a + d)$
$\quad = [(-d) + d] + (b + c).$ (6) Def. 4
(7) $0 + (a + d) = 0 + (b + c)$ (7) Def. 1
(8) $a + d = b + c$ (8) A4

Remarks: Step 4 uses Definition 4 to remove parentheses, step 5 uses Exercise 33 to commute various elements, and step 6 applies Definition 4 to insert parentheses again, so that $-b$ and b, $-d$ and d could be added. Note that *all* binary operations must be $+$ in order to apply Definition 4 and Exercise 33, so that step 3 is essential in this procedure.

Since we have proved Theorem 37 (1), we may now use it in the proof of Theorem 37 (2), by observing $a + d = a - (-d)$ (cf. Exercise 38).

Exercises

38. Prove Theorem 37 (2). [Remember, you can now use the statement of Theorem 37 (1) without going through the proof again.]

39. Solve the following, where t is a variable over R, and $a,b,c,d \in R$.
  (a) $ab - cd = a - t$.
  (b) $b - (t - c) = d + a$.
  (c) $b - (c - t) = d + a$.

2.7 A Proof by Contradiction

We now consider a theorem whose proof will be given by the method of *contradiction*. This method was used in Chapter 1 to prove statement 7 on sets: If A and B are sets such that $A \subset B$, then there exists an element of B which is not an element of A.

The idea of the proof was as follows: One observed that there were two alternatives:

1. There is an element of B not in A.
2. Every element of B is an element of A.

One of these alternatives must be correct.

Working on the *assumption* that (2) was correct led to a contradiction of the hypothesis that $A \subset B$. Hence (2) could not have been correct. Hence (1) was the only remaining possibility.

Sometimes, there are three (or more) possibilities to be considered. The way in which the possibilities are divided often depends upon the proof one is able to invent.

For example, one may wish to prove that an element a of the set of natural numbers is equal to 3. He may first attempt a proof by contradiction, considering two possibilities: Either (1) $a \neq 3$ or (2) $a = 3$.

He now tries to show that $a \neq 3$ leads to a contradiction. But in developing the proof, he sees that one argument is needed for a greater than 3, another for a less than 3.

He then changes his division of possibilities as follows:

"One and only one of the following can be true:
(1) a is greater than 3;
(2) a is less than 3;
(3) $a = 3$."

He gives one argument to show that "a is greater than 3" leads to a contradiction; a second argument to show that "a is less than 3" leads to a contradiction. The only possible conclusion is that $a = 3$.

Theorem 40. If $a \in R$ and $a \neq 0$, then $-a \neq 0$.

Proof:

(1)	$a \neq 0$	(1) Hyp.
(2)	Either $\quad -a = 0$ or $\quad\quad -a \neq 0$	(2) Listing of alternatives for a proof by contradiction
(3)	Suppose $-a = 0$	(3) Assumption to lead to a contradiction
(4)	$(-a) + a = 0 + a$	(4) Th. 5 (step 3)
(5)	$= a$	(5) A4
(6)	$(-a) + a = 0$	(6) Def. 1
(7)	$a = 0$	(7) Steps 5, 6
(8)	$-a = 0$ leads to a contradiction	(8) Step 7 contradicts step 1
(9)	$-a \neq 0$	(9) Steps 2, 8

Exercises

41. Prove the converse of Theorem 40. (*Hint:* Use Theorems 17 and 40.)
42. Prove: Let $a,b \in R$. Then $a \neq b$ if and only if $-a \neq -b$.

3. Theorems on Multiplication

3.1   Cancellation Laws; Uniqueness of Multiplicative Identity, Inverses

The definitions and theorems up to now involved only the postulates A1, A2, A3, A4, and A5, that is, the postulates for addition. We can state similar definitions and theorems for multiplication, and use M1, M2, M3, M4, and M5. Where we had + before, we have · now; where we had 0 before, we have 1 now. The only parts that do not carry over are those where we used an additive inverse, that is, A5. For A5 states that *every* real number has an additive inverse, whereas M5 states that each real number different from 0 has a multiplicative inverse. Thus in stating our theorems and definitions for multiplication, where we used A5 before, we must now stipulate that a be different from zero in order to use M5. With this in mind, the following parallels what we have done above, merely replacing $+$ by $\cdot$ and 0 by 1. We therefore list most of the theorems as exercises.

Exercises

43. Prove: If $a,b,c \in R$, $a \neq 0$, then $ab = ac$ if and only if $b = c$ (cf. Theorem 5).
44. Prove: If $a,b,c \in R$, $a \neq 0$, then $ba = ca$ if and only if $b = c$ (cf. Theorem 6).
45. Prove: If $1'$ is a multiplicative identity of R, then $1' = 1$ (cf. Theorem 8). Thus the multiplicative identity of R is unique.
46. Prove: If $a,b,c \in R$, $a \neq 0$, $ab = ac = 1$, then $b = c$ (cf. Theorem 9). Thus the multiplicative inverse of $a \neq 0$ in R is unique.

Definition 5. If $a \in R$, $a \neq 0$, then the unique multiplicative inverse of a in R shall be designated by 'a^{-1}' (cf. Definition 1).

Thus a^{-1} is the unique element in R such that

$$aa^{-1} = a^{-1}a = 1 \ ^5$$

Exercises

47. In Exercise 1, find 1^{-1}. In Exercise 2 find 1^{-1} and 2^{-1}.
48. Prove: $1^{-1} = 1$ (cf. Theorem 16).
49. Prove: Let $a,b \in R$ and $b \neq 0$. Then $ba = b$ if and only if $a = 1$.

3.2 Multiplication by Zero

At this point we must interrupt development of the analogues of the theorems of Section 2. For the analogue of Theorem 17 would read:

"If $a \in R$, $a \neq 0$, then $(a^{-1})^{-1} = a$."

But we do not yet know $a^{-1} \neq 0$, and so cannot apply Definition 5 to a^{-1}. Now $a^{-1} \cdot a = 1$. If we knew $0 \cdot a = 0$, we could not have $a^{-1} = 0$, since $0 \neq 1$. That $0 \cdot a = 0$ will be contained in Theorem 50.

Theorem 50. Let $a,b \in R$. Then $ab = 0$ if and only if $a = 0$ or $b = 0$.

Proof: (α) We first show if $a = 0$ or $b = 0$, then $ab = 0$. That is, we must show $0 \cdot b = 0$ (the case $a = 0$) or $a \cdot 0 = 0$ (the case $b = 0$). We shall show $0 \cdot b = 0$, the proof of $a \cdot 0 = 0$ being similar. ($a \cdot 0 = 0$ also follows from the result for $b = 0$ and the commutative law of multiplication applied to $0 \cdot a = 0$.)

---

[5] One generally says for '$-a$': "minus a"; for 'a^{-1}': "a inverse." Of course, one also calls $-a$ the *additive inverse* of a, and a^{-1} the *multiplicative inverse* of a.

Proof: (1) $0 \cdot b + 0 \cdot b = (0 + 0)b$ (1) D

(2) $= 0 \cdot b$ (2) A4

(3) $0 \cdot b = (0 \cdot b) - (0 \cdot b)$ (3) Th. 34

(4) $= 0$ (4) Ex. 21

Remarks: Step 2 shows that $0 \cdot b$ is a solution of $0 \cdot b + x = 0 \cdot b$. But the *unique* solution of this equation is $(0 \cdot b) - (0 \cdot b)$ by Theorem 34; hence these two solutions are the same, as noted in step 3.

[An alternative proof is the following:

(1) $0 \cdot b = (0 + 0)b$

(2) $= 0 \cdot b + 0 \cdot b$

(3) $0 \cdot b + 0 = 0 \cdot b + 0 \cdot b$

(4) $0 = 0 \cdot b$

The student should fill in the reasons.]

(β) We next show that if $ab = 0$, then $a = 0$ or $b = 0$. Another way of phrasing the conclusion is: If $a \neq 0$, then $b = 0$, or if $b \neq 0$, then $a = 0$. We shall therefore prove: If $ab = 0$ and $a \neq 0$, then $b = 0$. ("If $ab = 0$ and $b \neq 0$, then $a = 0$" is proved similarly or by use of the commutative law of multiplication.)

(1) $a \neq 0$ (1) Hyp.

(2) $ab = 0$ (2) Hyp.

(3) $b = 1 \cdot b$ (3) M4

(4) $= (a^{-1}a)b$ (4) Step 1, Def. 5

(5) $= a^{-1}(ab)$ (5) M2

(6) $= a^{-1} \cdot 0$ (6) Steps 2, 5

(7) $= 0$ (7) Th. 50 (α)

Remark: To apply Definition 5 in step 4, one had to know $a \neq 0$.

We know from M5 that if $a \in R$ and $a \neq 0$, then a has a multiplicative inverse. The question still remains as to whether 0 has a multiplicative inverse.

We may say either 0 has a multiplicative inverse, or 0 does not have a multiplicative inverse.

Considerable insight into this question is gained if we assume 0 has a multiplicative inverse.

Thus, assume *there exists $q \in R$ such that* [6] $0 \cdot q = 1$. But by Theorem 50, $0 \cdot q = 0$. Since $0 \cdot q = 1$ and $0 \cdot q = 0$, we have $1 = 0$. This contradicts postulate B.

Therefore we must conclude that 0 *does not have a multiplicative inverse.* Had M5 not excluded 0, therefore, we would have had an inconsistent set of postulates.

---

[6] The phrases "there exists" and "such that" arise so often that it is now common practice to use abbreviations. The symbol used for "there exists" is '∃,' and for "such that" is '∋.' Then the statement above would read: "Thus assume $\exists q \in R \ni 0 \cdot q = 1$."

Exercise

51. If $a \in R$ and $a \neq 0$, prove:
(a) $a^{-1} \neq 0$.
(b) $(a^{-1})^{-1} = a$ (cf. Theorem 17).

3.3 Division

Definition 6. If $a,b \in R$ and $b \neq 0$, then $\frac{a}{b}$ shall designate ab^{-1}; i.e.,

$\frac{a}{b} = ab^{-1}$ (cf. Definition 2).[7]

Exercises

52. In Exercise 2, find $\frac{0}{1}, \frac{0}{2}, \frac{1}{1}, \frac{1}{2}, \frac{2}{1}, \frac{2}{2}$.

53. Prove: If $a,b \in R$, $b \neq 0$, then $\frac{a}{b} \in R$.

54. Prove: If $a \in R$, $\frac{a}{1} = a$ (cf. Theorem 20).

55. Prove: If $a \in R$, $a \neq 0$, then $\frac{1}{a} = a^{-1}$ (cf. Theorem 22).

56. Prove: If $a \in R$, $a \neq 0$, then $\frac{a}{a} = 1$ (cf. Theorem 21).

3.4 Generalizations of M2 and M3

Definition 7. If $a,b,c \in R$, $abc = (ab)c$ (and also by M2)
$= a(bc)$ (cf. Definition 3)

Exercises

57. Prove: If $a,b,c,d \in R$, then $(abc)d = (ab)(cd) = a(bcd)$ (cf. Theorem 28).
58. Prove: If $a,b,c \in R$, then $abc = bac = bca = acb$, etc. (cf. Exercise 32).
59. Prove: Let $a,b,c \in R$. Then $abc = 0$ if and only if $a = 0$, $b = 0$, or $c = 0$.

Definition 8. If $a,b,c,d \in R$, then $abcd = (abc)d$ [and therefore by Exercise 57, $= (ab)(cd) = a(bcd)$] (cf. Definition 4).

Remark: It is clear how we would define $abcde$, $abcdef$, etc., and what theorems one should prove to show it does not matter how one inserts parentheses.

[7] Whenever writing $\frac{a}{b}$ one must be sure $b \neq 0$. Thus the rule assigning $\frac{a}{b}$ to the ordered pair (a, b) of R is not a binary operation on R, as it is not defined for $(1, 0)$, for example. It is, however, a binary operation on the set of real numbers distinct from 0. One calls this binary operation "division," and says "a divided by b" (or also "a over b") for $\frac{a}{b}$. This terminology is usually extended to $\frac{0}{b}$ as well.

Exercises

60. Prove: If $a,b,c,d \in R$, $abcd = abdc = adbc =$ etc. (cf. Exercise 33).
61. Prove: Let $a,b,c,d \in R$. Then $abcd = 0$ if and only if $a = 0$, $b = 0$, $c = 0$, or $d = 0$.

3.5   Solutions to Equations over R

Theorem 62. If $a,b \in R$, $a \neq 0$, and x is a variable over R, then the solution set of the equation $ax = b$ is $\left\{\dfrac{b}{a}\right\}$ (cf. Theorem 34).

Proof:

(α) We first show $\dfrac{b}{a}$ is a solution of $ax = b$.

(1) $a \cdot \dfrac{b}{a} = a(ba^{-1})$	(1) Def. 6
(2) $\quad\quad = aba^{-1}$	(2) Def. 7
(3) $\quad\quad = a^{-1}ab$	(3) Ex. 58
(4) $\quad\quad = (a^{-1}a)b$	(4) Def. 7
(5) $\quad\quad = 1 \cdot b$	(5) Def. 5
(6) $\quad\quad = b$	(6) M4

(β) We now show that if $ac = b$ where $c \in R$, then $c = \dfrac{b}{a}$.

(1) $a \neq 0$	(1) Hyp.
(2) $a\left(\dfrac{b}{a}\right) = b$	(2) Th. 62(α)
(3) $ac = b$	(3) Hyp.
(4) $ac = a\left(\dfrac{b}{a}\right)$	(4) Steps 2, 3
(5) $c = \dfrac{b}{a}$	(5) Steps 1, 4; Ex. 43

Theorem 63. If $a,b \in R$ and x is a variable over R, then the solution set of $(x - a)(x - b) = 0$ is $\{a, b\}$.

Proof: (α) We show a is a solution of $(x - a)(x - b) = 0$.

(1) $a - a = 0$	(1) Ex. 21
(2) $(a - a)(a - b) = 0 \cdot (a - b)$	(2) $\cdot$ is a binary operation
(3) $\quad\quad = 0$	(3) Th. 50

(β) To show b is a solution of $(x - a)(x - b) = 0$ is similar to the above.
(γ) We now show that a and b are the only solutions. That is, if $c \in R$ and $(c - a)(c - b) = 0$, we must show $c = a$ or $c = b$.

Proof: (1) $(c - a)(c - b) = 0$ (1) Hyp.
(2) $c - a = 0$ or $c - b = 0$ (2) Th. 50
(3) $c = a$ or $c = b$ (3) Ex. 35

[Note that this theorem does not tell how to solve equations of the type $(x - a)(x - b) = d$ for $d \neq 0$.]

Exercises

64. Prove: If $a,b,c \in R$ and x is a variable over R, then the solution set of $(x - a)(x - b)(x - c) = 0$ is $\{a, b, c\}$.

65. Prove: If $a,b,c,d \in R$ and x is a variable over R, then the solution set of $(x - a)(x - b)(x - c)(x - d) = 0$ is $\{a, b, c, d\}$.

66. Prove: If $a \in R$, $a \neq 0$, x a variable over R, then the solution set of $\dfrac{x}{a} = 0$ is $\{0\}$.

67. Solve the following, where $a,b,c,d \in R$, $a \neq 0$, x a variable over R:

(a) $ax + b = c$.

(b) $ax + b = 0$.

(c) $(ax + b)(cx + d) = 0$ for $c \neq 0$.

4. Informal Proofs

We have now studied formal proofs of many theorems. Actually, the proofs of theorems ordinarily encountered in mathematical literature are written much more informally, with sufficient reasoning given so that one could give the formal proof if he so desired. Therefore, we shall henceforth give informal proofs. It would be advisable for the student to construct informal proofs also, and proceed from these to the formal. When he feels he has sufficient experience in passing from informal proofs to formal proofs, he may then give only informal proofs.

Actually, with informal proofs one has the opportunity of making clearer the essential ideas of his arguments. That is, he can develop a style, ranging from lucid to obscure. Often what is lucid to one person is obscure to another and vice versa. Therefore if the student can improve upon the arguments given in the text, we encourage him to do so. He should remember that the object of writing out mathematical arguments is not only to clarify things for himself, but also to communicate his insights to others. To this end, any obscure arguments below are not purposely so conceived.

In this section we list most theorems to be proved as exercises.

Theorem 68. If $m,n \in R$, then $m - n = -(n - m)$.

Proof: By Definition 1, $-(n - m)$ is the *unique* additive inverse of $n - m$. Therefore, if we can show $m - n$ is also an additive inverse of $n - m$, the theorem will be established. Thus, we must show $(m - n) + (n - m) = 0$. But

$$\begin{aligned}(m - n) + (n - m) &= m + (-n) + n + (-m) \\ &= [m + (-m)] + [n + (-n)] \\ &= 0 + 0 \\ &= 0\end{aligned}$$

Remarks: Note that we did not indicate any reason in the steps of the proof. (We did, however, indicate the use of Definition 1.) But we outlined the argument in a way which makes the reasoning, in our estimation, apparent. One cannot say that we omitted *all* reasoning, since that would involve writing at once:

$$(m-n)+(n-m)=0$$

[Just this once(?), we repeat the proof formally. But the student is encouraged to attempt this independently.

Formal Proof of Theorem 68:

(1) $(m-n)+(n-m)=[m+(-n)]+[n+(-m)]$		(1) Def. 2
(2) $=m+(-n)+n+(-m)$		(2) Def. 4
(3) $=m+(-m)+n+(-n)$		(3) Ex. 33
(4) $=[m+(-m)]+[n+(-n)]$		(4) Def. 4
(5) $=0+0$		(5) Def. 1
(6) $=0$		(6) A4
(7) $m-n=-(n-m)$		(7) Def. 1 (step 6)

Remark: Step 6 states that $m-n$ is an additive inverse of $n-m$. By definition 1, the name of this unique additive inverse is '$-(n-m)$.' Hence $m-n=-(n-m)$, as given in step 7.]

Theorem 69. If $a,b \in R$, and $a,b \neq 0$, then $\dfrac{b}{a}=\left(\dfrac{a}{b}\right)^{-1}$.

Proof: By Definition 5, $\left(\dfrac{a}{b}\right)^{-1}$ is the unique multiplicative inverse of $\dfrac{a}{b}$. If we can show that $\dfrac{b}{a}$ is also a multiplicative inverse of $\dfrac{a}{b}$, it will follow that $\dfrac{b}{a}=\left(\dfrac{a}{b}\right)^{-1}$. Thus we must show $\dfrac{b}{a}\cdot\dfrac{a}{b}=1$. But

$$\frac{b}{a}\cdot\frac{a}{b}=(ba^{-1})(ab^{-1}) \qquad \text{Def. 6}$$
$$=ba^{-1}ab^{-1}$$
$$=aa^{-1}bb^{-1}$$
$$=(aa^{-1})(bb^{-1})$$
$$=1$$

Theorem 70. If $b,d \in R$ and $b,d \neq 0$, then $\dfrac{1}{bd}=\dfrac{1}{b}\cdot\dfrac{1}{d}$.

Proof: We first observe that if $b,d \neq 0$, then $bd \neq 0$ by Theorem 50. (For if $bd=0$, either $b=0$ or $d=0$.) Hence by Theorem 62, $(bd)x=1$ has the unique solution $\dfrac{1}{bd}$. If we can also show that $\dfrac{1}{b}\cdot\dfrac{1}{d}$ is a solution of this equation, the result will follow. Thus we wish to show $(bd)\left(\dfrac{1}{b}\cdot\dfrac{1}{d}\right)=1$. But

$$(bd) \cdot \left(\frac{1}{b} \cdot \frac{1}{d}\right) = (bd) \cdot (b^{-1} \cdot d^{-1}) \qquad \text{by Ex. 55}$$
$$= (bb^{-1})(dd^{-1})$$
$$= 1$$

Theorem 71a. If $a,b \in R$, then $a(-b) = (-a)b = -ab$.

[*Note:* $-ab$ means $-(ab)$; that is, $-ab$ is the additive inverse of ab.]

Proof: $-ab$ is the unique additive inverse of ab. If we can show $a(-b)$ and $(-a)b$ are also additive inverses of ab, the desired result will follow.

$$a(-b) + ab = a[(-b) + b] \qquad \text{by D}$$
$$= a \cdot 0$$
$$= 0 \qquad \text{by Th. 50}$$
$$(-a)b + ab = [(-a) + a]b \qquad \text{by D}$$
$$= 0 \cdot b$$
$$= 0$$

Remark: It follows from Theorem 71a that if $b \in R$, then $-b = (-1)b$. For according to Theorem 71a,

$$(-1)b = -(1 \cdot b)$$
$$= -b \qquad \text{by M4}$$

This proves:

Theorem 71b. If $b \in R$, $-b = (-1)b$.

Theorem 72. If $a,b \in R$, then $(-a)(-b) = ab$. [In particular, $(-1)(-1) = 1$.]

Proof: $(-a)(-b) = -[a(-b)] \qquad \text{by Th. 71}$
$$= -[-(ab)] \qquad \text{by Th. 71}$$
$$= ab \qquad \text{by Th. 17}$$

Exercises

73. If $a,b \in R$, then $-(a + b) = -a - b$.

74. If $a,b,c \in R$, then $a - b + c = a - (b - c)$.

75. If $a,b,c \in R$, then $a - b - c = a - (b + c)$.

76. If $a,b \in R$, $b \neq 0$, then $\dfrac{a}{b^{-1}} = ab$ (cf. Exercise 27).

77. If $a,b \in R$, $b \neq 0$, then $\dfrac{a}{b} = a \cdot \dfrac{1}{b}$.

78. If $a,b,c,d \in R$; $b,d \neq 0$; then $\dfrac{a}{b} = \dfrac{c}{d}$ if and only if $ad = bc$ (cf. Theorem 37).

79. If $a,b \in R$, $b \neq 0$, then $b \cdot \dfrac{a}{b} = a$.

80. If $a,b,c,d \in R$; $b,d \neq 0$; then $\dfrac{a}{b} \cdot \dfrac{c}{d} = \dfrac{ac}{bd}$.

81. If $a,b,c \in R$, $b \neq 0$, then $\dfrac{a}{b} \cdot c = \dfrac{ac}{b}$.

82. If $a,b,c,d,e,f \in R$; $b,d,f \neq 0$; then $\dfrac{a}{b} \cdot \dfrac{c}{d} \cdot \dfrac{e}{f} = \dfrac{ace}{bdf}$.

83. If $a,b,c,d,e,f,g,h \in R$; $b,d,f,h \neq 0$; then $\dfrac{a}{b} \cdot \dfrac{c}{d} \cdot \dfrac{e}{f} \cdot \dfrac{g}{h} = \dfrac{aceg}{bdfh}$.

84. If $a,b,c \in R$ and $b,c \neq 0$, then $\dfrac{ac}{bc} = \dfrac{a}{b}$.

85. If $a,b,c \in R$; $b,c \neq 0$, then $b \cdot \dfrac{a}{bc} = \dfrac{a}{c}$.

86. If $a,b,c,d \in R$; $a,b,c \neq 0$; then $\dfrac{b}{a} \cdot \dfrac{ad}{bc} = \dfrac{d}{c}$.

87. If $a,b,c,d \in R$; $b,c,d \neq 0$; then $\dfrac{a}{b} \Big/ \dfrac{c}{d} = \dfrac{ad}{bc}$.

88. If $a,b,c \in R$; $b,c \neq 0$; then $\dfrac{a}{b} \Big/ c = \dfrac{a}{bc}$.

89. If $a,b,c \in R$, then $a(b - c) = ab - ac$.

90. If $a,b,c,d \in R$, then $a(b \pm c \pm d) = ab \pm ac \pm ad$.[8]

91. If $a,b,c,d,e \in R$, $a(b \pm c \pm d \pm e) = ab \pm ac \pm ad \pm ae$.

92. If $a,b,c \in R$, then $(-a)(b \pm c) = -ab \mp ac$.[9]

93. If $a,b,c,d \in R$, $(-a)(b \pm c \pm d) = -ab \mp ac \mp ad$.

94. If $a,b,c,d,e \in R$, $(-a)(b \pm c \pm d \pm e) = -ab \mp ac \mp ad \mp ae$.

95. If $a,b,c,d \in R$, then:
   (a) $(a + b)(c + d) = ac + ad + bc + bd$.
   (b) $(a + b)(c - d) = ac - ad + bc - bd$.
   (c) $(a - b)(c - d) = ac - ad - bc + bd$.

96. If $a,b \in R$, then $(a + b)(a - b) = aa - bb$.

Theorem 97. If $a,b,c \in R$, $b \neq 0$, then $\dfrac{a}{b} \pm \dfrac{c}{b} = \dfrac{a \pm c}{b}$.

Proof: $\dfrac{a}{b} \pm \dfrac{c}{b} = a \cdot \dfrac{1}{b} \pm c \cdot \dfrac{1}{b}$ by Ex. 77

           $= (a \pm c) \cdot \dfrac{1}{b}$ by D for +, or Ex. 89 for −

           $= \dfrac{a \pm c}{b}$ by Ex. 77

[8] This is an abbreviation for four theorems:
  (1) $a(b + c + d) = ab + ac + ad$;
  (2) $a(b - c - d) = ab - ac - ad$ (cf. footnote 3);
  (3) $a(b + c - d) = ab + ac - ad$;
  (4) $a(b - c + d) = ab - ac + ad$.

[9] This abbreviates:
  (1) $(-a)(b + c) = -ab - ac$;
  (2) $(-a)(b - c) = -ab + ac$.

Theorem 98. If $a,b,c,d \in R$, $b,d \neq 0$, then $\dfrac{a}{b} \pm \dfrac{c}{d} = \dfrac{ad \pm bc}{bd}$.

Proof: $\dfrac{a}{b} \pm \dfrac{c}{d} = \dfrac{ad}{bd} \pm \dfrac{bc}{bd}$ by Ex. 84

$\qquad\qquad = \dfrac{ad \pm bc}{bd}$ by Th. 97

Theorem 99. If $a,b \in R$, $b \neq 0$, then $\dfrac{a}{-b} = \dfrac{-a}{b} = -\dfrac{a}{b}$.

Proof: $-\dfrac{a}{b}$ is the unique additive inverse of $\dfrac{a}{b}$ by Def. 1. Hence if we can show $\dfrac{a}{-b}$

and $\dfrac{-a}{b}$ are also additive inverses of $\dfrac{a}{b}$, the result will follow. But

$$\frac{a}{-b} + \frac{a}{b} = \frac{ab + a(-b)}{(-b)b} \qquad \text{by Th. 98}$$

$$= \frac{ab + [-(ab)]}{(-b)b} \qquad \text{by Th. 71}$$

$$= \frac{0}{(-b)b} \qquad \text{by Def. 1}$$

$$= 0 \qquad \text{by Ex. 66}$$

The remaining part of the theorem is listed as Exercise 100.

Exercises

100. Complete the proof of Theorem 99.

101. If $a,b \in R$, $b \neq 0$, then $\dfrac{-a}{-b} = \dfrac{a}{b}$.

102. If $a \in R$, $a \neq 0$, then $(-a)^{-1} = -(a^{-1})$.

103. If $a,b,c,d \in R$, then:
    (a) $(-a)(b)(-c) = abc$.
    (b) $(-a)(-b)(-c) = -abc$.
    (c) $(-a) \cdot b \cdot c \cdot d = -abcd$.

By this time, at the very least, the student will wonder if there is any end to this. The answer, of course, is that there is not. So perhaps we should stop here. For if we need any result later which was not included above, we can always prove it on the spot (as an exercise!).

5. Some Historical Remarks

In this chapter we have developed many of the properties of the real-number system from an initial set of postulates. This "postulational" (also called "axiomatic") approach is important if one wishes to delineate the assumptions clearly in his presentation of a deductive argument. Although mathematicians may benefit from a highly developed intuition, in the end all statements which are to become a subset of the mathematical literature must be deduced rigorously from a set of postulates and from the established theorems already derived from these.

Generally speaking, the Greek mathematician Pythagoras (569?–500? B.C.) is credited as being the first European to recognize the need for a strict deductive proof in geometry from a set of postulates.[10] Before this, mathematics was conceived of as a set of empirical rules. The introduction of the idea of a proof into the formal workings of mathematics was of tremendous significance. The possibility appears to exist that the Egyptians and Babylonians of about 2000 B.C. also observed the need for deductive proofs.[11]

Although today the words "axiom" and "postulate" are synonymous, perhaps it should be pointed out that at one time they had somewhat different meanings. Historically, they both referred to assumptions which were "self-evident," or which were "first principles impossible to prove." Aristotle (384–322 B.C.) used the word "axiom" for those "first principles" common to all sciences; and later writers used the word "postulates" for those "first principles" related to the specific science being considered.[12] Actually there was not a clear agreement among early Greek mathematicians between these words. Proclus (412–485), who wrote a commentary on Euclid's "Elements," [13] writes of the various distinctions encountered in the use of the words "axiom" and "postulate" by the early Greeks.[14] Generally speaking, at any rate, the axioms and postulates were assumptions from nature to be accepted, and were not thought of as being the creation of man.

The method of deducing theorems from "axioms and postulates" was beautifully demonstrated by Euclid (330?–275? B.C.) in his "Elements," which contains many of the theorems of geometry and number theory known in Euclid's time. For more than 2000 years this work has served as the basis for courses in plane and solid geometry. Its deductive methods have had a profound effect upon the development of mathematics to the present time.

And man was chained, for more than 2000 years, to the concept that postulates are found in nature. The freedom from this idea was achieved both in algebra and in geometry in the nineteenth century. In geometry,

[10] Cf. E. T. Bell, *Men of Mathematics,* p. 20, Simon & Schuster, New York, 1937.

[11] Cf. E. T. Bell, *Development of Mathematics,* p. 4, McGraw-Hill, New York, 1940.

[12] Cf. D. E. Smith, *History of Mathematics,* Vol. II, p. 280, Dover, New York, 1958 (reprinted from an earlier edition).

[13] Cf. W. W. Rouse Ball, *History of Mathematics,* p. 104, Macmillan, New York, 1888.

[14] Cf. H. Eves and C. V. Newsom, *An Introduction to the Foundations and Fundamental Concepts of Mathematics,* p. 37, Holt, New York, 1965.

this came about through a consideration of Euclid's fifth postulate, which stated that given a point—say P—and a line not passing through P—say l—then (1) there exists a line (in the plane of P and l) passing through P which does not meet (i.e., is parallel to) the line l; and (2) there exists in fact only one such line. There were many attempts to prove the second part of this postulate from the first (and the other axioms and postulates), but Nikolai Ivanovich Lobachevski (1793–1856) created a geometry in which he postulated that through the point P an indefinite number of lines may be drawn parallel to the line l, and János Bolyai (1802–1860) created a geometry in which he postulated that every line drawn through P will meet l (there are no parallel lines). What is more, both of these abstract geometric systems have realizations!

We should perhaps mention that the development of Euclid is by no means flawless by present standards of basing proofs exclusively upon a set of postulates. Hidden in some of Euclid's proofs were assumptions which remained undetected until the nineteenth century.

While most high-school students have been exposed to a postulational approach to geometry for a long time, it is only relatively recently that such an approach has been introduced into the early curriculum in the study of the arithmetic and algebra of the real-number system. In this chapter such a development was introduced, and we shall continue this postulational treatment in most of the remaining chapters of Part II. We shall have more to say concerning the historical aspects of the development of the number system later.

chapter vi

ARITHMETIC AND ALGEBRAIC COMPUTATIONS

The problems we undertake to consider in this chapter would be more logically deferred until a later one. For subsequent chapters treat some of the theorems which are needed to answer satisfactorily the problems in arithmetic and algebraic computations posed here. Indeed, even the addition and multiplication tables for the set of natural numbers will be derived later. We shall also make use of the "Fundamental Theorem of Arithmetic," even though its proof is not given until Chapter 9. Nevertheless, we consider these problems here for at least three reasons:

1. The student is ready to see how the theoretical development of Chapter 5 can be applied to solve problems he may have encountered in elementary arithmetic and algebra.

2. The problems presented serve as a preview and motivation for theoretical questions which will be considered later.

3. It is desirable that the student develop technical skills as early as possible.

1. The Integers

1.1 Assumptions

In Chapter 8 we shall define the set N of natural numbers. We shall then be able to derive the addition and multiplication tables for the set N of natural numbers. For the present, however, we shall assume a knowledge of these tables. We shall use the designations 'AN' and 'MN,' respectively, for the *A*ddition and *M*ultiplication tables for N. Thus if one wishes to specify a reason for statements such as $7 + 3 = 10$, he will give: AN; or for $7 \cdot 3 = 21$, the reason: MN.

It will also follow from the definition of N that $0 \notin N$ and $N \subseteq R$. For the present, we shall also consider these as assumptions. Thus, as the reason for the statement $7 \neq 0$, we give: $0 \notin N$. The assumption $N \subseteq R$ shall be labeled NR and will allow us to apply the theorems of Chapter 5 to N. (Note that the 1 in N is the same as the 1 in R given by M4. For if $1 \cdot 2 = 1' \cdot 2$, then $1 = 1'$, since $2 \neq 0$.)

In summary, then, we are assuming: (1) AN; (2) MN; (3) $0 \notin N$; (4) NR. From (3) and (4) we see that $N \subset R$.

1.2   Definition of the Set J of Integers

Definition 1. If $a \in R$, then a will be called an *integer* if any one of the following holds:

(a) $a \in N$;   (b) $a = 0$;   (c) $-a \in N$.

The set of all integers will be denoted by J. Thus $J \subseteq R$.

We see from (a) that $1, 2, 3, \ldots$ are integers; from (b) we have 0 is an integer (i.e., $0 \in J$); from (c), $-1, -2, -3, \ldots$ are integers.[1]

(a) $1, 2, 3, \ldots \in J$ i.e., $\{1, 2, 3, \ldots\} \subseteq J$
(b) $0 \in J$ i.e., $\{0\} \subseteq J$
(c) $-1, -2, -3, \ldots \in J$ i.e., $\{-1, -2, -3, \ldots\} \subseteq J$

Conversely, if s is an integer, then s is equal to one of the elements in (a), (b), or (c). For according to Definition 1, either $s \in N$, in which case s is one of the elements in (a); or $s = 0$, which is (b); or $-s \in N$. In this latter case, $-s$ is one of the elements in (a): say $-s = n \in N$. Then $s = -n$, so that s is one of the elements in (c).

If we denote by '$-N$' the set $\{-1, -2, \ldots\}$ we see that

$$J = N \cup \{0\} \cup -N$$

We have seen (5, 26) (i.e., Exercise 26 in Chapter 5) that if $m, n \in N$, then $-m = -n$ if and only if $m = n$. (We are using NR.) Thus $-7 \neq -22$, etc.

In a later chapter we shall see that N, $\{0\}$, $-N$ are disjoint (i.e., the intersection of each pair of these sets is the null set). It will then follow that $N \subset J \subseteq R$. Indeed, we shall show that $N \subset J \subset R$.

1.3   Computation of $a + b$, $a - b$, and ab in J

If $a, b \in N$, then we can find $a + b$ and ab by AN and MN. Thus $7 + 5 = 12$ by AN and $7 \cdot 5 = 35$ by MN. We now consider the computation of $a - b$, where $a, b \in N$.

(a) Find $7 - 3$.
     Solution: By (5, 34), $7 - 3$ is the unique solution of $3 + x = 7$. Since $3 + 4 = 7$ by AN, $7 - 3 = 4$.
     {More formally:
     [(1) $3, 7 \in R$ NR]
      (2) $3 + 4 = 7$ AN
      (3) $7 - 3 = 4$ Steps 1, 2; (5, 34)}.
(b) Find $7 - 7$.
     $7 - 7 = 0$ by (5, 21)
(c) Find $3 - 7$.

---

[1] -2 is an integer, for example, because it falls in class (c). For $-(-2) \in N$ [cf. Theorem 17, Chap. 5; we are using NR and this theorem to conclude $-(-2) = 2$].

$$3 - 7 = -(7 - 3) \qquad (5, 68)$$
$$= -4 \qquad \text{By the argument of example (a)}$$

We leave it to the student, in the following exercises, to consider the reasoning involved in the computation of $a + b$, $a - b$, ab for any $a,b \in J$.

Exercises

Find the following, indicating informal reasoning:

1. $0 - 0$.
2. $9 - 0$.
3. $8 \cdot 0$.
4. $8 - 8$.

5. $0 - 9$.
6. $-7 + 3$.
7. $-7 + (-3)$.

8. $(-7) - (-3)$.
9. $(-8) \cdot 0$.
10. $7 + (-3)$.

11. $(-8)(3)$.
12. $-(3 - 7 + 2)$ in two ways.
13. $5 + 9 - 12$ in two ways.

2. The Rational Numbers

Definition 2. If $a \in R$ and $a = \dfrac{m}{n}$, where $m,n \in J$ and $n \neq 0$, then a is said to be a rational number. The set of all rational numbers will be denoted by '$\bar{R}$.' $\left(m \text{ is called the numerator and } n \text{ the denominator of } \dfrac{'m'}{n}. \right)^2$

By (5, 54), if $m \in J$, then $m = \dfrac{m}{1} \in \bar{R}$. Hence we have $N \subset J \subseteq \bar{R} \subseteq R$. In a later chapter, when we conclude the list of postulates for R, we shall see that, in fact, $N \subset J \subset \bar{R} \subset R$.

We shall then call the elements of R which are not in $\bar{R}$ the *irrational numbers* of R.

According to our definition, examples of rational numbers are $\dfrac{3}{-2}$, $\dfrac{8}{6}$, $\dfrac{2}{-3}$, $\dfrac{-31}{82}$, $\dfrac{60}{84}$, $\dfrac{2}{3}$, $\dfrac{16}{12}$, $\dfrac{0}{2}$, $\dfrac{10}{2}$, $\dfrac{5}{1}$, $\dfrac{-5}{1}$, $\dfrac{5}{7}$, etc. Note that not all the rational numbers we have listed are distinct from one another. For example, $\dfrac{60}{84} = \dfrac{5}{7}$. This can be seen by applying (5, 78): Thus $60 \cdot 7 = 84 \cdot 5$ by MN; hence $\dfrac{60}{84} = \dfrac{5}{7}$. Another way to show this is to observe that $\dfrac{60}{84} = \dfrac{12 \cdot 5}{12 \cdot 7} = \dfrac{5}{7}$ [by

---

² If a and b are real numbers, a is called the numerator and b the denominator of '$\dfrac{a}{b}$'. Thus, although one often writes 2 is the numerator of $\frac{2}{3}$, and 3 is the denominator, this technically does not make sense since $\frac{2}{3} = \frac{4}{6} = \frac{6}{9}$, and one could equally well say in this language that 4 is the numerator and 6 the denominator. We see, then, that we mean that 2 is the numerator and 3 the denominator of the name '$\frac{2}{3}$' of the number $\frac{2}{3}$; or 4 is the numerator of '$\frac{4}{6}$'. Names of numbers are often called *numerals,* and numerals of the form $\dfrac{'a'}{b}$ are called *fractions.* Thus numerators and denominators refer to fractions. This being said, we will nevertheless continue to say 4 is the numerator of $\frac{4}{6}$, since it is clear that we mean of '$\frac{4}{6}$'. Similarly, we shall omit single quotes in many instances, in the sequel, where the meaning is not thereby obscured.

(5, 84)]. In showing that $\dfrac{60}{84} = \dfrac{5}{7}$ by this latter method, one had to be able to see that $60 = 12 \cdot 5$ and $84 = 12 \cdot 7$. That is, one had to know the *factors* of 60 and 84 in the following sense:

Definition 3. If $a, b \in J$, we say b is a *factor* of a (in J) if there exists $c \in J$ such that $a = bc$. (In this case c is also a factor of a.)

Thus the factors of 60 are $1, -1, 2, -2, 3, -3, 4, -4, 5, -5, 6, -6, 10, -10, 12, -12, 15, -15, 20, -20, 30, -30, 60, -60$; the factors of 84 are $1, -1, 2, -2, 3, -3, 4, -4, 6, -6, 7, -7, 12, -12, 14, -14, 21, -21, 28, -28, 42, -42, 84, -84$.

1 is a factor of 60, since $60 = 1 \cdot 60$; -2 is a factor of 84, since $84 = (-2)(-42)$; etc.

Every integer is a factor of 0. For example, 122 is a factor of 0, since $0 = 122 \cdot 0$.

If b is a factor of a, then so is $-b$. For if $a = b \cdot c$, then also $a = (-b)(-c)$ by (5, 72). Also $-a$ has the same factors as a does. For if b is a factor of a so that $a = b \cdot c$, then b is also a factor of $-a$, since then $-a = b \cdot (-c)$. Conversely, one sees that every factor of $-a$ is also a factor of a.

Thus to study the factors of integers, it is sufficient to study the factors of natural numbers. For example, the factors of -42 are precisely the same as the factors of 42. Moreover, one need only consider those factors which are in N. For if one determines, for example, that $1, 2, 3, 6, 7, 14, 21, 42$ are the factors in N of 42, then it follows that their additive inverses are the remaining factors, i.e., $-1, -2, -3, -6, -7, -14, -21, -42$.

Now to know the factors of a natural number requires knowing the multiplication table much more extensively than is required for multiplying any two specific elements of N. What are all the products, for example, yielding 11,742,793? We shall treat this question more systematically later, but to permit the student to gain experience in computations sooner, we present some of the ideas involved in the next section.

Exercises

14. List the factors in J of each of the natural numbers from 1 to 15.

15. What is the smallest number of factors a natural number (other than 1) can have? Which of the natural numbers from 2 to 20 have this property?

16. Using Definition 3, prove that if $p, q, r \in J$, and if p is a factor of q and q a factor of r, then p is a factor of r.

3. Factorization of Integers

3.1   The Fundamental Theorem of Arithmetic

We have seen that 60 has many factors. Consider any factor of 60 in N, excluding 1 and 60 itself: say 6. This leads to a factorization of 60 into two factors, namely $60 = 6 \cdot 10$. Now apply the same procedure to 6: namely, consider a factor of 6 in N excluding 1 and 6 itself: say 2. Then $6 = 2 \cdot 3$, so that $60 = 6 \cdot 10 = (2 \cdot 3) \cdot 10 = 2 \cdot 3 \cdot 10$. Similarly, for 10 we have $10 = 2 \cdot 5$, so that $60 = 2 \cdot 3 \cdot 2 \cdot 5$.

Every integer a distinct from 1 or -1 has $1, a, -1, -a$ as factors, since $a = 1 \cdot a = (-1)(-a)$. Thus $15 = 1 \cdot 15 = (-1)(-15)$ and $-8 = 1 \cdot (-8) = (-1) \cdot [-(-8)]$, etc. But in the case of 2, 3, 5 (and hence $-2, -3, -5$) these constitute all the factors. Such integers are called *prime integers* or *primes* (cf. Exercise 15).

Definition 4. If $a \, \epsilon \, J$, $a \neq 1, -1$, and the only factors of a are $1, -1, a, -a$, then a is called a *prime (integer)*. If $a \, \epsilon \, J$, $a \neq 0, 1, -1$, and a is not a prime, then a is said to be *composite* or a *composite integer*.

The primes *in N* up to 100 are:

2, 3, 5, 7, 11, 13, 17, 19, 23, 29, 31, 37, 41, 43, 47, 53, 59, 61, 67, 71, 73, 79, 83, 89, 97

If the above together with their additive inverses are considered, then one obtains the primes between -100 and 100.

To return to 60, then, $60 = 2 \cdot 3 \cdot 2 \cdot 5$ is factored into primes (in N). We obtained this factorization into primes by starting with $60 = 6 \cdot 10$ and then factored 6 and 10 in turn. But suppose we had begun with $60 = 4 \cdot 15$ or $60 = 12 \cdot 5$, and then factored the factors in turn. Would we obtain the same prime factorization? In $60 = 4 \cdot 15$, proceeding further we obtain $60 = 2 \cdot 2 \cdot 3 \cdot 5$; in $60 = 12 \cdot 5$ we obtain $60 = 3 \cdot 2 \cdot 2 \cdot 5$. Thus in these illustrations, the same prime factors in N appear with the same multiplicity: 2 appears twice, 3 once, and 5 once.

It is a theorem (called the *Fundamental Theorem of Arithmetic*) that *every natural number distinct from 1 can be factored into primes in N in one and only one way* (except for the possible order in which one writes the factors). This means that one can always factor a natural number distinct from 1 into prime factors in N, and no matter how he goes about it, the same primes will always appear and with the same multiplicity.[3] With this theorem, for example, one could answer the following:

Question: Without multiplying out, can you tell whether

$$5 \cdot 12 \cdot 11 \cdot 16 \cdot 25 \cdot (60)^3 \cdot (16)^2 \cdot (32)^3 = 7^4 \cdot 8^4 \cdot 9^4?$$

[Here, $(60)^3$ means $60 \cdot 60 \cdot 60$; 7^4 means $7 \cdot 7 \cdot 7 \cdot 7$; etc.]

Answer: The left side is unequal to the right. For the primes appearing in the factorization of the left are not identical with those appearing on the right.

[3] If the natural number involved is a prime, then it is to be regarded as already factored into primes, the number of factors being one. Thus a prime factorization of 5 is 5; of 10 is $2 \cdot 5$; etc.

For example, 7 appears on the right and not on the left. Or also on the right, 2 appears 12 times $[8^4 = (2 \cdot 2 \cdot 2)(2 \cdot 2 \cdot 2)(2 \cdot 2 \cdot 2)(2 \cdot 2 \cdot 2)]$, and on the left from 32^3 we have 2 appearing at least 15 times. In either case, by the fundamental theorem, we could not have equality. (We shall prove the fundamental theorem in a later chapter.)

We have said that a natural number has a unique factorization in N into prime factors. How about in J? Consider the following factorizations of 60 into primes in J:

$$
\begin{aligned}
60 &= 2 \cdot 2 \cdot 3 \cdot 5 \\
&= (-2)(-2) \cdot 3 \cdot 5 \\
&= (-2) \cdot 2 \cdot (-3) \cdot 5 \\
&= (-2) \cdot 2 \cdot 3 \cdot (-5) \\
&= (-2)(-2)(-3)(-5) \\
&= 2 \cdot 2 \cdot (-3)(-5)
\end{aligned}
$$

Except for rearrangement of the order, these are all the prime factorizations of 60 in J. If p is a prime appearing in the first factorization, then $1 \cdot p$ or $(-1) \cdot p$ appears in the remaining factorizations.

Definition 5. -1 and 1 are called the *units* of J (they are the factors of 1).

With this terminology, we may say that if 2 appears with multiplicity two in a prime factorization of 60 in N, then 2 multiplied by a unit appears with the same multiplicity in any prime factorization of 60 in J.

Definition 6. If $a \in J$, $a \neq 0$, and a is not a unit, then we say that a and b are *associates* if $b = au$, where u is a unit of J. (In this case we also have $a = bu$.)

Thus 2 and $(-1) \cdot 2$ are associates; -3 and $(-1)(-3)$ are associates; 4 and $1 \cdot 4$ are associates; etc.

With this terminology, we may say that every integer has a unique factorization into primes *in J* up to associates.[4]

That is, if one has two factorizations of an integer into primes, then if the primes are suitably arranged, primes appearing in a given place will either be equal or associates. Thus in all the factorizations of 60 given above, 2 or -2 appear in the first place, the same for the second, 3 or -3 in the third, and 5 or -5 in the fourth. Hence the same will be true for -60, an associate of 60. For example, $-60 = (-2)(2)(-3)(-5)$.

Another way one can express the Fundamental Theorem of Arithmetic

---

[4] We may say that a nonzero element of J is a prime if it is not a unit, and if its only factors are units and associates.

in J is: Every integer distinct from 0 or a unit can be written uniquely as a product of a unit and primes *in N*.

Thus $60 = 1 \cdot 2 \cdot 2 \cdot 3 \cdot 5$ and $-60 = (-1) \cdot 2 \cdot 2 \cdot 3 \cdot 5$ are the unique factorizations in this form.

One sees, then, that it is sufficient to work with elements of N and their factorizations into primes in N, since such factorizations easily lead to factorizations of integers in J. From a prime factorization of a natural number, one may determine all the factors of that number.

Example 1. Find all the factors in N of 60.
Solution: First we find *the* prime factorization of 60 in N:

$$60 = 2 \cdot 2 \cdot 3 \cdot 5$$

Now 1 and 60 are certainly factors of 60. Otherwise, if a is a factor distinct from 1 or 60, then $60 = ab$, where both a and b are different from 1 or 60. Factoring a and b into primes yields a prime factorization of 60, and by the fundamental theorem this factorization must agree with the above. Hence a can only be $2, 3, 5, 2 \cdot 2, 2 \cdot 3, 2 \cdot 5, 3 \cdot 5, 2 \cdot 2 \cdot 3, 2 \cdot 2 \cdot 5$, and $2 \cdot 3 \cdot 5$. Without multiplying out, these numbers are all distinct by the reasoning given in the question and answer above. Hence the factors of 60 are 1, 2, 3, 5, 4, 6, 10, 15, 12, 20, 30, 60.

Example 2. Find all the factors in N of 84.
Solution: $84 = 2 \cdot 2 \cdot 3 \cdot 7$. Hence all factors of 84 other than 1 and 84 are:

$$2, 3, 7, 2 \cdot 2, 2 \cdot 3, 2 \cdot 7, 3 \cdot 7, 2 \cdot 2 \cdot 3, 2 \cdot 2 \cdot 7, 2 \cdot 3 \cdot 7$$

Then all factors of 84 are:

$$1, 2, 3, 7, 4, 6, 14, 21, 12, 28, 42, 84$$

3.2 Highest Common Factor

In Section 2 we showed that $\frac{60}{84} = \frac{5}{7}$. One method was to observe that 12 was a *common factor* of 60 and 84. We now consider the following question:

Example 3. Find all the common factors in N of 60 and 84.
Solution: Of course one can find all the factors of 60, and all the factors of 84, and then see which ones are common to both. We give a more efficient method.

If a is a common factor in N of 60 and 84, then by definition there exists integers b and c such that

$$60 = ab$$
$$84 = ac$$

(In fact, b and c must be in N.)

Factoring a and b into primes yields a prime factorization of 60, and similarly a and c of 84. It follows that the primes appearing in a prime factorization of a must appear in both the prime factorizations of 60 and 84. Now

$$60 = \underline{2 \cdot 2 \cdot 3} \cdot 5$$
$$84 = \underline{2 \cdot 2 \cdot 3} \cdot 7$$

Thus any common factor of 60 and 84 is a factor of $2 \cdot 2 \cdot 3 = 12$. The common factors, then, are

$$1, 2, 3, 4, 6, 12$$

Definition 7. If a and b are nonzero integers, and if d is an integer such that:

(1) d is a common factor of a and b (i.e., d is a factor of a and d is a factor of b),
(2) any common factor of a and b is a factor of d,

then d is called a *highest common factor* (h.c.f.) or also a *greatest common divisor* (g.c.d.) of a and b.

Thus, a highest common factor of 84 and 60 is 12. It follows that -12 is also an h.c.f. of 84 and 60. Also -84 and 60, 84 and -60, and -84 and -60 all have the same highest common factors: 12 and -12.

When we refer to *the* h.c.f. of two integers, we shall mean the one in N. Thus the h.c.f. of -84 and 60 is 12.

The standard notation for the h.c.f. of a and b is '(a,b).' Although this notation is also used for denoting an ordered pair, it is usually clear from the context which is meant. Thus $(60,84) = (-60,84) = (60,-84) = (-60,-84) = 12$.

Example 4. Find each of the following:

(a) $(30,84)$.
$$30 = \underline{2 \cdot 3} \cdot 5$$
$$84 = \underline{2 \cdot 3} \cdot 2 \cdot 7$$
$$(30,84) = 6$$

(b) $(30,-60)$.
$$30 = \underline{2 \cdot 3 \cdot 5}$$
$$60 = \underline{2 \cdot 3 \cdot 5} \cdot 2$$
$$(30,-60) = 30$$

(c) $(12,35)$.
$$12 = 2 \cdot 2 \cdot 3$$
$$35 = 5 \cdot 7$$

There are no common primes, so the only factor in common with 12 and 35 is 1. Thus 1 satisfies the requirements of Definition 7.
$$(12,35) = 1$$

(d) $(-45, -54)$.
$$45 = \underline{3 \cdot 3} \cdot 5$$
$$54 = \underline{3 \cdot 3} \cdot 3 \cdot 2$$
$$(-45,-54) = 9$$

(e) $(-7,5) = 1$

The method of finding (a,b) for $a,b \in N$ as illustrated in Example 4 is as follows. One decomposes (i.e., factors) a and b into primes in N. The product of those primes (including repetitions) which appear in *both* is the h.c.f. of a and b. If there are none in common, the h.c.f. is 1. Thus from the Fundamental Theorem of Arithmetic, one sees that for every two natural numbers a and b there is one and only one *natural number d* satisfying (1) and (2) of Definition 7. If $a \in -N$, then one works with the associate of a which is in N, namely $-a$; similarly for b.

If $d = (a,b)$, then since d is a factor of a and of b, one can write

$$a = da'$$
$$b = db'$$

for some a', b' in J. Then a' and b' can have no common prime factors, and hence have 1 as their only common factor: $(a',b') = 1$.

Definition 8. If $r,s \in J$ and $(r,s) = 1$, then r and s are said to be *relatively prime.*

Thus if $d = (a,b)$ and $a = da'$, $b = db'$ as above, then a' and b' are relatively prime.

3.3   Least Common Multiple

Another number which turns out to be useful in computation problems is the *least common multiple* (l.c.m.) of two nonzero integers a and b.

Definition 9. If a and b are nonzero integers, and if w is an integer distinct from 0 such that:

(1) w is a common multiple of a and b (i.e., a and b are factors of w),
(2) any common multiple of a and b is a multiple of w,

then w is called a *least common multiple* (l.c.m.) of a and b.

Thus, a least common multiple of 4 and 6 is 12. For 12 is a multiple of 4 and of 6, since $12 = 4 \cdot 3$ and $12 = 6 \cdot 2$, and any common multiple of 4 and 6 must have 12 as a factor (i.e., must be a multiple of 12).

Also -12 is an l.c.m. of 4 and 6.

When we refer to *the* l.c.m. of two integers, we shall mean the one in N. Thus the l.c.m. of -4 and 6 is 12.

The standard notation for the l.c.m. of a and b is '$[a,b]$.' Thus $[4,6] = [-4,6] = [6,-4] = [-4,-6] = [-6,4] = 12$.

Example 5. Find $[60,84]$.
Solution: We write, as before,

$$60 = 2 \cdot 2 \cdot 3 \cdot 5$$
$$84 = 2 \cdot 2 \cdot 3 \cdot 7$$

Clearly, $60 \cdot 84$ is a common multiple of 60 and 84, as is in fact $60 \cdot 84 \cdot a$ for any $a \in J$. But none of these is equal to $[60,84]$, failing to satisfy the second requirement of Definition 9.

Now $2 \cdot 2 \cdot 3 \cdot 5$ must appear in the prime factorization of $[60,84]$, since 60 must be a factor of $[60,84]$. Similarly $2 \cdot 2 \cdot 3 \cdot 7$ must appear, since 84 must be a factor of $[60,84]$. The number $2 \cdot 2 \cdot 3 \cdot 5 \cdot 7$ satisfies both of these conditions, and clearly any number containing 60 and 84 as factors must also contain $2 \cdot 2 \cdot 3 \cdot 5 \cdot 7 = 420$ as a factor. Hence $420 = [60,84]$.

A technique for finding $[a,b]$ is as follows. Decompose a and b into primes as before. Select all prime factors of a and select those primes which appear in b but not in a (including proper multiplicity). The product of all such primes is $[a,b]$. Or to put it another way, the primes appearing in the factorization of $[a,b]$ are the primes appearing in the factorizations of a and of b. The multiplicity with which each such prime appears in $[a,b]$ is equal to the larger of the multiplicities with which it appears in a and in b. [If one takes the smaller of the multiplicities, one obtains (a,b).]

Example 6. Find each of the following:
(a) $[30,84]$.
$$30 = 2 \cdot 3 \cdot 5$$
$$84 = 2 \cdot 2 \cdot 3 \cdot 7$$
$$[30,84] = 2 \cdot 2 \cdot 3 \cdot 5 \cdot 7 = 420$$
(b) $[30,-60]$.
$$30 = 2 \cdot 3 \cdot 5$$
$$60 = 2 \cdot 2 \cdot 3 \cdot 5$$
$$[30,-60] = 2 \cdot 2 \cdot 3 \cdot 5 = 60$$
(c) $[-12,-35]$.
$$12 = 2 \cdot 2 \cdot 3$$
$$35 = 5 \cdot 7$$
$$[-12,-35] = 2 \cdot 2 \cdot 3 \cdot 5 \cdot 7 = 420$$
(d) $[45,54]$.
$$45 = 3 \cdot 3 \cdot 5$$
$$54 = 2 \cdot 3 \cdot 3 \cdot 3$$
$$[45,54] = 2 \cdot 3 \cdot 3 \cdot 3 \cdot 5 = 270$$
(e) $[7,5] = 5 \cdot 7 = 35$

Observe that for $a,b \in N$, if $d = (a,b)$ and $a = da'$, $b = db'$, then $[a,b] = da'b'$. In particular, $(a,b) = 1$ if and only if $[a,b] = ab$.

Exercises

17. Give a prime factorization in N (possibly with an additional factor of -1) for the following:
(a) the natural numbers from 52 to 60.   (c) -360.
(b) 216.   (d) -625.
18. Find all the factors in J of the numbers 26, -27, 28, -29, and 30.
19. Find the following:

(a) (216,360).   (d) [−14,27].
(b) [216,360].   (e) (−108,−144).
(c) (14,−27).   (f) [−108,−144].

20. Find the common factors in N of
(a) 216 and 360.
(b) −14 and −27.
(c) −108 and 144.

21. (a) How would one extend Definition 7 of the h.c.f. of two integers to three? to four?
(b) The same for the l.c.m. (Definition 9).

22. The answers to the following may be left in factored form:
(a) Find (112,−216,360); (260,104,520); (−546,770,−2145).
(b) Find [14,8,9]; [−42,−60,−105]; [35,55,−77].

23. If $(a,b) = [a,b]$, what values can a and b have (where $a,b \in N$)?

4. Computations in $\bar{R}$

4.1 Reducing Rationals to Lowest Terms

Example 7. Among the numbers $\dfrac{m}{n}$, where $m,n \in J$, $n \neq 0$, which are equal to $\dfrac{5}{7}$?

Solution: Now $(5,7) = 1$. If $\dfrac{m}{n} = \dfrac{5}{7}$, then $7m = 5n$ by (5, 78). (Clearly m and n cannot be zero.) By the fundamental theorem, $7m$ and $5n$ must contain the same primes in their prime decompositions. Thus m must contain 5 as a factor and n must contain 7. Thus $m = 5m'$, $n = 7n'$, and

$$7 \cdot 5 \cdot m' = 5 \cdot 7 \cdot n' \qquad \text{(where } m' \text{ and } n' \in J)$$

But then $m' = n'$ by (5, 43). Call this number r. Thus $m = 5r$, $n = 7r$ (and $r \neq 0$), and $\dfrac{m}{n} = \dfrac{5r}{7r}$. But conversely, $\dfrac{5r}{7r} = \dfrac{5}{7}$ by (5, 84) for all $r \neq 0$ in J.

Remark 1: In this example we used only the fact that 5 and 7 are relatively prime.

Remark 2: If $\dfrac{p}{q} = -\dfrac{5}{7}$, then $-\dfrac{p}{q} = \dfrac{5}{7}$ or $\dfrac{-p}{q} = \dfrac{5}{7}$ by (5, 99). Thus if $p,q \in J$, then $-p = 5r$ and $q = 7r$ for some $r \in J$ by the above example. But then $p = -5r = (-5)r$ by (5, 71). Hence $\dfrac{p}{q} = \dfrac{(-5)r}{7r}$. Of course, by (5, 99), we also have $\dfrac{p}{q} = \dfrac{5r}{(-7)r}$.

Conversely, $\dfrac{(-5)r}{7r} = -\dfrac{5r}{7r} = -\dfrac{5}{7}$ for all $r \neq 0$ in J.

Example 8. Find all rational numbers of the type $\dfrac{m}{n}$, where $m,n \in J$, $n \neq 0$, such that $\dfrac{m}{n} = \dfrac{28}{35}$.[5]

[5] Of course, technically, we should say "find all fractions $\dfrac{`m'}{n}$ where $m, n \in J$, $n \neq 0$, such that $\dfrac{m}{n} = \dfrac{28}{35}$." For there is only one rational number $\dfrac{28}{35}$ (cf. footnote 2).

Solution: We see that $28 = 2 \cdot 2 \cdot 7$ and $35 = 5 \cdot 7$, so that $(28,35) = 7$. Hence $28 = 7 \cdot 4$ and $35 = 7 \cdot 5$, and $(4,5) = 1$.

$$\frac{28}{35} = \frac{7 \cdot 4}{7 \cdot 5} = \frac{4}{5}$$

Hence by the method of Example 7, all such numbers are $\dfrac{4r}{5r}$ for $r \neq 0$ in J.

Note that $(4r,5r)$ is r or $-r$. Hence $4r$ and $5r$ are relatively prime when r is a unit. Thus $\dfrac{\text{‘4’}}{5}$ and $\dfrac{\text{‘$-4$’}}{-5}$ are the only designations of this rational number in which the numerator and denominator are relatively prime.

When representing the rational number in this way (i.e., as the "quotient" of two relatively prime integers) we say that the rational number has been *reduced to lowest terms*.

Similarly, $-\dfrac{28}{35}$ can also be reduced to lowest terms as $\dfrac{-4}{5}$ or $\dfrac{4}{-5}$, or also $-\dfrac{4}{5}.$[6]

Example 9. Reduce $\dfrac{84}{30}, \dfrac{-60}{30}, -\dfrac{12}{35}, \dfrac{45}{-54}, \dfrac{-7}{-5}$ to lowest terms.

Solution: $\dfrac{84}{30} = \dfrac{6 \cdot 14}{6 \cdot 5} = \dfrac{14}{5}$ [using the fact that $(84,30) = 6$].

$\dfrac{60}{30} = \dfrac{30 \cdot 2}{30 \cdot 1} = \dfrac{2}{1} = 2$. Hence the answer is -2 $\left(\text{or, if one wishes, also}\right.$ $\left.\dfrac{-2}{1}, \dfrac{2}{-1}, -\dfrac{2}{1}\right).$

$\frac{12}{35}$ is already in lowest terms. Thus the answer is $-\frac{12}{35}$ (or $\frac{-12}{35}$, or $\frac{12}{-35}$).

$\dfrac{45}{54} = \dfrac{9 \cdot 5}{9 \cdot 6} = \dfrac{5}{6}$. The answer is $-\dfrac{5}{6}$.

$\dfrac{7}{5}$ is in lowest terms, so that this is the answer. $\left(\text{So also is } \dfrac{-7}{-5}.\right)$

Exercises

24. Reduce to lowest terms:

(a) $\dfrac{216}{360}.$ (d) $\dfrac{27}{14}.$

(b) $\dfrac{-360}{216}.$ (e) $-\dfrac{108}{144}.$

(c) $\dfrac{-14}{-27}.$ (f) $\dfrac{144}{-108}.$

[6] Again, it is $\dfrac{\text{‘$-28$’}}{35}$ which is being reduced to lowest terms as $\dfrac{\text{‘$-4$’}}{5}$ or $\dfrac{\text{‘4’}}{-5}$ or $-\dfrac{\text{‘4’}}{5}$. For "reducing to lowest terms" refers to the representation of a rational number (cf. footnote 5).

4.2   Arithmetic in $\bar{R}$

To add or subtract any two rational numbers $\dfrac{a}{b}$ and $\dfrac{c}{d}$, one can apply (5, 98), and reduce the result to lowest terms.

Example 10. $\dfrac{2}{3} + \dfrac{4}{5} = \dfrac{2 \cdot 5 + 3 \cdot 4}{3 \cdot 5}$

$$= \frac{10 + 12}{15}$$

$$= \frac{22}{15} \text{ (already in lowest terms)}$$

Example 11. $\dfrac{5}{6} + \dfrac{7}{9} = \dfrac{5 \cdot 9 + 6 \cdot 7}{6 \cdot 9}$

$$= \frac{3 \cdot 3 \cdot 5 + 3 \cdot 2 \cdot 7}{3 \cdot 2 \cdot 9}$$

$$= \frac{3(3 \cdot 5 + 2 \cdot 7)}{3 \cdot 2 \cdot 9}$$

$$= \frac{3 \cdot 5 + 2 \cdot 7}{2 \cdot 9} \qquad (5, 84)$$

$$= \frac{15 + 14}{18}$$

$$= \frac{29}{18}$$

Of course, we could have also written

$$\frac{5}{6} + \frac{7}{9} = \frac{5 \cdot 9 + 6 \cdot 7}{6 \cdot 9}$$

$$= \frac{45 + 42}{54}$$

$$= \frac{87}{54}$$

$$= \frac{3 \cdot 29}{3 \cdot 18}$$

$$= \frac{29}{18}$$

The first method was used to show how one may sometimes avoid having to factor large numbers, in principle; although here, 87 and 54 are not that difficult to negotiate.

A more efficient technique for handling Example 11 is to make use of the l.c.m. of the denominators, in this case $[6,9] = 18$. As 6 and 9 are factors of 18, we have $6 \cdot 3 = 18$ and $9 \cdot 2 = 18$. Write $\frac{5}{6}$ as $\frac{5 \cdot 3}{6 \cdot 3}$ and $\frac{7}{9}$ as $\frac{7 \cdot 2}{9 \cdot 2}$; that is, so that the denominators become 18:

$$\frac{5}{6} + \frac{7}{9} = \frac{5 \cdot 3}{6 \cdot 3} + \frac{7 \cdot 2}{9 \cdot 2}$$

$$= \frac{15 + 14}{18} \qquad (5, 97)$$

$$= \frac{29}{18}$$

Thus instead of working with the denominator $54 = 18 \cdot 3$, we are able to cut down by a factor of 3 (and in general, by the h.c.f. of the denominators).

If $\frac{a}{b}$ and $\frac{c}{d}$ are rational numbers with $a,b,c,d \in J$ ($b,d \neq 0$), then $[b,d]$ is called the *least common denominator* of $\frac{a}{b}$ and $\frac{c}{d}$. Similarly, $[b,d,f]$ is the least common denominator of $\frac{a}{b}, \frac{c}{d}, \frac{e}{f}$, etc.[7]

Thus in adding rational numbers, we use a representation of each rational number in which the denominator appearing is the least common denominator of all rational numbers involved. Of course, it is more economical, first, to be sure that each rational number is expressed in lowest terms. If some of the rationals are actually integers, such as 3 or -4, then one may regard them, in this type of computation, as $\frac{3}{1}$ or $\frac{-4}{1}$. We then apply (5, 97), or an extension of it (5, 98) to more than two terms.

In the case of two terms, the method of Example 10 and the present method coincide when the denominators are relatively prime; or for more terms, when every pair of denominators is relatively prime.

Example 12. $\frac{5}{8} - \frac{10}{24} + \frac{19}{18} - 2$. We rewrite this as $\frac{5}{8} - \frac{5}{12} + \frac{19}{18} - \frac{2}{1}$. Then $[8,12,18,1] = 2 \cdot 2 \cdot 2 \cdot 3 \cdot 3$.

Our denominators are 8, 12, 18, and 1, and we wish to change them to $8 \cdot 9$, $12 \cdot 6$, $18 \cdot 4$, and $1 \cdot 72$: that is, to 72. Thus we obtain

$$\frac{5 \cdot 9}{8 \cdot 9} - \frac{5 \cdot 6}{12 \cdot 6} + \frac{19 \cdot 4}{18 \cdot 4} - \frac{2 \cdot 72}{1 \cdot 72} = \frac{45 - 30 + 76 - 144}{72} \qquad \text{[by an extension of (5, 97) to four terms]}$$

[7] Actually, $[b,d]$ is the least common denominator of the fractions $\frac{'a'}{b}$ and $\frac{'c'}{d}$.

$$= \frac{-53}{72} \quad \text{(by the methods of Section 1.3)}$$

We next consider an example of multiplication in $\bar{R}$.

Example 13. $\dfrac{7}{3} \cdot \dfrac{6}{14} \cdot \dfrac{9}{2} = \dfrac{7 \cdot 6 \cdot 9}{3 \cdot 14 \cdot 2}$ (5, 82)

$$= \frac{7 \cdot 2 \cdot 3 \cdot 3 \cdot 3}{3 \cdot 2 \cdot 7 \cdot 2}$$

$$= \frac{(2 \cdot 7 \cdot 3) \cdot (3 \cdot 3)}{(2 \cdot 7 \cdot 3) \cdot 2}$$

$$= \frac{3 \cdot 3}{2} \quad (5, 84)$$

$$= \frac{9}{2}$$

It may have been easier first to reduce $\frac{6}{14}$ to $\frac{3}{7}$. Note that it is unnecessary to multiply out numerator and denominator before common factors have been removed.

To find $\dfrac{7}{3} \cdot \dfrac{-6}{14} \cdot \dfrac{9}{2}$ one may first work Example 13 as above, and then give the answer as $-\frac{9}{2}$. Or one may carry along the '$-$' in the above computations.

As in addition, $\frac{7}{3} \cdot 6$ may be computed as $\frac{7}{3} \cdot \frac{6}{1}$.

We next consider the problem of finding $\dfrac{a}{b} \Big/ \dfrac{c}{d}$ where $a,b,c,d \in J$ $(b,c,d \neq 0)$.

There are two techniques which may be used:

1. One may apply (5, 87).
2. One may apply (5, 84).

The second procedure is usually more efficient. The methods coincide when $(b,d) = 1$.

The expression $\dfrac{a}{b} \Big/ \dfrac{c}{d}$ is meaningless if either b, c, or d is 0. If $a = 0$, the result is 0. (Why?)

Example 14. Find $\dfrac{\frac{3}{2}}{\frac{7}{4}}$.

Method 1: $\dfrac{\frac{3}{2}}{\frac{7}{4}} = \dfrac{3 \cdot 4}{2 \cdot 7}$ (5, 87)

$$= \frac{3 \cdot 2 \cdot 2}{2 \cdot 7}$$

$$= \frac{6}{7}$$

Method 2: Note that $[2,4] = 4$. In general, we multiply both numerator and denominator by $[b,d]$.

$$\frac{\dfrac{3}{2}}{\dfrac{7}{4}} = \frac{\dfrac{3 \cdot 2}{2 \cdot 2} \cdot 4}{\dfrac{7}{4} \cdot 4} \qquad (5, 84)$$

$$= \frac{6}{7} \qquad (5, 79)$$

Example 15. Find $\dfrac{\frac{3}{4} + \frac{7}{6}}{\frac{2}{9} + \frac{5}{8}}$.

One method is to reduce this to the form $\dfrac{a}{b} \Big/ \dfrac{c}{d}$ by first finding $\dfrac{3}{4} + \dfrac{7}{6}$ and $\dfrac{2}{9} + \dfrac{5}{8}$, and then proceed as in Example 14.

However, one can again make use of (5, 84).

$[4,6,9,8] = 2 \cdot 2 \cdot 3 \cdot 3 \cdot 2 = 72$ (one need not multiply out)

$$\frac{\dfrac{3}{4} + \dfrac{7}{6}}{\dfrac{2}{9} + \dfrac{5}{8}} = \frac{\left(\dfrac{3}{4} + \dfrac{7}{6}\right) \cdot 72}{\left(\dfrac{2}{9} + \dfrac{5}{8}\right) \cdot 72} \qquad (5, 84)$$

$$= \frac{\dfrac{3 \cdot 18}{4 \cdot 18} \cdot 72 + \dfrac{7 \cdot 12}{6 \cdot 12} \cdot 72}{\dfrac{2 \cdot 8}{9 \cdot 8} \cdot 72 + \dfrac{5 \cdot 9}{8 \cdot 9} \cdot 72} \qquad (D)$$

$$= \frac{54 + 84}{16 + 45} \qquad (5, 79)$$

$$= \frac{138}{61}$$

Exercises

In finding each of the following, show sufficient work to reveal the reasoning involved.

25. $\dfrac{1}{3} + \dfrac{2}{3}$.

26. $\dfrac{2}{5} - \dfrac{1}{3}$.

27. $\dfrac{2}{5} \cdot \dfrac{-1}{3} \cdot \dfrac{1}{2}$.

28. $\dfrac{\frac{3}{4}}{\frac{1}{2}}$.

29. $\dfrac{\frac{2}{5} \cdot \frac{1}{3}}{\frac{3}{2} \cdot 5}$.

30. $\dfrac{1}{60} - \dfrac{4}{15}$.

31. $\dfrac{5}{4} \cdot \dfrac{-1}{3} \cdot \dfrac{2}{-15} \cdot \dfrac{9}{7}.$

32. $\dfrac{\dfrac{-4}{3}}{\dfrac{2}{9}} + \dfrac{3}{2}.$

33. $\dfrac{\frac{1}{3} + \frac{1}{5}}{\frac{1}{9} - \frac{2}{3}}.$

34. $\dfrac{\frac{1}{3} + \frac{1}{5}}{3}.$

35. $\left(\dfrac{3}{4} + \dfrac{2}{5} - \dfrac{1}{6}\right) \cdot \left(\dfrac{-8}{3}\right).$

36. $\dfrac{9}{4} \cdot \dfrac{3}{5} \cdot \left(\dfrac{4}{15} - \dfrac{16}{25}\right).$

37. $\dfrac{\frac{2}{3} \cdot \frac{5}{7} - \frac{7}{4}}{\frac{3}{2} \cdot (-3) + \frac{1}{7}} \cdot \dfrac{\frac{2}{21} + \frac{1}{2}}{-2}.$

5. Algebraic Computations

5.1 *Determining Identities over R*

The methods developed in previous sections can be generalized to expressions involving arbitrary real numbers, or also to expressions involving variables over R.

Example 16. If $a \in R$, find $\dfrac{a}{3} + \dfrac{a+1}{2}$.

Solution: For $a \in R$,

$$\dfrac{a}{3} + \dfrac{a+1}{2} = \dfrac{2a + 3(a+1)}{2 \cdot 3} \qquad (5, 98)$$

$$= \dfrac{2a + (3a + 3)}{6} \qquad (D)$$

$$= \dfrac{(2a + 3a) + 3}{6} \qquad (A2)$$

$$= \dfrac{(2 + 3)a + 3}{6} \qquad (D)$$

$$= \dfrac{5a + 3}{6} \qquad (AN)$$

In this example we have shown that $\dfrac{a}{3} + \dfrac{a+1}{2} = \dfrac{5a+3}{6}$ for all $a \in R$. Another way of expressing this is to say: If x is a variable over R, the solution set of $\dfrac{x}{3} + \dfrac{x+1}{2} = \dfrac{5x+3}{6}$ is the set R; that is, this equation is an identity over R. Therefore, the above example is often given as follows:

Find $\dfrac{x}{3} + \dfrac{x+1}{2}$, where x is a variable over R.

One proceeds as before: For $x \in R$,

$$\dfrac{x}{3} + \dfrac{x+1}{2} = \dfrac{2x + 3(x+1)}{2 \cdot 3} \qquad (5, 98)$$

$$= \cdots$$

Thus if one uses a variable x in the above example, the theorems cited indicate that the corresponding statements become correct for all replacements of x by elements of R. Therefore the conclusion is an identity in one variable. In the examples following, x is assumed to be a variable over R.

Example 17. Find $(x + 2)(2x + 1)$ for all $x \in R$ (that is, x is a variable over R).

Solution: For $x \in R$,

$$
\begin{aligned}
(x + 2)(2x + 1) &= x(2x) + x(1) + 2(2x) + 2(1) \qquad (5, 95) \\
&= x \cdot 2 \cdot x + 1 \cdot x + (2 \cdot 2)x + 2 \\
&= 2 \cdot (x \cdot x) + (1 \cdot x + 4x) + 2 \\
&= 2(x \cdot x) + (1 + 4)x + 2 \\
&= 2x^2 + 5x + 2
\end{aligned}
$$

Hence $(x + 2)(2x + 1) = 2x^2 + 5x + 2$ is an identity over R.

Example 18. For $x \in R$, $x \neq 0$, find $\dfrac{x}{3} \Big/ \dfrac{2x}{5}$. (Here x is a variable over the set of non-zero real numbers.)

Solution: For $x \in R$, $x \neq 0$,

$$\frac{x}{3} \Big/ \frac{2x}{5} = \frac{5x}{3(2 \cdot x)} \qquad (5, 87)$$

$$= \frac{5 \cdot x}{(3 \cdot 2)x}$$

$$= \frac{5}{6} \qquad (5, 84)$$

Hence $\dfrac{x}{3} \Big/ \dfrac{2x}{5} = \dfrac{5}{6}$ has as solution set the set of all real numbers different from 0, so that we have an identity over this set.

The convention, however, is to call this an identity over R also, with the understanding that it holds for all elements of R for which both sides of the equation are real numbers.

Example 19. For all $x \in R$, find $(x + a)(x + b)$, where $a, b \in R$.

Solution: For $x \in R$,

$$
\begin{aligned}
(x + a)(x + b) &= x^2 + xb + ax + ab \\
&= x^2 + (a + b)x + ab
\end{aligned}
$$

Applications:

$$(x + 3)(x + 2) = x^2 + 5x + 6$$
$$(x - 2)(x + 1) = x^2 - x - 2$$
$$[\text{for } (x - 2)(x + 1) = (x + (-2))(x + 1) = x^2 + (-2 + 1)x + (-2)(1)]$$
$$(x + \tfrac{1}{2})(x - \tfrac{1}{3}) = x^2 + (\tfrac{1}{2} - \tfrac{1}{3})x - \tfrac{1}{2} \cdot \tfrac{1}{3}$$
$$= x^2 - \tfrac{1}{6}x - \tfrac{1}{6}$$

Example 20. For all $x \in R$, $(cx + a)(dx + b) = (cd)x^2 + (ad + bc)x + ab$ where $a,b,c,d \in R$. (Exercise.)

Applications: $(3x + 1)(2x - 2) = 6x^2 - 4x - 2$

$$\left(\frac{1}{2}x - 2\right)\left(x + \frac{1}{3}\right) = \frac{1}{2}x^2 + \left(\frac{1}{6} - 2\right)x - \frac{2}{3}$$

$$= \frac{x^2}{2} - \frac{11}{6}x - \frac{2}{3}$$

Remark: Example 19 could be treated as an identity in three variables or Example 20 as an identity in five variables. But our aim was to show how to apply these examples to obtain numerous identities in a single variable, and therefore stated the problems as identities in the single variable x over R. Observe that Example 17 is a special case of Example 20.

Example 21. For all $x \neq 0, -2$ in R, find $\dfrac{x + 4}{x} - \dfrac{x + 1}{x + 2}$.

Solution: For $x \neq 0, -2$,

$$\frac{x + 4}{x} - \frac{x + 1}{x + 2} = \frac{(x + 4)(x + 2) - x(x + 1)}{x(x + 2)} \qquad (5, 98)$$

$$= \frac{(x^2 + 6x + 8) - x^2 - x}{x(x + 2)}$$

$$= \frac{(x^2 - x^2) + (6x - x) + 8}{x(x + 2)}$$

$$= \frac{0 + (6 - 1)x + 8}{x(x + 2)}$$

$$= \frac{5x + 8}{x(x + 2)}$$

Example 22. Find $\left(\dfrac{2}{x} - \dfrac{1}{y^2}\right) \Big/ \left(\dfrac{3}{x^2} + \dfrac{1}{y}\right)$ for all $x, y \in R$; $x, y \neq 0$; $\dfrac{3}{x^2} + \dfrac{1}{y} \neq 0$; x and y variables over R.

Solution (α): $\dfrac{\dfrac{2}{x} - \dfrac{1}{y^2}}{\dfrac{3}{x^2} + \dfrac{1}{y}} = \dfrac{\left(\dfrac{2}{x} - \dfrac{1}{y^2}\right)x^2y^2}{\left(\dfrac{3}{x^2} + \dfrac{1}{y}\right)x^2y^2}$ $\qquad (5, 84)$

$$= \frac{\dfrac{2x^2y^2}{x} - \dfrac{x^2y^2}{y^2}}{\dfrac{3x^2y^2}{x^2} + \dfrac{x^2y^2}{y}}$$

$$= \frac{2xy^2 - x^2}{3y^2 + x^2y}$$

$$= \frac{x(2y^2 - x)}{y(3y + x^2)}$$

Solution (β):

$$\dfrac{\dfrac{2}{x} - \dfrac{1}{y^2}}{\dfrac{3}{x^2} + \dfrac{1}{y}} = \dfrac{\dfrac{2y^2 - x}{xy^2}}{\dfrac{3y + x^2}{x^2 y}} \qquad (5,\,98)$$

$$= \dfrac{(2y^2 - x)x^2 y}{(3y + x^2)xy^2} \qquad (5,\,87)$$

$$= \dfrac{x(2y^2 - x)}{y(3y + x^2)} \qquad (5,\,84)$$

Exercises

38. Find $(x + 1)(x + 1)$.
39. Find $(x + 4)(x - 2)$.
40. Find $(2x + 3)(x + 1)$.
41. Find $(25x + 5)(4x + 4)$.
42. Find $\dfrac{x + 1}{x - 2} + \dfrac{4}{x}$ for all $x \neq 0,2$ in R.
43. Find $\dfrac{1}{x + 1} - \dfrac{3}{x + 3}$ for all $x \neq -1,-3$ in R.
44. Find $\left(\dfrac{1}{x} + \dfrac{1}{y}\right) \Big/ \left(\dfrac{1}{x} - \dfrac{1}{y}\right)$ for all x,y; $x \neq y$, $x \neq 0$, $y \neq 0$, in R.
45. Find $\left(\dfrac{x}{x + 2} + \dfrac{5}{x - 3}\right) \Big/ \dfrac{1}{x + 2}$ for all $x \neq -2,3$ in R.

5.2   Factoring

In Section 4.1 we applied (5, 84) to reduce rational numbers to lowest terms, by factoring both numerator and denominator into prime numbers. For example, $\dfrac{4}{6} = \dfrac{2 \cdot 2}{3 \cdot 2} = \dfrac{2}{3}$. One can simplify expressions in one or more variables by the same procedure, but the factors are no longer necessarily integers.

For example, $\dfrac{x^2 - 4}{x^2 + 4x + 4} = \dfrac{(x + 2)(x - 2)}{(x + 2)(x + 2)} = \dfrac{x - 2}{x + 2}$, where $x \neq -2$.

This is an identity in one variable over R. (This is according to our convention stated after Example 18 in the last section.) Here we "factor" $x^2 - 4$ into $(x - 2)(x + 2)$. The problem is how to recognize that an expression such as $x^2 - 4$ can be factored into $(x - 2)(x + 2)$. The procedure is similar to that in arithmetic. One learns the multiplication table before he gains experience in the reverse procedure. (At least for now!)

The concept of factoring depends upon the set in which one is working. As we are working in R, we may say it depends on the subset of R under consideration. We have considered the factorization theory in J (or better, the nonzero elements of J) under multiplication. If one worked in $\bar{R}$, this theory would be of no interest, since every nonzero rational is a factor of every other nonzero rational. For example, $\frac{1}{3}$ is a factor in $\bar{R}$ of $\frac{2}{7}$. Namely,

$$\tfrac{2}{7} = \tfrac{1}{3} \cdot \tfrac{6}{7}$$

In particular, in $\bar{R}$ all nonzero elements are factors of 1, and all elements would be units. For the units are simply the factors of 1. Thus in $\bar{R}$ there are no primes.

Now expressions in a variable x of the type $x^2 - 4$ and $x^2 + 4x + 4$, where the constants appearing are integers (or rationals, or reals) also have a factorization theory. Over J, the units are 1 and -1. Over $\bar{R}$, the units are all the nonzero elements of $\bar{R}$. Over R, the units are all the nonzero elements of R.

Two such expressions are associates if one is a unit multiplied by the other. Thus over J, $x - 2$ and $2 - x$ are associates since $x - 2 = (-1)(2 - x)$. Similarly, $x + \frac{2}{3}$ and $3x + 2$ are associates over $\bar{R}$. For $x + \frac{2}{3} = \frac{1}{3}(3x + 2)$, where $\frac{1}{3}$ is a unit in $\bar{R}$. Also $3x + 2 = 3 \cdot (x + \frac{2}{3})$, 3 being a unit.

We shall see, for example, that $x^2 - 2$ can be factored over R, but cannot be factored over $\bar{R}$. For the present we consider factorization over J, although the identities we obtain are still over R.

Analogous to our work in J, we shall say that, 1, -1, $x + 2$, $x - 2$, $(-1)(x + 2)$, $(-1)(x - 2)$ are factors of $x^2 - 4$ (over J). For example,

$$x^2 - 4 = [(-1)(x + 2)][(-1)(x - 2)]$$
$$= (-x - 2)(-x + 2)$$

which shows that $(-1)(x + 2)$, i.e., $-x - 2$, is a factor of $x^2 - 4$.

A highest common factor of $x^2 - 4$ and $x^2 + 4x + 4$ is $x + 2$, and hence also $-(x + 2)$.

Similarly a least common multiple of $x^2 - 4$ and $x^2 + 4x + 4$ is

$$(x + 2)(x + 2)(x - 2) = x^3 + 2x^2 - 4x - 8$$

Also $-(x + 2)(x + 2)(x - 2) = -x^3 - 2x^2 + 4x + 8$ is an l.c.m. of $x^2 - 4$ and $x^2 + 4x + 4$.

$(x^2 - 4, x^2 + 4x + 4)$ shall refer to "the" h.c.f. of $x^2 - 4$ and $x^2 + 4x + 4$, and $[x^2 - 4, x^2 + 4x + 4]$ to "the" l.c.m. Although we use the word "the," it will not matter which choice one makes. As before, these are unique "up to associates."

The h.c.f. of $x - 2$ and $2 - x$ is $x - 2$ (or also $2 - x$). For $x - 2$ is a factor of both $x - 2$ and $2 - x$: namely, $2 - x = (-1)(x - 2)$.

To be able to find the h.c.f. and l.c.m., we must know the "prime" factors. Later, these terms — h.c.f., l.c.m., and prime factors — will be defined more carefully for the above situation. But for now we can consider some methods of factoring, and some examples involving these notions.

In Example 19 of Section 5.1, we saw that

$$(x + a)(x + b) = x^2 + (a + b)x + ab$$

Hence to factor $x^2 - x - 6$, one looks for numbers a and b for which $a + b = -1$ and $ab = -6$. Repeated trials reveal -3 and 2 are such numbers, so that $x^2 - x - 6 = (x - 3)(x + 2)$.

We shall list below the identities which will be of use in factoring:

(1) $xy \pm xz = x(y \pm z)$
     $xy \pm xz \pm xw = x(y \pm z \pm w)$
(2) $(cx + a)(dx + b) = (cd)x^2 + (ad + bc)x + ab$
     $(x + a)(x + b) = x^2 + (a + b)x + ab$
(3) $x^2 - a^2 = (x + a)(x - a)$
(4) $(x + a)^2 = x^2 + 2ax + a^2$
     $(x - a)^2 = x^2 - 2ax + a^2$
(5) $x^3 - a^3 = (x - a)(x^2 + ax + a^2)$
     $x^3 + a^3 = (x + a)(x^2 - ax + a^2)$
(6) $(x + a)^3 = x^3 + 3ax^2 + 3a^2x + a^3$
     $(x - a)^3 = x^3 - 3ax^2 + 3a^2x - a^3$

The letters appearing in these formulas may be regarded either as real numbers or as variables over R, depending upon the use one wishes to make of them.

Exercises

46. Verify identity (3).
47. Verify identities (4).
48. Verify identities (5).
49. Verify identities (6).
In Exercises 50 to 61 factor the expressions.
50. $x^2 + 3x + 2$.
51. $x^2 - 1$.
52. $(p + q)^2 - r^2$.
53. $xy^2 - x$.
54. $st + tu + t^3$.
55. $x^3 + 3x^2 + 3x + 1$.
56. $6x^2 - x - 2$.
57. $x^2 + 4x + 4 - y^2$.
58. $x^3 - 6x^2 + 12x - 8$.

59. $x^3 - 8$.

60. $6x^3 + x^2 - 2x$.

61. $(a + b)^2 - c^4$.

62. Find $(x^2 - 9, x^2 + x - 6)$, i.e., the h.c.f. of $x^2 - 9$ and $x^2 + x - 6$.

63. Find $[x^2 - 9, x^2 + x - 6]$, i.e., the l.c.m. of $x^2 - 9$ and $x^2 + x - 6$.

64. Find $[x - 2, x^2 - 9, x^2 + x - 6]$.

65. Find $(x - 2, x^2 - 9, x^2 + x - 6)$.

66. Find $[a^2 - b^2, a^2 + 2ab - 3b^2]$.

67. Find $(a^2 - b^2, a^2 + 2ab - 3b^2)$.

68. Find $(a^2 - b^2, a^2 + 2ab - 3b^2, a^2 + 4ab + 3b^2)$.

69. Find $[a^2 - b^2, a^2 + 2ab - 3b^2, a^2 + 4ab + 3b^2]$.

70. Find $(x - 2, 4 - x^2)$.

71. Find $(x - 2, 2 - x, x^2 - 4)$.

72. Find $[x - 2, 4 - x^2]$.

73. Find $[x - 2, 2 - x, x^2 - 4]$.

5.3   Identities Continued

Example 23. Find $\dfrac{x^2 - 9}{x^2 + 2x} \cdot \dfrac{x + 2}{x + 3}$.

Solution: $\dfrac{x^2 - 9}{x^2 + 2x} \cdot \dfrac{x + 2}{x + 3} = \dfrac{(x + 3)(x - 3)(x + 2)}{x(x + 2)(x + 3)}$

$$= \frac{x - 3}{x}$$

Note that $((x + 3)(x - 3)(x + 2), x(x + 2)(x + 3)) = (x + 2)(x + 3)$. Thus the procedure here is similar to reducing a rational number to lowest terms. In adding expressions of this type, one can use the l.c.m. of the denominators (i.e., the least common denominator), as in adding rational numbers.

Example 24. Find $\dfrac{3 - x}{x^2 - 2x} + \dfrac{x}{2 - x}$.

Solution: The denominators are $x^2 - 2x$ and $2 - x$, or $x(x - 2)$ and $2 - x$.

Now $2 - x = (-1)(x - 2)$. Thus we see that

$$[x(x - 2), 2 - x] = x(x - 2)$$

$$\frac{3 - x}{x^2 - 2x} + \frac{x}{2 - x} = \frac{3 - x}{x(x - 2)} + \frac{x(-1) \cdot x}{(2 - x)(-1)x}$$

$$= \frac{3 - x - x^2}{x(x - 2)} \qquad (5, 97)$$

$$= \frac{-(x^2 + x - 3)}{x(x - 2)}$$

Remark: It is assumed without specifically stating so that $x \neq 0, 2$. In working this example, one might also have proceeded as follows:

$$\frac{3-x}{x^2-2x}+\frac{x}{2-x}=\frac{3-x}{x(x-2)}+\frac{x}{-(x-2)} \qquad (5, 68)$$

$$=\frac{3-x}{x(x-2)}-\frac{x}{x-2} \qquad (5, 99)$$

$$=\frac{3-x}{x(x-2)}-\frac{x\cdot x}{x(x-2)}$$

$$=\frac{3-x-x^2}{x(x-2)} \qquad (5, 97)$$

$$=\frac{-(x^2+x-3)}{x(x-2)}$$

Example 25. $\dfrac{x}{x^2-5x+6}+\dfrac{x}{x^2-2x-3}-\dfrac{2x}{x^2+3x+2}$

$$=\frac{x}{(x-3)(x-2)}+\frac{x}{(x-3)(x+1)}-\frac{2x}{(x+2)(x+1)}$$

$$=\frac{x(x+1)(x+2)}{(x-3)(x-2)(x+1)(x+2)}+\frac{x(x-2)(x+2)}{(x-3)(x+1)(x-2)(x+2)}$$

$$-\frac{2x(x-3)(x-2)}{(x+2)(x+1)(x-3)(x-2)} \qquad (5, 84)$$

$$=\frac{x(x+1)(x+2)+x(x-2)(x+2)-2x(x-3)(x-2)}{(x-3)(x-2)(x+1)(x+2)}$$

$$\qquad\qquad (5, 97-\text{extended to three terms})$$

$$=\frac{x^3+3x^2+2x+x^3-4x-2x(x^2-5x+6)}{(x-3)(x-2)(x+1)(x+2)}$$

$$=\frac{2x^3+3x^2-2x-2x^3+10x^2-12x}{(x-3)(x-2)(x+1)(x+2)}$$

$$=\frac{13x^2-14x}{(x-3)(x-2)(x+1)(x+2)}$$

$$=\frac{x(13x-14)}{(x-3)(x-2)(x+1)(x+2)}$$

The last step may be omitted, as it does not lead to any factors in the numerator which appear in the denominator, so that no further simplification is forthcoming.

We could have used other common multiples of the denominators, such as $(x-3)(x-2)(x-3)(x+1)(x+2)(x+1)$, or $(x-3)(x-2)(x+1)(x+2)(x^2-16)$, etc., but the first of these multiples would lead to more common factors to be removed from numerator and denominator, and the second would in addition lead to arguments valid only for $x \notin \{3,2,-1,-2,4,-4\}$ instead of for $x \notin \{3,2,-1,-2\}$. Thus it is better to use the least common multiple of the denominators, that is, the least common denominator.

Exercises

74. Find $\dfrac{2x}{2x^2 + 7x + 3} - \dfrac{1}{x + 3}$. What values of x are excluded?

75. Find $\dfrac{x + 1}{x^2 - 2x} - \dfrac{x + 2}{x^2 - x - 2} - \dfrac{1}{x^3 - x^2 - 2x}$. What values of x are excluded?

76. Simplify $\dfrac{a^2 + ab}{a^2 - b^2} \Big/ \dfrac{a^3 + a^2b + ab^2}{a^3 - b^3}$.

77. Find $\dfrac{4x + 3y}{x^2 - y^2} - \dfrac{3}{y - x}$. What values of x and y are excluded?

78. Find $\left(\dfrac{x}{x^2 - y^2} + \dfrac{1}{x - y}\right) \Big/ \dfrac{2x - y}{x^2 - y^2}$. What values of x and y are excluded?

79. Show that the following are identities, specifying which values are excluded:

(a) $\dfrac{x + 2}{x - 2} + \dfrac{x}{2 - x} = \dfrac{2}{x - 2}$.

(b) $\dfrac{3x^2 + 2x}{(2x - 1)(3x + 2)} + \dfrac{x - 1}{2x - 1} - 1 = 0$.

(c) $\dfrac{\dfrac{x}{x - 2} + \dfrac{x^2}{4 - x^2}}{\dfrac{x^3}{2 - x}} = \dfrac{-2}{x^2(2 + x)}$.

6. Solving Equations

6.1   Equations in One Variable

If x is a variable over R, the following are examples of equations in one variable:

(1) $3(x - 2) = 5x + 8$

(2) $\dfrac{x + 3}{9} - \dfrac{x}{6} = 1$

(3) $\dfrac{2}{x - 1} = \dfrac{5}{x + 2}$

(4) $\dfrac{x^2 - x}{x} = x - 1$

(5) $3x^2 - 2x - 8 = 0$

(6) $\dfrac{2}{x + 3} + \dfrac{2}{x^2 + 5x + 6} = -1$

The problem is to find the solution set for each of these equations. In (3), 1 and -2 cannot be solutions. For 1, the left side of (3) is undefined and for -2 the right side is undefined. Similarly 0 cannot be a solution of (4); and -3, -2 cannot be solutions of (6).

As in Chapter 4, the technique for solving these equations will be algebraic. That is, we shall derive an equivalent equation (one having the same solution set) from which the solutions can be seen by inspection.

The three basic techniques used to derive an equivalent equation will be:

(α) The use of identities over R.

(β) Theorem (5, 5): $a + c = b + c$ if and only if $a = b$.

(γ) Theorem (5, 43): If $c \neq 0$, then $ac = bc$ if and only if $a = b$.

[In (β) and (γ), of course, $a,b,c \in R$.]

Solution of Equation (1):

We begin by using the distributive law, which in this case yields that $3(x - 2) = 3x - 6$ is an identity. Thus we begin as follows:

(a) $3(x - 2) = 5x + 8$

(b) $3x - 6 = 5x + 8$ (D)

That is, equation (b) is equivalent to equation (a), since the left sides of (a) and (b) yield the same element of R upon any replacement of the variable by a real number. We shall now attempt to obtain an equivalent equation in the form $ax = b$ for some $a,b \in R$. For this purpose, we make use of (β).

According to (5, 5), we can add any element to both sides of (b) and obtain an equivalent equation. Thus we may add $-5x$ to simplify the right side and 6 to simplify the left. This can be accomplished at once by adding $-5x + 6$:

(c) $(-5x + 6) + (3x - 6) = (-5x + 6) + (5x + 8)$

Now applying identities to left and right yields

(d) $(-5x + 3x) + (6 - 6) = (-5x + 5x) + (6 + 8)$

(e) $-5x + 3x = 14$

(f) $(-5 + 3)x = 14$ [We used the fact that $-5x = (-5)x$ is an identity. Hence we may apply D to rewrite $(-5)x + 3x$ as $(-5 + 3)x$, which yields (f).]

(g) $(-2)x = 14$

Since $-\frac{1}{2} \neq 0$, we have by (5, 43) that the following is equivalent to (g):

(h) $(-\frac{1}{2}) \cdot [(-2)x] = (-\frac{1}{2}) \cdot 14$

(i) $[(-\frac{1}{2})(-2)]x = -7$

(j) $x = -7$

Since equations (a), (b), . . . , (j) are all equivalent, solving any one of them solves all the others. But the solution set of (j) is clearly $\{-7\}$. Hence this is also the solution set of (a).

Solution of (2):

(a) $\dfrac{x + 3}{9} - \dfrac{x}{6} = 1$

Multiply both sides of the equation by the least common denominator of all terms appearing on the left and right. For this purpose, the right side is regarded as $\frac{1}{1}$. Thus $[9,6,1] = 18$.

(b) $18\left(\dfrac{x+3}{9} - \dfrac{x}{6}\right) = 18 \cdot 1$ (5, 43)

(c) $2(x+3) - 3 \cdot x = 18$ etc.

Solution of (3):

(a) $\dfrac{2}{x-1} = \dfrac{5}{x+2}$

Note that $[x-1, x+2] = (x-1)(x+2)$. Multiplying through, we obtain

(b) $(x-1)(x+2) \cdot \dfrac{2}{x-1} = (x-1)(x+2) \cdot \dfrac{5}{x+2}$ (5, 43)

We applied (5, 43) to state that (a) and (b) are equivalent.

But this is true only if $(x-1)(x+2) \neq 0$, which means $x-1 \neq 0$ and $x+2 \neq 0$ by (5, 50). But since 1 and -2 are not solutions of (a), we see that (a) and (b) are equivalent if we assume the variable x to be over the set of real numbers distinct from 1 and -2. Over this set, we may proceed:

(c) $(x+2) \cdot 2 = (x-1) \cdot 5$
(d) $\quad 2x + 4 = 5x - 5$
(e) $\quad\quad 9 = 3x$
(f) $\quad\quad 3 = x$

Since (a) and (f) are equivalent if 1 and -2 are excluded, the solution set of (a) is $\{3\}$.

Solution of (4):

(a) $\dfrac{x^2 - x}{x} = x - 1$

Regarding $x - 1$ as $\dfrac{x-1}{1}$, we see that $[x,1] = x$.

(b) $\dfrac{x \cdot (x^2 - x)}{x} = x \cdot (x-1)$ [equivalent to (a) for $x \neq 0$ by (5, 43)]

(c) $x^2 - x = x^2 - x$

Here (c) is an identity over R, but is equivalent to (a) only for $x \neq 0$ in R. Hence the solution set of (a) is the set of all real numbers distinct from 0. (When we say "for $x \neq 0$ in R," we mean "for x regarded as a variable over the set of real numbers excluding 0.")

Solution of (5):

$$3x^2 - 2x - 8 = 0$$
$$\tfrac{1}{3}(3x^2 - 2x - 8) = \tfrac{1}{3} \cdot 0 \quad (5, 43)$$
$$x^2 - \tfrac{2}{3}x - \tfrac{8}{3} = 0$$

$$(x + \tfrac{4}{3})(x - 2) = 0$$

Solution Set is $\{-\tfrac{4}{3}, 2\}$ (5, 63)

Or, one could have proceeded as follows:

$$3x^2 - 2x - 8 = 0$$
$$(3x + 4)(x - 2) = 0$$

By (5, 50), the solution set is then the union of the solution sets of $3x + 4 = 0$ and $x - 2 = 0$, i.e., $\{-\tfrac{4}{3}\} \cup \{2\}$, or $\{-\tfrac{4}{3}, 2\}$.

Of course, we had to be able to factor $x^2 - \tfrac{2}{3}x - \tfrac{8}{3}$ in the first method, or $3x^2 - 2x - 8$ in the second. A more inclusive method will be considered in Part III.

Solution of (6):

(a) $\dfrac{2}{x + 3} + \dfrac{2}{x^2 + 5x + 6} = -1$

Observe that $[x + 3, x^2 + 5x + 6, 1] = (x + 3)(x + 2)$.

(b) $(x + 3)(x + 2)\left[\dfrac{2}{x + 3} + \dfrac{2}{(x + 3)(x + 2)}\right] = (x + 3)(x + 2)(-1)$ (5, 43)

(c) $2(x + 2) + 2 = -(x^2 + 5x + 6)$

(d) $x^2 + 5x + 6 + 2x + 4 + 2 = 0$ (5, 5)

(e) $x^2 + (5x + 2x) + (6 + 4 + 2) = 0$

(f) $x^2 + (5 + 2)x + 12 = 0$ (D)

(g) $x^2 + 7x + 12 = 0$

(h) $(x + 4)(x + 3) = 0$

Now (h) is equivalent with (a), but not for x as a variable over R, but rather over all elements of R distinct from -3 and -2. Thus all solutions of (h) distinct from -3 and -2 are solutions of (a).

The solution set of (a) is therefore $\{-4\}$.

6.2   Some Notation

It is convenient, and customary, to use the following notation:

$$\{x \in R / \cdots\}$$

to mean "the set of all x in R such that . . . ." For example,

$$\{x \in R / x \neq 2\}$$

is read "the set of all x in R such that $x \neq 2$." This in turn means that an element is in this set if replacing it for x one obtains a correct statement. Thus:

3 is an element of R such that $3 \neq 2$.
Hence $3 \in \{x \in R / x \neq 2\}$,
$2 \notin \{x \in R / x \neq 2\}$.

Similarly, $\{x \in R/3(x-2) = 5x+8\}$ refers to the solution set of the equation $3(x-2) = 5x+8$, where x is a variable over R. In Example 1 in Section 6.1 we saw that

$$\{x \in R/3(x-2) = 5x+8\} = \{-7\}$$

In Example 4 of Section 6.1 we saw that

$$\left\{x \in R \middle/ \frac{x^2 - x}{x} = x - 1\right\} = \{x \in R/x \neq 0\}$$

In Example 5 we saw that

$$\{x \in R/3x^2 - 2x - 8 = 0\} = \{x \in R/3x + 4 = 0\} \cup \{x \in R/x - 2 = 0\}$$
$$= \{-\tfrac{4}{3}, 2\}$$

In Example 6 we have

$$\left\{x \in R \middle/ \frac{2}{x+3} + \frac{2}{x^2 + 5x + 6} = -1\right\}$$
$$= \{x \in R/(x+4)(x+3) = 0\} \cap \{x \in R/x \neq -2, -3\}$$
$$= \{-4\}$$

Of course,

$$\left\{x \in N \middle/ \frac{2}{x+3} + \frac{2}{x^2 + 5x + 6} = -1\right\} = \varnothing$$

Exercises

Solve the following equations (a) where x is a variable over R and (b) where x is a variable over J. Indicate your reasoning; in particular, state where you use (5, 5) and (5, 43). In the application of (5, 43), state for which subset of R your reasoning is valid. In (100) and (101), x and y are variables over R.

80. $4x - 3 = 2x + 5$.

81. $x - 7 = 3x + 2$.

82. $\dfrac{1}{x+3} + \dfrac{2}{x-3} = 0$.

83. $\dfrac{x-2}{4} + \dfrac{2x}{3} = 0$.

84. $x^2 + x - 6 = 0$.

85. $12x^2 - 5x = 3$.

86. $(x^2 + 3x + 2)(x - 1) = 0$.

87. $\dfrac{x}{3-x} + \dfrac{7}{x} = \dfrac{-9}{x^2 - 3x}$.

88. $(x+4)(x+3) = 2$.

89. $2x^2 + x - 6 = 0$.

90. $\dfrac{2}{x-3} + \dfrac{x-3}{2} = 2$.

91. $\dfrac{x^3 + 2x^2 - x - 2}{x^2 - 1} - 3x^2 = x^3 - 1$.

92. $\dfrac{x^2(x-a)^2(x-b)}{(a-x)x} = 0$.

93. $\dfrac{x^3 - x^2 - 2x + 2}{x^2 - 2} + x^2 - 2 = 3$.

94. $\dfrac{x^2 - 1}{x - 1} = x + 1.$

95. $\dfrac{x^2 + 3x}{x^2 - 3x} = 0.$

96. $\dfrac{x^2 + 3x}{x - 3} = 0.$

97. $\dfrac{1}{x + 3} + \dfrac{2}{x - 3} = 0.$

98. $\dfrac{x^2}{x} = 0.$

99. $3y - 4x = 12 - xy.$

100. $\dfrac{3}{x} - \dfrac{4}{y} = \dfrac{12}{xy} - 1.$

chapter vii

THE ORDERING OF THE REAL NUMBERS

In this chapter we return to our theoretical development of the real-number system. We postulate the existence of a subset P of R, whose elements we call the positive elements of R, satisfying certain prescribed conditions (cf. postulate $\mathcal{O}$ below). We are then able to define the negative elements of R, and to distinguish between such rules as "negative times negative is positive" and "$(-a)(-b) = ab$." We then define the concept of one real number being greater (or less) than another real number.

Now that the student has been initiated into computational problems, we apply our theoretical development to further such problems as we go along. Thus, the ordering postulate and its derived consequences are used to solve "inequalities." Furthermore, after defining the absolute value of a real number, we turn to the solution of equations and inequalities involving absolute values.

To delineate further the real-number system, as well as the natural-number system, it is useful to introduce the concepts of upper and lower bounds of nonempty subsets of R. These ideas depend strongly on the ordering of the real numbers which has been introduced. We then distinguish subsets of R as to whether they are bounded above, bounded below, or bounded. We conclude the chapter with the definitions of the least upper bound and greatest lower bound, and the greatest and least elements of a set (when these exist).

1. The Ordering Postulate for the Real Numbers

1.1   Statement of Postulate $\mathcal{O}$

Up to now we have considered properties of real numbers based on the postulate that they form a field. This concerns the properties of the binary operations. Thinking of the real numbers as applied to measuring distances on a line from a fixed point O on that line, we discern another aspect of the real numbers, their order. Thus in the diagram,

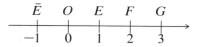

F follows E, G follows F, O follows $\bar{E}$, etc., if we think of moving from left to right (or in case one accidentally turns this page upside down, in

131

moving in the direction from O to E). We can think of the real numbers as being of three types: (a) those to the right of O (which we shall call positive), (b) 0, and (c) those to the left of O (which we shall call negative). We shall then wish to show that N is a subset of the positive reals and $-N$ a subset of the negative reals. In thinking of addition of two real numbers a and b as meaning first walk a units from O to A and then b units from A, we conclude that the sum of two positive reals is positive. In thinking of the product of two positive reals as used for measuring area, we shall also want the product of two positive real numbers to be positive. But all this is by way of motivation for the formulation of our next postulate.

Postulate $\mathcal{O}$: There exists a subset $P \subseteq R$ such that:

($\mathcal{O}_1$) If $a,b \in P$, then $a + b \in P$ (i.e., P is closed under addition)
($\mathcal{O}_2$) If $a,b \in P$, then $ab \in P$ (i.e., P is closed under multiplication)
($\mathcal{O}_3$) If $a \in R$, then one and only one of the following holds:
(a) $a \in P$
(b) $a = 0$
(c) $-a \in P$

Definition 1. The elements of P are called the *positive* real numbers; those satisfying $\mathcal{O}_3$ (c) are called the *negative* real numbers. We shall denote the set of negative real numbers by $-P$.

Thus:

$$R = P \cup \{0\} \cup -P$$

where each of the three subsets $P, \{0\}, -P$ is disjoint from the others.

According to $\mathcal{O}_3$, in terms of Definition 1, if $a \in R$ then a is either positive, zero, or negative; and only one of these is possible.

1.2   Elementary Consequences

Theorem 1. If $a \in R$, then a is positive if and only if $-a$ is negative (thus a is negative if and only if $-a$ is positive).

Proof: (α) Suppose a is positive. We wish to show $-a$ is negative. Thus we must show that $-(-a) \in P$ according to $\mathcal{O}_3$ (c). But $-(-a) = a$ by (5, 17), and a is given to be in P.
(β) Suppose $-a$ is negative. Thus $-(-a) \in P$, according to $\mathcal{O}_3$ (c). Again $-(-a) = a$, so that $a \in P$ and a is positive.
(γ) The remark in parentheses follows if one replaces 'a' by '$-a$' in the statement of the theorem.

Theorem 2. If $a,b \in -P$ (i.e., a and b are negative), then $a + b \in -P$. (This theorem states that the set of negative real numbers is closed under addition.)

Proof: $a,b \in -P$ by hypothesis

Hence $-a, -b \in P$	Def. 1
$(-a) + (-b) \in P$	By $\mathcal{O}_1$
$-(a + b) \in P$	(5, 73)
$a + b \in -P$	Def. 1

Exercises

3. Prove:
   (a) If $a,b \in P$, then $ab \in P$.   [(pos.)(pos.) = pos.]
   (b) If $a \in P$, $b \in -P$, then $ab \in -P$.   [(pos.)(neg.) = neg.]
   [*Hint:* Use (5, 71).]
   (c) If $a \in -P$, $b \in P$, then $ab \in -P$.   [(neg.)(pos.) = neg.]
   (d) If $a,b \in -P$, then $ab \in P$.   [(neg.)(neg.) = pos.]

Remark: The rule in Exercise 3d is not the same as the rule $(-a)(-b) = ab$. This latter rule holds for all real numbers, whereas the former rule states that if one takes two elements from a certain subset, their product is in a certain other subset of R.

Theorem 4. If $a \in R$, $a \neq 0$, then $a^2 \in P$. In particular, 1 is positive and -1 is negative.

Proof: (1) If $a \in P$, then $a^2 \in P$ by $\mathcal{O}_2$.
(2) If $a \in -P$, then $(-a) \in P$; and then $(-a)^2 \in P$ by $\mathcal{O}_2$. Since $(-a)^2 = a^2$ by (5, 72), it follows that $a^2 \in P$.
(3) If $a \neq 0$, then either $a \in P$ or $a \in -P$ by $\mathcal{O}_3$, and hence (1) and (2) include all cases.
(4) Since $1 \in R$, $1 \neq 0$, it follows that $1^2 \in P$, and since $1^2 = 1$, we have $1 \in P$.
(5) By Theorem 1 we have $-1 \in -P$.

Ordinarily, one defines 2 to be $1 + 1$, so that 2 is positive and hence -2 is negative. Similarly 3 is defined to be $2 + 1$, and 4 to be $3 + 1$, etc.; so that 3 and 4 are positive and -3 and -4 are negative.

Suppose, however, that we defined $2 = (-1) + (-1)$ and $3 = (-2) + 1$. Then 2 would be negative (since -1 is negative by Theorem 4; and the sum of two negative numbers is negative by Theorem 2). Hence -2 would be positive. Then $3 = (-2) + 1$ would be positive. Thus we would have:

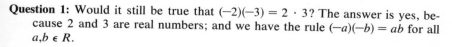

Question 1: Would it still be true that $(-2)(-3) = 2 \cdot 3$? The answer is yes, because 2 and 3 are real numbers; and we have the rule $(-a)(-b) = ab$ for all $a,b \in R$.

Question 2: Would $2 \cdot 3$ be positive or negative? The answer is that $2 \cdot 3$ would be negative. For 2 is negative and 3 is positive; and by Exercise 3c, (negative) $\cdot$ (positive) is negative.

Of course, we shall adopt the usual definitions of 2 and 3 hereafter. But we wished to emphasize the distinction between the rules given in (5, 71 and 72) and those given in Exercise 3 (cf. the remark following Exercise 3).

Exercises

Prove the following:

5. If $a \in R$, $a \neq 0$, then a and $a^{-1} = \dfrac{1}{a}$ are either both positive or both negative.

6. (a) If $a,b \in P$, then $\dfrac{a}{b} \in P$. $\left[\dfrac{\text{pos.}}{\text{pos.}} = \text{pos.}\right]$

(b) If $a \in P$, $b \in -P$, then $\dfrac{a}{b} \in -P$. $\left[\dfrac{\text{pos.}}{\text{neg.}} = \text{neg.}\right]$

(c) If $a \in -P$, $b \in P$, then $\dfrac{a}{b} \in -P$. $\left[\dfrac{\text{neg.}}{\text{pos.}} = \text{neg.}\right]$

(d) If $a,b \in -P$, then $\dfrac{a}{b} \in P$. $\left[\dfrac{\text{neg.}}{\text{neg.}} = \text{pos.}\right]$

7. Show that in Exercises (5, 1 and 2) there is no subset satisfying $\mathcal{O}_1$, $\mathcal{O}_2$, and $\mathcal{O}_3$. (Fields that satisfy the conditions stated in postulate $\mathcal{O}$ are called *ordered fields*. Thus, we are assuming R is an ordered field. This exercise reveals two examples of fields which are not ordered fields.)

8. Define, as usual, $2 = 1 + 1$; also $3 = 2 + 1$; $4 = 3 + 1$; etc. Prove the following:

(a) $2 \in P$. (f) $3 \in P$.
(b) $2 \neq 1$. (g) $4 \in P$.
(c) $2^{-1} \in P$. (h) $\frac{1}{3} \in P$.
(d) $-2 \in -P$. (i) $\frac{1}{4} \in P$.
(e) $2 \neq 2^{-1}$. (j) $2 + 2 = 4$.

2. The Relations $<$, $\leqq$, $>$, and $\geqq$

2.1 $a > b$

Definition 2. If $a,b \in R$, $a > b$ shall mean $a - b \in P$. For $a > b$ we shall also write $b < a$. If $a > b$, we shall say a is greater than b or also b is less than a. (One ordinarily says a is *greater than* b when using '$a > b$,' and b is *less than* a when using '$b < a$.' However, both mean precisely the same thing, namely, $a - b$ is positive.)

Theorem 9. If $a, b \in R$, one and only one of the following holds:
(a) $a > b$
(b) $a = b$
(c) $a < b$

Proof: We may apply $\mathcal{O}_3$ to $a - b$:
  (1) One and only one of the following holds:
      (a) $a - b \in P$
      (b) $a - b = 0$
      (c) $-(a - b) \in P$
  (2) (a) holds if and only if $a > b$ by Definition 2.
      (b) holds if and only if $a = b$ by (5, 35).
      (c) holds if and only if $b - a \in P$ by (5, 68), which in turn holds if and only if $a < b$ by Definition 2.

Exercises

Prove the following:
10. (a) If $a \in R$, a is positive if and only if $a > 0$.
   (b) If $a \in R$, a is negative if and only if $a < 0$.
11. Let $a, b \in R$.
   (a) $ab > 0$ if and only if $a > 0$ and $b > 0$, or $a < 0$ and $b < 0$.
   (b) $ab < 0$ if and only if $a > 0$ and $b < 0$, or $a < 0$ and $b > 0$.
12. Let $a, b \in R$.
   (a) $a - b < 0$ if and only if $a < b$.
   (b) If $a \in P$, $b \in -P$, then $a > b$.

2.2 Cancellation Rules

Theorem 13. Let $a, b, c \in R$. Then $a + c > b + c$ if and only if $a > b$.

Proof: (1) $a - b = [a + (-b)] + [c + (-c)]$ A4
                   $= (a + c) + [(-b) + (-c)]$
                   $= (a + c) - (b + c)$ (5, 73)
  (2) Hence $a - b \in P$ if and only if $(a + c) - (b + c) \in P$, or by Definition 2, $a > b$ if and only if $a + c > b + c$.

Theorem 14. Let $a, b, c \in R$.
(a) If $c > 0$, then $ac > bc$ if and only if $a > b$.
(b) If $c < 0$, then $ac > bc$ if and only if $a < b$.

Proof: (a) $c > 0$. By Exercise 11, $(a - b)c > 0$ if and only if $a - b > 0$. Since $(a - b)c = ac - bc$, we have $ac - bc > 0$ if and only if $a - b > 0$. This means (Exercise 10) that $ac - bc$ is positive if and only if $a - b$ is positive; or by Definition 2, $ac > bc$ if and only if $a > b$.
   (b) $c < 0$ (cf. Exercise 15).

Exercises

15. Prove Theorem 14b.
16. This exercise may be regarded as a continuation of Exercise 8.
  (a) Prove $2 > 1$.
  (b) Prove $2^{-1} < 1$.
  (c) Is $-3 > -2$? Justify your answer.
  (d) Is $-1 < 3$? Justify your answer.

2.3 $a \geq b$; $a > b > c$

Definition 3. If $a,b \in R$, then $a \geq b$ (also $b \leq a$) means $a > b$ or $a = b$.

Thus $1 \geq 0$, since $1 > 0$; and $1 \geq 1$, since $1 = 1$.

Definition 4. Let $a,b,c \in R$.
  (1) $a > b > c$ means $a > b$ and $b > c$.
  (2) $a \geq b > c$ means $a \geq b$ and $b > c$.
  (3) $a > b \geq c$ means $a > b$ and $b \geq c$.
  (4) $a \geq b \geq c$ means $a \geq b$ and $b \geq c$.
In the case of (1), we say b is between a and c.

Exercises

17. Let $a \in R$. Prove:
  (a) If $0 < a < 1$, then $0 < a^2 < 1$.
  (b) If $1 < a$, then $1 < a^2$.
18. Let $a,b \in R$. Prove:
  (a) $ab \geq 0$ if and only if $a \geq 0$ and $b \geq 0$, or $a \leq 0$ and $b \leq 0$.
  (b) $ab \leq 0$ if and only if $a \geq 0$ and $b \leq 0$, or $a \leq 0$ and $b \geq 0$.
  (c) $a - b \leq 0$ if and only if $a \leq b$.
19. Prove: If $a,b,c \in R$, then $a + c \geq b + c$ if and only if $a \geq b$.
20. Let $a,b,c \in R$. Prove:
  (a) If $c > 0$, then $ac \geq bc$ if and only if $a \geq b$.
  (b) If $c < 0$, then $ac \geq bc$ if and only if $a \leq b$.
21. Let $a,b,c \in R$. Prove:
  (a) If $a > b > c$, then $a > c$.
  (b) If $a \geq b \geq c$, then $a \geq c$.
  (c) State and prove corresponding statements for parts (2) and (3) of Definition 4.
22. If $a,b \in R$, prove that $a \leq b$ and $a \geq b$ if and only if $a = b$.
23. (a) If $a,b \in R$, prove that $a < b$ if and only if $\exists c \in P \ni a + c = b$.
  (b) If in part (a) we have $0 < a < b$, prove that $c < b$.
24. Prove that if $a,b \in R$ and $a < b$, then $\exists d \in R \ni a < d < b$. (This means that between every two distinct real numbers, there exists another real number.)
25. Let $a,b,c,d \in R$. Prove that if $a > b$ and $c > d$, then $a + c > b + d$. (Similarly, if $a \geq b$ and $c \geq d$, then $a + c \geq b + d$.)

Theorem 26. Let $a,b,c,d \in R$. If $a > b > 0$ and $c > d > 0$, then $ac > bd$.

Proof: (1) Since $a > b > 0$, we have $a > 0$ by Exercise 21. Thus $a > 0$, $b > 0$. Similarly $c > 0$, $d > 0$ so that a, b, c, d are positive. (Indeed, we might have stated the theorem: "Let $a,b,c,d \in P$. If $a > b$, $c > d$, then $ac > bd$.")

(2) Since $a > b$ and $c > 0$, we have $ac > bc$ by Theorem 14a. Similarly, $c > d$ and $b > 0$ implies $bc > bd$.

(3) But $ac > bc > bd$ implies $ac > bd$.

Exercises

27. State and prove theorems analogous to Theorem 26 for one or more appearances of '$\geq$' for '$>$.'

28. Let $a,b \in P$. Prove:
   (a) $a < b$ if and only if $a^2 < b^2$.
   (b) $a < b$ if and only if $a^3 < b^3$.
   (c) $a < b$ if and only if $a^4 < b^4$.
   (d) $a = b$ if and only if $a^2 = b^2$.
   (e) $a = b$ if and only if $a^3 = b^3$.
   (f) $a = b$ if and only if $a^4 = b^4$.
   (Similar rules for '$\leq$' are consequences of the above.)

29. Let $a,b \in P$. Prove that $a < b$ if and only if $a^{-1} > b^{-1}$.

3. Solving Inequalities

Statements of equality, such as $5 = 2$, $7 = 5 + 2$, etc., were called equations, as were $5 + x = 2$, $3x + 2y = 1$, $x^2 - 3 = 2x^2 + 5x$. Statements such as $5 < 2$, $2 < 5$, $7 \geq 4$, $3 + x \leq 4 - x$, $2x + 3y < 5$, $x^2 - 3 > 2x^2 + 5x$, etc., are called *inequalities*. As with equations, inequalities can be in no variables, or in one or more variables.

We say $a \in R$ is a *solution* of an inequality in the variable x over R if upon replacing x by a wherever x appears, we obtain a correct statement. The *solution set* of an inequality in one variable is the set $S \subseteq R$ consisting of all the solutions of the inequality.

Similarly, we say $(a,b) \in R \times R$ is a *solution* of an inequality in the variables x, y over R if upon replacing x by a wherever x appears and y by b wherever y appears, we obtain a correct statement. The *solution set* of an inequality in two variables is the set $S \subseteq R \times R$ consisting of all solutions of the inequality. It is now clear how we would define solutions and solution sets for inequalities in more than two variables.

To *solve an inequality* means to determine its solution set. The technique is to proceed from the given inequality to an equivalent one (i.e., having the same solution set), from which the solutions are easily seen.

To solve inequalities, we shall make use of the identities established in Chapter 5. But corresponding to (5, 5) and (5, 43) used for solving equations, we shall use Theorems 13 and 14, also Exercises 19 and 20.

Example 1. If x is a variable over R, solve $4x + 7 < 2x + 1$.

Solution: $4x + 7 < 2x + 1$

$$(4x + 7) + (-2x - 7) < (2x + 1) + (-2x - 7) \qquad \text{(Th. 13)}$$
$$2x < -6$$
$$\tfrac{1}{2} \cdot (2x) < \tfrac{1}{2} \cdot (-6) \qquad \text{(Th. 14a)}$$
$$x < -3$$

The above inequalities are all equivalent to one another.

Thus the solution set is $\{x \in R/x < -3\}$. Or, we may also say,

$$\{x \in R/4x + 7 < 2x + 1\} = \{x \in R/x < -3\}.$$

We may picture R by means of a line, and then mark off the solution set (shaded below):

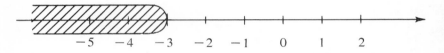

We use the curved line through -3 to indicate that -3 *is not* included in the solution set.

In the second line of the above solution we added $-2x$ (and also -7) to both sides of the inequality to eliminate the appearance of the variable from the right side. We could also have eliminated the variable from the left side. To do this, we would add $-4x$ (and also -1 to eliminate the 1 on the right at the same time) to both sides and obtain

$$(4x + 7) + (-4x - 1) < (2x + 1) + (-4x - 1) \qquad \text{(Th. 13)}$$
$$6 < -2x$$
$$(-\tfrac{1}{2}) \cdot 6 > (-\tfrac{1}{2})(-2x) \qquad \text{(Th. 14b)}$$
$$-3 > x$$

Of course, $x < -3$ and $-3 > x$ mean the same thing.

Example 2. The solution set of $4x + 7 \leq 2x + 1$ is $\{x \in R/x \leq -3\}$ as can be verified by applying Exercises 19 and 20 in place of Theorems 13 and 14 in Example 1. We indicate the solution set as follows:

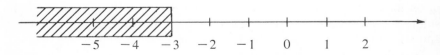

We use the straight line through -3 to indicate that -3 *is* included in the solution set.

Example 3. If $3 \leqq 7$ is an inequality in one variable over R, find the solution set.
   Answer: R. (In two variables, the answer would be $R \times R$; in three, $R \times R \times R$, etc.)

Example 4. If $3 > 7$ is an inequality in one variable over R, find the solution set.
   Answer: $\varnothing$. (In two, three, . . . variables, the answer is also $\varnothing$.)

Example 5. Find $\left\{x \; \epsilon \; R \; \middle/ \; \dfrac{x-3}{-6} < \dfrac{4+x}{9}\right\}$.

Solution: $\dfrac{x-3}{-6} < \dfrac{4+x}{9}$ is equivalent to:

$$\left(\frac{x-3}{-6}\right)(-18) > \left(\frac{4+x}{9}\right)(-18) \qquad \text{(Th. 14b)}$$
$$(x-3) \cdot 3 > (4+x)(-2)$$
$$3x - 9 > -8 - 2x$$
$$5x > 1 \qquad \text{(Th. 13)}$$
$$x > \tfrac{1}{5} \qquad \text{(Th. 14a)}$$

The solution set is $\{x \; \epsilon \; R/x > \tfrac{1}{5}\}$:

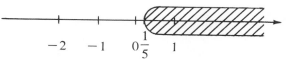

Example 6. If x is a variable over R, solve

$$(x-3)(x-1) \geqq 0$$

Solution: By Exercise 18a, α is a solution of $(x-3)(x-1) \geqq 0$ [i.e., $(\alpha-3)(\alpha-1) \geqq 0$] if and only if $\alpha - 3 \geqq 0$ and $\alpha - 1 \geqq 0$, or $\alpha - 3 \leqq 0$ and $\alpha - 1 \leqq 0$. We may phrase it this way: Let

$$A = \{x \; \epsilon \; R/x - 3 \geqq 0\}$$
$$B = \{x \; \epsilon \; R/x - 1 \geqq 0\}$$
$$C = \{x \; \epsilon \; R/x - 3 \leqq 0\}$$
$$D = \{x \; \epsilon \; R/x - 1 \leqq 0\}$$

Then the solution set of $(x-3)(x-1) \geqq 0$ is

$$(A \cap B) \cup (C \cap D)$$

We may write $A = \{x \; \epsilon \; R/x \geqq 3\}$ and $B = \{x \; \epsilon \; R/x \geqq 1\}$. Since any solution of $x \geqq 3$ is also a solution of $x \geqq 1$ (why?), we see that $A \subseteq B$ so that $A \cap B = A$.

Similarly, $C = \{x \; \epsilon \; R/x \leqq 3\}$, $D = \{x \; \epsilon \; R/x \leqq 1\}$ and $D \subseteq C$. Hence $C \cap D = D$.

Hence $(A \cap B) \cup (C \cap D) = A \cup D = \{x \; \epsilon \; R/x \geqq 3\} \cup \{x \; \epsilon \; R/x \leqq 1\}$. (We could also write this solution set as $\{x \; \epsilon \; R/x \geqq 3 \text{ or } x \leqq 1\}$.)

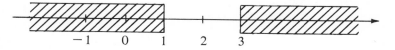

Example 7. If x is a variable over R, solve $(2x + 1)(x - 2) < 0$.

Solution: Let $A = \{x \in R/2x + 1 > 0\}$. One easily sees that we may write $A = \{x \in R/x > -\frac{1}{2}\}$. Similarly, let

$$B = \{x \in R/x - 2 < 0\} = \{x \in R/x < 2\}$$
$$C = \{x \in R/2x + 1 < 0\} = \{x \in R/x < -\frac{1}{2}\}$$
$$D = \{x \in R/x - 2 > 0\} = \{x \in R/x > 2\}$$

By Exercise 11b,

$$\{x \in R/(2x + 1)(x - 2) < 0\} = (A \cap B) \cup (C \cap D)$$
$$A \cap B = \{x \in R/-\tfrac{1}{2} < x < 2\}$$
$$C \cap D = \varnothing$$

Hence $A \cap B$ is the solution set:

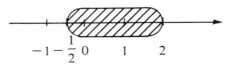

Remark: We have shown that the solution set of $(2x + 1)(x - 2) < 0$ over R is $\{x \in R/-\frac{1}{2} < x < 2\}$. But this is the same as $\{x \in R/(2x + 1)(x - 2) < 0\}$, so that this is also the solution set, given with a different designation. Thus what we mean by finding the solution set of $(2x + 1)(x - 2) < 0$ is to find an alternative designation of $\{x \in R/(2x + 1)(x - 2) < 0\}$ from which the solutions can be seen by inspection.

Example 8. Find $\left\{x \in R \middle/ \dfrac{x - 3}{x + 1} < 5\right\}$.

Solution: $\dfrac{x - 3}{x + 1} < 5$

Note that the left side is undefined for $x + 1 = 0$. Thus -1 cannot be in the solution set.

The desire is to multiply both sides of the inequality by $x + 1$, by applying Theorem 14. But we have to apply Theorem 14a when $x + 1 > 0$ and 14b when $x + 1 < 0$. The point is that we are multiplying both sides by an expression involving a variable. We thus have to separate the procedure into two cases: one when we multiply both sides by a positive number, the other by a negative. That is, we have to apply one method for those values of x for which $x + 1 > 0$, another for $x + 1 < 0$. (The case $x + 1 = 0$ may be excluded as noted above.)

If the case $x + 1 > 0$ leads to a solution set A, then the solutions we select are in $A \cap \{x \in R/x + 1 > 0\}$. Similarly, if $x + 1 < 0$ leads to solution set B, then $B \cap \{x \in R/x + 1 < 0\}$ yields solutions for our problem. The union of these two sets is then the desired solution set.

Case 1: $x + 1 > 0$ (i.e., $x > -1$)

$$x - 3 < 5(x + 1) \qquad \text{(Th. 14a)}$$
$$-8 < 4x \qquad \text{(Th. 13)}$$
$$-2 < x \qquad \text{(Th. 14a)}$$

This yields $\{x \in R/x > -2\} \cap \{x \in R/x > -1\}$. This set is equal to $\{x \in R/x > -1\}$:

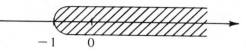

Case 2: $x + 1 < 0$ (i.e., $x < -1$)

$$x - 3 > 5(x + 1) \qquad \text{(Th. 14b)}$$
$$-8 > 4x$$
$$-2 > x$$

This yields $\{x \in R/x < -2\} \cap \{x \in R/x < -1\}$. This set is equal to $\{x \in R/x < -2\}$:

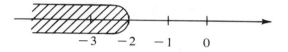

The union of the sets arising from case 1 and case 2 is:

$$\{x \in R/x > -1\} \cup \{x \in R/x < -2\} = \{x \in R/x > -1 \text{ or } x < -2\}$$

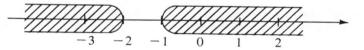

Example 9. Solve $\dfrac{2}{x - 3} > \dfrac{3}{x + 1}$, x a variable over R.

Solution: We multiply both sides by $(x - 3)(x + 1)$, the l.c.m. of $x - 3$ and $x + 1$.

(I) For $(x - 3)(x + 1) > 0$ we obtain $2(x + 1) > 3(x - 3)$ by Theorem 14a.

(II) For $(x - 3)(x + 1) < 0$ we obtain $2(x + 1) < 3(x - 3)$ by Theorem 14b.

Let

$$S = \{x \in R/(x - 3)(x + 1) > 0\}$$
$$T = \{x \in R/(x - 3)(x + 1) < 0\}$$
$$H = \{x \in R/2(x + 1) > 3(x - 3)\}$$
$$K = \{x \in R/2(x + 1) < 3(x - 3)\}$$

Then the solution set to our example is

$$(S \cap H) \cup (T \cap K)$$

One sees that $S \cap H$ arises from (I) and $T \cap K$ from (II).

From $2(x + 1) > 3(x - 3)$ we obtain

$$2x + 2 > 3x - 9$$
$$11 > x$$

Thus $H = \{x \in R/x < 11\}$. Similarly, $K = \{x \in R/x > 11\}$.

The method for computing S and T has been given in Examples 6 and 7.

We compute S. Thus let $A = \{x \in R/x > 3\}$, $B = \{x \in R/x > -1\}$, $C = \{x \in R/x < 3\}$, $D = \{x \in R/x < -1\}$.

Then $S = (A \cap B) \cup (C \cap D)$. Since $A \subseteq B$, we have $A \cap B = A$. Similarly $C \cap D = D$. Then $S = \{x \in R/x > 3$ or $x < -1\}$:

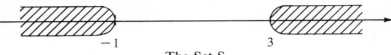

The Set S

Since S is the solution set of $(x - 3)(x + 1) > 0$, and $\{3, -1\}$ is the solution set of $(x - 3)(x + 1) = 0$, it follows that T (being the solution set of $(x - 3)(x + 1) < 0$) consists of all real numbers not in S and not in $\{3, -1\}$. Thus $T = \{x \in R/-1 < x < 3\}$:

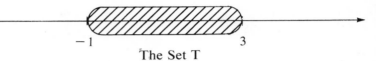

The Set T

Then
$$S \cap H = \{x \in R/x < -1 \text{ or } x > 3\} \cap \{x \in R/x < 11\}$$
$$= \{x \in R/x < -1 \text{ or } 3 < x < 11\}$$
$$T \cap K = \{x \in R/-1 < x < 3\} \cap \{x \in R/x > 11\}$$
$$= \varnothing$$

The solution set is then $\{x \in R/x < -1 \text{ or } 3 < x < 11\}$.
Of course, this may also be written

$$\{x \in R/x < -1\} \cup \{x \in R/3 < x < 11\}$$

Example 10. Find:

(a) $\left\{ x \in N \;\middle/\; \dfrac{2}{x - 3} > \dfrac{3}{x + 1} \right\}$

(b) $\left\{ x \in J \;\middle/\; \dfrac{2}{x - 3} > \dfrac{3}{x + 1} \right\}$

Solution: Having solved the problem over R, it is now an easy matter to specialize to N and to J. Referring to Example 9, then, the answers are:

(a) $\{4, 5, 6, 7, 8, 9, 10\}$

(b) $\{4, 5, 6, 7, 8, 9, 10, -2, -3, -4, \ldots\}$

Example 11. Find $\left\{ x \in R \;\middle/\; \dfrac{x}{x + 2} > \dfrac{2}{x - 1} \right\}$.

Solution: For $(x + 2)(x - 1) > 0$ we obtain $x(x - 1) > 2(x + 2)$ by Theorem 14a. For $(x + 2)(x - 1) < 0$ we obtain $x(x - 1) < 2(x + 2)$ by Theorem 14b. Let

$$E = \{x \in R/(x + 2)(x - 1) > 0\}$$
$$F = \{x \in R/(x + 2)(x - 1) < 0\}$$
$$U = \{x \in R/x(x - 1) > 2(x + 2)\}$$
$$V = \{x \in R/x(x - 1) < 2(x + 2)\}$$

Then the solution set is

$$(E \cap U) \cup (F \cap V)$$

(1) We determine E. If

$$A = \{x \in R/x + 2 > 0\}$$
$$B = \{x \in R/x - 1 > 0\}$$
$$C = \{x \in R/x + 2 < 0\}$$
$$D = \{x \in R/x - 1 < 0\}$$

then $E = (A \cap B) \cup (C \cap D)$.

$$A \cap B = \{x \in R/x > -2 \text{ and } x > 1\} = \{x \in R/x > 1\}$$
$$C \cap D = \{x \in R/x < -2 \text{ and } x < 1\} = \{x \in R/x < -2\}$$

Thus $E = \{x \in R/x < -2 \text{ or } x > 1\}$:

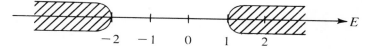

(2) It follows that $F = \{x \in R/-2 < x < 1\}$:

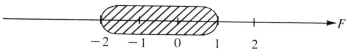

(3) We determine U:

$$x(x - 1) > 2(x + 2)$$
$$x^2 - x > 2x + 4$$
$$x^2 - 3x - 4 > 0$$
$$(x - 4)(x + 1) > 0$$

Thus, as in (1), $U = \{x \in R/x > 4\} \cup \{x \in R/x < -1\}$:

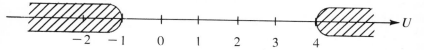

(4) Similarly, $V = \{x \in R/-1 < x < 4\}$:

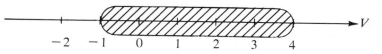

Thus

$$E \cap U = \{x \in R/x < -2 \text{ or } x > 4\}$$
$$F \cap V = \{x \in R/-1 < x < 1\}$$

The solution set is

$$\{x \in R/x < -2 \text{ or } -1 < x < 1 \text{ or } 4 < x\}$$

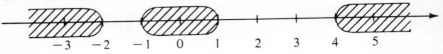

Exercises

Solve the following inequalities, where x is a variable over R, and indicate the graphs of the solution sets:

30. $2 - 4x < 1$.

31. $3 + 2x > 4$.

32. $4 - 3x \leqq 5x + 2$.

33. $2x - 3 > 4x + 2$.

34. $4 - \dfrac{x}{2} < 0$.

35. $3x > \dfrac{x - 3}{3}$.

36. $3x - 2 > \dfrac{5x + 4}{-2}$.

37. $\dfrac{x}{2} - 3 + \dfrac{2x - 1}{3} > -1$.

38. $x^2 < 9$.

39. $x^2 < -9$.

40. $x^3 - x^2 > 0$.

41. $x^3 - x^2 < 0$.

42. $x^3 - x^2 \leqq 0$.

43. $x^2 \leqq 0$.

44. $x^2 \geqq 0$.

45. $x^2 - x - 6 < 0$.

46. $2x^2 + 3x - 2 \leqq 0$.

47. $3x^2 - 1 \geqq 1 + x - 3x^2$.

48. $x(x - 1) < 0$.

49. $x^2 (x - 1) < 0$.

50. $x^3 \geqq 0$.

51. $x^3 < 0$.

52. $x^4 > 0$.

53. $x^4 < 0$.

54. $x^4 + x^2 + 1 < 0$.

55. $x^2 > x(x - 1)$.

56. $x^2 - 2 > (x + 1)(x - 1)$.

57. $\dfrac{3x}{-2} + 1 \geqq -5$.

58. $\dfrac{2}{x} < \dfrac{x}{2}$.

59. $\dfrac{4}{x^2} < 1$.

60. $\dfrac{2}{1 - x^2} > \dfrac{1}{1 - x}$.

61. $\dfrac{x}{x - 1} \leqq \dfrac{6}{7 - x}$.

62. $(x^2 - 1)(x - 1) < 0$.

63. $(x^2 - 1)(x - 1) > 0$.

64. $x^2 > 0$.

65. $(x - 1)^2 \geqq 0$.

66. $(x - 1)^2 < 0$.

67. $(2x - 3)^2 \leqq 0$.

68. $(x - 1)^3 \geqq 0$.

69. $(x - 1)^3 < 0$.

70. $x^2(x + 1)^2 > 0$.

71. $x + \dfrac{1}{x} > 0$.

72. $x(x - 1)^2 > 0$.

73. $x^2(x - 1) > 0$.

74. $x^2(2x - 3)^2 \leqq 0$.

75. $(2x + 2)^2 < 0$.

76. $x^2 + 1 \leqq 0$.

77. $x^2 + 1 > 0$.

78. $(x - 1)(x + 2)(x - 3) \geqq 0$.

79. $(x - 1)(x + 2)(x - 3) < 0$.

80. $\dfrac{2}{x} < \dfrac{3}{x - 1}$.

81. $\dfrac{5}{x + 1} < \dfrac{2}{x - 1}$.

82. $\dfrac{3}{2x + 1} \geqq \dfrac{4}{x - 2}$.

83. $\dfrac{2}{x + 1} \geqq \dfrac{3}{x + 1}$.

84. $\dfrac{1}{x^2} \leqq \dfrac{1}{x^2 + 1}$.

85. $\dfrac{2x}{x - 1} < \dfrac{x + 1}{x}$.

86. $\dfrac{x+1}{2-x} < \dfrac{1}{x+2}.$ **89.** $\dfrac{4x}{x+1} > x+1.$

87. $\dfrac{x}{2x-1} \leqq \dfrac{x+4}{x+10}.$ **90.** $\dfrac{x}{x-2} > \dfrac{x-1}{x+5}.$

88. $\dfrac{2}{x} < \dfrac{1}{x}.$

4. Absolute Value of a Real Number

Definition 5. If $a \in R$, the *absolute value* of a, designated by '$|a|$,' is defined to be:

(a) a if $a \in P$
(b) 0 if $a = 0$
(c) $-a$ if $a \in -P$

Note that $|a|$ is a real number.

Examples. $|1| = 1$ since $1 \in P$
$|0| = 0$
$|-1| = -(-1) = 1$ since $-1 \in -P$
$|-\tfrac{1}{2}| = -(-\tfrac{1}{2}) = \tfrac{1}{2}$
$|\tfrac{1}{2}| = \tfrac{1}{2}$

The following is an immediate consequence of the definition.

Theorem 91. $|a| \geqq 0$ for all $a \in R$; $|a| = 0$ if and only if $a = 0$.

Proof: If $a \in R$, then $a \in P$, or $a = 0$, or $a \in -P$ by $\mathcal{O}$.
(a) If $a \in P$, then $|a| = a$ by Definition 5a, so that $|a| \in P$ and $|a| > 0$.
(b) $|0| = 0$ by Definition 5b.
(c) If $a \in -P$, then $|a| = -a$ by Definition 5c. But if $a \in -P$, then $-a \in P$, so that $|a| > 0$.

We may also say: If $a \in R$, then $|a| = \max \{a, -a\}$.

Exercises

92. If $a, b \in R$, prove:
(a) $|a| = |-a|$.   (b) $|a|^2 = |a^2|$.   (c) $|a - b| = |b - a|$.
93. If $a \in R$, prove that $a \leqq |a|$ and $-a \leqq |a|$.
94. Prove if $a, b \in R$, then $|a| \leqq b$ if and only if $a \leqq b$ and $-a \leqq b$. (Similarly $|a| < b$ if and only if $a < b$ and $-a < b$.)
95. Prove if $a, b \in R$, then $|a| \geqq b$ if and only if $a \geqq b$ or $-a \geqq b$. (Similarly $|a| > b$ if and only if $a > b$ or $-a > b$.)
96. Let $a \in R$. Prove:
(a) $0 < |a| < 1$ if and only if $0 < a^2 < 1$.
(b) $1 < |a|$ if and only if $1 < a^2$.

97. If $a,b, \epsilon R$, prove that $|a| < |b|$ if and only if $a^2 < b^2$.

98. Prove: If $a,b \epsilon R$, then $|a+b| \le |a| + |b|$. When does equality hold? (*Hint:* $a \le |a|$, $b \le |b|$; hence $a + b \le |a| + |b|$. $-a \le |a|$, $-b \le |b|$; hence $-(a+b) \le |a| + |b|$. Apply Exercise 94.)

99. Prove if $a,b \epsilon R$, then $|a-b| \ge ||a| - |b||$. (*Hint:* $a = (a-b) + b$. Hence $|a| \le |a-b| + |b|$ or $|a| - |b| \le |a-b|$. Similarly show $|b| - |a| \le |a-b|$.)

100. (a) If $a,b \epsilon R$, prove $|a| \cdot |b| = |ab|$.

   (b) If $a,b \epsilon R$ and $b \ne 0$, prove $\dfrac{|a|}{|b|} = \left|\dfrac{a}{b}\right|$.

101. (a) If $a,b \epsilon R$, prove that $|a| = |b|$ if and only if $a = b$ or $a = -b$.

   (b) If $a,b \epsilon R$ and $b \ne 0$, prove that $|a| < |b|$ if and only if $-1 < \dfrac{a}{b} < 1$.

   (Similarly, $|a| \le |b|$ if and only if $-1 \le \dfrac{a}{b} \le 1$.)

5. Equations and Inequalities Involving Absolute Value

In Section 4 we developed the basic theorems (mainly through exercises) for expressions containing absolute value. These theorems may be used systematically for determining solutions of equations and inequalities, as presented in examples below.

Example 12. Solve: $|x| = 5$ where x is a variable over R.
Solution: (1) For $x \epsilon P$, $|x| = x$; thus $|x| = 5$ is equivalent to $x = 5$ in this case. The solution one obtains for this case is $P \cap \{x \epsilon R/x = 5\}$. This is clearly $\{5\}$.
(2) For $x \epsilon -P$, $|x| = -x$; thus $|x| = 5$ is equivalent to $-x = 5$, or $x = -5$. The solution one obtains for this case is $-P \cap \{x \epsilon R/x = -5\}$. This is clearly $\{-5\}$.
(3) The solution set is the union of the sets in (1) and (2): $\{5\} \cup \{-5\} = \{5, -5\}$.

Of course, if one applies Exercise 101a, one may write the solution set as $\{5, -5\}$ immediately.

Example 13. Solve: $|x - 3| = 2, x \epsilon R$.
Solution: Again by Exercise 101a, the solution set is the following:

$$\{x \epsilon R/x - 3 = 2\} \cup \{x \epsilon R/x - 3 = -2\} \text{ or } \{5, 1\}$$

Examples 12 and 13 may be interpreted geometrically. If $a,b \epsilon R$, it is easy to see intuitively that $b - a$ represents the directed distance from a to b. That is $b - a$ is positive if b is to the right of a, and negative if b is to the left of a.

Thus if $a = 2$ and $b = -3$, the directed distance from a to b (i.e., from 2 to -3) is $b - a = (-3) - (2)$ or -5. That is, the (undirected) distance is 5 and -3 is to the left of 2.

If we are interested in the distance without regard to direction, then we consider $|b - a| = |a - b|$.

Thus $|b - a| = 2$ geometrically means that the (undirected) distance between a and b is 2.

It follows that any solution to Example 13 is a number whose distance to the number 3 is 2, and conversely. Such numbers are 5 and 1:

Distance 2   Distance 2

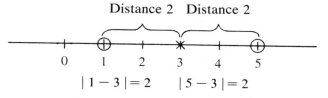

$|1 - 3| = 2$ $\quad$ $|5 - 3| = 2$

Of course the geometry will be used only for intuition. The reasoning for the solution set {5, 1} has already been given.

In Example 12 we may regard the equation $|x| = 5$ as $|x - 0| = 5$. Thus we are seeking numbers whose distance to 0 is 5. As we have seen, such numbers are 5 and -5.

Distance 5 $\qquad\qquad\qquad$ Distance 5

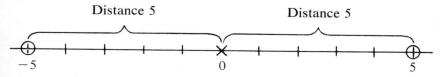

The directed distance from -5 to 0 is 5; from 0 to -5 is -5. The directed distance from 0 to 5 is 5; from 5 to 0 is -5.

Example 14. Find $\{x \in R/ \, |x - 2| > -1\}$. Geometrically, we are seeking the "points" whose distance from 2 is greater than -1. This is certainly all of R. We now prove this.

Solution: By Theorem 91, $|a| \geq 0$ for all $a \in R$, and since $0 > -1$, we see that $|a| > -1$ for all $a \in R$. Hence $\{x \in R/ \, |x - 2| > -1\} = R$.

Example 15. Find $\{x \in R/ \, |x + 2| \leq 3\}$. Thinking of $|x + 2|$ as $|x - (-2)|$, we see that we are seeking the points whose distance to -2 is less than or equal to 3.

This is, intuitively, the numbers from -5 to 1 inclusive:

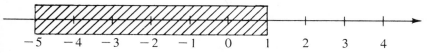

Solution: Applying Exercise 94, we see that the solution set is
$$\{x \in R/x + 2 \leq 3\} \cap \{x \in R/-(x + 2) \leq 3\}$$
$$= \{x \in R/x \leq 1\} \cap \{x \in R/x \geq -5\}$$
$$= \{x \in R/-5 \leq x \leq 1\}$$

Example 16. Find $\{x \in R/ \, |4x - 5| < 7\}$.

Solution: Again by Exercise 94, we see that the solution set is

$$\{x \in R/4x - 5 < 7\} \cap \{x \in R/-(4x - 5) < 7\}$$
$$= \{x \in R/x < 3\} \cap \{x \in R/-\tfrac{1}{2} < x\}$$
$$= \{x \in R/-\tfrac{1}{2} < x < 3\}$$

Of course, since $|4x - 5| = |4(x - \tfrac{5}{4})| = |4||x - \tfrac{5}{4}| = 4|x - \tfrac{5}{4}|$ are identities, $|4x - 5| < 7$ is equivalent to $|x - \tfrac{5}{4}| < \tfrac{7}{4}$. Thus we found the points whose distance to $\tfrac{5}{4}$ is less than $\tfrac{7}{4}$.

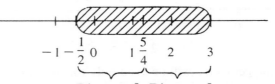

Distance $\tfrac{7}{4}$ Distance $\tfrac{7}{4}$

Example 17. $\{x \in R/ \mid 3 - x \mid = -5\} = \varnothing$.

Example 18. Find $\{x \in R/ \mid 3 - x \mid = \mid 2x + 1 \mid\}$.

Solution: By Exercise 101a, the solution set is

$$\{x \in R/3 - x = 2x + 1\} \cup \{x \in R/3 - x = -(2x + 1)\}$$
$$= \{x \in R/x = \tfrac{2}{3}\} \cup \{x \in R/x = -4\}$$
$$= \{\tfrac{2}{3}, -4\}$$

Example 19. Solve: $|3x + 7| = 5(1 + x)$ where x is a variable over R.

Solution: The right side must be greater than or equal to zero. Thus the solution set is

$$\{x \in R/ \mid 3x + 7 \mid = \mid 5(1 + x) \mid\} \cap \{x \in R/5(1 + x) \geqq 0\}$$
$$= \{x \in R/3x + 7 = 5(1 + x) \text{ or } 3x + 7 = -5(1 + x)\} \cap \{x \in R/x \geqq -1\} \text{ (by Ex. 101a)}$$
$$= \{x \in R/x = 1 \text{ or } x = -\tfrac{3}{2}\} \cap \{x \in R/x \geqq -1\}$$
$$= \{1\}$$

Example 20. $|5x - 2| < 2x + 1$.

Solution: Apply Exercise 94. The solution set is

$$\{x \in R/5x - 2 < 2x + 1\} \cap \{x \in R/-(5x - 2) < 2x + 1\}$$
$$= \{x \in R/x < 1\} \cap \{x \in R/x > \tfrac{1}{7}\}$$
$$= \{x \in R/\tfrac{1}{7} < x < 1\}$$

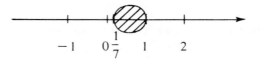

Example 21. $|3x - 1| < |2x - 5|$.

Solution: One can apply Exercise 101b, but it is just as easy (and difficult) to work directly from the definition. This method, then, is one which may always be applied (cf. Example 12).

(a) $|3x - 1| = 3x - 1$ when $3x - 1 \geqq 0$.
(b) $|3x - 1| = -(3x - 1)$ when $3x - 1 < 0$.
(c) $|2x - 5| = 2x - 5$ when $2x - 5 \geqq 0$.
(d) $|2x - 5| = -(2x - 5)$ when $2x - 5 < 0$.

Let

$$A = \{x \in R / 3x - 1 \geqq 0\}$$
$$B = \{x \in R / 3x - 1 < 0\}$$
$$C = \{x \in R / 2x - 5 \geqq 0\}$$
$$D = \{x \in R / 2x - 5 < 0\}$$

$|3x - 1| < |2x - 5|$ may be written as:

(e) $3x - 1 < 2x - 5$ for $x \in A \cap C$.
(f) $3x - 1 < -(2x - 5)$ for $x \in A \cap D$.
(g) $-(3x - 1) < 2x - 5$ for $x \in B \cap C$.
(h) $-(3x - 1) < -(2x - 5)$ for $x \in B \cap D$.

Let

$$P = \{x \in R / 3x - 1 < 2x - 5\}$$
$$Q = \{x \in R / 3x - 1 < -(2x - 5)\}$$
$$R = \{x \in R / -(3x - 1) < 2x - 5\}$$
$$S = \{x \in R / -(3x - 1) < -(2x - 5)\}$$

The solution set is then

$$(A \cap C \cap P) \cup (A \cap D \cap Q) \cup (B \cap C \cap R) \cup (B \cap D \cap S)$$

(1) $A \cap C \cap P = \{x \in R / x \geqq \tfrac{1}{3}\} \cap \{x \in R / x \geqq \tfrac{5}{2}\} \cap \{x \in R / x < -4\}$
   $= \emptyset$
(2) $A \cap D \cap Q = \{x \in R / x \geqq \tfrac{1}{3}\} \cap \{x \in R / x < \tfrac{5}{2}\} \cap \{x \in R / x < \tfrac{6}{5}\}$
   $= \{x \in R / \tfrac{1}{3} \leqq x < \tfrac{6}{5}\}$
(3) $B \cap C \cap R = \{x \in R / x < \tfrac{1}{3}\} \cap \{x \in R / x \geqq \tfrac{5}{2}\} \cap \{x \in R / \tfrac{6}{5} < x\}$
   $= \emptyset$
(4) $B \cap D \cap S = \{x \in R / x < \tfrac{1}{3}\} \cap \{x \in R / x < \tfrac{5}{2}\} \cap \{x \in R / x > -4\}$
   $= \{x \in R / -4 < x < \tfrac{1}{3}\}$

The union of (1), (2), (3), and (4) is then

$$\{x \in R / -4 < x < \tfrac{6}{5}\}$$

Example 22. $|x - 3| > 5 + x$.
Solution: We use Exercise 95. Let

$$A = \{x \in R / x - 3 > 5 + x\}$$
$$B = \{x \in R / -(x - 3) > 5 + x\}$$

Then according to Exercise 95, the solution set is $A \cup B$.

$$A \cup B = \{x \in R / -3 > 5\} \cup \{x \in R / x < -1\}$$
$$= \{x \in R / x < -1\}$$

Exercises

102. If x is a variable over R, solve:
  (a) $|x| = 0$.   (d) $|x| \geq 0$.
  (b) $|x| > 0$.   (e) $|x| \leq 0$.
  (c) $|x| < 0$.   (f) $|x - a| = 0$, where $a \in R$.

103. If x is a variable over R, $a,b \in R$, solve:
  (a) $|x| = a$.
  (b) $|x - b| = a$.
  (c) How many solutions are there in (a) and (b) if $a < 0$? $a = 0$?
  (d) $|x - b| < a$ (assume $a \in P$). (*Hint:* Apply Exercise 94 to see that the solution set is the intersection of the solution sets of $x - b < a$ and $-(x - b) < a$.)
  (e) $|x| > a$:
      (i) if $a < 0$.
      (ii) if $a = 0$.
      (iii) if $a > 0$.
  (f) $|x - b| \geq a$. Consider cases as in (e).
  (g) $|x - 2| = |2x + 3|$.

104. If x is a variable over R, solve and indicate the graph of:
  (a) $|x| = 7$.   (f) $|3x| < 5$.
  (b) $|x| = -3$.   (g) $|x - 4| > 8$.
  (c) $|2x| = 8$.   (h) $|2x - \frac{3}{2}| \geq \frac{1}{3}$.
  (d) $|2x| = 2x$.   (i) $|x - \frac{1}{3}| \leq \frac{3}{4}$.
  (e) $|x + 4| = |x| + 4$.

105. If x is a variable over R, solve and graph the following:
  (a) $|x + 1| < |2x - 3|$.   (f) $|x| \geq x - 1$.
  (b) $|x| \leq |x - 1|$.   (g) $x \geq |x - 1|$.
  (c) $|2x - 3| \geq |x + 2|$.   (h) $|2x - 3| \geq x + 2$.
  (d) $|x + 1| < 2x - 3$.   (i) $2x - 3 < |x + 2|$.
  (e) $x + 1 < |2x - 3|$.

6. Bounds of a Set

6.1 Upper and Lower Bounds

We have seen examples, in graphing inequalities, of sets of real numbers which extend indefinitely to the right, to the left, or both.

For example, $\{x \in R/x > 3\}$ extends indefinitely to the right:

Also $\{x \in R/x < -1\}$ extends indefinitely to the left.

The set $\{x \in R/x < -1 \text{ or } x > 3\}$ extends indefinitely to the right and to the left, as does R.

There are also sets which do not extend indefinitely in either direction. Examples are:

$$\{x \in R/-1 < x \leq 2\}$$
$$\{x \in R/1 \leq x < 2\} \cup \{x \in R/2 < x \leq 3\}$$

To discuss these differences concerning subsets of R, we introduce the notion of upper and lower bounds of a set.

Definition 6. If S is a nonempty subset of R (i.e., $S \subseteq R$ and $S \neq \emptyset$), then $a \in R$ is said to be an *upper bound* of S if $a \geq s$ for all $s \in S$. [Note that a itself need *not* be in S!]

If such an upper bound exists, we say *S has an upper bound* or *is bounded above*.

Definition 7. Similarly if $a \in R$ and $a \leq s$ for all $s \in S$, a is said to be a *lower bound* of S.

If such a lower bound exists, we say *S has a lower bound* or *is bounded below*.

Definition 8. If S is both bounded above and bounded below, we say *S is bounded*.

Example 23. Let $A = \{-2, 0, 1\}$.
  (a) 2 is an upper bound of A. For $2 \geq -2$ (in fact, $2 > -2$), $2 \geq 0$, $2 \geq 1$. Thus $2 \geq a$ for every $a \in A$.
  (b) 3 is an upper bound of A.
  (c) Every $b \in R$ with $b \geq 1$ is an upper bound of A.
  (d) A is bounded above. For example, one may use (a), (b), or (c) to see this. To show that A is bounded above, it is sufficient to show the existence of one upper bound of A.
  (e) A is bounded below. -2 is a lower bound; so is -3; so is any $c \in A$ with $c \leq -2$.
  (f) A is bounded. This follows from (d) and (e).

Example 24. We consider the set P of positive real numbers, i.e., $\{x \in R/x > 0\}$.
  (a) P is not bounded above. For suppose $b \in R$ and b is an upper bound of P. We shall show that this leads to a contradiction. If b is an upper bound of P, then $b \geq 1$, and since $1 > 0$ we see from Exercise 21c that $b > 0$. Hence $b \in P$. It follows from $\mathcal{O}_1$ that $b + 1 \in P$. But this would mean that $b \geq b + 1$ (b being an upper bound of P and $b + 1 \in P$). This certainly is impossible. Hence no such upper bound exists in R.
  (b) P is bounded below. By Exercise 10a, 0 is a lower bound; or by Exercise 12b any negative number is a lower bound.

Example 25. Let $Q = \{u \in R/0 < u < 1\}$; $V = \{x \in R/x \leqq 1\}$.

(a) Q is bounded above, e.g., 2 is an upper bound.
(b) V is bounded above, e.g., 1 is an upper bound.
(c) If $a \in R$ and $a < 1$, then a is not an upper bound of Q.
If $a \leqq 0$, this is clear. Thus suppose $0 < a < 1$. Then by Exercise 24, $\exists d \in R \ni a < d < 1$. Hence $d \in Q$, and $a \ngeqq d$. Hence a is not an upper bound of Q.
(d) Q is bounded below.
(e) V is not bounded below.
(f) Q is bounded.

Theorem 106. If S is a nonempty subset of R, and q is an upper bound of S, then every element of $\{t \in R/t \geqq q\}$ is also an upper bound of S.

Proof: Let $a \in \{t \in R/t \geqq q\}$. Thus, $a \geqq q$. We wish to show a is an upper bound of S.

Let s be any element of S. We must show $a \geqq s$. But since q is an upper bound of S, $q \geqq s$; since also $a \geqq q$, by Exercise 21b we see that $a \geqq s$.

Exercises

For each of the following subsets S of R in Exercises 107 to 115, answer the following:

(a) Is S bounded above? If so, exhibit an upper bound.
(b) If S is bounded above, is there an upper bound a of S such that $a \leqq b$ for *all* upper bounds b of S (i.e., does there exist an upper bound of S which is less than all other upper bounds of S)?
(c) Is S bounded below? If so, exhibit a lower bound.
(d) If S is bounded below, does there exist a lower bound a of S such that $a \geqq b$ for *all* lower bounds b of S (i.e., does there exist a lower bound of S which is greater than all other lower bounds of S)?
(e) If S is bounded above, is one of the upper bounds of S an element of S itself?
(f) If S is bounded below, is one of the lower bounds of S an element of S?
(g) Is S bounded?
(h) Graph S.

107. $S = \{x \in R/-3 \leqq x < 0 \text{ or } 1 < x\}$.
108. $S = \{x \in R/2 < x \leqq 3\}$.
109. $S = \{x \in R/2 \leqq x < 3\}$.
110. $S = \{x \in R/x \leqq -2\} \cup \{x \in R/-1 < x < 5\}$.
111. $S = \{x \in R/0 < |x| < 1\}$.
112. $S = \{1\}$.
113. $S = \{1, 2\}$.
114. $S = \{x \in R/x = 1 \text{ or } x < \frac{1}{2}\}$.
115. $S = \{x \in R/x < \frac{1}{2} \text{ or } x = 1 \text{ or } x \geqq 2\}$.
116. State and prove a theorem analogous to Theorem 106 for lower bounds.

6.2   Least Upper and Greatest Lower Bounds of a Set

In part (b) of Exercises 107 to 115, the student was asked to consider all upper bounds (if any existed) of a set, and to find one which was less than all the other upper bounds.

If $A = \{x \in R/x < 2\}$, then 2 is such an element.

If $B = \{x \in R/x \leq 2\}$, then again 2 is such an element. That is, 2 is an upper bound of A and B, and if c is any upper bound of A (or B), then $c \geq 2$.

We shall call 2 the *least upper bound* of A (also of B), in accordance with the following:

Definition 9. Let S be a nonempty subset of R. If there exists an upper bound $a \in R$ of S such that $a \leq b$ for all upper bounds b of S, we shall say that a is a *least upper bound* (lub) of S.

Definition 10. If there exists a lower bound $a \in R$ of S such that $a \geq b$ for all lower bounds b of S, we shall say that a is a *greatest lower bound* (glb) of S [cf. part (d) of Exercises 107 to 115].

Other terminology used is "supremum" (sup) for "least upper bound," and "infimum" (inf) for "greatest lower bound."

Theorem 117. If S is a nonempty subset of R and if S has a least upper bound, then it is unique. The statement also holds for a greatest lower bound of S.

Proof: Suppose a and a' are both least upper bounds of S. We must show they are equal.

Since a is a least upper bound, and a' is an upper bound, according to Definition 9, $a \leq a'$.

Similar reasoning leads to the conclusion that $a' \leq a$.

By Exercise 22, $a = a'$.

The proof is similar for the uniqueness of the greatest lower bound (when it exists).

Theorem 117 allows us to refer to *the* lub of a set, when it exists; similarly *the* glb of a set.

Exercises

118. Let S be a nonempty subset of R. Suppose $a \in R$ is an upper bound of S, and that furthermore $a \in S$. Prove that a is the lub of S.

119. State and prove a similar theorem (as in Exercise 118) for a set bounded below.

6.3   The Greatest and Least Elements of a Set

Definition 11. If S is a nonempty subset of R which has a lub q, and if furthermore $q \in S$, then q is called the *greatest element* of S.

Definition 12. If $S \subseteq R$, $S \neq \varnothing$, has a glb p, and if furthermore $p \in S$, then p is called the *least element* of S.

Examples. (1) $\{x \in R / 0 < x < 1\}$ has no least and no greatest element. The glb is 0, the lub is 1, but neither of these is an element of the set.
(2) $\{x \in R / 0 < x \leq 1\}$ has a greatest element (namely 1) but no least element.
(3) $\{x \in R / 5 \leq x\}$ has a least element, but no greatest element.
(4) In $\{-3, -2, -1\}$, -3 is the least element and -1 is the greatest element.

Exercises

120. For the sets of Exercises 107 to 115, list the lub, glb, greatest elements, and least elements, where they exist.
121. Under what circumstances can a real number be *both* a lower bound and an upper bound of the same set?

7. Historical Remarks

As the reader will undoubtedly realize, numbers were used long before the idea arose of giving a postulational treatment, and certainly before history was recorded. In the early history of the development of the number concept, different words would be used for a given number depending upon the concrete objects being associated. For example, the word for "two" as used in designating two women would be different from that used for designating two men. Also the use of large numbers slowly evolved from a time when people only recognized the concept of one object versus more than one object. But with the growth of civilization, the need for numbers also grew. This was particularly true when it came to trade and commerce, but also in early engineering projects, agriculture, and the construction of calendars. And of course, it was important to be able to compute the area of land or the yield of crops in order to be able to assess taxes properly. With the increased use of numbers, an arithmetic of numbers gradually developed independent of the objects associated. Eventually it was found useful to have people who could instruct others in this arithmetic, and the discipline of mathematics emerged. For an account of the evolution of the number concept, we should like to recommend the book by Tobias Dantzig, *Numbers, The Language of Science*, 4th ed., Doubleday (Anchor Books), New York, 1954.

In the concluding remarks to Part I we observed that the early Egyptians had signs for $+$ and $-$. The $-$ sign as used here involves the idea of subtraction of a smaller natural number from a larger one, which one encounters in elementary or pre-elementary school arithmetic. Thus from 5 one takes 3 to obtain 2. But this does not involve the use of negative numbers. It only answers the question: What must be added to 3 to obtain 5? And yet if the reader can imagine himself in an early civilization adding 2 to 3 to obtain 5, or 4 to 5 to obtain 9, perhaps he can imagine the difficulty involved in initiating the use of subtraction, $5 - 3 = 2$, $9 - 5 = 4$, as another formal operation.

The Indians appear to be the first to have considered negative numbers as such. This was with the idea of positive numbers being used for possessions and negative ones for debts; or positive numbers for one direction on a line and negative for the other.[1] This does not mean that negative numbers were merely around waiting to be found, just as subtraction was not. They were created by man and used by him in the solution of specific problems.

The rule that $(-a)(-b) = ab$, or $(-a)b = -(ab)$ historically stemmed from the rule that negative times negative is positive; or negative times positive is negative. We hope we have clarified the distinction between these rules in this chapter. It is true, however, that $-a$ (or some other symbol representing $-$) originally meant a negative number. Thus -5 or -2 were recognized concepts before $-(-5)$ or $-(-2)$ came into being. In this sense, '$-$' would mean negative and '$+$' positive. There is no reason any longer to maintain this connection between $-$ and negative, and $+$ and positive.

But let us return to the rule $(-a)(-b) = ab$ from an historical point of view. It stemmed from the early observation that $(7 + 2)(5 + 3)$ could be found by the usual method of multiplying $(a + b)(c + d)$ to obtain $ac + ad + bc + bd$. Eventually it was observed that this rule worked for computing $(7 - 2) \cdot (5 - 3)$ if one took as a working rule that $(-2)(-3) = (2) \cdot (3)$. In this sense, this rule was first recognized by Diophantus (ca. 275 A.D.).

By the sixteenth century the use of negative numbers was clearly established. Hieronymus (or Girolamo) Cardan (1501–1576) treated negative numbers in his *Ars Magna*, published in 1545. The use of a letter $-$ with no plus or minus sign preceding it $-$ to represent either a positive or negative number appears to have been introduced by Johann Hudde (1628?–1704).[2]

Long before negative numbers were introduced, "fractions" were used by the Babylonians with the idea of dividing a given length, say, into 8

[1] Cf. Florian Cajori, *A History of Mathematics*, p. 93, Macmillan, New York, 1894.
[2] Cf. D. E. Smith, *History of Mathematics*, Vol. II, p. 259, Dover, New York, 1958.

equal parts, each part thereby having length $\frac{1}{8}$. In the Ahmes Papyrus (ca. 1550 B.C.), one found not only "unit" fractions — i.e., fractions with 1 in the numerator — but also the idea of 2 or 3, etc., being divided into an equal number of parts.[3] By the time of Pythagoras in the sixth century B.C., then, positive rational numbers had long been used to represent lengths of line segments. Before the use of these numbers came into being, divisions of units had to be made by introducing smaller units, e.g., so many ounces rather than some fraction of a pound. But while the Greeks and the Romans were familiar with the positive rational numbers, the number zero was another matter. The origin of this number does not seem to be known, but Smith writes that "the earliest undoubted occurrence of a zero in India is seen in an inscription of 876 at Gavalior." [4]

At any rate, with the positive rational numbers, zero, and then the negative rational numbers, we have all the rational numbers. They form an example of what today is called a *field*, which is a generalization one obtains if he attempts to bring out the essential algebraic features of the system of rational numbers. Indeed, one used the phrase "domain of rationality" for "field" in the earlier literature. Although the postulates of a field were explicitly given at the beginning of this century, they nevertheless were first implicitly recognized in the work of Niels Henrich Abel (1802–1829) and Evariste Galois (1811–1832). They were also seen, in more restrictive applications, in the work of Julius Wilhelm Richard Dedekind (1831–1916) and Leopold Kronecker (1823–1891).[5]

E. T. Bell [7] writes:

The passage to final abstractness took about a quarter of a century.

The turning point was Hilbert's work on the foundations of geometry in 1899.[6] Although this did not concern algebra or arithmetic directly, it set a new and high standard of definiteness and completeness in the statement of all mathematical definitions or, what is equivalent, in the construction of postulate systems. Compared to what came after 1900 in this basic kind of work, that before 1900 now seems incredibly slack. With abundant resources at hand to continue the Euclidean program of stating explicitly what a mathematical argument is to be about, the majority of the nineteenth-century mathematicians left their readers to guess exactly what was postulated. Neglect to state all the intended assumptions incurred its own penalties in faulty proofs and false propositions. The change for the better after 1900 was most marked, but there is still room for improvement. . . .

[3] Cf. *ibid.,* pp. 208–228.
[4] *Ibid.,* p. 69.
[5] E. T. Bell, *Development of Mathematics,* pp. 196–199, McGraw-Hill, New York, 1940.
[6] David Hilbert: 1862–1943.
[7] E. T. Bell, *Development of Mathematics,* pp. 196–199, McGraw-Hill, New York, 1940.

chapter viii

MATHEMATICAL INDUCTION

Up to now we have been unable to state and prove theorems depending upon deeper properties of the natural numbers. In Chapter 6 we did make use of the addition and multiplication tables for N, and we used the Fundamental Theorem of Arithmetic. In Chapter 5 we stated and proved the associative, commutative, and distributive laws in R for several terms, but had no technique for proving these laws for *any finite* number of terms. By *any finite* number of terms, we mean n terms, where n is any element of N. Proving a statement to be true for the first million natural numbers, for example, does not mean it is true for every natural number. Thus one might be able to show that the statement: "If $n \in N$, then n is less than a billion" is true for values of n up to 500 million, but this does not constitute a proof for all $n \in N$.

We see a need, then, for a sharper delineation of the natural numbers. In this chapter we shall define the set N of natural numbers and we shall thereupon derive consequences. As a result, we shall be able to prove such theorems as the generalized associative, commutative, and distributive laws for any finite number of terms. The powerful technique used in these proofs is known as *mathematical induction*. One of the important purposes of this chapter is to initiate the student into the experience of constructing proofs involving the method of mathematical induction.

1. The Natural Numbers

1.1   An Intuitive Look at the Natural Numbers

One's first acquaintance with the natural numbers was with their use as counting numbers. The important idea, at that time, was "one more." That is, if one had a penny, then one more penny would give him two pennies; one more than that would give three, one more four, and so on. To see that two pennies and three more pennies gave five, one would at first count one by one: two and one is three; and one is four; and one is five. If one memorized the names in order: 'one,' 'two,' 'three,' 'four,' etc., the earliest idea he would have about these numbers was that each was one more than the preceding.

Eventually, rather than always associating these numbers with collections of pennies, or chocolate bars, etc., one was able to answer such questions as:

How much is 2 and 1?   *Answer:* 3
How much is 3 and 1?   *Answer:* 4
How much is 6 and 1?   *Answer:* 7

One soon recognized that for any counting number a, $a + 1$ was also a counting number.

We may express the above observations by saying that N is a subset of R with the following two properties:

(a) $1 \in N$;
(b) If $a \in N$, then $a + 1 \in N$.

Now there are certainly other subsets of R with these two properties; e.g., $J, \bar{R}$, and R, to name only a few. But if S is *any* subset of R satisfying properties (a) and (b) above, it seems intuitively clear that N would be a subset of S. It is this observation which we use to formulate a definition of N.

1.2   Definition of the Set N of Natural Numbers

Definition 1. Let N be the intersection of all subsets S of R satisfying:

(a) $1 \in S$;
(b) If $a \in S$, then $a + 1 \in S$.

[Thus $x \in N$ means $x \in S$ for every subset S of R satisfying (a) and (b).] We call the elements of N *natural numbers.*

Although N is the intersection of subsets of R satisfying (a) and (b), we now check that N itself satisfies (a) and (b), and that no proper subset of N satisfies (a) and (b).

Theorem 1. N satisfies the following:

(a) $1 \in N$;
(b) If $a \in N$, then $a + 1 \in N$;
(c) If M is any subset *of* N satisfying (a) and (b), then $M = N$.

Conversely, if N' is any subset of R satisfying (a), (b), (c), then $N' = N$.

Proof: Let $\mathscr{F}$ be the collection of subsets of R satisfying (a) and (b).

(a) Since $1 \in S$ for every $S \in \mathscr{F}$, it follows that $1 \in N$.[1]
(b) Suppose $a \in N$. Then $a \in S$ for every $S \in \mathscr{F}$. But then $a + 1 \in S$ for every $S \in \mathscr{F}$. Hence $a + 1 \in N$. We have therefore shown that N satisfies (a) and (b).
(c) Suppose $M \subseteq N$, and that M satisfies (a) and (b). Then by definition of N we have $N \subseteq M$. But $M \subseteq N$ and $N \subseteq M$ implies $M = N$.

---

[1] This would not follow if $\mathscr{F}$ were empty, as then there would be no S in $\mathscr{F}$ for which $1 \in S$. But $\mathscr{F}$ is clearly not empty, as, in particular, $R \in \mathscr{F}$.

(d) Finally suppose N' satisfies (a), (b), and (c). Since N' satisfies (a) and (b), by Definition 1 we have $N' \supseteq N$. But then by property (c) for N', we have $N = N'$.

2. The Method of Mathematical Induction (First Principle)

2.1 Proofs by Mathematical Induction

The properties (a), (b), (c) of Theorem 1 offer a characterization of N as a subset of R. We now show how Theorem 1 may be used to derive various other facts about N.

Theorem 2. $N \subseteq P$.

Remarks: We wish to prove that every element of N is positive. In any case, we may consider the set M of all natural numbers which *are* positive. Our aim would then be to prove that $M = N$. Theorem 1(c) offers an approach.

Proof: Let $M = \{x \in N / x \in P\}$, so that $M \subseteq N$.
(a) Since $1 \in N$ by Theorem 1(a), and $1 \in P$ by (7, 4), we have $1 \in M$.
(b) Suppose $a \in M$. This means $a \in N$ and $a \in P$. But then $a + 1 \in N$ by Theorem 1(b), and $a + 1 \in P$ by postulate $\mathcal{O}_1$. Hence $a + 1 \in M$.
Since M satisfies (a) and (b), and $M \subseteq N$, it follows from Theorem 1(c) that $M = N$.

Note that by definition, $N \subseteq R$; and by Theorem 2, $0 \notin N$. Thus the assumptions NR and $0 \notin N$ of Chapter 6 were not really needed; they were assumed there only to offer practice in technical facility sooner.

We have defined $J = N \cup \{0\} \cup -N$. It now follows that these sets are disjoint.

Definition 2. The elements of N are called *positive integers* (as well as natural numbers), the elements of $-N$, *negative integers*.

Theorem 3. $1 \leq n$ for all $n \in N$. (That is, 1 is the least element of N.)

Proof: Let $M = \{x \in N / 1 \leq x\}$.
(a) $1 \in M$, since $1 \leq 1$.
(b) Suppose $a \in M$, so that $1 \leq a$. Since $a < a + 1$, we have $1 \leq a < a + 1$. By (7, 21), $1 \leq a + 1$. Hence $a + 1 \in M$.
By Theorem 1(c), $M = N$, and this proves the theorem.

In Chapter 7 we were able to prove $1 \in P$, and $2 \in P$ (where $2 = 1 + 1$), and $3 \in P$ (where $3 = 2 + 1$), and $4 \in P$ (where $4 = 3 + 1$). Similarly we could prove $2 > 1$; $3 > 1$; $4 > 1$. We may phrase this as follows:
(a) Let $P(n)$ be the proposition that $n \in P$ for $n \in N$. Then in Chapter 7 we could prove $P(1)$, $P(2)$, $P(3)$, and $P(4)$ to be theorems.

(b) Let $P(n)$ be the proposition that $1 \leq n$ for $n \in N$. Then in Chapter 7 we could prove $P(1)$, $P(2)$, $P(3)$, and $P(4)$ to be theorems. (Since $2 \neq 1$, $3 \neq 1$, and $4 \neq 1$, this leads to $2 > 1$, $3 > 1$, and $4 > 1$.)

But Theorem 2 proves $P(n)$ in (a) to be a theorem *for all $n \in N$*. And Theorem 3 proves $P(n)$ in (b) to be a theorem *for all $n \in N$*. Both of these theorems, then, represent a vast improvement over our earlier results, and it is worth analyzing their proofs.

In both Theorems 2 and 3, we are asked to prove that a proposition $P(n)$ is a theorem for all $n \in N$. We then let

$$M = \{x \in N / P(x) \text{ is a theorem}\}$$

The object is then to prove that $M = N$, i.e., that $P(n)$ is a theorem for all $n \in N$.

To prove $M = N$, we use Theorem 1. Thus we prove:
  (a) $1 \in M$;
  (b) If $a \in M$, then $a + 1 \in M$.
By Theorem 1(c) it follows that $M = N$.
We shall rephrase this method, in the next theorem, in general terms.

Theorem 4. Let $P(n)$ be a proposition involving the natural number n. Suppose:
  (a) $P(1)$ is a theorem;
  (b) If $P(a)$ is a theorem (for $a \in N$), then $P(a + 1)$ is a theorem.
Then $P(n)$ is a theorem for all $n \in N$.

We have really given the proof above, but we repeat it. Thus let $M = \{x \in N / P(x) \text{ is a theorem}\}$. Then by (a), we have $1 \in M$. And by (b), if $a \in M$, then $a + 1 \in M$. Hence by Theorem 1, $M = N$ and $P(n)$ is a theorem for all $n \in N$.

Theorem 4 is called the *first principle of mathematical induction*. A proof using this theorem is called a *proof by mathematical induction*. As Theorem 4 is merely a formalization of the use of Theorem 1 in proofs of theorems, a proof using Theorem 1 is also a proof by mathematical induction.

We illustrate the use of Theorem 4 in our next result.

Theorem 5. N is closed under addition.

Proof: Let $P(n)$ be the proposition that $m + n \in N$ for all $m \in N$. We wish to prove $P(n)$ is a theorem for all $n \in N$. We prove this by mathematical induction.
  (a) $P(1)$ states that $m + 1 \in N$ for all $m \in N$. This follows from Theorem 1(b). Hence $P(1)$ is a theorem.
  (b) Suppose $P(a)$ is a theorem for $a \in N$; i.e., suppose $m + a \in N$ for all $m \in N$. We must show that $P(a + 1)$ is a theorem. That is, we must show

$m + (a + 1) \in N$ for all $m \in N$. But $m + (a + 1) = (m + a) + 1$. Here $m + a \in N$ since P(a) is a theorem. Hence $(m + a) + 1 \in N$ by Theorem 1(b), so that $m + (a + 1) \in N$. This shows that $P(a + 1)$ is a theorem.

By Theorem 4, $P(n)$ is a theorem for all $n \in N$.

[If we wished to introduce the set M as in the proofs of Theorems 2 and 3, we would have proceeded as follows: Let $M = \{x \in N / m + x \in N$ for all $m \in N\}$. Then since $m + 1 \in N$ for all $m \in N$ by Theorem 1(b), we have $1 \in M$. Suppose $a \in M$. Then we must show $a + 1 \in M$. That is, we must show $m + (a + 1) \in N$ for all $m \in N$. But $m + (a + 1) = (m + a) + 1$ and $m + a \in N$ since $a \in M$. Hence $(m + a) + 1 \in N$ by Theorem 1(b), and hence $m + (a + 1) \in N$. Thus M satisfies properties (a) and (b) and by Theorem 1(c), $M = N$. Of course, the proof of Theorem 4 shows that this method is equivalent to the proof we have given above.]

Exercise

6. Prove that N is closed under multiplication. (*Hint:* Use mathematical induction and Theorem 5.)

2.2 Definition by Induction (Recursive Definitions)

Not only are we able to use Theorem 1 to establish the basis for proofs by mathematical induction (Theorem 4), but also for definitions by mathematical induction.

For example, suppose we wish to define r^n for $r \in R$ and $n \in N$.

Definition 3. Let $r \in R$ and $k \in N$.
  (a) $r^1 = r$;
  (b) $r^{k+1} = r^k \cdot r$.

Now Definition 3 defines r^n for all $n \in N$. For if

$$S = \{x \in N / r^x \text{ has been defined}\}$$

then $1 \in S$ by (a); and if $k \in S$ so that r^k is defined, then $k + 1 \in S$ by (b).

Example 1. According to Definition 3, write out completely the meaning of r^5.
  (Here $5 = 4 + 1$, $4 = 3 + 1$, $3 = 2 + 1$, and $2 = 1 + 1$.)
Solution: $r^5 = r^{4+1}$
$\qquad = r^4 \cdot r$ by Def. 3(b) with $k = 4$
$\qquad = r^{3+1} \cdot r$
$\qquad = (r^3 \cdot r) \cdot r$ by Def. 3(b) with $k = 3$
$\qquad = (r^{2+1} \cdot r) \cdot r$
$\qquad = ((r^2 \cdot r) \cdot r) \cdot r$ by Def. 3(b) with $k = 2$
$\qquad = ((r^{1+1} \cdot r) \cdot r) \cdot r$
$\qquad = (((r^1 \cdot r) \cdot r) \cdot r) \cdot r$ by Def. 3(b) with $k = 1$
$\qquad = (((r \cdot r) \cdot r) \cdot r) \cdot r$ by Def. 3(a)

Definition 4. We define $k!$ for all $k \in N$ as follows:

(a) $1! = 1$;

(b) $(n + 1)! = (n + 1)n!$.

One says for "$k!$": "k factorial."

Example 2. $4! = 4 \cdot 3!$ by Def. 4(b)

$= 4 \cdot (3 \cdot 2!)$ by Def. 4(b)

$= 4 \cdot (3 \cdot (2 \cdot 1!))$ by Def. 4(b)

$= 4 \cdot (3 \cdot (2 \cdot 1))$ by Def. 4(a)

Of course, assuming the multiplication table, this is 24.

Definitions 3 and 4 are illustrations of *inductive definitions* (or *definitions by induction* or *recursive definitions*). Namely, to define something for every $k \in N$, one defines it:

(a) for 1;

(b) for $n + 1$ in terms of the definition for n.

Example 3. Prove $1^n = 1$ for all $n \in N$.

Solution: We use mathematical induction.

(a) $1^1 = 1$ by Def. 3(a). Hence the result is true for $n = 1$.

(b) Assume $1^n = 1$. We must show $1^{n+1} = 1$. But

$$1^{n+1} = 1^n \cdot 1 \text{ by Def. 3(b)}$$

$$= 1 \cdot 1 \text{ by "inductive hypothesis" that } 1^n = 1$$

$$= 1$$

By Theorem 4, the theorem is proved for all $n \in N$.

Example 4. Prove $2^n > n$ for all $n \in N$.

Solution: (a) $2^1 = 2$ by Def. 3(a), and $2 > 1$ {cf. [7, 16(a)]}. Hence $2^1 > 1$ and the result is true for $n = 1$.

(b) Assume $2^k > k$ for $k \in N$. We must show $2^{k+1} > k + 1$. Since $2^k > k$ by inductive hypothesis, and $2 > 1$, it follows from (7, 26) that $2^k \cdot 2 > k \cdot 2$. Hence $2^{k+1} > 2k$. But $2k = (1 + 1)k = k + k \geq k + 1$ (since $k \geq 1$ by Theorem 3). Hence $2^{k+1} > 2k \geq k + 1$ and $2^{k+1} > k + 1$.

Exercises

7. Find: (a) $\dfrac{6!}{2!4!}$; (b) $\dfrac{6!}{3!3!}$; (c) $\dfrac{7!}{3!4!}$.

8. For $k \in N$, define $a_k \in R$ as follows:

(a) $a_1 = 2$;

(b) $a_{n+1} = a_n + 3$.

Compute: a_2; a_3; a_4; a_5; a_6; a_7.

9. If $a \in R$ and $a \neq 0$, prove $a^n \neq 0$ for all $n \in N$.

0. If $a \in P$, prove $a^n \in P$ for all $n \in N$.

11. If $a \in R$ and $0 < a < 1$, prove $0 < a^n < 1$ for all $n \in N$.
12. If $a \in R$ and $1 < a$, prove $1 < a^n$ for all $n \in N$.
13. (a) Prove that if $a \in P$ and $a^k < 1$ for some $k \in N$, then $0 < a < 1$. (*Hint:* Use Example 3 and Exercise 12.)
    (b) Prove that if $a \in P$ and $a^k > 1$ for some $k \in N$, then $a > 1$.
    (c) Prove that if $a \in P$ and $a^k = 1$ for some $k \in N$, then $a = 1$.
14. If $a = bc$, where $a,b,c \in N$, prove that $b \le a$ and $c \le a$. {*Hint:* If, say, $b > a$, one may conclude $bc > a$ [cf. Theorem 3 and (7, 27)].}
15. (a) Prove $(-1)^{2n} = 1$ for all $n \in N$. (As usual, $2 = 1 + 1$.)
    (b) Prove $2n - 1 \in N$ for all $n \in N$.
    (c) Prove $(-1)^{2n-1} = -1$ for all $n \in N$.

3. Further Properties of the Natural Numbers

Our intuitive view of the natural numbers suggests that for every natural number n, the next natural number is $n + 1$; and unless $n = 1$, the preceding natural number is $n - 1$. This is the content of our next two theorems.

Theorem 16. If $n \in N$ and $n \ne 1$, then $n - 1 \in N$. (Of course if $n = 1$, then $n - 1 \notin N$, since $1 - 1 = 0 \notin N$.)

Theorem 17. For every $n \in N$, there is no natural number between n and $n + 1$. (That is, $n < a < n + 1$ is impossible for n and a in N. Or also, if $n,a \in N$ and $n \le a \le n + 1$, then either $a = n$ or $a = n + 1$.)

Proof of Theorem 16: We give a proof by contradiction. Thus suppose there exists some $c \in N$ with $c \ne 1$ such that $c - 1 \notin N$.

Let $S = \{x \in N / x \ne c\}$. We shall prove that $S = N$, which will contradict the fact that $c \notin S$. We shall then be able to conclude that no such $c \in N$ exists satisfying $c \ne 1$ and $c - 1 \notin N$, and our theorem will be proved.
(a) $1 \in S$ since we are given $c \ne 1$.
(b) Suppose $n \in S$. Thus $n \in N$ and $n \ne c$. Then $n + 1 \in N$, by Theorem 1(b). But also, $n + 1 \ne c$, for if $n + 1 = c$ we would have $n = c - 1$, contrary to the fact $c - 1 \notin N$. Hence $n + 1 \in S$.
By Theorem 1(c), $S = N$.

Proof of Theorem 17: We give a proof by induction.
(a) We must first show that $1 < a < 1 + 1$ is impossible for $a \in N$. But if $1 < a < 1 + 1$, then $1 - 1 < a - 1 < (1 + 1) - 1$ or $0 < a - 1 < 1$. Since $a \in N$ and $a \ne 1$, by Theorem 16 we have that $a - 1 \in N$. This shows the existence of a natural number less than 1, contrary to Theorem 3.
(b) We may assume there exists no natural number between n and $n + 1$ for $n \in N$, and must show that there is then no natural number between $n + 1$ and $(n+1)+1$. But if $n+1 < a < (n+1)+1$, then $n < a-1 < n+1$. This would be impossible by inductive hypothesis if we could show $a - 1 \in N$.

But since $1 < n + 1 < a$, we have $1 < a$ and $a \neq 1$. Hence $a - 1 \in N$, by Theorem 16.

By Theorem 4, this proves Theorem 17.

Theorem 3 states that $n \geq 1$ for all $n \in N$. Thus Theorem 16 may be stated: If $n \in N$ and $n > 1$, then $n - 1 \in N$. The next theorem generalizes this result, stating that if $n,m \in N$ and $n > m$, then $n - m \in N$. Conversely, if $n,m \in N$ and $n - m \in N$, then $n > m$. This may be stated as follows:

Theorem 18. Let $m,n \in N$. Then $n > m$ if and only if there exists $r \in N$ such that $n = m + r$ (i.e., if and only if $n - m = r \in N$).

Proof: (1) If $r \in N$ exists such that $n = m + r$, then $n - m = r \in N$; and since $N \subseteq P$, we have $n - m \in P$. Hence $n > m$.

(2) Suppose $n > m$. We must show there exists $r \in N$ such that $n = m + r$. We use induction on m. Thus let $P(m)$ be the proposition that if $n > m$ for $n \in N$, then there exists $r \in N$ such that $n = m + r$.

(a) Proof of $P(1)$: Suppose $n \in N$ and $n > 1$. Then $n - 1 \in N$ by Theorem 16. Take $r = n - 1$. Thus $n = 1 + (n - 1)$.

(b) Assume $P(k)$ is a theorem. We must prove $P(k + 1)$. Thus assume $n > k + 1$ for $n \in N$. Then since $k + 1 > 1$, we have $n > 1$, so that $n - 1 \in N$. Thus $n - 1 > k$, where $n - 1 \in N$. By inductive hypothesis [i.e., by $P(k)$], there exists $t \in N$ such that $n - 1 = k + t$. But then $n = (k + 1) + t$, where $t \in N$.

By Theorem 4, this proves $P(m)$ for all $m \in N$.

We now prove an important theorem relating to the set of natural numbers. It generalizes Theorem 3. For Theorem 3 states that N has a least element (namely, 1). We now show that this applies to every nonempty subset of N.

Theorem 19. Every nonempty subset of N has a least element.

Proof: Suppose A is any nonempty subset of N. We wish to show there exists $a \in A$ such that $a \leq r$ for all $r \in A$. We prove this by contradiction. Hence assume A does not have a least element. Let $S = \{x \in N / p \notin A \text{ for all } p \in N \text{ with } p \leq x\}$. Note that if $n \in S$, then $b \notin A$ for all $b \in N$ with $b \leq n$. In particular $n \notin A$. Hence if we can show that $S = N$, this will provide a contradiction to the fact that A is nonempty.

(a) $1 \in S$: For otherwise, $1 \in A$. But then Theorem 3 would show that 1 is the least element of A, and we are assuming no such least element exists.

(b) Suppose $n \in S$. We must show $n + 1 \in S$. Since $n \in S$, it follows that $p \notin A$ for all $p \in N$ with $p \leq n$. Hence if $r \in A$, then $r \geq n + 1$ by Theorem 17. If furthermore, $n + 1 \in A$, then $n + 1$ would be the least element of A, whereas none such exists. Hence $n + 1 \notin A$, so that $n + 1 \in S$.

By Theorem 1(c), $S = N$.

Exercises

20. Let $m,n \in N$. Prove:
    (a) $m < n$ if and only if $m \leq n - 1$.
    (b) $m < n$ if and only if $m + 1 \leq n$.
21. Let $2 = 1 + 1$, $3 = 2 + 1$, $4 = 3 + 1$.
    (a) Prove that 2 is a prime integer.
    (b) Prove that 3 is a prime integer.
    (c) Prove that 4 is a composite integer.
    (*Hint:* Cf. Exercise 14.)
22. Prove that there is no integer between s and $s + 1$ for every $s \in J$.
23. (a) Prove J is closed (i) under $+$, (ii) under $-$, and (iii) under $\cdot$.
    (b) Prove $\bar{R}$, the set of rational numbers (cf. Definition 2 of Chapter 6), forms
    a *subfield* of R. By this we mean that $\bar{R}$ is a subset of R such that when the
    addition and multiplication defined on R are restricted to $\bar{R}$, then $\bar{R}$ be-
    comes a field. Thus these operations restricted to $\bar{R}$ satisfy A1, A2, A3,
    A4, A5, M1, M2, M3, M4, M5, B, and D of Chapter 5.
24. Theorem 4 states that to prove a proposition $P(n)$ to be a theorem for all
    $n \in N$, it is sufficient to prove: (a) $P(1)$ a theorem; and then to prove: (b)
    $P(n + 1)$ a theorem on the assumption that $P(n)$ is a theorem, for $n \in N$.
    Rather than prove $P(n)$ a theorem for all $n \in N$ (i.e., for all $n \in J$ with $n \geq 1$),
    one often wishes to prove $P(n)$ a theorem for all $n \geq m$ for some $m \in J$. (For
    an example with $m = 4$, cf. the next exercise.) Here m may be positive, nega-
    tive, or zero. To do this it is sufficient to prove: (a) $P(m)$ a theorem, and
    then to prove: (b) $P(n + 1)$ a theorem on the assumption $P(n)$ is a theorem, for
    $n \in J$ with $n \geq m$. Prove this last contention.
    [*Hint:* Let $S = \{x \in N/P(x + m - 1)$ is a theorem$\}$. Observe that $1 \in S$ and
    that if $n \in S$, so is $n + 1 \in S$. Conclude that $S = N$. Hence $P(s + m - 1)$ is a
    theorem for all $s \in N$. Show that $r \geq m$ if and only if $r = s + m - 1$ for some
    $s \in N$.]
25. Prove: $2^r < r!$ for all $r \in N$ with $r \geq 4$. [*Hint:* Apply Exercise 24. Thus first
    prove $P(4)$, and then on the assumption $P(n)$ is a theorem, $n \geq 4$, prove that
    $P(n + 1)$ is a theorem.]

4. The Generalized Associative, Distributive, and Commutative Laws

We have considered ordered pairs (or "2-tuples") and ordered triples
(or "3-tuples") of real numbers in earlier chapters. We now wish to extend this to the concept of n-tuples of real numbers for every $n \in N$.

The idea of a 2-tuple is that there is a first and a second real number.
Or in a 3-tuple, there is a first, a second, and a third. Thus if (a,b,c) is a
3-tuple, we may think of a assigned to the first position, b to the second,
and c to the third. That is, to 1 we assign the real number a, to 2 the number b, and to 3 the number c.

A 3-tuple may then be regarded as a rule assigning to each of the natural numbers 1, 2, and 3 a real number. If we denote by 'a_1' the real number assigned to 1, by 'a_2' the real number assigned to 2, and by 'a_3' the real number assigned to 3, then the corresponding 3-tuple is designated '(a_1,a_2,a_3).'

It is this idea which leads us to a definition of an n-tuple.

Definition 5. An n-tuple of real numbers is a rule assigning to each $i \in N$ with $1 \leq i \leq n$ a real number a_i. We denote such an n-tuple by '$(a_1,a_2, \ldots ,a_n)$.'

With each n-tuple $(a_1, \ldots ,a_n)$ in R we wish to define a sum

$$a_1 + \cdots + a_n$$

of the real numbers $a_1, \ldots ,a_n$.

Definition 6.
(a) A sum of a 1-tuple (a_1) is the element a_1 itself.
(b) $a_1 + \cdots + a_{k+1} = (a_1 + \cdots + a_k) + a_{k+1}$.

Thus $a_1 + a_2 + a_3$ is defined by (b) to be $(a_1 + a_2) + a_3$. Once a meaning for $a_1 + a_2 + a_3$ is known, again by (b),

$$a_1 + a_2 + a_3 + a_4 = (a_1 + a_2 + a_3) + a_4$$

These are seen to agree with our earlier definitions.

In Definition 6, in place of R we could have used any set, and in place of $+$ any binary operation.

Example 5. Let $Q = \{a, b, c, d\}$ and $\circ$ the binary operation of Table 8.1.

Table 8.1

$\circ$	a	b	c	d
a	a	b	c	d
b	c	b	c	a
c	d	a	b	c
d	a	c	d	a

Then

$$
\begin{aligned}
a \circ b \circ c \circ b &= (a \circ b \circ c) \circ b \\
&= [(a \circ b) \circ c] \circ b \\
&= (b \circ c) \circ b \\
&= c \circ b \\
&= a
\end{aligned}
$$

One may consider a different insertion of parentheses:

$$(a \circ b) \circ (c \circ b) = b \circ a$$
$$= c$$

Thus in this example, $a \circ b \circ c \circ b \neq (a \circ b) \circ (c \circ b)$.

Example 6. A product of k real numbers can be defined analogously to the sum of k real numbers.

In Definition 6 we defined a sum of $a_1, \ldots, a_n$. Let $i \in N$ with $1 \leq i < n - 1$ ($n \geq 3$). Then the sum $a_1 + \cdots + a_i$ is defined as is the sum $a_{i+1} + \cdots + a_n$. [These sums correspond, respectively, to the i-tuple $(a_1, \ldots, a_i)$ and $(a_{i+1}, \ldots, a_n)$. The latter is an $(n-i)$-tuple (since $i < n, n - i \in N$), in which a_{i+1} is assigned to $1, \ldots, a_{i+(n-i)} = a_n$ to $n - i$.] The question arises as to whether the sum of these two real numbers, i.e.,

$$(a_1 + \cdots + a_i) + (a_{i+1} + \cdots + a_n)$$

is equal to $a_1 + \cdots + a_n$, as defined in Definition 6. Note that $a_1 + \cdots + a_n = (a_1 + \cdots + a_{n-1}) + a_n$, which is the case $i = n - 1$. This is the reason for our restriction $i < n - 1$.

Theorem 26. (The Generalized Associative Law). Let $i \in N$ with $1 \leq i < n - 1$ and $n \geq 3$. Then $(a_1 + \cdots + a_i) + (a_{i+1} + \cdots + a_n) = a_1 + \cdots + a_n$.

Proof: We use induction. According to the ordinary associative law of addition, $a_1 + (a_2 + a_3) = (a_1 + a_2) + a_3$. The right side is $a_1 + a_2 + a_3$ by definition, and the left side is the case $i = 1$, which is the only case to consider if $1 \leq i < 3 - 1$.

Assume the theorem has been proved for $n = k$. Let $1 \leq i < (k+1) - 1$; i.e., $1 \leq i < k$. We must show $a_1 + \cdots + a_{k+1} = (a_1 + \cdots + a_i) + (a_{i+1} + \cdots + a_{k+1})$.

Since $i < k$, then $i + 1 \leq k$ (cf. Exercise 20), and we have

$(a_1 + \cdots + a_i) + (a_{i+1} + \cdots + a_{k+1})$
$= (a_1 + \cdots + a_i) + [(a_{i+1} + \cdots + a_k) + a_{k+1}]$ by Def. 6
$= [(a_1 + \cdots + a_i) + (a_{i+1} + \cdots + a_k)] + a_{k+1}$ by A2, the ordinary associative law of addition
$= (a_1 + \cdots + a_k) + a_{k+1}$ by inductive hypothesis if $i < k - 1$, and by Def. 6 if $i = k - 1$
$= a_1 + \cdots + a_{k+1}$ by Def. 6

We remark that the proof of Theorem 26 used only the ordinary associative law of addition. The same argument, therefore, applies to any set with a binary operation which is associative. In particular, we therefore shall take the generalized associative law of multiplication in R to be a theorem. Thus in any expression in R involving only the binary operation of addition, or only the binary operation of multiplication, we may insert or remove parentheses as we please.

Example 7. Let $P(r)$ be the proposition that the sum of the first r natural numbers is one-half the product of r and $r+1$; i.e., $1+2+\cdots+r=\dfrac{r(r+1)}{2}$. Thus

$$P(4) \text{ states that } 1+2+3+4=\frac{4(4+1)}{2}$$

$$P(2) \text{ states: } 1+2=\frac{2(2+1)}{2}$$

$$P(1) \text{ states: } 1=\frac{1(1+1)}{2}$$

$$P(k) \text{ states: } 1+2+\cdots+k=\frac{k(k+1)}{2}$$

$$P(t^2) \text{ states: } 1+2+\cdots+t^2=\frac{t^2(t^2+1)}{2}$$

Proof: (a) That $P(1)$ is true can be seen by inspection.

      (b) Assume $P(n)$ is a theorem:

$$1+2+\cdots+n=\frac{n(n+1)}{2}$$

Then adding $n+1$ to both sides, we obtain

$$1+2+\cdots+n+(n+1)=\frac{n(n+1)}{2}+(n+1)$$
$$=\frac{n^2+n+2n+2}{2}$$
$$=\frac{n^2+3n+2}{2}$$
$$=\frac{(n+1)(n+2)}{2}$$

and this is $P(n+1)$. Hence $P(r)$ is a theorem for all $r \in N$.

Example 8. Let $P(r)$ be the proposition: If $a_1, \ldots, a_r \in P$, then $a_1 \ldots a_r \in P$. Then $P(r)$ is a theorem for all $r \in N$.

Proof: (a) $P(1)$ states that if $a_1 \in P$, then $a_1 \in P$, and this is clearly so.

      (b) Assume $P(n)$ to be true. Suppose $a_1, a_2, \ldots, a_n, a_{n+1} \in P$. Then by $P(n)$, $a_1 \ldots a_n \in P$. Since $a_1 \ldots a_n$ and a_{n+1} are positive, it follows from $\mathcal{O}_2$ that $(a_1 \ldots a_n)a_{n+1} = a_1 \ldots a_{n+1} \in P$. Hence $P(n+1)$ is proved.

Example 9. The same argument as in Example 8 applies to the sum of any number of positive real numbers. One uses $\mathcal{O}_1$ instead of $\mathcal{O}_2$.

Theorem 27. If $a, b_1, \ldots, b_r \in R$, then

$$a(b_1+\cdots+b_r)=ab_1+\cdots+ab_r$$
$$(b_1+\cdots+b_r)a=b_1a+\cdots+b_ra$$

(This is the generalized distributive law of multiplication with respect to addition.)

Proof: (a) For $r = 1$, the theorem is obvious.

(b) $a(b_1 + \cdots + b_{n+1})$

$$= a[(b_1 + \cdots + b_n) + b_{n+1}] \qquad \text{Def. 6}$$
$$= a(b_1 + \cdots + b_n) + ab_{n+1} \qquad \text{D (the ordinary distributive law)}$$
$$= (ab_1 + \cdots + ab_n) + ab_{n+1} \qquad \text{Inductive hypothesis}$$
$$= ab_1 + \cdots + ab_{n+1} \qquad \text{Def. 6}$$

Similarly, $(b_1 + \cdots + b_r)a = b_1 a + \cdots + b_r a$. Or also, this follows by applying the commutative law to the rule just proved above.

We wish, next, to state and prove the generalized commutative law of addition (and of multiplication). This is a generalization of the results established in Chapter 5, stating that a sum (or product) of three, four, five, or six terms does not depend upon the order in which the terms appear. Thus $a_1 + a_2 + a_3 = a_1 + a_3 + a_2 = a_2 + a_1 + a_3$, etc.

Theorem 28. Let $P(r)$ be the proposition that for all $a_1, a_2, \ldots, a_r \in R$ the sum of these r numbers is independent of the order in which it is performed. Then $P(r)$ is a theorem for all $r \in N$ (generalized commutative law of addition).

Proof: (1) $P(1)$ is clearly true.

(2) Assume $P(n)$ has been proved for some $n \in N$, $n \geq 1$.

Let $b_1, \ldots, b_{n+1}$ be any rearrangement of $a_1, \ldots, a_{n+1}$.

(a) If $b_{n+1} = a_{n+1}$, then $b_1, \ldots, b_n$ is a rearrangement of $a_1, \ldots, a_n$ so that by $P(n)$, $a_1 + \cdots + a_n = b_1 + \cdots + b_n$ and hence

$$a_1 + \cdots + a_n + a_{n+1} = b_1 + \cdots + b_n + b_{n+1}.$$

(b) Assume $b_{n+1} \neq a_{n+1}$. Then $b_i = a_{n+1}$ for some i with $1 \leq i \leq n$. The sum $b_1 + \cdots + b_n$ will not be changed if we interchange b_i and b_1 by $P(n)$. Thus we may assume $b_1 = a_{n+1}$. Now

$$b_1 + b_2 + \cdots + b_{n+1} = b_1 + (b_2 + \cdots + b_{n+1})$$
$$= (b_2 + \cdots + b_{n+1}) + b_1$$

Now since $b_1 = a_{n+1}$, it follows that $b_2, \ldots, b_{n+1}$ is a rearrangement of $a_1, \ldots, a_n$. Hence by $P(n)$, $b_2 + \cdots + b_{n+1} = a_1 + \cdots + a_n$, so that

$$(b_2 + \cdots + b_{n+1}) + b_1 = (a_1 + \cdots + a_n) + a_{n+1},$$

or

$$b_1 + \cdots + b_{n+1} = a_1 + \cdots + a_{n+1}.$$

Hence $P(n + 1)$ is established, and the generalized commutative law of addition is proved.

Remark: A similar argument yields the generalized commutative law of multiplication in R.

Exercises

29 Let $P(r)$ be the proposition: If $a_1, \ldots, a_r, b_1, \ldots, b_r \in R$ and $a_1 > b_1, \ldots, a_r > b_r$, then $a_1 + \cdots + a_r > b_1 + \cdots + b_r$.

(a) Write out $P(1)$, $P(2)$, $P(3)$, $P(4)$, $P(5)$, and $P(s)$.

(b) Prove $P(r)$ for all $r \in N$.

30. Let $P(r)$ be the proposition:

$$1^2 + 2^2 + \cdots + r^2 = \frac{r(r+1)(2r+1)}{6}$$

(a) State $P(1)$, $P(2)$, $P(3)$, $P(4)$, and $P(5)$.

(b) Verify that the propositions in (a) are theorems.

(c) Prove that $P(r)$ is a theorem for all $r \in N$.

31. (i) Let $P(n)$ be the proposition

$$2 + 4 + \cdots + 2n = n(n+1)$$

(a) State $P(1)$, $P(2)$, $P(3)$, $P(4)$, and $P(13)$.

(b) Prove $P(n)$ for all $n \in N$.

(ii) Let $P(t)$ be the proposition

$$1 + 3 + \cdots + (2t - 1) = t^2$$

(a) State $P(1)$, $P(2)$, $P(8)$, $P(2k)$, $P(k^2)$, and $P(2k - 1)$.

(b) Prove $P(t)$ for all $t \in N$.

32. Let $a, \lambda \in R$, $\lambda \neq 1$. Prove that $a + a\lambda + \cdots + a\lambda^n = \dfrac{a - a\lambda^{n+1}}{1 - \lambda}$ where $n \in N$.

33. (a) If $a_1, \ldots, a_n$ are negative real numbers, prove $a_1 + \cdots + a_n$ is negative.

(b) If $a_1, \ldots, a_n$ are in N, prove $a_1 + \cdots + a_n$ and $a_1 a_2 \cdots a_n$ are in N.

5. The Method of Mathematical Induction (Second Principle)

5.1   Basic Theorem

In applying the first principle of induction (cf. Theorem 4), we were able to use the inductive hypothesis $P(n)$ in presenting a proof for $P(n + 1)$. Actually, we shall see that we could even have used $P(k)$ for all $k \in N$ with $k < n + 1$ to prove $P(n + 1)$. That is, this latter procedure would also prove that $P(r)$ is a theorem for all $r \in N$. The fact that this is so will be based on the following:

Theorem 34. Let S be a subset of N satisfying the following conditions:

(a) $1 \in S$;

(b) If $1, 2, \ldots, n$ are elements of S, then $n + 1 \in S$.

Then $S = N$.

Proof: Let $T = \{x \in N / x \notin S\}$. Suppose $T \neq \varnothing$. Then T has a least element, say m. By (a), $1 \notin T$ so that $m \neq 1$.

If $k \in N$, and $k < m$, then $k \notin T$, so that $k \in S$. Hence $1, 2, \ldots, m - 1$ are elements of S, so that by (b) $m \in S$. This contradicts the fact that $m \in T$. Therefore, T could not have been nonempty, and $T = \varnothing$. Thus, $S = N$.

5.2   Recursive Definitions (Continued)

We discussed recursive definitions in Section 2.2. There one defined a concept involving $n + 1$ in terms of the definition for n.

By Theorem 34 we see that we can also define a concept for each $r \in N$ by defining it for $r = 1$, and by defining it for $r = n + 1$ on the assumption that it has already been defined for $r = 1, 2, \ldots, n$.

Example 10. We define a_r for $r \in N$ as follows:
(a) $a_1 = 1$;
(b) $a_{n+1} = a_1 + \cdots + a_n$.
Thus

$$a_2 = a_1 = 1$$
$$a_3 = a_1 + a_2 = 1 + 1 = 2$$
$$a_4 = a_1 + a_2 + a_3 = 1 + 1 + 2 = 4$$
$$a_5 = 1 + 1 + 2 + 4 = 8$$

Example 11. We define b_r for $r \in N$ as follows:
(a) $b_1 = 1$;
(b) $b_2 = 2$;
(c) $b_{n+1} = b_{n-1} + b_n$, $n \geq 2$.
Thus

$$b_3 = b_1 + b_2 = 1 + 2 = 3$$
$$b_4 = b_2 + b_3 = 2 + 3 = 5$$
$$b_5 = b_3 + b_4 = 3 + 5 = 8$$

Analogous to Exercise 23, we can give definitions for all $n \in J$ with $n \geq m$ for any fixed $m \in J$.

Example 12. Define a_r for $r \in J$ and $r \geq -3$ as follows:
(a) $a_{-3} = 2$;
(b) $a_{n+1} = a_n + 3$ (for $n \geq -3$).
Then

$$a_{-2} = a_{-3} + 3 = 2 + 3 = 5$$
$$a_{-1} = a_{-2} + 3 = 5 + 3 = 8$$
$$a_0 = a_{-1} + 3 = 8 + 3 = 11$$
$$a_1 = 14 \qquad a_2 = 17 \qquad \text{etc.}$$

Example 13. Define a_r for $r = 0, 1, \ldots$ as follows:
(a) $a_0 = -1$;
(b) $a_1 = 1$;
(c) $a_{n+1} = a_{n-1}a_n$, $n \geq 1$.
Then

$$a_2 = a_0 a_1 = -1$$
$$a_3 = a_1 a_2 = -1$$
$$a_4 = a_2 a_3 = 1 \qquad \text{etc.}$$

Exercises

35. Define c_r for $r \in N$ as follows:
(a) $c_1 = -1$;
(b) $c_{n+1} = c_1 \cdot c_2 \cdots c_n$.
Compute c_1, c_2, c_3, c_4, and c_5.

36. Define d_r for $r \in N$ as follows:

(a) $d_1 = 0$;

(b) $d_2 = -1$;

(c) $d_{n+1} = d_{n-1} \cdot d_n + d_{n-1}$.

Compute d_1, d_2, d_3, d_4, and d_5.

5.3 The Second Principle of Mathematical Induction

Theorem 37. (Second Principle of Mathematical Induction). Suppose $P(r)$ is a proposition stated for the natural number r. Suppose further that:

(1) $P(1)$ is a theorem.

(2) If $P(k)$ is a theorem for all $k \in N$ with $k \leq n$, then $P(n + 1)$ is a theorem.

Then $P(r)$ is a theorem for all $r \in N$.

As in Exercise 24, we may replace (1) by "$P(m)$ is a theorem for any fixed $m \in J$." The statement then becomes "$P(r)$ is a theorem for all $r \in J$ with $r \geq m$."

Example 14. Let $P(r)$ be the proposition: r can be written as the product of a finite number of primes in N. Then $P(r)$ is a theorem for all $r \in N$ with $r \geq 2$.

Proof: (1) $P(2)$ is a theorem by Exercise 21a.

(2) Suppose $n \in N$ and $n \geq 2$. Assuming $P(k)$ has been proved for all $k \in N$ with $2 \leq k \leq n$, we must prove $P(n + 1)$.

(a) If $n + 1$ is a prime, then $P(n + 1)$ is a theorem, since then $n + 1$ can be written as a product of one prime.

(b) If $n + 1$ is not a prime, then $n + 1 = ab$ where $a,b \in N$ and neither a nor b are 1 (or hence $n + 1$). By Exercise 14, $1 < a < n + 1$, $1 < b < n + 1$. By Exercise 20, $2 \leq a \leq n$, $2 \leq b \leq n$.

We therefore may assume $P(a)$ and $P(b)$ to have been proved, so that a and b can be written as the product of a finite number of primes. If $a = p_1 \cdots p_s$ and $b = q_1 \cdots q_t$, then

$$n + 1 = ab = p_1 \cdots p_s q_1 \cdots q_t$$

This establishes $P(n + 1)$, so that $P(r)$ is a theorem for all $r \in N$ with $r \geq 2$.

6. Cardinality of Finite Sets

In Definition 5 we stated the meaning of an n-tuple of real numbers for $n \in N$. We could as easily have given the definition of an n-tuple of any set. Thus an n-tuple of a set X is a rule assigning to each $i \in N$ with $1 \leq i \leq n$ an element a_i of X. As before, we denote such an n-tuple by '$(a_1, \ldots, a_n)$.'

Definition 7. If, in the above, each of the elements $a_1, \ldots, a_n$ are distinct from one another, we say that the subset $\{a_1, \ldots, a_n\}$ of X has n elements; or also that the *cardinality* of $\{a_1, \ldots, a_n\}$ is n. In particular, if

$X = \{a_1, \ldots, a_n\}$, the cardinality of X is n. If $X = \emptyset$, we say X has cardinality 0, or has 0 elements.

Definition 8. If X is a set whose cardinality is n for some $n \in N$, or if $X = \emptyset$, we call X a *finite* set. A set which is not finite is said to be *infinite*.

The following theorem is well known to one's intuitive knowledge of finite sets, but we give a proof by induction.

Theorem 38. Let X and Y be finite sets of cardinality m and n, respectively, and suppose that $X \cap Y = \emptyset$. Then $X \cup Y$ has cardinality $m + n$.

Proof: We use induction on n.
  (1) Suppose X has m elements and Y has 1 element. Then $X = \{a_1, \ldots, a_m\}$ and $Y = \{b_1\}$. The rule assigning to i the element a_i if $1 \leq i \leq m$, and to $m + 1$ the element b_1 shows that $X \cup Y$ has $m + 1$ elements.
  (2) Suppose X has m elements and Y has $k + 1$ elements. Then $X = \{a_1, \ldots, a_m\}$ and $Y = \{b_1, \ldots, b_{k+1}\}$. Let $Y_0 = \{b_1, \ldots, b_k\}$. Then Y_0 has k elements. By our inductive hypothesis, $X \cup Y_0$ has $m + k$ elements. But then $(X \cup Y_0) \cup \{b_{k+1}\}$ has $(m + k) + 1 = m + (k + 1)$ elements. Hence $X \cup Y$ has $m + (k + 1)$ elements.

Theorem 39. Let X and Y be finite sets of cardinality m and n, respectively. Then $X \times Y$ has cardinality mn.

Proof: We use induction on n.
  (1) Suppose X has m elements and Y has 1 element. Then $X = \{a_1, \ldots, a_m\}$, $Y = \{b_1\}$. The rule assigning to each i the element (a_i, b_1), $1 \leq i \leq m$, shows that $X \times Y$ has $m = m \cdot 1$ elements.
  (2) Suppose X has m elements and Y has $k + 1$ elements. Then $X = \{a_1, \ldots, a_m\}$, $Y = \{b_1, \ldots, b_{k+1}\}$. Let $Y_0 = \{b_1, \ldots, b_k\}$. Then $X \times Y = (X \times Y_0) \cup \{(a_1, b_{k+1}), \ldots, (a_m, b_{k+1})\}$. $X \times Y_0$ has mk elements by our inductive hypothesis. $\{(a_1, b_{k+1}), \ldots, (a_m, b_{k+1})\}$ has m elements by the argument of part (1). By Theorem 38, $X \times Y$ has $mk + m$ or $m(k + 1)$ elements.

Theorems 38 and 39 can be generalized to any finite number of sets. We give the generalization of Theorem 38, and leave that of Theorem 39 to Exercise 44.

Theorem 40. Let $X_1, \ldots, X_r$ be a finite number of sets, with $r \in N$, having cardinalities $n_1, \ldots, n_r$, respectively, and suppose $X_i \cap X_j = \emptyset$ for $i \neq j$. Then $X_1 \cup \cdots \cup X_r$ has $n_1 + \cdots + n_r$ elements.[2]

Proof: For $r = 1$, the result is obvious. Assume the theorem has been proved for $r = k$. Let $X_1, \ldots, X_{k+1}$ be $k + 1$ sets satisfying the hypotheses. Then

---

[2] The meaning of '$X_1 \cup \cdots \cup X_r$' is given in Definition 6 according to the remark following that definition.

$$X_1 \cup \cdots \cup X_{k+1} = (X_1 \cup \cdots \cup X_k) \cup X_{k+1} \qquad \text{Def. 6}$$

But $X_1 \cup \cdots \cup X_k$ has $n_1 + \cdots + n_k$ elements by inductive hypothesis, and X_{k+1} has n_{k+1} elements by hypothesis. By Theorem 38, $X_1 \cup \cdots \cup X_{k+1}$ has $(n_1 + \cdots + n_k) + n_{k+1}$ elements; i.e., $n_1 + \cdots + n_{k+1}$ elements.

We have defined what it means for a set to have n elements. But it still remains to check, on the basis of this definition, that a set cannot have two different cardinalities.

Theorem 41. Suppose X has cardinality m and also cardinality n. Then $m = n$.

Proof: We are given that there exists a rule assigning to each i with $1 \leq i \leq n$ an element $a_i \in X$, and that $X = \{a_1, \ldots, a_n\}$, where the elements $a_1, \ldots, a_n$ are all distinct. Similarly, there is also a rule assigning to each i with $1 \leq i \leq m$ an element $b_i \in X$; also $X = \{b_1, \ldots, b_m\}$ and $b_1, \ldots, b_m$ are all distinct.

If $b_m \neq a_n$, we may determine $c_1, \ldots, c_m$ with $X = \{c_1, \ldots, c_m\}$, $c_1, \ldots, c_m$ distinct, and $c_m = a_n$. Namely, suppose $b_h = a_n$. Then assign to each i with $1 \leq i \leq m$ the element c_i, where

$$c_i = \begin{cases} b_i & \text{if } i \neq h \text{ and } i \neq m \\ b_m & \text{if } i = h \\ b_h & \text{if } i = m \end{cases}$$

Hence we may assume to begin with that

$$X = \{a_1, \ldots, a_n\} = \{b_1, \ldots, b_m\}$$

where $b_m = a_n$, since otherwise we may replace $\{b_1, \ldots, b_m\}$ by $\{c_1, \ldots, c_m\}$ as constructed above.

We now prove the theorem by induction on m.
(1) If $m = 1$, then $\{a_1, \ldots, a_n\} = \{b_1\}$, where $b_1 = a_n$. But since $a_1, \ldots, a_n$ are distinct, we must have $n = 1$.
(2) Assume $m = k + 1$:

$$\{a_1, \ldots, a_n\} = \{b_1, \ldots, b_{k+1}\}$$

Then $n \neq 1$, since otherwise the argument in (1) shows $k + 1 = 1$. Since $a_n = b_{k+1}$, we have

$$\{a_1, \ldots, a_{n-1}\} = \{b_1, \ldots, b_k\}$$

and this is a set of cardinality $n - 1$ and k. By our inductive hypothesis, $n - 1 = k$. Hence $n = k + 1$, and the theorem is proved.

In Chapter 1 we discussed the power set $[X]$ of a set X. If X has n elements, we shall soon be in a position to prove that $[X]$ has 2^n elements. We shall first investigate, however, the number of subsets of X having a given number of elements. For example, if $X = \{a_1, a_2, a_3, a_4\}$, then X has 1 subset having 0 elements, namely, $\emptyset$; X has 4 subsets having 1 element, namely, $\{a_1\}$, $\{a_2\}$, $\{a_3\}$, and $\{a_4\}$; X has 6 subsets having 2 elements, namely, $\{a_1,a_2\}, \{a_1,a_3\}, \{a_1,a_4\}, \{a_2,a_3\}, \{a_2,a_4\}$, and $\{a_3,a_4\}$; X has 4 subsets having 3 elements, namely, $\{a_1,a_2,a_3\}$, $\{a_1,a_2,a_4\}$, $\{a_1,a_3,a_4\}$, and $\{a_2,a_3,a_4\}$; and finally X has 1 subset having 4 elements, namely, $\{a_1,a_2,a_3,a_4\}$.

Definition 9. The number of subsets having cardinality r of a set X having cardinality n is called *the combinations of n things r at a time and* is denoted by $C(n,r)$.[3]

We have shown above that $C(4,0) = 1$, $C(4,1) = 4$, $C(4,2) = 6$, $C(4,3) = 4$, and $C(4,4) = 1$. It then follows that $[X]$ has

$$C(4,0) + C(4,1) + C(4,2) + C(4,3) + C(4,4)$$

elements; i.e., $1 + 4 + 6 + 4 + 1$, or 16 elements. In general, if X has n elements, then $[X]$ will have

$$C(n,0) + C(n,1) + C(n,2) + \cdots + C(n,n)$$

elements. This follows from Theorems 40 and 41 (and, of course, Definition 9).

We shall prove that $C(n,r) = \dfrac{n!}{r!(n-r)!}$. This will be true if $r = 0$, provided that we define $0! = 1$.

For example,

$$C(4,0) = \frac{4!}{0!4!} = 1$$

$$C(4,1) = \frac{4!}{1!3!} = \frac{4 \cdot 3!}{3!} = 4$$

$$C(4,2) = \frac{4!}{2!2!} = \frac{4 \cdot 3 \cdot 2!}{2!2!} = 6$$

$$C(4,3) = \frac{4!}{3!1!} = 4$$

$$C(4,4) = \frac{4!}{4!0!} = 1$$

In Definition 4(b) [i.e., $(n+1)! = (n+1)n!$], it is assumed that $n \in N$. If one defines $0! = 1$, Definition 4(b) remains correct if $n = 0$.

Thus the following definition includes Definition 4.

Definition 10. We define $k!$ for all $k \in J$ with $k \geq 0$ as follows:
(a) $0! = 1$;
(b) $(n+1)! = (n+1)n!$

To prove $C(n,r) = \dfrac{n!}{r!(n-r)!}$, we shall need the following result.

---

[3] Among other notations found in the literature are C_r^n, $_nC_r$, and $C_{n,r}$.

Theorem 42. Suppose $r,n \in N$ and $r \leq n$. Then

$$\frac{n!}{r!(n-r)!} + \frac{n!}{(r-1)!(n-r+1)!} = \frac{(n+1)!}{r!(n+1-r)!}$$

Before proving this theorem, we give several examples.

Example 15. In Exercise 7, one showed $\dfrac{6!}{2!4!} = 15, \dfrac{6!}{3!3!} = 20$, and $\dfrac{7!}{3!4!} = 35$. Thus

$\dfrac{6!}{3!3!} + \dfrac{6!}{2!4!} = \dfrac{7!}{3!4!}$. This is the case $n = 6$, $r = 3$ of Theorem 42.

Example 16. $\dfrac{5!}{1!4!} + \dfrac{5!}{0!5!} = \dfrac{6!}{1!5!}$, since the left side is $5 + 1$ and the right side is 6.

This is the case $n = 5$, $r = 1$.

Remark: Note that under the hypotheses of Theorem 42, the conclusion involves terms which have been defined. For if $r \leq n$, then either $r < n$, in which case $n - r$ is in N; or $r = n$ in which case $n - r = 0$. In either case $(n - r)!$ has been defined. Also $n - r + 1 \in N$, so that $(n - r + 1)!$ is defined.

Proof of Theorem 42:

$$\frac{n!}{r!(n-r)!} + \frac{n!}{(r-1)!(n-r+1)!}$$

$$= \frac{n!}{r(r-1)!(n-r)!} + \frac{n!}{(r-1)!(n-r+1)(n-r)!}$$

$$= \frac{n!(n-r+1) + n!r}{r(r-1)!(n-r+1)(n-r)!}$$

$$= \frac{n!(n-r+1+r)}{r!(n+1-r)!}$$

$$= \frac{(n+1)n!}{r!(n+1-r)!}$$

$$= \frac{(n+1)!}{r!(n+1-r)!}$$

Theorem 43. Let r and n be nonnegative integers with $r \leq n$. Then $C(n,r) = \dfrac{n!}{r!(n-r)!}$. That is, if X is a set having n elements, the number of subsets having r elements is $\dfrac{n!}{r!(n-r)!}$, where $0 \leq r \leq n$ in J.

Proof: We use induction on the number of elements in X.

(1) Let X be a set with 0 elements. Thus $X = \varnothing$. Then we must have $r = 0$ since $0 \leq r \leq n$. The number of subsets of X having 0 elements is 1, namely, $\varnothing$. Hence $C(0,0) = 1$. But $\dfrac{n!}{r!(n-r)!} = \dfrac{0!}{0!0!} = 1$ for $r = n = 0$.

Hence the formula holds in this case.

(2) Assume the theorem holds for n, and let X be a set of cardinality $n + 1$.

(a) $C(n+1,0) = 1$, since the only subset of X with 0 elements is the empty set.

(b) $C(n+1,n+1) = 1$, since the only subset of X with $n+1$ elements is X itself.

(c) $\dfrac{(n+1)!}{0!(n+1-0!)} = 1$, which checks with (a), so that the formula holds for $r = 0$.

(d) $\dfrac{(n+1)!}{(n+1)!((n+1)-(n+1))!} = \dfrac{(n+1)!}{(n+1)!0!} = 1$, which checks with (b), so that the formula holds for $r = n+1$.

(e) To prove the theorem completely, it remains to consider the case $1 \leq r \leq n$. We are given $X = \{a_1, \ldots, a_{n+1}\}$. Let $X_0 = \{a_1, \ldots, a_n\}$, so that X_0 has cardinality n. Let A be a subset of X having r elements. If A does not contain a_{n+1}, then A is a subset of X_0. If A does contain a_{n+1}, then we may write $A = A_0 \cup \{a_{n+1}\}$, where A_0 is a subset of X_0 of cardinality $r-1$.

Thus the subsets of X having r elements are those of X_0 having r elements together with those of X_0 having $r-1$ elements with a_{n+1} added. That is,

$$C(n+1,r) = C(n,r) + C(n,r-1)$$

But the right side can be computed by our inductive hypothesis:

$$C(n,r) + C(n,r-1) = \frac{n!}{r!(n-r)!} + \frac{n!}{(r-1)!(n-r+1)!}$$

$$= \frac{(n+1)!}{r!(n+1-r)!} \quad \text{by Th. 42}$$

Hence $C(n+1,r) = \dfrac{(n+1)!}{r!(n+1-r)!}$. But this is just our formula for the case $n+1$, and the theorem is proved.

Corollary. $C(n,r) + C(n,r-1) = C(n+1,r);\ r \leq n$ in N.

Proof: This was demonstrated in part (e) of the proof. Or one may replace each term in Theorem 42 according to Theorem 43.

Exercises

44. (a) If $X_1, \ldots, X_r$ are r sets, for $r \in N$, define $X_1 \times \cdots \times X_r$ by induction.

(b) If, in (a), $X_1, \ldots, X_r$ are finite sets having $n_1, \ldots, n_r$ elements, respectively, prove that $X_1 \times \cdots \times X_r$ has $n_1 \cdots n_r$ elements.

45. Verify Theorems 42 and 43 in the following cases:

(a) $r = 2$, $n = 4$.   (d) $r = 4$, $n = 6$.

(b) $r = 1$, $n = 4$.   (e) $r = 4$, $n = 7$.

(c) $r = 1$, $n = 5$.   (f) $r = 5$, $n = 5$.

46. Prove $C(n,r) = C(n,n-r)$. (*Hint:* Use Theorem 43.)

47. Let A consist of the ten members of a club.
  (a) How many distinct subcommittees of three can be formed?
  (b) How many distinct subcommittees of at most three can be formed? (Include the vacuous subcommittee.)
  (c) How many distinct subcommittees of more than seven can be formed?
  (d) How many of at least seven?
  (e) How many less than two?

48. If a deck of cards consists of 52 cards, and a bridge hand of 13 cards, how many distinct bridge hands are there?

7. Further Applications of Mathematical Induction

The next theorem is known as the *Binomial Theorem*. It gives a formula for computing $(a + b)^n$, for $n \in N$. For example,

$$(a + b)^2 = a^2 + 2ab + b^2$$
$$(a + b)^3 = a^3 + 3a^2b + 3ab^2 + b^3$$
$$(a + b)^4 = a^4 + 4a^3b + 6a^2b^2 + 4ab^3 + b^4$$

By trying further examples ($n = 5,6, \ldots$), one expects the formula for $(a + b)^n$ to be of the form

$$(a + b)^n = a^n + (\ \ )a^{n-1}b^1 + (\ \ )a^{n-2}b^2 + \cdots + (\ \ )a^1b^{n-1} + b^n$$

where in the parentheses appear certain integers. Actually the coefficient of $a^{n-r}b^r$ turns out to be $\dfrac{n!}{r!(n-r)!}$, which we have seen is $C(n,r)$.

Theorem 49. Let $a,b \in R$ and $n \in N$. Then

$$(a + b)^n = C(n,0)a^n + C(n,1)a^{n-1}b + \cdots + C(n,r)a^{n-r}b^r + \cdots + C(n,n)b^n$$

(the Binomial Theorem).

Proof: (1) The theorem holds for $n = 1$, since it states in this case that

$$(a + b)^1 = C(1,0)a^1 + C(1,1)b^1$$

and one sees that one obtains $a + b$ on the left and on the right.
  (2) We assume the theorem for n. That is, we assume

$$(a + b)^n = C(n,0)a^n + C(n,1)a^{n-1}b + \cdots + C(n,n)b^n$$

Multiply both sides by $a + b$.

$(a + b)(a + b)^n$
$= (a + b)[C(n,0)a^n + C(n,1)a^{n-1}b + \cdots + C(n,n)b^n]$
$= a[C(n,0)a^n + C(n,1)a^{n-1}b + \cdots + C(n,n)b^n]$
$\quad + b[C(n,0)a^n + C(n,1)a^{n-1}b + \cdots + C(n,n)b^n]$ by D
$= [C(n,0)a^n \cdot a + C(n,1)a^{n-1} \cdot a \cdot b + \cdots + C(n,n) \cdot a \cdot b^n]$

$+ [C(n,0)a^nb + C(n,1)a^{n-1}b \cdot b + \cdots + C(n,n)b^n \cdot b]$ by the generalized distributive law

$= [C(n,0)a^{n+1} + C(n,1)a^nb + \cdots + C(n,n)ab^n]$
$\quad + [C(n,0)a^nb + C(n,1)a^{n-1}b^2 + \cdots + C(n,n)b^{n+1}]$ by Def. 3

$= C(n,0)a^{n+1} + (C(n,1) + C(n,0))a^nb + \cdots + (C(n,n) + C(n,n-1))ab^n$
$\quad + C(n,n)b^{n+1}$ by the generalized commutative and associative laws of addition, and D

$= C(n,0)a^{n+1} + C(n+1,1)a^nb + \cdots + C(n+1,n)ab^n + C(n,n)b^{n+1}$ by the corollary to Theorem 43

$= C(n+1,0)a^{n+1} + C(n+1,1)a^nb + \cdots + C(n+1,n)ab^n + C(n+1,n+1)b^{n+1}$
since $C(n+1,0) = C(n,0) = C(n,n) = C(n+1,n+1) = 1$

This proves the theorem for $n + 1$, and the binomial theorem is proved.

Corollary. If X is a set of cardinality n, then $[X]$ has cardinality 2^n.

Proof: $[X]$ has cardinality

$$C(n,0) + C(n,1) + \cdots + C(n,n)$$

But by the binomial theorem,

$$2^n = (1 + 1)^n = C(n,0)1^n + C(n,1)1^{n-1} \cdot 1 + \cdots + C(n,n) \cdot 1^n$$
$$= C(n,0) + C(n,1) + \cdots + C(n,n)$$
$$= \text{the cardinality of } [X]$$

In expanding $(a + b)^n$ according to the binomial theorem, the integers $C(n,0), C(n,1), \ldots, C(n,n)$ are known as the *binomial coefficients*. We shall write the binomial coefficients for $(a + b)^1$, $(a + b)^2$, $(a + b)^3$, and $(a + b)^4$ on separate lines as follows:

$$\begin{array}{ccccccc}
& & & 1 & & & \\
(a+b)^1: & & & 1 & 1 & & \\
(a+b)^2: & & 1 & 2 & 1 & & \\
(a+b)^3: & & 1 & 3 & 3 & 1 & \\
(a+b)^4: & 1 & 4 & 6 & 4 & 1 &
\end{array}$$

The 1 appearing on the first line refers to $(a + b)^0$, which will later be defined to be 1. In the line for $(a + b)^4$, the 6 arises from $C(4,2)$. Now $C(4,2) = C(3,1) + C(3,2)$. $C(3,1)$ and $C(3,2)$ appear on the previous line to the left and to the right of the 6. Thus one adds 3 and 3 on the previous line to obtain 6. This procedure works in general since $C(n,r-1) + C(n,r) = C(n+1,r)$. Thus to obtain the coefficients for $(a + b)^5$, one begins with 1. Then adding the first two coefficients of $(a + b)^4$ yields 5, the second coefficient of $(a + b)^5$. Similarly $4 + 6$ yields the third coefficient of $(a + b)^5$, etc.:

$$1 \quad 5 \quad 10 \quad 10 \quad 5 \quad 1$$

The coefficients are always symmetric—the same whether one starts with the first or the last—since $C(n,r) = C(n,n - r)$ by Exercise 46.

The array of coefficients, when arranged in the above manner, is known as the *Pascal triangle*.

We conclude this section with several results (Theorems 50 to 52) which will be useful in later chapters.

Theorem 50. Let $a_1, \ldots ,a_r,b_1, \ldots ,b_s \in R$, where $r,s \in N$. Then

$$(a_1 + \cdots + a_r)(b_1 + \cdots + b_s)$$

$$= a_1b_1 + \cdots + a_1b_s + a_2b_1 + \cdots + a_2b_s + \cdots + a_rb_1 + \cdots + a_rb_s$$

Proof: We use induction on r.
(1) For $r = 1$, this follows from the generalized distributive law.
(2) Assume the theorem proved for $r = n$.

$$(a_1 + \cdots + a_n + a_{n+1})(b_1 + \cdots + b_s)$$
$$= [(a_1 + \cdots + a_n) + a_{n+1}](b_1 + \cdots + b_s)$$
$$= (a_1 + \cdots + a_n)(b_1 + \cdots + b_s) + a_{n+1}(b_1 + \cdots + b_s) \qquad \text{by D}$$
$$= [a_1b_1 + \cdots + a_1b_s + \cdots + a_nb_1 + \cdots + a_nb_s] + a_{n+1}(b_1 + \cdots + b_s)$$
by inductive hypothesis
$$= [a_1b_1 + \cdots + a_1b_s + \cdots + a_nb_1 + \cdots + a_nb_s] + (a_{n+1}b_1 + \cdots + a_{n+1}b_s)$$
by the generalized distributive law

This proves the result for $n + 1$ (the parentheses may be removed by the generalized associative law), so that the theorem is proved.

Theorem 51. $a^n - b^n = (a - b)(a^{n-1} + a^{n-2}b + \cdots + ab^{n-2} + b^{n-1})$ for all $a,b \in R$ and $n \in N$ with $n \geq 2$.

For $n = 2$, this states $a^2 - b^2 = (a - b)(a^1 + b^1)$;
$\qquad n = 3: a^3 - b^3 = (a - b)(a^2 + ab + b^2)$;
$\qquad n = 4: a^4 - b^4 = (a - b)(a^3 + a^2b + ab^2 + ab^3)$.

Proof: We may prove this directly (i.e., without the use of induction):

$$(a - b)(a^{n-1} + a^{n-2}b + \cdots + ab^{n-2} + b^{n-1})$$
$$= a \cdot a^{n-1} + a \cdot a^{n-2}b + \cdots + a \cdot ab^{n-2} + ab^{n-1} + (-b)a^{n-1} + (-b)a^{n-2}b$$
$$+ \cdots + (-b)ab^{n-2} + (-b)b^{n-1} \qquad \text{by Th. 50}$$
$$= a^n + a^{n-1}b + \cdots + a^2b^{n-2} + ab^{n-1} - a^{n-1}b - a^{n-2}b^2 - \cdots - ab^{n-1} - b^n$$
$$= a^n + (a^{n-1}b + (-a^{n-1}b)) + \cdots + (ab^{n-1} + (-ab^{n-1})) - b^n \qquad \text{by the generalized commutative and associative laws of addition}$$
$$= a^n - b^n$$

Remark: Because a proposition is stated in terms of the natural number r does not mean one must use an inductive proof. Indeed, we suggest that the student try to prove the above by induction, and see what happens. An inductive proof involves making use of $P(k)$ for one or more $k \leq n$, in order to establish $P(n + 1)$ [as well as, of course, proving $P(1)$ or $P(m)$ for some $m \in J$]. If one establishes $P(n + 1)$ without making use of such an inductive hypothesis, he is really giving a direct proof.

Theorem 52. Let $\alpha \in R$ with $\alpha > 1$. Suppose $a_0, a_1, \ldots, a_r$ are $r + 1$ real numbers, where $0 \leq a_i \leq \alpha - 1$ for $i = 0, 1, \ldots, r$. (That is, $0 \leq a_0 \leq \alpha - 1, 0 \leq a_1 \leq \alpha - 1, \ldots, 0 \leq a_r \leq \alpha - 1$.) Then

$$\alpha^{r+1} > a_r \alpha^r + a_{r-1} \alpha^{r-1} + \cdots + a_1 \alpha^1 + a_0$$

Proof: We use induction on r.

(1) For $r = 0$, the statement is that

$$\alpha^1 > a_0$$

which is given.

(2) We wish to show that the theorem is true for $r = n + 1$; that is:

$$\alpha^{n+2} > a_{n+1} \alpha^{n+1} + a_n \alpha^n + \cdots + a_1 \alpha + a_0$$

where we may assume the theorem to have been proved for $0 \leq k \leq n$. Thus we know that

(a) $\alpha^{n+1} > a_n \alpha^n + \cdots + a_1 \alpha + a_0$.
   Since $\alpha - 1 \geq a_{n+1} \geq 0$, multiplying both sides by α^{n+1} yields
(b) $(\alpha - 1)\alpha^{n+1} \geq a_{n+1}\alpha^{n+1}$
   Adding (a) and (b) we obtain

$$\alpha^{n+2} > a_{n+1}\alpha^{n+1} + a_n \alpha^n + \cdots + a_1 \alpha + a_0$$

For instance, Example 3 shows that

$$8^4 > 6 \cdot 8^3 + 7 \cdot 8^2 + 5 \cdot 8 + 3$$

Exercises

53. Multiply:

(a) $(x + y - 2)(x^2 - y + 1)$.
(b) $(a_1 + a_2 + a_3 + a_4)(b_1 + b_2 + b_3)$.

54. Factor $x^5 - 1$ as in Theorem 51.

55. Expand the following according to the binomial theorem:

(a) $(x + y)^6$.   (b) $(x - y)^6$.   (c) $(a + b)^8$.   (d) $(a - b)^8$.

56. In the expansion of $(a + b)^n$ the coefficient of $a^{n-r}b^r$ is $C(n,r)$. This is the $(r + 1)$st term in the expansion.

(a) What is the third coefficient in $(a + b)^{10}$? The eighth coefficient?
(b) What is the coefficient of $a^2 b^{48}$ in $(a + b)^{50}$?
(c) Does $42130a^{42}b^{10}$ appear as a term in $(a + b)^{60}$? Justify your answer.

57. If a set has 9 elements, how many elements does its power set have?

8. The Theory of Positive Integral Exponents

If $a \in R$ and n is a positive integer, we have defined a^n. We call n the exponent and a the base in a^n. It shall be our aim in the sequel to give a meaning to a^α, where α is any real number. We shall do this in such a way that the theorems on exponents continue to hold. It will be necessary, for this purpose, to restrict a to be positive.

In this section we consider exponents which are positive integers and allow a to be any real number. We are then able to prove the following:

Theorem 58. Let $a,b \in R$, and $m,n \in N$. Then

(1) $a^m \cdot a^n = a^{m+n}$

(2) $\dfrac{a^m}{a^n} = \begin{cases} a^{m-n} & \text{if } m > n \\ 1 & \text{if } m = n \\ \dfrac{1}{a^{n-m}} & \text{if } m < n \end{cases}$

     where $a \neq 0$

(3) $(a^m)^n = a^{mn}$

(4) $(ab)^n = a^n b^n$

(5) $\left(\dfrac{a}{b}\right)^n = \dfrac{a^n}{b^n}$ where $b \neq 0$

Proof: (1) Let $P(r)$ be the proposition that $a^m \cdot a^r = a^{m+r}$ for all $a \in R$ and all $m \in N$.

    (a) $P(1)$ states $a^m \cdot a^1 = a^{m+1}$, which is true by Definition 3.

    (b) Assume $P(n)$; we give a proof for $P(n+1)$:

$$\begin{aligned} a^m \cdot a^{n+1} &= a^m \cdot (a^n \cdot a) & \text{by Def. 3} \\ &= (a^m \cdot a^n)a \\ &= a^{m+n} \cdot a & \text{by } P(n) \\ &= a^{m+n+1} & \text{by Def. 3} \end{aligned}$$

    This establishes $P(n+1)$, and hence (1).

(2) Suppose $m > n$. Then $m - n \in N$ by Theorem 18 and a^{m-n} is defined.

$$\begin{aligned} a^n \cdot a^{m-n} &= a^{n+(m-n)} & \text{by part (1)} \\ &= a^m \end{aligned}$$

Hence $a^{m-n} = \dfrac{a^m}{a^n}$ (cf. Exercise 9).

The remaining cases ($m = n$ and $m < n$) are left as exercises (cf. Exercise 59).

(3) Let $P(r)$ be the proposition that $(a^m)^r = a^{mr}$ for all $a \in R$, $m \in N$.

    (a) $P(1)$ states $(a^m)^1 = a^{m \cdot 1}$, which is clearly so.

    (b) Assume $P(n)$. Then

$$\begin{aligned} (a^m)^{n+1} &= (a^m)^n \cdot (a^m) & \text{Def. 3} \\ &= a^{mn} \cdot a^m & P(n) \\ &= a^{mn+m} & \text{by part (1)} \\ &= a^{m(n+1)} \end{aligned}$$

    which establishes $P(n+1)$.

(4) and (5) are left as exercises (cf. Exercise 59).

Exercises

59. Prove the following:
  (a) Theorem 58(2) for $m = n$ and $m < n$.
  (b) Theorem 58(4).
  (c) Theorem 58(5).

60. (a) Expand $(a^m + b^n)^p$ for $m,n,p \in N$ and $a,b \in R$.

  (b) Expand $\left(2^9 + \dfrac{1}{2^{13}}\right)^8$ and simplify. (You need not compute powers of 2.)

61. Prove: If $a \in R$ and $0 < a < 1$, then $0 < a^n < a$ for all $n \in N$ with $n > 1$.

62. Prove $n^2 > n$ for all $n \in N$ with $n > 1$.

63. Let $a \in P$ and $m,n \in N$. Prove:
  (a) For $a > 1$: $a^m > a^n$ if and only if $m > n$.
  (b) For $0 < a < 1$: $a^m > a^n$ if and only if $m < n$.

64. Suppose $m,n \in N$ and $m > 1$, $n > 1$. Prove $n^m > n$.

65. If $a,b \in P$, prove that $a < b$ if and only if $a^n < b^n$ where $n \in N$.

9. The Peano Postulates

In this chapter we have defined the set N of natural numbers. The following are among the results one can establish concerning natural numbers:

  (1) $1 \in N$.
  (2) If $a \in N$, then $a + 1 \in N$. We call $a + 1$ the successor of a.
  (3) If $a,b \in N$ and if $a + 1 = b + 1$, then $a = b$.
  (4) There is no natural number n for which $n + 1 = 1$. (That is, $0 \notin N$.)
  (5) If M is a subset of N such that
    (a) $1 \in N$,
    (b) $a \in N$ implies $a + 1 \in N$,
    then $M = N$.

To prove these results, one uses the definition of N and the previous properties concerning the real numbers.

What is interesting about the above five statements is that all the properties of the natural numbers are derivable from them. That is, instead of starting with the real-number system and defining the particular subset which constitutes the natural numbers, Giuseppi Peano (1858–1932) assumed the existence of a set (whose elements are to be called the natural numbers) in which '1' and 'successor' were taken to be primitive terms. The postulates he gave were:

  (1) $1 \in N$.
  (2) For each $a \in N$, there exists exactly one successor in N, which we shall denote by a^+.
  (3) If $a^+ = b^+$, then $a = b$.

(4) 1 is not the successor of any natural number.

(5) If M is a subset of N such that

    (a) $1 \in N$,

    (b) $a \in N$ implies $a^+ \in N$,

    then $M = N$.

The fifth postulate is the so-called *induction postulate*.

We should remark that Blaise Pascal (1623–1662) was the first to formulate explicitly the principle of mathematical induction.[4]

Now as we said, one can derive all the properties of N—for example, those established in this chapter—from the Peano postulates. In such a development, one would have to define addition and multiplication along the way. One could then *construct* the set J of integers and develop results in J. (In the laboratory exercise following Chapter 10, we shall outline how, from the real numbers, a larger system of numbers—called the *complex numbers*—can be constructed.) Once one develops suitable theorems within J, one can then construct the set of rational numbers. And finally, one can then construct from the rational numbers a larger system of numbers—called the *real numbers*—and now *prove as theorems* what we have taken to be postulates (including the postulate stated in Chapter 10). For this rigorous development from the Peano postulates for the natural numbers to the construction and properties of the real and complex numbers, we refer the reader to E. G. H. Landau's book, *Foundations of Analysis*, Chelsea, New York, 1951.

The student may now have become aware of the chronology involved in one's study of mathematics today. He begins somewhere in the middle, where he is given enough assumptions so that he can develop from them as many results as possible. With further study, he reaches the unsolved problems, and hopefully makes his contribution in proving theorems. This is one frontier toward which one proceeds. At the same time, however, he reaches further back into the foundations. Thus after assuming postulates for the reals, later in his work he learns how to obtain the reals from assumptions concerning the rationals. Still later he reaches the Peano postulates, and after that derives the Peano postulates from the *theory of sets*. At this end—that is, at the foundations—he reaches another frontier. Thus there are professional mathematicians working at each end of the structure today. And as with trees, each end consists of many ends.

---

[4] Cf. Tobias Dantzig, *Number, the Language of Science*, p. 71, Doubleday (Anchor Books), New York, 1930.

chapter ix

ARITHMETIC OF NATURAL
NUMBERS AND POLYNOMIALS

In this chapter we apply our previous theory to derive the addition and multiplication tables for the set of natural numbers. In so doing we unfold the reasoning involved behind the usual algorithms (calculating procedures) for addition, subtraction, multiplication, and division. At the outset of the chapter, we establish a notation for the natural numbers (based on Theorem 2). We do this both for base ten (the familiar notation) and for bases other than ten.

Some of the reasoning used in deriving algorithms for the arithmetic of natural numbers can also be applied to the addition, subtraction, multiplication, and division of certain algebraic expressions called *polynomials*.

At the conclusion of the chapter, we give a proof of the Fundamental Theorem of Arithmetic, as well as a proof of the theorem that there are infinitely many prime natural numbers.

In Chapter 6 we assumed (1) AN, (2) MN, (3) $0 \notin N$, (4) NR, and finally the Fundamental Theorem of Arithmetic. For at that point we had not yet defined the set N of natural numbers. In Chapter 8 this definition was given, and (3) and (4) were then consequences. In this chapter (1), (2), and the Fundamental Theorem of Arithmetic are derived. Hence had we deferred Chapter 6, as we could have, the development thus far would depend upon the postulates given in Chapters 5 and 7. The list of postulates for R will be completed in the next chapter.

1. Notation for Natural Numbers

1.1 Base Ten

The usual notation used to designate natural numbers involves the use of "base 10." In this base, one uses only the symbols '0,' '1,' '2,' '3,' '4,' '5,' '6,' '7,' '8,' and '9' in the designation of any natural number. For example, 2306, 100, and 919 involve only the foregoing symbols. These symbols are defined formally as follows:

Definition 1. $2 = 1 + 1, 3 = 2 + 1, 4 = 3 + 1, 5 = 4 + 1, 6 = 5 + 1, 7 = 6 + 1,$ $8 = 7 + 1,$ and $9 = 8 + 1.$ These numbers are called, respectively, "two, three, four, five, six, seven, eight, and nine."

Definition 2. The number $9 + 1$ is called "ten."

By 2306, we mean $2(\text{ten})^3 + 3(\text{ten})^2 + 0 \cdot (\text{ten})^1 + 6$. Thus 2306 is defined completely by means of terms which have previously been defined. Similarly, 5895 means $5(\text{ten})^3 + 8(\text{ten})^2 + 9(\text{ten})^1 + 5$; also 72010 means $7(\text{ten})^4 + 2(\text{ten})^3 + 0 \cdot (\text{ten})^2 + 1(\text{ten})^1 + 0$.

Of course, 002306 is seen to be equal to 2306. Thus one usually uses the shorter designation, where the first symbol is distinct from 0.

10 means $1(\text{ten})^1 + 0$, so that the notation for ten, when working in base ten, is '10.'

By Exercise (8, 33b), all the above numbers are in N. The question arises as to whether one obtains all natural numbers in this way. The fact that this is so is contained in Theorem 2, which when stated for base ten is:

Let $a \in N$. Then

$$a = a_n(\text{ten})^n + a_{n-1}(\text{ten})^{n-1} + \cdots + a_1(\text{ten})^1 + a_0$$

where $a_n, a_{n-1}, \ldots, a_0$ are each one of the integers $0, 1, 2, 3, 4, 5, 6, 7, 8, 9$, and $a_n \neq 0$. The integers n, a_n, a_{n-1}, $\ldots$, a_0 are uniquely determined by a.

For example, if $a = 72010$, then $n = 4$ and $a_4 = 7$, $a_3 = 2$, $a_2 = 0$, $a_1 = 1$, $a_0 = 0$.

Exercises

In each of the following, we give the natural number a in standard notation. Write the values of n, a_n, a_{n-1}, $\ldots$, a_0.

1. 380.	**4.** 720,031.	**7.** 10,000.
2. 47.	**5.** 10.	**8.** 70,001.
3. 6.	**6.** 1.	**9.** 7,400,293.

1.2   Theoretical Justification

One observes that in the representation of natural numbers considered above, one makes repeated use of a finite number of symbols: namely, 0, 1, 2, 3, 4, 5, 6, 7, 8, and 9 (for base ten). The justification that every natural number can be represented as in the above examples is contained, as we have said, in Theorem 2. For this purpose, we shall need the following important result.

Theorem 1 (Division Algorithm). Let $a, b \in N$. Then $\exists q, r \in J$ with $0 \leq r < b$ and $0 \leq q$ such that

$$a = bq + r \qquad (*)$$

Moreover, q and r are uniquely determined.

This theorem is the basis for the usual process of division. Thus in dividing 74 by 8, one asks how many 8's go into 74. The answer is that there are 9, leaving a remainder of 2:

$$74 = 8 \cdot 9 + 2$$

In this illustration, $a = 74$, $b = 8$, $q = 9$, and $r = 2$.

Proof of Theorem 1:

(a) If $a < b$, then $a = b \cdot 0 + a$ is a representation as given in (*), with $q = 0$ and $r = a$.

(b) Assume $a \geq b$. We consider multiples of b: $1b, 2b, \ldots$. There are some multiples of b which are greater than a, for example, $(a + 1)b$.

Let $T = \{t \in N / tb > a\}$, and let m be the least element of T. Since $a \geq b$, $1 \notin T$ and $m > 1$.

We have $mb > a$, but $(m - 1)b \leq a$. (In the illustration preceding this proof, $m - 1$ would be 9.)

Let $q = m - 1$. Then

$$qb \leq a \qquad \text{and} \qquad (q + 1)b > a$$

(i) Since $qb \leq a$, $a - qb \geq 0$. We set $r = a - qb$, so that $r \geq 0$.

(ii) Since $(q + 1)b > a$, adding $-qb$ to both sides yields

$$(q + 1)b - qb > a - qb$$
$$b > r$$

From (i) and (ii) we have $0 \leq r < b$, and since $r = a - qb$, we have $a = bq + r$.

(c) We now show uniqueness. That is, we show that if

$$a = bq_1 + r_1 \tag{†}$$

with $0 \leq q_1$ and $0 \leq r_1 < b$ ($q_1, r_1 \in J$), then $q = q_1$ and $r = r_1$.

From (*) and (†) we obtain

$$qb + r = q_1 b + r_1$$

Say $q \geq q_1$. Then $(q - q_1)b = r_1 - r$ and $r_1 - r \geq 0$; i.e., $r_1 \geq r$. If $q > q_1$, then $q - q_1 \geq 1$ and $(q - q_1)b \geq b$. Since $(q - q_1)b = r_1 - r$, if we show $r_1 - r < b$, this would be a contradiction. Certainly if $r = 0$, $r_1 - r < b$. Suppose $r > 0$. Then $b > b - r > r_1 - r$. This establishes the contradiction, so that we cannot have $q > q_1$. Hence $q = q_1$, and from $(q - q_1)b = r_1 - r$ we obtain $r = r_1$.

Remark: It follows from the uniqueness part of Theorem 1 that b is a factor of a if and only if $r = 0$.

Definition 3. If $a, b \in N$, then to *divide* a by b means to find the q and r given by Theorem 1. We call q the *quotient* and r the *remainder* of a divided by b.

We shall consider examples of division presently. If one finds q and r, then one can write $\dfrac{a}{b} = q + \dfrac{r}{b}$, where $0 \leqq \dfrac{r}{b} < 1$. For example, 7 divided by 3 is 2 (the quotient) with remainder 1. This means $7 = 3(2) + 1$ or $\frac{7}{3} = 2 + \frac{1}{3}$. One sometimes writes $2 + \frac{1}{3}$ as $2\frac{1}{3}$ (which should not be confused with $2 \cdot \frac{1}{3} = \frac{2}{3}$). At any rate, the representation of a positive rational number $\dfrac{a}{b}$ as $q + \dfrac{r}{b}$ shows that every positive rational number can be written as the sum of a nonnegative integer and a nonnegative rational number less than 1.

We now turn to Theorem 2, which generalizes the idea of representing a natural number in base ten to any base $r \, \epsilon \, N$ with $r > 1$.

Theorem 2. Let $r \, \epsilon \, N, r \neq 1$. Then every $a \, \epsilon \, N$ can be written in the form

$$a = a_n r^n + a_{n-1} r^{n-1} + \cdots + a_1 r + a_0$$

where $a_i \, \epsilon \, J$, $0 \leqq a_i \leqq r - 1$ for $i = 0,1,2, \ldots ,n$, and $a_n \neq 0$.
Moreover, n and $a_0, a_1, \ldots ,a_n$ are uniquely determined by a.

Proof: (α) Let $P(a)$ be the proposition that $a = a_n r^n + \cdots + a_0$ for some $n \, \epsilon \, J$ with $n \geqq 0$ and $a_0, \ldots ,a_n \, \epsilon \, J$ with $0 \leqq a_i \leqq r - 1$, and $a_n \neq 0$.
    (1) Clearly $P(1)$ is a theorem. Namely, take $n = 0$ and $a_0 = 1$.
    (2) Assume $P(k)$ for $k = 1,2, \ldots ,a$. We then prove $P(a + 1)$. $a + 1 = qr + a_0$, where $0 \leqq a_0 < r$ by Theorem 1.
      (a) If $q = 0$, then $a + 1 = a_0$ is a representation of the required type, with $n = 0$.
      (b) If $q \neq 0$, then $q < a + 1$. (Why?) Then by $P(q)$, $q = b_m r^m + \cdots + b_0$, where $0 \leqq b_i \leqq r - 1$, and $b_m \neq 0$. Thus

$$\begin{aligned} a + 1 &= qr + a_0 \\ &= (b_m r^m + \cdots + b_0)r + a_0 \\ &= b_m r^{m+1} + \cdots + b_0 r + a_0 \\ &= a_n r^n + \cdots + a_1 r + a_0 \end{aligned}$$

where $n = m + 1$, $a_n = b_m, \ldots ,a_1 = b_0$.
    Hence $P(a + 1)$ is established.
    (β) It remains to prove uniqueness. Now if there were an element a which did not have a unique representation, there would be a least such (cf. 8, 19), say b.

$$\begin{aligned} b &= a_n r^n + \cdots + a_0 = b_m r^m + \cdots + b_0 \\ &= (a_n r^{n-1} + \cdots + a_1)r + a_0 = (b_m r^{m-1} + \cdots + b_1)r + b_0 \end{aligned}$$

Hence

$$a_n r^{n-1} + \cdots + a_1 = b_m r^{m-1} + \cdots + b_1 \text{ and } a_0 = b_0 \qquad \text{by Th. 1}$$

But $a_n r^{n-1} + \cdots + a_1 < b$ (why?) and hence has a unique representation. So $m = n$, and $a_n = b_n, \ldots, a_1 = b_1$. This means b could not have had two distinct representations, a contradiction. Hence every $a \in N$ has a unique representation.

Definition 4. In the above representation of the natural number a, we call r the *base* or also the *radix*. We write

$$a = (a_n a_{n-1} \cdots a_0)_r$$

if $a = a_n r^n + \cdots + a_0$. If $r = $ ten, it is customary to omit the r. Thus

$$a = (a_n a_{n-1} \cdots a_0)_{\text{ten}} = a_n a_{n-1} \cdots a_0{}^1$$

We shall use the usual names eleven, twelve, and thirteen, etc., for the numbers $(11)_{\text{ten}}$, $(12)_{\text{ten}}$, and $(13)_{\text{ten}}$, regardless of the base we are working in. Thus, although five may have different designations, depending upon the base, we shall always mean by 'five' the number $1 + 1 + 1 + 1 + 1$.

1.3   Bases Other than Ten

To represent natural numbers in the base ten, we needed the symbols $0, 1, 2, \ldots, 9$. In general, to represent natural numbers in the base r, we shall need symbols for $0, 1, \ldots, r - 1$.

Thus in base five, we use $0, 1, 2, 3,$ and 4 as defined in Definition 1.

In base eleven we need $0, 1, 2, 3, 4, 5, 6, 7, 8,$ and 9 and also a symbol for $9 + 1$. We shall use u for $9 + 1$ when working in base eleven.

In base twelve we shall define $v = u + 1$. Here we need the symbols $0, 1, \ldots, 9, u, v$.

$$(324)_{\text{five}} = 3(\text{five})^2 + 2(\text{five}) + 4$$
$$(1u0v)_{\text{twelve}} = 1 \cdot (\text{twelve})^3 + u(\text{twelve})^2 + 0 \cdot (\text{twelve}) + v$$
$$(10)_{\text{five}} = 1 \cdot (\text{five}) + 0, \text{ which is five}$$
$$(10)_{\text{twelve}} = 1 \cdot (\text{twelve}) + 0, \text{ which is twelve}$$
$$(10)_r = 1 \cdot r + 0 \quad \text{or} \quad r$$

Thus we may write

$$(324)'_{\text{five}} = 3 \cdot (10)_{\text{five}}{}^2 + 2(10)_{\text{five}} + 4$$
$$(1u0v)_{\text{twelve}} = 1 \cdot (10)_{\text{twelve}}{}^3 + u \cdot (10)_{\text{twelve}}{}^2 + 0 \cdot (10)_{\text{twelve}} + v$$
$$789 = (789)_{\text{ten}} = 7 \cdot (10)_{\text{ten}}{}^2 + 8 \cdot (10)_{\text{ten}} + 9 = 7(10)^2 + 8(10) + 9$$

We shall now turn to *algorithms* (i.e., methods of calculations) for the addition, subtraction, multiplication, and division of natural numbers.

---

[1] In this notation, $a_n a_{n-1} \cdots a_0$ may be confused with $a_n \cdot a_{n-1} \cdots a_0$. For this reason, one always writes $5 \cdot 9$ (or 5×9, etc.) for 45, rather than writing 59.

2. Addition of Natural Numbers

To add two natural numbers which are represented in base r, one must know first the addition table for $1,2, \ldots ,r - 1$.

2.1   Base Ten

In base ten, $10 = 9 + 1$, $11 = 10 + 1$, $12 = 10 + 2$, $13 = 10 + 3$, $14 = 10 + 4$, $15 = 10 + 5$, $16 = 10 + 6$, $17 = 10 + 7$, $18 = 10 + 8$ by Definition 4.

From $10 = 9 + 1$, we may derive other rules of addition:

$$10 = 9 + 1$$
$$= (8 + 1) + 1 \qquad \text{Def. 1}$$
$$= 8 + (1 + 1)$$
$$= 8 + 2 \qquad \text{Def. 1}$$

This yields $8 + 2 = 10$.

In a similar fashion, one derives $7 + 3 = 10$, $6 + 4 = 10$, and $5 + 5 = 10$. Similar results are obtained from $11 = 10 + 1, \ldots , 18 = 10 + 8$. Or also from $8 + 1 = 9$, $7 + 1 = 8$, etc. By this procedure, one may—in a finite amount of time—derive the addition table shown in Table 9.1.

Table 9.1

+	1	2	3	4	5	6	7	8	9
1	2	3	4	5	6	7	8	9	10
2	3	4	5	6	7	8	9	10	11
3	4	5	6	7	8	9	10	11	12
4	5	6	7	8	9	10	11	12	13
5	6	7	8	9	10	11	12	13	14
6	7	8	9	10	11	12	13	14	15
7	8	9	10	11	12	13	14	15	16
8	9	10	11	12	13	14	15	16	17
9	10	11	12	13	14	15	16	17	18

With this table we can now compute $a + b$ for $a,b \in N$, and $a,b \leq 9$. To compute $a + b$, where either a or b is greater than 9, we shall make use of the (generalized) associative, commutative, and distributive laws to reduce the problem to the above table.

Example 1. Add 321 and 76.

Solution:
$$321 + 76 = (3 \cdot 10^2 + 2 \cdot 10 + 1) + (7 \cdot 10 + 6)$$
$$= 3 \cdot 10^2 + (2 \cdot 10 + 7 \cdot 10) + (1 + 6)$$
$$= 3 \cdot 10^2 + (2 + 7) \cdot 10 + (1 + 6)$$
$$= 3 \cdot 10^2 + 9 \cdot 10 + 7$$
$$= 397$$

Example 2

$$331 + 96 = (3 \cdot 10^2 + 3 \cdot 10 + 1) + (9 \cdot 10 + 6)$$
$$= 3 \cdot 10^2 + (3 \cdot 10 + 9 \cdot 10) + (1 + 6)$$
$$= 3 \cdot 10^2 + (3 + 9) \cdot 10 + (1 + 6)$$
$$= 3 \cdot 10^2 + (12) \cdot 10 + 7$$

But this is not of the form of Theorem 2, since 12 is not less than 10. We therefore continue as follows:

$$331 + 96 = 3 \cdot 10^2 + (1 \cdot 10 + 2) \cdot 10 + 7$$
$$= 3 \cdot 10^2 + (1 \cdot 10^2 + 2 \cdot 10) + 7$$
$$= (3 \cdot 10^2 + 1 \cdot 10^2) + 2 \cdot 10 + 7$$
$$= (3 + 1) \cdot 10^2 + 2 \cdot 10 + 7$$
$$= 4 \cdot 10^2 + 2 \cdot 10 + 7$$
$$= 427$$

A convenient organization for this work is as follows:

$$\frac{\begin{array}{r} 331 \\ 96 \end{array}}{427}$$

One starts from the right column, called the *units* column, going left to the "tens" column, then to the "hundreds" column, etc.

Thus, one begins: $6 + 1 = 7$; then, 3 tens and 9 tens are 12 tens, which is 2 tens and $1(10)^2$, that is, 2 tens and 1 hundred; then, 3 hundreds and the 1 hundred carried over is 4 hundreds.

Example 3. Compute $587 + 80246 + 908$.
Solution:

$$587 + 80246 + 908$$
$$= (5 \cdot 10^2 + 8 \cdot 10 + 7) + (8 \cdot 10^4 + 2 \cdot 10^2 + 4 \cdot 10 + 6) + (9 \cdot 10^2 + 8)$$
$$= 8 \cdot 10^4 + (5 \cdot 10^2 + 2 \cdot 10^2 + 9 \cdot 10^2) + (8 \cdot 10 + 4 \cdot 10) + (7 + 6 + 8)$$
$$= 8 \cdot 10^4 + (5 + 2 + 9)10^2 + (8 + 4)10 + (7 + 6 + 8)$$

This is the basis for writing the numbers in columns:

$$\begin{array}{r} 587 \\ 80246 \\ 908 \end{array}$$

Thus the $(7 + 6 + 8)$ corresponds to the column on the right, the $(8 + 4)$ to the tens column, the $(5 + 2 + 9)$ to the hundreds, and the 8 to the ten thousands column.

We shall work from right to left to imitate the usual algorithm; thus, we first compute $7 + 6 + 8$. This is $13 + 8$:

$$
\begin{array}{rl}
13 & \text{(a) } 3 + 8 = 11, \text{ which is 1 ten and 1} \\
\underline{8} & \text{(b) 1 ten and the 1 ten from (a)} \\
21 & \text{yields 2 tens}
\end{array}
$$

Of course with practice, one learns to do these computations by sight. At any rate, we obtain

$$8 \cdot 10^4 + (5 + 2 + 9)10^2 + (8 + 4)10 + (2 \cdot 10 + 1)$$
$$= 8 \cdot 10^4 + (5 + 2 + 9)10^2 + (8 + 4 + 2)10 + 1$$
$$= 8 \cdot 10^4 + (5 + 2 + 9)10^2 + (1 \cdot 10 + 4)10 + 1$$
$$= 8 \cdot 10^4 + (5 + 2 + 9 + 1)10^2 + 4 \cdot 10 + 1$$
$$= 8 \cdot 10^4 + (1 \cdot 10 + 7)10^2 + 4 \cdot 10 + 1$$
$$= 8 \cdot 10^4 + 1 \cdot 10^3 + 7 \cdot 10^2 + 4 \cdot 10 + 1$$

Thus the answer is 81741.

The theoretical basis for the usual algorithm for addition should now be clear.

Exercises

Compute the following, as in Examples 1, 2, and 3. Check for yourself how your work corresponds to each step of the usual algorithm for addition as outlined after Example 2:

10. $87023 + 2894$.
11. $99 + 999$.
12. $10021 + 473 + 8098$.
13. $732 + 89 + 8634 + 98$.
14. $74 + 3729 + 9600 + 488 + 3969$.

Prove the following (cf. Definitions 1 and 4):

15. $2 + 2 = 4$.
16. $7 + 5 = 12$.
17. $1 + 7 = 8$.
18. $5 + 9 = 14$.
19. $5 + 1 = 6$.

2.2   Other Bases

In other bases, one again needs only the basic addition table.

Example 4. Base eight.

We need the definition: $1 + 1 = 2$, $2 + 1 = 3$, $3 + 1 = 4$, $4 + 1 = 5$, $5 + 1 = 6$, and $6 + 1 = 7$. The base eight is $7 + 1$.

It then follows that $7 + 1 = (10)_{\text{eight}}$, $(11)_{\text{eight}} = (10)_{\text{eight}} + 1$, $(12)_{\text{eight}} = (10)_{\text{eight}} + 2$, $(13)_{\text{eight}} = (10)_{\text{eight}} + 3$, $(14)_{\text{eight}} = (10)_{\text{eight}} + 4$, $(15)_{\text{eight}} = (10)_{\text{eight}} + 5$, $(16)_{\text{eight}} = (10)_{\text{eight}} + 6$, $(17)_{\text{eight}} = (10)_{\text{eight}} + 7$: all by Definition 4. We may then compute the table for 1, 2, 3, 4, 5, 6, and 7.

We obtain Table 9.2, all designations being in base eight.

Table 9.2

+	1	2	3	4	5	6	7
1	2	3	4	5	6	7	10
2	3	4	5	6	7	10	11
3	4	5	6	7	10	11	12
4	5	6	7	10	11	12	13
5	6	7	10	11	12	13	14
6	7	10	11	12	13	14	15
7	10	11	12	13	14	15	16

Let us agree to write the base–eight, in this example–always in the base ten designation, when used as a subscript. Thus we shall write

$$(10)_8 \text{ for } (10)_{\text{eight}}$$
$$(13)_8 \text{ for } (13)_{\text{eight}}$$

Then

$$
\begin{aligned}
(231)_8 + (64)_8 &= [2 \cdot (10)_8{}^2 + 3 \cdot (10)_8 + 1] + [6 \cdot (10)_8 + 4] \\
&= 2 \cdot (10)_8{}^2 + [3 \cdot (10)_8 + 6 \cdot (10)_8] + (1 + 4) \\
&= 2 \cdot (10)_8{}^2 + (3 + 6) \cdot (10)_8 + (1 + 4) \\
&= 2 \cdot (10)_8{}^2 + (3 + 6)(10)_8 + 5 \\
&= 2 \cdot (10)_8{}^2 + [1(10)_8 + 1](10)_8 + 5 \\
&= (2 + 1) \cdot (10)_8{}^2 + 1 \cdot (10)_8 + 5 \\
&= 3 \cdot (10)_8{}^2 + 1 \cdot (10)_8 + 5 \\
&= (315)_8
\end{aligned}
$$

where we worked from right to left to correspond to the usual algorithm. The work is organized as follows:

$$
\begin{array}{r}
(231)_8 \\
(64)_8 \\
\hline
(315)_8
\end{array}
$$

In the units column, we have $1 + 4 = 5$; in the eights column, we have 3 eights and 6 eights are $(11)_8$ eights, i.e., 1 (eight)^2 and 1 eight; then 2 (eight)^2's and the 1 (eight)^2 carried over is 3 (eight)^2's.

One sees there is no difference in the algorithm for base eight and base ten. The principles are the same.

Example 5. To find $(12022)_3 + (21101)_3$, the table we need is Table 9.3. All designations in Table 9.3 are, of course, in base three.

$$
\begin{array}{r}
(12022)_3 \\
(21101)_3 \\
\hline
(110200)_3
\end{array}
$$

Table 9.3

+	1	2
1	2	10
2	10	11

Example 6. We show how to check work in bases other than ten by working in base ten. However, one needs to know how to multiply in base ten (which is first explained in Section 4 on p. 197).

(a) In Example 4, we found

$$(231)_8 + (64)_8 = (315)_8$$

Now

$$(231)_8 = 2(10)_8^2 + 3(10)_8 + 1$$
$$= 2 \cdot 8^2 + 3 \cdot 8 + 1 \qquad \text{in base ten}$$
$$= 128 + 24 + 1$$
$$= 153$$

Similarly,

$$(64)_8 = 6 \cdot 8 + 4 \qquad \text{in base ten}$$
$$= 52$$

Finally,

$$(315)_8 = 3 \cdot 8^2 + 1 \cdot 8 + 5 \qquad \text{in base ten}$$
$$= 192 + 13$$
$$= 205$$

Therefore, we should have $153 + 52 = 205$, and this appears to be so.

(b) In Example 5 we showed $(12022)_3 + (21101)_3 = (110200)_3$.

$$(12022)_3 = 1 \cdot 3^4 + 2 \cdot 3^3 + 2 \cdot 3 + 2 = 81 + 54 + 6 + 2 = 143$$
$$(21101)_3 = 2 \cdot 3^4 + 1 \cdot 3^3 + 1 \cdot 3^2 + 1 = 162 + 27 + 9 + 1 = 199$$
$$(110200)_3 = 1 \cdot 3^5 + 1 \cdot 3^4 + 2 \cdot 3^2 = 243 + 81 + 18 = 342$$

Therefore, we should have $143 + 199 = 342$.

Exercises

20. (a) Write out an addition table for radix four (i.e., for 1, 2, 3) and use it to compute $(10232)_4 + (3133)_4$. Convert to radix ten and check your result.

(b) Compute $(2031)_4 + (333)_4 + (1003)_4$. Check in base ten.

(c) Compute $(32)_4 + (22)_4 + (10)_4 + (300)_4 + (21)_4 + 2$. Check in base ten.

21. (a) Write out a table for base twelve (i.e., for $1,2,3,\dots,9,u,v$) and use it to compute $(29u)_{12} + (v7v)_{12}$. Check in base ten.

(b) Compute $(7804)_{12} + (uu29)_{12} + (v00u)_{12}$. Check in base ten.

22. (a) Write out a table for base two and use it to compute $(10011)_2 + (101101)_2$. Check in base ten.

(b) Compute $(101)_2 + (11)_2 + (10)_2 + 1 + (111)_2$. Check in base ten.

23. (a) Write out a table for base seven and use it to compute $(326)_7 + (1402)_7$. Check in base ten.

   (b) Compute $(442)_7 + (5616)_7 + (6043)_7 + (505)_7$. Check in base ten.

3. Subtraction of Natural Numbers

We consider in this section the algorithm for determining $a - b$ where $a, b \in N$ and $a > b$. [For $a = b$, the answer is 0; and for $a < b$ compute $b - a$; the answer is then $-(b - a)$.]

3.1   Base Ten

Example 7. Find $8761 - 628$.
Solution:

$$8761 - 628 = (8 \cdot 10^3 + 7 \cdot 10^2 + 6 \cdot 10 + 1) - (6 \cdot 10^2 + 2 \cdot 10 + 8)$$
$$= 8 \cdot 10^3 + (7 - 6) \cdot 10^2 + (6 - 2) \cdot 10 + (1 - 8)$$

Now $1 - 8 < 0$. In such a case we add 10, and take it away from the $(6 - 2) \cdot 10$. Thus we obtain

$$8 \cdot 10^3 + (7 - 6) \cdot 10^2 + (6 - 1 - 2) \cdot 10 + (11 - 8)$$

As $11 - 8$ is the unique solution of $8 + x = 11$, we make use of the addition table to obtain 3:

$$8 \cdot 10^3 + (7 - 6) \cdot 10^2 + (6 - 1 - 2) \cdot 10 + 3$$

$$= 8 \cdot 10^3 + (7 - 6) \cdot 10^2 + \left(\begin{matrix} 5 - 2 \\ \text{or} \\ 6 - 3 \end{matrix}\right) \cdot 10 + 3$$

$$= 8 \cdot 10^3 + (7 - 6) \cdot 10^2 + 3 \cdot 10 + 3$$

$$= 8 \cdot 10^3 + 1 \cdot 10^2 + 3 \cdot 10 + 3$$

$$= 8133$$

The work may be organized as follows:

$$\begin{array}{r} 8761 \\ 628 \\ \hline 8133 \end{array}$$

We work from right to left as before. We first ask what added to 8 yields $1 + 10$ (since $1 < 8$), and this is 3. We may then add 1 to 2 or take away 1 from 6 in the tens column to make up for the 10 added in the units column. Thus we either say 3 and what make 6, or 2 and what make 5. This is 3, with no carry over necessary. As $6 + 1 = 7$, we obtain 1 in the hundreds column.

If one prefers to learn a subtraction table, then Table 9.4 may be derived from the addition table and is all that is needed in the above algorithm for subtraction.

Table 9.4

−	1	2	3	4	5	6	7	8	9
1	0								
2	1	0							
3	2	1	0						
4	3	2	1	0					
5	4	3	2	1	0				
6	5	4	3	2	1	0			
7	6	5	4	3	2	1	0		
8	7	6	5	4	3	2	1	0	
9	8	7	6	5	4	3	2	1	0
10	9	8	7	6	5	4	3	2	1
11		9	8	7	6	5	4	3	2
12			9	8	7	6	5	4	3
13				9	8	7	6	5	4
14					9	8	7	6	5
15						9	8	7	6
16							9	8	7
17								9	8
18									9

Example 8. Compute $4876 - 5230$.
Solution

$$5230 - 4876 = (5 \cdot 10^3 + 2 \cdot 10^2 + 3 \cdot 10 + 0) - (4 \cdot 10^3 + 8 \cdot 10^2 + 7 \cdot 10 + 6)$$
$$= (5 - 4) \cdot 10^3 + (2 - 8) \cdot 10^2 + (3 - 7) \cdot 10 + (0 - 6)$$
$$= (5 - 4) \cdot 10^3 + (2 - 8) \cdot 10^2 + (3 - 7 - 1) \cdot 10 + (10 - 6)$$
$$= (5 - 4) \cdot 10^3 + (2 - 8) \cdot 10^2 + (3 - 8) \cdot 10 + 4$$
$$= (5 - 4) \cdot 10^3 + (2 - 8 - 1) \cdot 10^2 + (10 + 3 - 8) \cdot 10 + 4$$
$$= (5 - 4) \cdot 10^3 + (2 - 9) \cdot 10^2 + (13 - 8) \cdot 10 + 4$$
$$= (5 - 4) \cdot 10^3 + (2 - 9) \cdot 10^2 + 5 \cdot 10 + 4$$
$$= (5 - 4 - 1) \cdot 10^3 + (12 - 9) \cdot 10^2 + 5 \cdot 10 + 4$$
$$= 3 \cdot 10^2 + 5 \cdot 10 + 4$$
$$= 354$$

The answer is therefore -354.

Exercises

Compute the following as in Examples 7 and 8. Check for yourself how your work corresponds to each step of the usual algorithm for subtraction as outlined after Example 7.

24. $80012 - 9643$.
25. $6278 - 13724$.
26. $32199 - 4067$.
27. $21101 - 30221$.

3.2 Other Bases

Example 9. Find $(4172)_8 - (277)_8$.
Solution: $(4172)_8$

$$\frac{(277)_8}{(3673)_8}$$

In the units column, we observe $7 + \underline{3} = (12)_8$. In the 10's place, $(10)_8 + \underline{7} = (17)_8$. In the 100's place $3 + \underline{6} = (11)_8$. In the 1000's place, $1 + \underline{3} = 4$.

In working this problem, we suggest that the student try to live within base eight. Thus, to go from 7 to $(12)_8$ involves the steps 7, $(10)_8$, $(11)_8$, and $(12)_8$, which is three steps. Or, 7 is 1 less than the radix, $(12)_8$ is 2 more. Of course, one would eventually learn the basic subtraction table if he continued to work in base eight.

Exercises

Compute the following, and check in base ten.

28. $(6716)_8 - (717)_8$.
29. $(1100010)_2 - (11001)_2$.
30. $(31021)_4 - (2102123)_4$.
31. $(491u)_{12} - (382v)_{12}$.
32. $(924)_{11} - (835)_{11}$.
33. $(23014)_5 - (31123)_5$.

4. Multiplication of Natural Numbers

To multiply two natural numbers using the usual algorithm, one has to know the multiplication table for $1, 2, \ldots, r - 1$.

4.1 Base Ten

Example 10. Compute $(843)(263)$.
Solution

$$(843)(263) = (8 \cdot 10^2 + 4 \cdot 10 + 3)(2 \cdot 10^2 + 6 \cdot 10 + 3)$$

We apply the (generalized) distributive law in the form

$$a(b + c + d) = ab + ac + ad$$

where $a = 8 \cdot 10^2 + 4 \cdot 10 + 3$. Thus we obtain

$$(8 \cdot 10^2 + 4 \cdot 10 + 3)(2 \cdot 10^2) + (8 \cdot 10^2 + 4 \cdot 10 + 3)(6 \cdot 10) + (8 \cdot 10^2 + 4 \cdot 10 + 3) \cdot 3$$
$$= [(8 \cdot 10^2 + 4 \cdot 10 + 3) \cdot 2] \cdot 10^2 + [(8 \cdot 10^2 + 4 \cdot 10 + 3) \cdot 6] \cdot 10$$
$$+ [(8 \cdot 10^2 + 4 \cdot 10 + 3) \cdot 3]$$

We now work within each bracket, starting from the right:

$$(8 \cdot 10^2 + 4 \cdot 10 + 3) \cdot 3 = 24 \cdot 10^2 + 12 \cdot 10 + 9 \qquad \text{using the multiplication}$$
$$\text{table for } 1, 2, \ldots, 9$$

$$= 24 \cdot 10^2 + 1 \cdot 10^2 + 2 \cdot 10 + 9$$
$$= (24 + 1) \cdot 10^2 + 2 \cdot 10 + 9$$
$$= 25 \cdot 10^2 + 2 \cdot 10 + 9$$
$$= 2 \cdot 10^3 + 5 \cdot 10^2 + 2 \cdot 10 + 9$$

Similarly, we see that

$$(8 \cdot 10^2 + 4 \cdot 10 + 3)6 = 5 \cdot 10^3 + 5 \cdot 10 + 8$$
$$(8 \cdot 10^2 + 4 \cdot 10 + 3)2 = 1 \cdot 10^3 + 6 \cdot 10^2 + 8 \cdot 10 + 6$$

Thus

$$(843)(263) = [1 \cdot 10^3 + 6 \cdot 10^2 + 8 \cdot 10 + \underline{6}] \cdot 10^2$$
$$+ [5 \cdot 10^3 + 5 \cdot 10 + 8] \cdot 10 + [2 \cdot 10^3 + 5 \cdot 10^2 + 2 \cdot 10 + 9]$$
$$= (1 \cdot 10^5 + 6 \cdot 10^4 + 8 \cdot 10^3 + 6 \cdot 10^2) + (5 \cdot 10^4 + 5 \cdot 10^2$$
$$+ 8 \cdot 10) + (2 \cdot 10^3 + 5 \cdot 10^2 + 2 \cdot 10 + 9)$$
$$= 168600 + 50580 + 2529$$

One may now add by the method of Section 2:

$$
\begin{array}{r}
2529 \\
50580 \\
168600 \\
\hline
221709
\end{array}
$$

One may organize the procedure as follows:

$$
\begin{array}{r}
843 \\
263 \\
\hline
2529 \leftarrow 1 \\
50580 \leftarrow 2 \\
168600 \leftarrow 3 \\
\hline
221709 \leftarrow 4
\end{array}
$$

On line 1 appears the result of $(843)(3)$. Here we work from right to left, as before. Thus $3 \cdot 3 = 9$, $3(4 \cdot 10) = 12 \cdot 10 = 1 \cdot 10^2 + 2 \cdot 10$. Thus we write 2 and carry the 1 to the 10^2 place. Next, $3 \cdot (8 \cdot 10^2) = 24 \cdot 10^2$; the $1 \cdot 10^2$ carried yields $25 \cdot 10^2 = 2 \cdot 10^3 + 5 \cdot 10^2$. Line 2 indicates the result of multiplying 843 by $6 \cdot 10$, which is $(843 \cdot 6) \cdot 10$. Hence one multiplies $843 \cdot 6$, and places a 0 in the last position. It is now clear how line 3 is obtained, and the addition yields line 4. In practice, one often omits the zeros arising from the 10, 10^2, 10^3, ... Thus

$$
\begin{array}{r}
843 \\
263 \\
\hline
2529 \\
5058 \\
1686 \\
\hline
221709
\end{array}
$$

Also, for easier reading, the practice is to place commas to separate every three figures, beginning from the right:

$$221709 = 221,709$$
$$58104 = 58,104$$

To derive the multiplication table for $1, 2, \ldots, 9$, we give an illustration: $6 \cdot 4 = 6 \cdot (3 + 1) = 6 \cdot 3 + 6$ and the problem reduces to finding $6 \cdot 3$. Similarly, $6 \cdot 3 = 6 \cdot (2 + 1) = 6 \cdot 2 + 6$. Finally, $6 \cdot 2 = 6(1 + 1) = 6 + 6 = 12$.

It is thus clear that on the basis of addition, one can derive the multiplication table.

4.2   Other Bases

Example 11. Find $(312)_4(2032)_4$.
Solution: First observe the multiplication table (Table 9.5).

Table 9.5

	1	2	3
1	1	2	3
2	2	10	12
3	3	12	21

Thus we have

$$
\begin{array}{r}
2032 \\
312 \\
\hline
10130 \\
2032 \\
12222 \\
\hline
1313310
\end{array}
$$

All designations are in base four.

If one wishes to see how this looks in base ten, we have

$$(2032)_4 = 2 \cdot 4^3 + 3 \cdot 4 + 2 = 142$$
$$(312)_4 = 3 \cdot 4^2 + 1 \cdot 4 + 2 = 54$$
$$(1,313,310)_4 = 1 \cdot 4^6 + 3 \cdot 4^5 + 1 \cdot 4^4 + 3 \cdot 4^3 + 3 \cdot 4^2 + 1 \cdot 4 + 0 = 7668$$

Checking, in base ten, we have

$$142$$
$$54$$
$$\overline{568}$$
$$710$$
$$\overline{7668}$$

Exercises

34. Find $(201210)_3(12210)_3$. Convert to radix ten and check your result.

35. Find $(9uv)_{12}(u6)_{12}$. Check in base ten.

36. Find $(78216)_9 \cdot (348)_9$. Check in base ten.

37. Find $(2500)_6 \cdot (103)_6$. Check in base ten.

38. Find $(100110)_2 \cdot (1010)_2$. Check in base ten.

5. Division of Natural Numbers

As stated in Definition 3, to divide a by b means to find q and r of Theorem 1, so that $a = bq + r$, where $0 \leq q$ and $0 \leq r < b$.

If $a < b$, then part (a) of the proof of Theorem 1 applies. That is, the quotient is 0 and the remainder is a.

If $a \geq b$, then we saw in the proof of part (b) of Theorem 1 that

$$qb \leq a < (q + 1)b$$

Thus q is the largest natural number whose product with b remains less than or equal to a.

Once q is determined, one may find r as $a - bq$.

In base ten, if $q = q_n 10^n + q_{n-1} 10^{n-1} + \cdots + q_0$, then in the algorithm presented below, we shall first determine n, then $q_n, q_{n-1}, \ldots, q_0$, and finally r.

5.1   Base ten

Example 12. Divide 23913 by 84.

Solution: (a) We first determine n such that $(84)10^n \leq 23913 < (84)10^{n+1}$. Since $8400 \leq 23913 < 84000$, we see that $n = 2$.

It follows that $10^2 \leq q < 10^3$.

Thus $q = q_2 10^2 + q_1 10^1 + q_0$, where $1 \leq q_2 \leq 9$, $0 \leq q_1 \leq 9$, $0 \leq q_0 \leq 9$. If one writes

$$84\,\overline{)23913}$$

and places the quotient above the 23913, then q_2 appears in the hundreds place, q_1 in the tens, and q_0 in the units:

$$\begin{array}{r} q_2\,q_1\,q_0 \\ 84\overline{)2\ 3\ 9\ 1\ 3} \end{array}$$

(b) Suppose we determine q_2, q_1, q_0, and r as follows:

(i) q_2 as the largest integer such that

   (α) $84(q_2 \cdot 10^2) \leq 23913$

(ii) then q_1 as the largest integer such that

   (β) $84(q_1 \cdot 10) \leq 23913 - 84(q_2 \cdot 10^2)$

(iii) then q_0 as the largest integer such that

   (γ) $84 \cdot q_0 \leq 23913 - 84(q_2 \cdot 10^2) - 84(q_1 \cdot 10)$

(iv) finally, let $r = 23913 - 84(q_2 \cdot 10^2 + q_1 \cdot 10 + q_0)$, so that

$$23913 = 84(q_2 \cdot 10^2 + q_1 \cdot 10 + q_0) + r$$

Since $84 \cdot 10 \cdot 10^2 > 23913$ [by part (a)], we see from (α) that $q_2 \leq 9$. In (ii), if $q_1 \geq 10$, then from (β) we would have

$$84 \cdot 10 \cdot 10 \leq 23913 - 84(q_2 \cdot 10^2)$$

or

$$84(q_2 + 1) \cdot 10^2 \leq 23913$$

contrary to the choice of q_2 in (i). So $q_1 \leq 9$.

In (iii) if $q_0 \geq 10$, then from (γ) we would have

$$84 \cdot 10 \leq 23913 - 84(q_2 \cdot 10^2) - 84(q_1 \cdot 10)$$

or

$$84 \cdot (q_1 + 1) \cdot 10 \leq 23913 - 84(q_2 \cdot 10^2)$$

contrary to the choice of q_1 in (ii).

Finally, from the choice of q_0 in (γ), we may conclude that

$$84(q_0 + 1) > 23913 - 84(q_2 \cdot 10^2) - 84(q_1 \cdot 10)$$

or

$$84 > 23913 - 84(q_2 \cdot 10^2) - 84(q_1 \cdot 10) - 84q_0$$

the right side being r.

Thus this procedure leads to $q = q_2 \cdot 10^2 + q_1 \cdot 10 + q_0$ and r such that $23913 = 84q + r$, $0 \leq q$, $0 \leq r < 84$. By the uniqueness part of Theorem 1, this leads us to the quotient and remainder we are seeking.

In (i), we may try $84 \cdot (1 \cdot 10^2)$, $84 \cdot (2 \cdot 10^2)$, ..., $84 \cdot (9 \cdot 10^2)$, since $q_2 \leq 9$. As soon as one reaches a number larger than 23913, then the preceding one will determine q_2. If all these numbers do not exceed 23913, then $q_2 = 9$.

In (ii) we try $84(1 \cdot 10)$, $84(2 \cdot 10)$, ..., $84(9 \cdot 10)$. As soon as one reaches a number larger than $23913 - 84(q_2 \cdot 10^2)$, then the preceding one will determine q_1.

Finally in (iii), one tries $84 \cdot 1$, $84 \cdot 2$, ..., $84 \cdot 9$. The procedure for finding q_0 is then analogous to the ones for q_1 and q_2.

One may organize the work as follows:

$$
\begin{array}{r}
284 \\
84\overline{)23913} \\
16800 \\
\hline
7113 \\
6720 \\
\hline
393 \\
336 \\
\hline
57
\end{array}
$$

Thus 2 appears in the quotient, since $84(2 \cdot 10^2) = 16800$ and

$$84 \cdot (3 \cdot 10^2) = 25200$$

the latter being too large. Then one subtracts 16800 from 23913 to obtain 7113. Then according to (ii), q_1 is chosen as the largest integer such that $84(q \cdot 10) \leqq 7113$. Since $84(8 \cdot 10) = 6720$ and $84(9 \cdot 10) = 7560$, we see that 9 is too large, and $q_1 = 8$. We then subtract 6720 from 7113 to obtain 393. Now q_0 is determined as in (iii), that is, so that q_0 is the largest integer for which $84q_0 \leqq 393$. We see that $q_0 = 4$, since $4 \cdot 84 = 336$ is less than 393 and $5 \cdot 84 = 420$ is greater than 393. According to (iv), subtracting 336 from 393 must yield r.

The part within the dotted lines is usually omitted.

Thus we have $q = 284$, $r = 57$. That is, $23913 = (84)(284) + 57$, or

$$\frac{23913}{84} = 284 + \frac{57}{84}$$

5.2   Other Bases

Example 13. Divide $(21220111)_3$ by $(10212)_3$.
Solution

$$
\begin{array}{r}
2001 \\
10212\overline{)21220111} \\
21201 \\
\hline
12111 \\
10212 \\
\hline
1122
\end{array}
$$

(a) One determines n as 3, since

$$(10212000)_3 \leqq (21220111)_3 < (102120000)_3$$

(b) Since $2 \cdot (10)_3^3 \cdot (10212)_3 \leqq (21220111)_3$, $q_3 = 2$.
(c) Subtracting $(21201000)_3$ from $(21220111)_3$ yields $(12111)_3$.
(d) Since $1 \cdot (10)_3^2 \cdot (10212)_3 > (12111)_3$, we have $q_2 = 0$.
(e) Since $1 \cdot (10)_3 \cdot (10212)_3 > (12111)_3$, we have $q_1 = 0$.
(f) Finally, $q_0 = 1$.

Although usually abbreviated as above, the solution worked out in more detail would be

$$
\begin{array}{r}
2001 \\
10212\overline{)21220111} \\
21201\dot{0}\dot{0}\dot{0} \\
\hline
121\dot{1}1 \\
0\dot{0}0 \\
\hline
1211\dot{1} \\
0\dot{0} \\
\hline
12111 \\
10212 \\
\hline
1122
\end{array}
$$

One may check in base ten by observing that

$$(21220111)_3 = 5764$$
$$(10212)_3 = 104$$
$$(2001)_3 = 55$$
$$(1122)_3 = 44$$

Thus, dividing 5764 by 104 should yield a quotient of 55 and remainder of 44.

Exercises

39. Divide $(7286)_9$ by $(62)_9$. Check in base ten.
40. Divide $(130123)_4$ by $(13)_4$. Check in base ten.
41. Divide $(4124201)_5$ by $(203)_5$. Check in base ten.
42. Divide $(21uv96)_{12}$ by $(3u0)_{12}$. Check in base ten.

6. Change of Base

Once one knows the algorithms for multiplication and division, it is an easy matter to change from representation of a natural number in one base to that of another.

Example 14. Change $(804)_{ten}$ to a representation in base six.
Solution: Method 1. One must first determine the representation of ten and of the digits appearing in 804 in base six. Thus $8 = (12)_6$, $0 = (0)_6$, $4 = (4)_6$, and $10 = (14)_6$.
[For example, one thinks of 10 as $6 + 4$, or $(10)_6 + (4)_6 = (14)_6$.] Then

$$804 = 8 \cdot 10^2 + 0 \cdot 10 + 4$$
$$= (12)_6 \cdot (14)_6^2 + 0 \cdot (14)_6 + (4)_6$$

One then applies the methods of multiplication and addition to obtain $(3420)_6$.
Method 2. The more usual method is to use division. Thus observe that

$$804 = a_n 6^n + a_{n-1}6^{n-1} + \cdots + a_1 \cdot 6 + a_0$$

since every natural number may be represented in base six. Here we have $0 \leqq a_n < 6, 0 \leqq a_{n-1} < 6, \ldots, 0 \leqq a_0 < 6$. Thus

$$804 = (a_n 6^{n-1} + a_{n-1} 6^{n-2} + \cdots + a_1) \cdot 6 + a_0,$$

so that a_0 must be the remainder upon dividing 804 by 6. The quotient is $a_n 6^{n-1} + \cdots + a_1$. Dividing this quotient by 6 yields remainder a_1 and quotient $a_n 6^{n-2} + \cdots + a_2$, since

$$a_n 6^{n-1} + \cdots + a_2 \cdot 6 + a_1 = (a_n 6^{n-2} + \cdots + a_2) \cdot 6 + a_1.$$

In this way one obtains $a_0, a_1, \cdots$. Thus $6\overline{)804}$ has remainder 0. Hence $a_0 = 0$.

$$
\begin{array}{r}
22 \\
6\overline{)134} \\
12 \\
\overline{14} \\
12 \\
\overline{2}
\end{array}
$$

Hence $a_1 = 2$.

$$
\begin{array}{r}
3 \\
6\overline{)22} \\
18 \\
\overline{4}
\end{array}
$$

Hence $a_2 = 4$.

$$
\begin{array}{r}
0 \\
6\overline{)3} \\
0 \\
\overline{3}
\end{array}
$$

Hence $a_3 = 3$.

$$
\begin{array}{r}
0 \\
6\overline{)0} \\
0 \\
\overline{0}
\end{array}
$$

Hence $a_4 = 0$; similarly $a_5 = 0$, etc. Thus $804 = (3420)_6$.

Example 15. Change $(3420)_6$ to base seven.

Solution: (1) The digits 3, 4, 2, 0, and 6 are unchanged in base seven.

$$(3420)_6 = (3)_7 (6)_7^3 + (4)_7 (6)_7^2 + (2)_7 (6)_7 + (0)_7$$

One then performs the computation on the right in base seven.

(2) A second solution, as in Example 14, is to use division by 7, but expressed in base six: $7 = (11)_6$.

Then the process is as before:

$$
\begin{array}{r}
310 \\
11\overline{)3420} \\
33 \\
\overline{12} \\
11 \\
\overline{10}
\end{array}
$$

Thus $a_0 = 6$ [that is, $(10)_6 = (6)_7$].

$$
\begin{array}{r}
24 \\
11\overline{)310} \\
22 \\
\hline
50 \\
44 \\
\hline
2
\end{array}
$$

Hence $a_1 = 2$.

$$
\begin{array}{r}
2 \\
11\overline{)24} \\
22 \\
\hline
2
\end{array}
$$

Hence $a_2 = 2$.

$$
\begin{array}{r}
0 \\
11\overline{)2} \\
0 \\
\hline
2
\end{array}
$$

Hence $a_3 = 2$.
Clearly $a_4 = 0$, $a_5 = 0$, etc.
Thus $(3420)_6 = (2226)_7 = 2 \cdot 7^3 + 2 \cdot 7^2 + 2 \cdot 7 + 6$.
(3) A third method is to combine the methods of (1) and (2) so as to perform all computations in base ten (or any other base one likes to work in).
(a) Change $(3420)_6$ to base ten.

$$
\begin{aligned}
(3420)_6 &= 3 \cdot 6^3 + 4 \cdot 6^2 + 2 \cdot 6 \\
&= 3(216) + 4(36) + 12 \\
&= 648 + 144 + 12 \\
&= 804
\end{aligned}
$$

(b) Now convert 804 to base seven.

$$
\begin{array}{ll}
804 = 7(114) + 6 & a_0 = 6 \\
114 = 7(16) + 2 & a_1 = 2 \\
16 = 7(2) + 2 & a_2 = 2 \\
2 = 7(0) + 2 & a_3 = 2 \\
0 = 7(0) + 0 & a_4 = 0
\end{array}
$$

So $804 = (2226)_7$.

Exercises

43. Change the following to designations in base ten:
(a) $(35012)_6$.   (d) $(u964)_{11}$.
(b) $(1uvu)_{12}$.   (e) $(53600)_8$.
(c) $(100101001)_2$.

44. The following numbers are designated in base ten. Convert them to bases two, three, five, eight, eleven, and twelve.

(a) 762. (d) 49.
(b) 94001. (e) 6.
(c) 3000. (f) 8.

45. Convert each of the following to the bases indicated. Use all three methods illustrated in the text.

(a) $(72041)_9$ to base four and base eleven.
(b) $(1010011)_2$ to base three and base eight.
(c) $(61200)_7$ to base two and base twelve.
(d) $(196u)_{11}$ to base five and base twelve.

7. Polynomials

In Chapter 6 we added, subtracted, and multiplied such expressions as $2x^2 - x + 1$ and $3x^3 + 2x^2 - 2$ to obtain identities in the variable x over R. The methods are similar to those we used in our preceding work with natural numbers. Thus, using the associative and commutative laws of addition and multiplication, and the distributive law of addition with respect to multiplication (and our work of Chapter 5), one obtains

$$(2x^2 - x + 1) + (3x^3 + 2x^2 - 2) = 3x^3 + (2 + 2)x^2 - x + (1 - 2)$$
$$(2x^2 - x + 1) - (3x^3 + 2x^2 - 2) = -3x^3 + (2 - 2)x^2 - x + (1 + 2)$$
$$(2x^2 - x + 1) \cdot (3x^3 + 2x^2 - 2)$$
$$= (2x^2 - x + 1)3x^3 + (2x^2 - x + 1)2x^2 + (2x^2 - x + 1)(-2)$$

(1) For addition we may work in column form as follows:

$$
\begin{array}{r}
2x^2 - x + 1 \\
3x^3 + 2x^2 + 0 \cdot x - 2 \\
\hline
3x^3 + 4x^2 - x - 1
\end{array}
$$

(2) Subtraction may be referred to addition by considering

$$(2x^2 - x + 1) - (3x^3 + 2x^2 - 2)$$

as

$$(2x^2 - x + 1) + (-3x^3 - 2x^2 + 2)$$

(3) Multiplication may be organized as follows:

$$
\begin{array}{r}
2x^2 - x + 1 \\
3x^3 + 2x^2 + 0.x - 2 \\
\hline
-4x^2 + 2x - 2 \\
4x^4 - 2x^3 + 2x^2 \\
6x^5 - 3x^4 + 3x^3 \\
\hline
6x^5 + x^4 + x^3 - 2x^2 + 2x - 2
\end{array}
$$

The procedures are thus the same as for working with natural numbers in terms of a given base, except that here one does not concern himself with the carryovers. Thus $2x$ remains $2x$, whereas in $2 \cdot 7$ we would write 4 and carry the 1.

These procedures apply to any two "polynomials" in the variable x over R in the sense of the following:

Definition 5. An expression of the type $a_n x^n + a_{n-1} x^{n-1} + \cdots + a_0$ in the variable x over R, where $a_n, a_{n-1}, \ldots, a_0 \in R$, is called a *polynomial* (*in the variable x over R*).[2] The numbers $a_n, a_{n-1}, \ldots, a_0$ are called the *coefficients of the polynomial*. If $a_n \neq 0$, we call n the *degree of the polynomial* and a_n the *leading coefficient*. If the coefficients are all 0, we shall say the polynomial has no degree.[3]

Following are examples of polynomials in the variable x over R, together with their respective degrees:

$5x^4 - \frac{1}{2}x$	Degree 4
$2x^3 - x^2 + x - 1$	Degree 3
6	Degree 0 ⎱ Polynomials of degree 0
0	No degree ⎰ and the zero polynomial are called *constant polynomials*
$6x^8 + 4x^6 - 3x^5 + x - 2$	Degree 8

Thus, we can add, subtract, and multiply polynomials,

$$a_n x^n + \cdots + a_0$$

and

$$b_m x^m + \cdots + b_0$$

using the above procedures. Our main purpose in this section is to consider division of polynomials, and to this end we have the following analogue of Theorem 1:

Theorem 3. Let α and β be polynomials, where β is a nonzero polynomial. Thus $\alpha = a_n x^n + \cdots + a_0$ and $\beta = b_m x^m + \cdots + b_0$, where $b_m \neq 0$. Then there exist polynomials λ and ρ such that

$$\alpha = \beta \lambda + \rho \tag{*}$$

and where either the degree of ρ is less than that of β, or ρ is the zero polynomial.

Theorem 3 is called the *division algorithm for polynomials*.

---

[2] We may also define polynomials over other fields. For the present, however, we shall consider polynomials in which the constants are in R and the variable over R.

[3] It is also current practice to say that the zero polynomial has degree -1.

Proof: (1) If the degree of α is less than that of β, or if α is the zero polynomial, then

$$\alpha = \beta \cdot 0 + \alpha$$

is a representation of the type given in (∗).

(2) Thus, assume the degree of α is greater than or equal to the degree of β.

Let $P(n)$ be the proposition that $\exists \lambda$ and ρ satisfying (∗), n being the degree of α.

If $n = 0$, $\alpha = a_0$ and $\beta = b_0$, where $b_0 \neq 0$. Then let $\lambda = b_0^{-1} \cdot a$ and $\rho = 0$. We then have $\alpha = \beta \lambda + \rho$, where ρ is the zero polynomial, and $P(0)$ is a theorem.

Assume $P(k)$ for all $k < n$. We must then prove $P(n)$. We have $\alpha = a_n x^n + \cdots + a_0$, $\beta = b_m x^m + \cdots + b_0$, $n \geq m$, and $b_m \neq 0$.

$$\alpha - a_n b_m^{-1} x^{n-m} \beta \quad \text{(where } x^{n-m} \text{ means 1 if } n = m)$$

$$= (a_n x^n + \cdots + a_0) - a_n b_m^{-1} x^{n-m}(b_m x^m + \cdots + b_0)$$

$$= a_n x^n + a_{n-1} x^{n-1} + \cdots + a_0 - a_n x^n - a_n b_m^{-1} b_{m-1} x^{n-1} - \cdots - a_n b_m^{-1} b_0 x^{n-m}$$

$$= (a_{n-1} - a_n b_m^{-1} b_{m-1}) x^{n-1} + \cdots$$

Let $\gamma = \alpha - a_n b_m^{-1} x^{n-m} \beta$. Then we have shown that γ is a polynomial of degree less than n or else is the zero polynomial.

(a) If $\gamma = 0$, then $\alpha = a_n b_m^{-1} x^{n-m} \beta$. Thus $P(n)$ holds with $\lambda = a_n b_m^{-1} x^{n-m}$ and $\rho = 0$.

(b) Assume $\gamma \neq 0$, so that γ has a degree which is greater than or equal to zero. Then by our inductive hypothesis

$$\gamma = \beta \bar{\lambda} + \rho$$

where $\rho = 0$, or the degree of ρ is less than that of β. Then

$$\alpha - a_n b_m^{-1} x^{n-m} \beta = \beta \bar{\lambda} + \rho \quad \text{and} \quad \alpha = (a_n b_m^{-1} x^{n-m} + \bar{\lambda})\beta + \rho$$

This proves $P(n)$ with $\lambda = a_n b_m^{-1} x^{n-m} + \bar{\lambda}$.

Definition 6. If α and β are polynomials, and $\beta \neq 0$, then to *divide* α by β means to find the λ and ρ as determined in the proof of Theorem 3. We call λ the *quotient* and ρ the *remainder* of α divided by β.

The proof of Theorem 3 provides the method for dividing two polynomials:

Example 16. Divide $2x^3 - 3x^2 + 1$ by $3x^2 + 2x - 2$.
Solution: Multiply $3x^2 + 2x - 2$ by a polynomial so that the leading coefficient becomes $2x^3$. Thus

$$(3x^2 + 2x - 2)(\tfrac{2}{3}x) = 2x^3 + \tfrac{4}{3}x^2 - \tfrac{4}{3}x$$

Now subtract this from $2x^3 - 3x^2 + 1$:

(1) $$(2x^3 - 3x^2 + 1) - (2x^3 + \tfrac{4}{3}x^2 - \tfrac{4}{3}x) = (-3 - \tfrac{4}{3})x^2 + \tfrac{4}{3}x + 1$$

$$= -\tfrac{13}{3}x^2 + \tfrac{4}{3}x + 1$$

Now work with $-\frac{13}{3}x^2 + \frac{4}{3}x + 1$ and $3x^2 + 2x - 2$ as before.

$$(3x^2 + 2x - 2)(-\tfrac{13}{9}) = -\tfrac{13}{3}x^2 - \tfrac{26}{9}x + \tfrac{26}{9}$$

(2) Then

$$(-\tfrac{13}{3}x^2 + \tfrac{4}{3}x + 1) - (-\tfrac{13}{3}x^2 - \tfrac{26}{9}x + \tfrac{26}{9}) = (\tfrac{4}{3} + \tfrac{26}{9})x + (1 - \tfrac{26}{9})$$

$$= \tfrac{38}{9}x - \tfrac{17}{9}$$

This has degree less than that of $3x^2 + 2x - 2$, so we stop. By (1) we have

$$(2x^3 - 3x^2 + 1) - (3x^2 + 2x - 2)(\tfrac{2}{3}x) = -\tfrac{13}{3}x^2 + \tfrac{4}{3}x + 1$$

By (2) we have

$$(-\tfrac{13}{3}x^2 + \tfrac{4}{3}x + 1) - (3x^2 + 2x - 2)(-\tfrac{13}{9}) = \tfrac{38}{9}x - \tfrac{17}{9}$$

Combining these we have

$$(2x^3 - 3x^2 + 1) - (3x^2 + 2x - 2)(\tfrac{2}{3}x) - (3x^2 + 2x - 2)(-\tfrac{13}{9}) = \tfrac{38}{9}x - \tfrac{17}{9}$$

Hence $2x^3 - 3x^2 + 1 = (3x^2 + 2x - 2)(\tfrac{2}{3}x - \tfrac{13}{9}) + (\tfrac{38}{9}x - \tfrac{17}{9})$. The quotient is therefore $\tfrac{2}{3}x - \tfrac{13}{9}$, the remainder $\tfrac{38}{9}x - \tfrac{17}{9}$.

The work may be organized as follows:

$$
\begin{array}{r}
\tfrac{2}{3}x - \tfrac{13}{9} \leftarrow \text{quotient} \\
3x^2 + 2x - 2\,\overline{)\,2x^3 - 3x^2 + 0\cdot x + 1} \\
\underline{2x^3 + \tfrac{4}{3}x^2 - \tfrac{4}{3}x} \\
-\tfrac{13}{3}x^2 + \tfrac{4}{3}x + 1 \\
\underline{-\tfrac{13}{3}x^2 - \tfrac{26}{9}x + \tfrac{26}{9}} \\
\tfrac{38}{9}x - \tfrac{17}{9} \leftarrow \text{remainder}
\end{array}
$$

Thus $2x^3 - 3x^2 + 1 = (3x^2 + 2x - 2)(\tfrac{2}{3}x - \tfrac{13}{9}) + (\tfrac{38}{9}x - \tfrac{17}{9})$ is an identity in the variable x over R.

Exercises

46. Perform the indicated additions:

(a) $(3x^2 - \tfrac{1}{3}x + 2) + (-\tfrac{4}{3}x + \tfrac{1}{2})$.

(b) $(x^4 - 3x^2 + 2x - 1) + (3x^3 - 2x^2 + 5x + 3) + (-2x^4 - x^3 + x + 1)$.

(c) $(ax^2 + bx + c) + (2x^2 - x + 1)$, where $a,b,c \in R$.

(d) $(7x^5 + 2x^2) + (4x^4 - 3x^3 + x^2 - x) + (-3x^5 + 2x^3 + x - 1)$.

47. Perform the indicated subtractions:

(a) $(3x^2 - \tfrac{1}{3}x + 2) - (\tfrac{4}{3}x - \tfrac{1}{2})$.

(b) $(\tfrac{4}{3}x - \tfrac{1}{2}) - (3x^2 - \tfrac{1}{3}x + 2)$.

(c) $(x^4 - 3x^2 + 2x - 1) - (-3x^3 + 2x^2 - 5x - 3)$.

(d) $(3x^3 - 2x^2 + 5x + 3) - (2x^4 + x^3 - x - 1)$.

(e) $(ax^2 + bx + c) - (-2x^2 + x - 1)$, where $a,b,c \in R$.

(f) $(7x^5 + 2x^2) - (3x^5 - 2x^3 - x + 1)$.

48. Perform the indicated multiplications:

(a) $(3x^2 - \tfrac{1}{3}x + 2)(-\tfrac{4}{3}x + \tfrac{1}{2})$.

(b) $(x^4 - 3x^2 + 2x - 1)(-2x^4 - x^3 + x + 1)$.

    (c) $(ax^2 + bx + c)(2x^2 - x + 1)$.
    (d) $(7x^5 + 2x^2)(4x^4 - 3x^3 + x^2 - x)$.

49. Divide:

    (a) $3x^2 - \frac{1}{3}x + 2$ by $-\frac{4}{3}x + \frac{1}{2}$.
    (b) $-\frac{4}{3}x + \frac{1}{2}$ by $3x^2 - \frac{1}{3}x + 2$.
    (c) $x^5 + x^4 + x^2 + x$ by $x^3 + 1$.
    (d) $x^4 - 3x^2 + 2x - 1$ by $3x^3 - 2x^2 + 5x + 3$.
    (e) $-2x^4 - x^3 + x + 1$ by $2x^2 - x + 1$.
    (f) $ax^2 + bx + c$ by $2x^2 - x + 1$, where $a,b,c \in R$.
    (g) $7x^5 + 2x^2$ by $2x^2 - x + 1$.
    (h) $x^4 - x^3 + 2x^2 - x + 1$ by $x^2 - x + 1$.
    (i) $-3x^5 + 2x^3 + x - 1$ by $x^2 + 1$.
    (j) $7x^5 + 2x^2$ by $-3x^5 + 2x^3 + x - 1$.

50. Divide:

    (a) $3x^2 - \frac{1}{3}x + 2$ by $x - 1$.   (f) $x^3 - 3x^2 + x + 1$ by $x + 1$.
    (b) $x^2 - x - 6$ by $x + 3$.   (g) $x^3 - 3x^2 + x + 1$ by $x - 1$.
    (c) $x^2 - x - 6$ by $x - 3$.   (h) $2x^4 - x^2 + 2x$ by $x + 1$.
    (d) $x^2 - x - 6$ by $x + 2$.   (i) $2x^4 - x^2 + 2x$ by $x - 1$.
    (e) $x^2 - x - 6$ by $x - 2$.

8. Fundamental Theorem of Arithmetic and Euclid's Theorem

8.1 Proof of Fundamental Theorem

    In Chapter 6 we assumed AN and MN; but in the previous sections we have seen that AN and MN are consequences of our field postulates and the ordering postulate. We shall now see that the Fundamental Theorem of Arithmetic (cf. Chapter 6) can also be deduced. It has already been shown that every $a \in N$, $a \neq 1$ has a factorization into primes.[4] It remains to show that this factorization is unique.

    We use induction. Since 2 is prime, $P(2)$ is a theorem. Assume $P(k)$ is a theorem for all $k \in N$ *with* $Q \leq k < a$. We shall deduce that $P(a)$ is also a theorem. This is clearly so if a is prime.

    Thus suppose a is composite and has two factorizations into primes.

$$a = p_1 p_2 \cdots p_r = q_1 q_2 \cdots q_s$$

If any p_i appeared as a q_j, one would obtain two factorizations of a number smaller than a by dropping the p_i and q_j from both sides, contrary to our inductive hypothesis. Hence we may assume that the primes p_i are all distinct from the primes q_j.

    By rearranging if necessary, we may assume $p_1 \leq p_i$, $i = 1,2, \ldots ,r$ and $q_1 \leq q_j$ for $j = 1,2, \ldots ,s$. Since a is composite, $r \geq 2$ and $s \geq 2$. Hence $a \geq p_1 p_2 \geq p_1^2$ and $a \geq q_1 q_2 \geq q_1^2$. Since $p_1 \neq q_1$, we must have $p_1 > q_1$

---

[4] Cf. Example 14 of Chapter 8.

or $q_1 > p_1$. Say $p_1 > q_1$. Then $p_1^2 > p_1 q_1$, and $a \geq p_1^2 > p_1 q_1$ yields $a > p_1 q_1$.

Hence $a - p_1 q_1$ is a positive integer, is less than a, and hence has a unique factorization. Moreover, since p_1 is a factor of a and of $p_1 q_1$, p_1 is a factor of $a - p_1 q_1$ and must appear in *the* factorization of $a - p_1 q_1$. The same is true for q_1. Hence $a - p_1 q_1 = p_1 q_1 b$. Hence if we set $c = 1 + b$, $a = p_1 q_1 c = p_1 p_2 \cdots p_r$. Hence $q_1 c = p_2 \cdots p_r$, and is smaller than a.

Again, by induction, $q_1 c = p_2 \cdots p_r$ has a unique factorization. But this is impossible, since q_1 appears in the factorization on the left but not on the right.

Hence a has only one factorization, and the Fundamental Theorem of Arithmetic is now completely proved.

8.2 Euclid's Theorem

One may ask whether or not there are a finite number of primes. It perhaps seems plausible that very large numbers must be composite. However, due to Euclid, we have the following:

Theorem 4. There are an infinite number of primes.

Proof: Suppose there are only a finite number of primes, say $p_1, p_2, \ldots, p_n$. Let $a = p_1 p_2 \cdots p_n + 1$. Then $a = (p_2 \cdots p_n)p_1 + 1$, and a divided by p_1 yields a remainder of 1. Hence p_1 is not a factor of a. Similarly, neither is p_2, or $p_3, \cdots$, or p_n. But the fundamental theorem states that a has a factorization into primes, so that there must exist a prime factor of a distinct from $p_1, \ldots, p_n$. This contradicts the assumption that $p_1, \ldots, p_n$ were all the primes.

Hence there must be an infinite number of primes.

How can one tell whether a number is prime or not? Of course, he can divide by all numbers preceding it (greater than 1), and see if any lead to a zero remainder (which would mean that it was not prime). However, one can reduce this labor by making the following observation. If a is the number we are testing, and $b^2 > a$, then one need only test whether a has factors less than b. For if $a = a_1 a_2$ and $a_1 \geq b$, then $a_2 < b$, for otherwise $a_1 a_2 \geq b^2 > a$. Hence if a has a factor, it has one which is less than b. Hence it has a prime factor less than b.

For example, if one wishes to determine whether any integer from 2 to 99 is prime, since $10^2 > 99$, one need only check whether 2, 3, 4, 5, 6, 7, 8, and 9 are factors. Now $9 = 3^2$ is not a prime, nor is $8 = 2^3$, $6 = 2 \cdot 3$, $4 = 2^2$. To test whether 3 is a prime, we need only test whether 2 is a factor. But $2^2 > 3$. Hence 3 is prime. For 5 we need only try 2, since $3^2 > 5$. But $5 \div 2$ leaves remainder 1, and 5 is prime. The same holds for 7.

The only primes, then, between 1 and 9 are 2, 3, 5, and 7. It follows that if one lists the integers from 2 to 99, and crosses out all multiples of

2, of 3, of 5, of 7, then what remains are the other primes between 2 and 99.

Exercise

51. List the primes between 100 and 150.

8.3 *Historical Remarks*

The Fundamental Theorem of Arithmetic and the theorem of Euclid are two important theorems from the branch of mathematics known as number theory. This subject is concerned with the study of the natural numbers. Although one of the most difficult subjects of mathematics, many of the problems in number theory still unsolved today can be easily stated in an introductory textbook. One such is the celebrated "Fermat's Last Theorem": [5]

Let n be any natural number greater than 2. Then there are no natural numbers a, b, c such that

$$a^n + b^n = c^n$$

For $n = 2$, such natural numbers can be found. For example, take $a = 3$, $b = 4$, $c = 5$; or also $a = 5$, $b = 12$, $c = 13$. Thus $3^2 + 4^2 = 5^2$ and $5^2 + (12)^2 = (13)^2$. In some notes written in the margin of a book, Fermat writes, referring to the above theorem: "I have found for this a truly wonderful proof, but the margin is too small to hold it." [6]

Actually no proof has yet been found despite a great amount of effort by eminent mathematicians, and it remains a question as to whether Fermat really had discovered a proof. He did present a proof for the case $n = 4$, and Leonard Euler (1707–1783) proved the theorem for $n = 3$. Ernst Eduard Kummer (1810–1893) developed the theory of ideals, a branch of "modern algebra," in his efforts to attack this problem, and much of the recent efforts make use of Kummer's ideas. J. L. Selfridge, C. A. Nichol, and H. S. Vandiver have shown that Fermat's last theorem is true for all prime natural numbers not exceeding 4002. [7]

Another unsolved problem is the long-standing conjecture that there are infinitely many positive integers m such that $m - 1$ and $m + 1$ are prime numbers. For example, $m = 4, 6, 12$ are such integers. Thus 3 and 5, 5 and 7, and 11 and 13 are examples of "twin primes," i.e., primes which differ by 2. There are more than one hundred thousand such twins known. [8]

---

[5] Pierre de Fermat, 1601–1665.

[6] Cf. Florian Cajori, *A History of Mathematics*, p. 179, Macmillan, New York, 1894.

[7] "Proof of Fermat's Last Theorem for all prime exponents less than 4002," *Proc. Natl. Acad. Sci.*, **41**, 970–973 (1955).

[8] Cf. the excellent book by Daniel Shanks, *Solved and Unsolved Problems in Number Theory*, p. 30, Spartan Books, Washington, D.C., 1962, for remarks on this and many other open questions in number theory.

There is the famous Goldbach conjecture that every positive even integer greater than 2 is the sum of two primes. Thus $4 = 2 + 2$, $6 = 3 + 3$, $8 = 5 + 3$, $10 = 7 + 3 = 5 + 5$, and $12 = 7 + 5$.

We have given Euclid's proof that there are infinitely many primes, but there are few procedures for telling whether a given number is prime. One method was given at the end of the previous section. But this will be of little value in determining whether 2,305,843,009,213,693,951 is a prime. (Of course, it is!)

The literature of number theory is rich, and many other results and open questions can be given. But perhaps in this introductory textbook it would be well to stop at this point to raise a disturbing question. Suppose it is shown that there are infinitely many pairs of twin primes, or that $a^n + b^n = c^n$ for $n > 2$ never has a solution in the natural numbers. So what? Is it important to know these answers because there are definite applications? Or is it perhaps because some day—in a year, a hundred years, or a billion years—there may conceivably be an application?

Of course it is unknown to this writer whether there are today applications awaiting the solution of these problems, but he assumes there probably are no such applications. If there were, this would certainly be an important reason to work on these problems. And it is admittedly true that it is wise to encourage basic research in mathematics, along with all other basic research, in the hope that out of the vast number of results or ideas a few may become useful at a given time in the future.

The reader is undoubtedly aware that many mathematicians, however, will work with great determination and dedication on problems such as given above without the slightest concern for the application. And certainly their reasons are highly individual ones—compulsiveness, the desire for promotion, need for an increase in salary, the necessity to have one's name in print—to name but a few which may occur to some readers.

But the fact is that the development of mathematics has not yet reached the stage, apparently, in which solutions to the above conjectures can be settled. And so these questions provide a focus for working on the creation of new techniques which will help overcome such limitations in insight. For it is reasonably certain that should such new developments in mathematics be achieved, the solution to these problems will be only a partial reward. One would expect to acquire a greater comprehension of numerous other aspects of the subject. Could the mathematician then close up shop someday, all outstanding questions having been settled? Alas, it is well known that the solution of any open question usually gives one the insight to raise at least two more. Such is the story of mathematics.

chapter x

THE LEAST UPPER BOUND POSTULATE FOR R

Thus far we have assumed the existence of a set R on which two binary operations $+$ and $\cdot$ are defined with respect to which R is a field (Chapter 5). Furthermore, we assumed the existence of a subset P of R satisfying Postulate $\mathcal{O}$ (Chapter 7). In this chapter we introduce our final postulate for R, namely, that every nonempty subset S of R which is bounded above has a least upper bound in R (not necessarily in S). On the basis of this postulate and our previous work, we are able to deduce that if a is a positive real number, then the equation $x^n = a$ for $n \in N$ has a *unique positive* solution in R. If $a \in N$, we shall apply the fundamental theorem of arithmetic to investigate the conditions under which such a solution is a rational number or an irrational number.

The above unique positive solution of $x^n = a$ allows us to extend the meaning of exponents to the positive rational numbers. We then develop the theory of rational exponents and finally define the meaning of any real exponent.

The chapter concludes with the development of the decimal notation (as well as other bases) for the real numbers.

1. The Least Upper Bound Postulate and Some Consequences

1.1 Statement of Postulate LUB

The postulates listed up to now do not distinguish $\bar{R}$ from R. That is, the set of rational numbers satisfies A_1 to A_5, M_1 to M_5, $\mathcal{O}$, if we replace 'R' by '$\bar{R}$.' However we shall see that in $\bar{R}$ there is no solution of $x^2 = 2$. As stated in the introduction to Part II, however, we should expect a solution to this equation in R. We now introduce our final postulate for R, then, and on the basis of this postulate (and our previous development) we shall be able to prove the existence in R of a solution to the above equation, and more generally to the equation $x^n = a$ for every $n \in N$ and $a \in P$.

Postulate LUB. *Every nonempty subset of R which is bounded above has a least upper bound in R.*

1.2   Statement of Some Consequences

We now present five consequences of postulate LUB. For those who wish to defer reading their proofs for the present, we shall present the statements of these theorems in this section and the proofs in Section 2.

Theorem 1. Every nonempty subset of R which is bounded below has a greatest lower bound in R.

> One could have made Theorem 1 the final postulate. Then postulate LUB would have been our first theorem. There are other alternatives to postulate LUB, which in our development become theorems. For example, the following could have been taken as a postulate in place of LUB:
>
> "Let S and T be two nonempty subsets of R satisfying the following:
>
> (1) $S \cup T = R$;
> (2) For every $s \in S$ and $t \in T$, $s < t$.
>
> Then $\exists \, \alpha \in R \ni \alpha$ is an upper bound of S and a lower bound of T." This is known as the *axiom of Dedekind.*

The next theorem is obvious intuitively on geometric grounds. Namely, suppose one takes any positive real number, say $\tfrac{4}{3}$, for example. Consider the set $\{1 \cdot \tfrac{4}{3}, 2 \cdot \tfrac{4}{3}, 3 \cdot \tfrac{4}{3}, \ldots\}$.

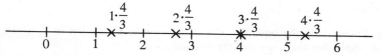

If the set of real numbers, as delineated by our postulates, is to represent our intuitive conception of the line, the set $\{1 \cdot \tfrac{4}{3}, 2 \cdot \tfrac{4}{3}, \ldots\}$ should not be bounded above. That is, if b is any real number, then there should be some $n \in N$ for which $n \cdot \tfrac{4}{3} > b$. That this is so is the content of the next theorem.

Theorem 2. If $a,b \in P$ then $\exists \, n \in N \ni na > b$. In particular, there is no real number larger than every natural number.

The latter statement of the theorem is obtained from the former by taking $a = 1$. Then for any $b \in P$, $\exists \, n \in N \ni n \cdot 1 > b$.

We have seen that if $a,b \in R$ and $a < b$, then there exists a real number between a and b $\left(\text{e.g.,} \dfrac{a+b}{2}\right)$. The next theorem states that between every two distinct real numbers, there in fact exists a rational number.

Theorem 3. If $a,b \in R$ and $a < b$, then there exists a rational number s such that $a < s < b$.

The next theorem is used in the proof of Theorem 5. Consider any $a \in P$ and $n \in N$. Then $a^n \in P$.

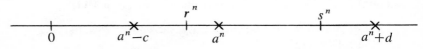

Consider any point to the left of a^n and any point to the right. The point to the left is $a^n - c$ for some $c \in P$ and the one to the right $a^n + d$ for some $d \in P$.

Then $\exists r,s \in P$ such that r^n is between $a^n - c$ and a^n, and s^n is between a^n and $a^n + d$. In fact, r and s may be chosen to be rational.

Theorem 4.[1] Suppose $a \in P$ and $n \in N$. Then if, $c,d \in P$, $\exists r,s \in P \ni$ $a^n - c < r^n < a^n < s^n < a^n + d$. Furthermore, we may choose r and s to be rational.

Finally, we come to the theorem referred to in Section 1.1.

Theorem 5. Let $a \in R$, $a > 0$. Then if x is a variable over P, $x^n = a$ has a unique solution (in P).

Exercises

6. By Theorem 5, the equation $x^2 = 2$ has a unique solution in P. Using this fact, show that there are exactly two solutions in R.
7. The equation $x^3 = 2$ has a unique solution in P. Using this fact, show that it has a unique solution in R.
8. Using the fact that $x^3 = 2$ has a unique solution in R (cf. Exercise 7), show that the equation $x^3 = -2$ has a unique solution in R. What can be said about the solution set of $x^2 = -2$?
9. (a) We say an integer n is even if $n = 2n'$ for some integer n'. We call $n \in J$ odd if $n = 2n' + 1$ for some $n' \in J$. Use Theorem (9, 1) to show that every integer is either even or odd and not both.
   (b) If n is a positive even integer, and $a \in P$, show that $x^n = a$ has exactly two solutions in R. (*Hint:* Let $n = 2n'$. Show that if c is the unique solution in P, then $-c$ is the unique solution in $-P$.)
   (c) If n is a positive even integer, and $a \in -P$, show that there is no solution in R of $x^n = a$.
   (d) If n is a positive odd integer, and $a \in P$, show that there is a unique solution in R of $x^n = a$.

[1] The statement of this theorem may be omitted by those who wish to omit Section 2 at this reading.

(e) If n is a positive odd integer, and $a \in -P$, show that there is a unique solution in R of $x^n = a$. (Namely, if c is the unique solution of $x^n = |a|$, then $-c$ is the unique solution of $x^n = a$.)

2. Proofs of Theorems 1 to 5

Although the proofs given in this section are logically accessible to the student, they may require concentrated study, particularly the proofs of Theorems 4 and 5. Those who choose to omit the proofs at this time should nevertheless carefully study the statements of the theorems in the preceding section (except for Theorem 4, which is given as a tool for proving Theorem 5).

2.1 Proof of Theorem 1

Let S be a nonempty subset of R which is bounded below. Let $-S = \{x \in R / -x \in S\}$. Thus $s \in S$ if and only if $-s \in -S$. If $\ell \leq s$, then $-\ell \geq -s$. It follows that if ℓ is a lower bound of S, then $-\ell$ is an upper bound of $-S$. Hence since S is bounded below, $-S$ is bounded above.

By LUB, $-S$ has a least upper bound, say u. We shall prove the theorem by showing that $-u$ is the greatest lower bound of S.

(a) $-u$ is a lower bound of S: For suppose $s \in S$. Then since u is an upper bound of $-S$, $u \geq -s$. Hence $-u \leq s$.
(b) If ℓ is any lower bound of S, $\ell \leq -u$: For if ℓ is a lower bound of S, then $-\ell$ is an upper bound of $-S$. Hence $-\ell \geq u$ since u is the lub of $-S$. Thus, $\ell \leq -u$.

2.2 Proof of Theorem 2

Let $S = \{a, 2a, 3a, \ldots\} = \{x \in R / x = ma$ for some $m \in N\}$. We wish to show there is some element of S which is greater than b. Suppose no such element exists. Then b is an upper bound of S.

By LUB, S has a least upper bound, say u. Since $u - a < u$, it follows that $u - a$ is not an upper bound of S. Hence $\exists\, ma \in S \ni ma > u - a$, where $m \in N$. But then $ma + a > u$ or $(m + 1)a > u$. Since $m + 1 \in N$, we must have $(m + 1)a \in S$. This is a contradiction to the fact that u is an upper bound of S. Hence S could not have been bounded above by b, which proves the theorem.

2.3 Proof of Theorem 3

(α) Since 1 and $b - a$ are positive, by Theorem 2, $\exists$ a positive integer $n \ni n(b - a) > 1$.
(β) Again by Theorem 2, there exist positive integers larger than na, where the n is selected as in (α). Hence by (8, 19) there exists a least such, say m. Thus, m is the smallest integer for which

$$\text{(i) } na < m$$

so that

$$\text{(ii) } m - 1 \le na$$

(γ) From (βi), we see that $a < \dfrac{m}{n}$.

(δ) From (βii) we see that

$$
\begin{aligned}
m &\le na + 1 \\
&< na + n(b - a) \qquad \text{by } (\alpha) \\
&= nb
\end{aligned}
$$

[A list involving inequalities, such as above, means:

$$m \le na + 1 < na + n(b - a) = nb$$

so that the conclusion is $m < nb$.]

Since $m < nb$, it follows that $\dfrac{m}{n} < b$.

(ϵ) From (γ) and (δ) we obtain

$$a < \frac{m}{n} < b$$

Hence we have $a < s < b$ where s is rational:

$$s = \frac{m}{n}$$

2.4   Proof of Theorem 4

(α) Suppose $n = 1$.
   (i) If $a - c < 0$, choose r with $0 < r < a$ (say by Theorem 3).
       Then $r \in P$ and $a - c < r < a$.
   (ii) If $a - c \ge 0$, use Theorem 3 again to determine r with

$$a - c < r < a$$

   (iii) Finally, choose s such that $a < s < a + d$.
(β) We now consider the case $n > 1$. Let $M = a^{n-1} \cdot n$.

   (i) By Theorem 3, $\exists\, t_1 \in R \ni 0 < t_1 < \dfrac{c}{M}$.

   (ii) Also $\exists\, t_2 \in R \ni 0 < t_2 < a$. Let $t = \min\{t_1, t_2\}$.
   Then by (i), we have

   (iii) $0 < t < \dfrac{c}{M}$
   and by (ii)

(iv) $a - t > 0$.

(v) Let $r = a - t$, so that $0 < r < a$ and $r^n < a^n$.

Then $a^n - r^n = (a - r)(a^{n-1} + a^{n-2}r + \cdots + r^{n-1})$ by (8, 51)

$\qquad\qquad < (a - r)(a^{n-1} + a^{n-2}a + \cdots + a^{n-1})$

$\qquad\qquad\qquad$ by (8, 65) and (8, 29), since $0 < r < a$

$\qquad\qquad = t \cdot (n \cdot a^{n-1})$

$\qquad\qquad = tM$

$\qquad\qquad < \dfrac{c}{M} \cdot M$ by (iii)

$\qquad\qquad = c$

Hence $a^n - r^n < c$ so that

(vi) $a^n - c < r^n$.

Combining (v) and (vi) yields

(vii) $a^n - c < r^n < a^n$.

[By Theorem 3 and (8, 65) we may, if we wish, take r to be rational and satisfying (vii).]

(γ) Let $b = \dfrac{d}{a^n + d}$ so that $0 < b < 1$. Regarding 1 as 1^n, we may apply part (β) to obtain:

(i) $1 - b < w^n < 1$ for some $w \in P$. ($1 - b > 0$ since $b < 1$.)

Taking multiplicative inverses in (i) reverses the inequalities [cf. (7, 29)]:

$$\frac{1}{1 - b} > \frac{1}{w^n} > 1$$

Since $\dfrac{1}{w^n} = \left(\dfrac{1}{w}\right)^n$ [cf. (8, 58(5))], we have, upon replacing b by $\dfrac{d}{a^n + d}$:

(ii) $\dfrac{a^n + d}{a^n} > \left(\dfrac{1}{w}\right)^n > 1$.

Let $s = \dfrac{a}{w}$, so that $\left(\dfrac{1}{w}\right)^n = \dfrac{s^n}{a^n}$. Then (ii) becomes

$$\frac{a^n + d}{a^n} > \frac{s^n}{a^n} > 1$$

or multiplying through by a^n,

$$a^n + d > s^n > a^n$$

[As in (β) we may, if we wish, take s to be rational.]

This proves the theorem completely.

2.5   *Proof of Theorem 5*

Let $S = \{x \in P/x^n \leqq a\}$ and $T = \{y \in P/y^n \geqq a\}$.

(a) S is nonempty:
   (i) If $a \leqq 1$, then $a^n \leqq a$ (8, 61). Hence in this case $a \in S$.
   (ii) If $a > 1$, then choose any r with $0 < r < 1$. Then $0 < r^n < 1 < a$, so that $r \in S$.

(b) T is nonempty: Since $a + 1 > 1$, we have [2] $(a + 1)^n \geqq a + 1 > a$, so that $a + 1 \in T$.

(c) S is bounded above and T is bounded below: Any element of T is an upper bound of S and any element of S is a lower bound of T [cf. (8, 65)].

(d) It follows that S has a lub, say α, and T a glb, say β.

(e) $\alpha \leqq \beta$: Since S is nonempty, it is clear that $0 < \alpha$. Since every element of T is an upper bound of S, $\alpha \leqq t$ for all $t \in T$. Hence α is a lower bound of T. But β is the glb of T. Hence $\alpha \leqq \beta$.

(f) $\alpha = \beta$: For suppose $\alpha < \beta$ [the only other alternative by (e)]. If c is any real number (and there would exist such) with $\alpha < c < \beta$, then $c \notin S$ and $c \notin T$. Hence $c^n \not\leqq a$ and $c^n \not\geqq a$. This contradicts (7, 9).

(g) $\alpha^n = a$: Either $\alpha^n < a$, $\alpha^n = a$, or $\alpha^n > a$ [by (7, 9)].
   (i) Suppose $\alpha^n < a$. Then if $d = a - \alpha^n$, $d > 0$. By Theorem 4, $\exists s \in R$ with $\alpha^n < s^n < \alpha^n + d$. The first inequality $\alpha^n < s^n$ yields $\underline{\alpha < s}$ [by (8, 65)]. The second inequality $s^n < \alpha^n + d$ yields $s^n < a$ [since $\alpha^n + d = \alpha^n + (a - \alpha^n) = a$]. But $s^n < a$ means $s \in S$ so that $\underline{s \leqq \alpha}$. The two underlined statements are contradictory.
   (ii) Suppose $\alpha^n > a$. Then if $c = \alpha^n - a$, $c > 0$. By Theorem 4, $\exists r \in P$ with $\alpha^n - c < r^n < \alpha^n$. The first inequality yields $a < r^n$, so that $r \in T$ and hence $\underline{r \geqq \alpha}$. The second inequality $r^n < \alpha^n$ yields $\underline{r < \alpha}$. We therefore reach a contradiction.
   It follows that $\alpha^n = a$.

We have therefore shown that $x^n = a$ has a solution in P, namely, α.

(h) The solution of $x^n = a$ in P is unique: For suppose γ is a solution, where $\gamma \in P$: $\gamma^n = a$. Then $\gamma^n = \alpha^n$, and by (8, 65) we have $\gamma = \alpha$.

3.   The Theory of Positive Rational Exponents

3.1   *The Aim of the Theory of Exponents Stated*

Theorem (8, 58) summarizes the rules for positive integral exponents. Our aim shall be to extend the meaning of a^α to any $\alpha \in R$ in such a way that (8, 58) remains true. In fact, since we shall have negative exponents,

---

[2] Use (8, 63a) in the following way: Since $a + 1 > 1$, we have $(a + 1)^n > (a + 1)^1$ if $n > 1$. Of course we have equality if $n = 1$.

it would be best if (8, 58(2)) would read $\dfrac{a^m}{a^n} = a^{m-n}$ without exception, that is, regardless of whether $m < n$, $m = n$, or $m > n$. We shall see that all this is possible, but only if we restrict a to be positive. Thus our aim shall be to define a^α for $a \in P$ and $\alpha \in R$ such that the following becomes a theorem:

"If $a,b \in P$ and $\alpha,\beta \in R$, then

$$(1)\quad a^\alpha a^\beta = a^{\alpha+\beta}$$

$$(2)\quad \frac{a^\alpha}{a^\beta} = a^{\alpha-\beta}$$

$$(3)\quad (a^\alpha)^\beta = a^{\alpha\beta}$$

$$(4)\quad (ab)^\alpha = a^\alpha b^\alpha$$

$$(5)\quad \left(\frac{a}{b}\right)^\alpha = \frac{a^\alpha}{b^\alpha}\text{ "}$$

We shall first consider the theory for positive rational exponents, then for all rational exponents, and finally for all real exponents.

3.2   Positive Rational Exponents Defined

Suppose we begin by attempting to give a meaning to $a^{1/n}$, where $n \in N$. Then if rule (3) is to hold, we would have

$$(a^{1/n})^n = a^{(1/n)n} = a^1 = a$$

Thus $a^{1/n}$ would be a solution of $x^n = a$ [i.e., $(a^{1/n})^n = a$]. For $n = 2$ and a negative, such a solution does not exist (cf. Exercise 9c). Restricting a to be positive, however, we are assured of a unique positive solution of $x^n = a$ according to Theorem 5. We are therefore led to define $a^{1/n}$ according to the following:

Definition 1. The unique positive real number which is a solution to the equation $x^n = a$, where $a \in P$, will be denoted by '$a^{1/n}$' or '$\sqrt[n]{a}$,' and will be called the nth *root* of a. Thus $a^{1/n}$ is the unique positive real number for which $(a^{1/n})^n = a$ (similarly for $\sqrt[n]{a}$, $(\sqrt[n]{a})^n = a$). For $a^{1/2}$ or $\sqrt[2]{a}$, we shall also use the notation '$\sqrt{a}$.'

Remark: For $n = 1$, we obtain $a^{1/1}$ as the unique solution of $x^1 = a$. Since this solution is a, Definition 1 here agrees (when applicable, namely when $n = 1$) with our old Definition (8, 3a).

Examples: (1) Since $x^3 = 8$ is satisfied by 2, we have $8^{1/3} = 2$ (or also $\sqrt[3]{8} = 2$).
(2) $16^{1/4} = 2$, since $2^4 = 16$.
(3) $(\frac{1}{9})^{1/2} = \frac{1}{3}$, since $(\frac{1}{3})^2 = \frac{1}{9}$.
(4) $2^{1/2}$ is the unique positive solution of $x^2 = 2$. Thus, $(2^{1/2})^2 = 2$.
(5) $\sqrt{3}$ is the unique positive solution of $x^2 = 3$. Thus, $(\sqrt{3})^2 = 3$.
(6) $(\frac{1}{8})^{1/3} = \frac{1}{2}$, since $(\frac{1}{2})^3 = \frac{1}{8}$.

The above are all examples of the notation introduced in Definition 1.

Now, to define a^r, where r is any positive rational number, we write r as the ratio of two positive natural numbers: thus, $r = \frac{m}{n}$, where $m, n \in N$. Again if rule (3) is to hold, $(a^{1/n})^m$ must equal $a^{m/n}$. One is therefore tempted to define $a^{m/n}$ to be $(a^{1/n})^m$. But if $r = \frac{m}{n}$, then we also have, for example, $r = \frac{2m}{2n}$. Thus we would also have $a^r = a^{2m/2n} = (a^{1/2n})^{2m}$. How do we know that '$(a^{1/2n})^{2m}$' and '$(a^{1/n})^m$' designate the same real number?

To emphasize this problem, suppose one decides to define $2^{m/n}$ to be $\frac{2m}{2n}$. Then we would have $2^{2/3} = \frac{2^2}{2^3} = \frac{1}{2}$; and we would also have $2^{4/6} = \frac{2^4}{2^6} = \frac{1}{4}$. Thus, one would not really be defining a *rational number* as an exponent, but rather an *ordered pair of natural numbers*, where $(2,3) \neq (4,6)$. Whether one used the notation '$\frac{2}{3}$' or '(2,3)' for the exponent would be irrelevant. Since $2^{2/3}$ and $2^{4/6}$ are different, $\frac{2}{3}$ and $\frac{4}{6}$ could not be thought of as rational numbers, since otherwise '$2^{2/3}$' and '$2^{4/6}$' would have to designate the same element.

Thus, if the following were not a theorem, we would have to terminate our development of a theory for rational exponents.

Theorem 10. If $m, n, p, q \in N$ and $a \in P$, and if $\frac{m}{n} = \frac{p}{q}$, then

$$(a^{1/n})^m = (a^{1/q})^p$$

Proof: Since $\frac{m}{n} = \frac{p}{q}$, $mq = pn$. Hence $x^{mq} = a^{pm}$ and $x^{pn} = a^{pm}$ are the same equations.

We shall show $(a^{1/n})^m$ and $(a^{1/q})^p$ are solutions of this equation. By the uniqueness part of Theorem 5, we shall be able to conclude that they are equal.

$$\begin{aligned}
[(a^{1/n})^m]^{pn} &= (a^{1/n})^{mpn} & &\text{by [8, 58(3)]} \\
&= [(a^{1/n})^n]^{mp} & &\text{by [8, 58(3)]} \\
&= a^{mp} & &\text{by Def. 1} \\
[(a^{1/q})^p]^{mq} &= (a^{1/q})^{pmq} & & \\
&= [(a^{1/q})^q]^{mp} & & \\
&= a^{mp} & &
\end{aligned}$$

Definition 2. If r is a positive rational number, and a is a positive real number, then 'a^r' shall designate the real number $(a^{1/n})^m$ where $r = \frac{m}{n}$ and $m, n \in N$. By Theorem 10, a^r depends only on r, and not upon the representation of r as a quotient of natural numbers.

Remarks: If r is a positive integer, then $r = \frac{r}{1}$. Then Definition 2 states that $a^{r/1} = (a^{\frac{1}{1}})^r = a^r$. Hence in the case r is a positive integer, Definition 2 agrees with our old Definition (8, 3). Also if $r = \frac{1}{n}$, Definition 2 agrees with Definition 1.

Examples: (1) $25^{3/2} = (25^{1/2})^3 = 5^3 = 125.$

(2) $8^{4/6} = 8^{2/3} = (8^{1/3})^2 = 2^2 = 4.$

(3) $(\frac{1}{32})^{2/5} = [(\frac{1}{32})^{1/5}]^2 = (\frac{1}{2})^2 = \frac{1}{4}.$

(4) $(\frac{27}{8})^{4/3} = [(\frac{27}{8})^{1/3}]^4 = (\frac{3}{2})^4 = \frac{81}{16}.$

Exercises

11. Simplify the following:

(a) $4^{5/2}$.

(b) $\sqrt{\frac{16}{81}}$.

(c) $\sqrt[4]{\frac{16}{81}}$.

(d) $(\frac{16}{81})^{2/8}$.

(e) $(\frac{1}{64})^{1/3}$.

(f) $64^{1/2}$.

(g) $(\sqrt{16})^3$.

(h) $(3^{1/100})^{100}$.

(i) $(\sqrt{3,281})^2$.

(j) $(\sqrt[n]{d})^n$ $(d \in P)$.

(k) $\left(\dfrac{1}{\sqrt{2}}\right)^2$.

(l) $(\sqrt{\frac{3}{2}})^2$.

12. If r is a positive rational number, prove that $1^r = 1$.

13. If $a \in P$ and r is a positive rational number, prove that $a^r \in P$.

3.3   The Main Theorem for Positive Rational Exponents

Theorem 14. If $a,b \in P$, and r, s are positive rational numbers, then

(1) $a^r \cdot a^s = a^{r+s}$

(2)
$$\frac{a^r}{a^s} = \begin{cases} a^{r-s} & \text{if } r > s \\ 1 & \text{if } r = s \\ \dfrac{1}{a^{s-r}} & \text{if } r < s \end{cases}$$

(3) $(a^r)^s = a^{rs}$

(4) $(ab)^r = a^r b^r$

(5) $\left(\dfrac{a}{b}\right)^r = \dfrac{a^r}{b^r}$

Proof: Let $r = \dfrac{m}{n}$, $s = \dfrac{p}{q}$ where $m,n,p,q \in N$.

(1) $a^r \cdot a^s = a^{m/n} \cdot a^{p/q}$

$= a^{mq/nq} \cdot a^{np/nq}$ Th. 10

$= (a^{1/nq})^{mq} \cdot (a^{1/nq})^{np}$ Def. 2

$= (a^{1/nq})^{mq+np}$ (8, 58)

$= a^{(mq+np)/nq}$ Def. 2

$= a^{m/n+p/q}$ (5, 98)

$= a^{r+s}$

(2) (a) Suppose $r > s$, so that $r - s$ is a positive rational number. Then

$$a^s \cdot a^{r-s} = a^{s+(r-s)} \qquad \text{Th. 14(1)}$$
$$= a^r$$

Hence $a^{r-s} = \dfrac{a^r}{a^s}$. (Of course, $a^s \neq 0$ by Exercise 13.)

(b) If $r = s$, then $\dfrac{a^r}{a^s} = 1$ [by (5, 56)].

(c) $r < s$ is left as an exercise (cf. Exercise 15).

(3) $(a^r)^s = (a^{m/n})^{p/q}$ and $a^{rs} = a^{mp/nq}$.

We raise both of these to the nq power. If the results are equal, then the original numbers are equal, since for any $c \, \epsilon \, P$, $c^{1/nq}$ is uniquely determined (Theorem 5).

$$
\begin{aligned}
[(a^{m/n})^{p/q}]^{nq} &= \{[(a^{m/n})^{1/q}]^p\}^{nq} & \text{Def. 2}\\
&= [(a^{m/n})^{1/q}]^{pnq} & (8, 58)\\
&= \{[(a^{m/n})^{1/q}]^q\}^{pn} & (8, 58)\\
&= (a^{m/n})^{pn} & \text{Def. 1}\\
&= [(a^{1/n})^m]^{pn} & \text{Def. 2}\\
&= (a^{1/n})^{mpn} & (8, 58)\\
&= [(a^{1/n})^n]^{mp} & (8, 58)\\
&= a^{mp} & \text{Def. 1}\\
(a^{mp/nq})^{nq} &= [(a^{1/nq})^{mp}]^{nq} & \text{Def. 2}\\
&= (a^{1/nq})^{mpnq} & (8, 58)\\
&= [(a^{1/nq})^{nq}]^{mp} & (8, 58)\\
&= a^{mp} & \text{Def. 1}
\end{aligned}
$$

(4) We show that $(ab)^{m/n}$ and $a^{m/n}b^{m/n}$ when raised to the nth power both yield $a^m b^m$. It will then follow that $(ab)^{m/n} = a^{m/n}b^{m/n}$.

$$
\begin{aligned}
[(ab)^{m/n}]^n &= (ab)^{(m/n)\cdot n} & \text{Th. 14(3)}\\
&= (ab)^m\\
&= a^m b^m & (8, 58)\\
(a^{m/n}b^{m/n})^n &= (a^{m/n})^n (b^{m/n})^n & (8, 58)\\
&= a^{(m/n)\cdot n} b^{(m/n)\cdot n} & \text{Th. 14(3)}\\
&= a^m b^m
\end{aligned}
$$

(5) (i) $\left(b \cdot \dfrac{1}{b}\right)^r = 1^r = 1$ (Ex. 12).

(ii) $\left(b \cdot \dfrac{1}{b}\right)^r = b^r \cdot \left(\dfrac{1}{b}\right)^r$ [Th. 14(4)].

From (i) and (ii) we obtain

(iii) $b^r \cdot \left(\dfrac{1}{b}\right)^r = 1$ or $\left(\dfrac{1}{b}\right)^r = \dfrac{1}{b^r}$. Hence

$$\left(\frac{a}{b}\right)^r = \left(a \cdot \frac{1}{b}\right)^r$$
$$= a^r \cdot \left(\frac{1}{b}\right)^r \qquad \text{Th. 14(4)}$$

$$= a^r \cdot \frac{1}{b^r} \qquad \text{(iii)}$$

$$= \frac{a^r}{b^r}$$

Exercises

15. Complete the proof of Theorem 14(2).

16. To compute $(8^5)^{1/3}$, it is easier to compute $(8^{1/3})^5$. How can one tell by inspection that these are equal?

17. State and prove a general rule for which Exercise 16 becomes a particular example.

18. If $c, d \in P$, prove that $\sqrt{cd} = \sqrt{c}\sqrt{d}$.

19. Show that $\sqrt{8} = 2\sqrt{2}$.

20. If $c, d \in P$, prove that $\sqrt[n]{cd} = \sqrt[n]{c}\sqrt[n]{d}$.

21. Show that $16^{1/3} = 2\sqrt[3]{2}$.

22. Find $2^{2/3}\sqrt[3]{2}$. (*Answer:* 2.)

23. Show that $4^{1/3} - 2^{2/3} = 0$.

4. The Theory of Rational Exponents

4.1 Zero and Negative Rational Exponents Defined

We have now defined the meaning of a^r when r is a positive rational number, and $a \in P$. We now turn to a definition of a^0 and a^{-r}. As stated in Section 3.1, we wish to do this in such a way that the five rules stated there hold.

Thus, if the theory of exponents is to hold, we should have $a^0 \cdot a^1 = a^{0+1}$ according to the first rule. But this would mean

$$a^0 \cdot a^1 = a^1$$
$$a^0 = 1$$

Definition 3. If $a \in P$, then $a^0 = 1$.

Examples: $8^0 = 1$, $(\sqrt{2})^0 = 1$, $(8a)^0 = 1$ (where $a \in P$), $8a^0 = 8$, $2^{1/3}3^0 2^{2/3} = 2$, and $(2^{1/3}3^0 2^{2/3})^0 = 1$.

Again to define a^{-r}, where r is a positive rational number, in such a way that rule (1) holds, we must have

$$a^r \cdot a^{-r} = a^{r+(-r)} = a^0 = 1$$

That is, we must have $a^{-r} = \dfrac{1}{a^r}$.

Definition 4. If $a \in P$ and r is a positive rational number, then $a^{-r} = \dfrac{1}{a^r}$.

Remark: The only previous use of the notation 'a^{-r}' for r a positive rational number has been 'a^{-1}' as the inverse of a. Thus a^{-1} by our previous definition was the unique real number for which $a \cdot a^{-1} = 1$. In our present definition, $a^{-1} = \dfrac{1}{a}$. As 'a^{-1}' in both cases designates the same real number, our present definition offers no difficulty.

Examples: (1) $8^{-2/3} = \dfrac{1}{8^{2/3}} = \dfrac{1}{4}$.

(2) $4^{-1/2} = \dfrac{1}{\sqrt{4}} = \dfrac{1}{2}$.

(3) $\left(\dfrac{1}{8}\right)^{-1/3} = \dfrac{1}{(\frac{1}{8})^{1/3}} = \dfrac{1}{\frac{1}{2}} = 2$.

(4) $(2^{-5/4} \cdot 3^{1/3})^0 = 1$.

According to Definition 4, $a^{-\alpha} = \dfrac{1}{a^\alpha}$ if α is a positive rational number. We now show that this remains true for all α in $\bar{R}$.

Theorem 24. Let $a \in P$ and $\alpha \in \bar{R}$. Then $a^{-\alpha} = \dfrac{1}{a^\alpha}$.

Proof: (i) If $\alpha > 0$, the result follows from Definition 4.
(ii) If $\alpha = 0$, the result follows from the fact that $-0 = 0$ and Definition 3.
(iii) Suppose $\alpha < 0$.

$$\frac{1}{a^\alpha} = \frac{1}{a^{-(-\alpha)}}$$

$$= \frac{1}{\left(\dfrac{1}{a^{-\alpha}}\right)} \qquad \text{by Def. 4, since } -\alpha \text{ is a positive rational number}$$

$$= a^{-\alpha}$$

Exercises

25. Prove that $1^\alpha = 1$ for all $\alpha \in \bar{R}$.
26. Prove that if $a \in P$ and $\alpha \in \bar{R}$, then $a^\alpha \in P$.
27. Simplify the following:
    (a) $4^{-5/2}$.
    (b) $\left(\frac{16}{81}\right)^{-1/2}$.
    (c) $\left(\frac{16}{81}\right)^{-1/4}$.
    (d) $64^{-1/2}$.
    (e) $\left(\frac{1}{64}\right)^{-1/3}$.
    (f) $(\sqrt{16})^{-3}$.
    (g) $(3^{1/100})^{-100}$.
    (h) $(\sqrt{3,281})^{-2}$.
    (i) $(\sqrt[n]{d})^{-n}$ $(d \in P)$.
    (j) $(\sqrt{\frac{3}{2}})^{-2}$.

28. Prove that if $a,b \in P$ and $\alpha \in \bar{R}$, then $\left(\dfrac{a}{b}\right)^{-\alpha} = \left(\dfrac{b}{a}\right)^\alpha$. [*Hint:* Use Theorem 14(5).]
29. Use Exercise 28 in parts (b), (c), and (e) of Exercise 27.

4.2   The Main Theorem for Rational Exponents

Theorem 30. If $a,b \in P$ and $r,s \in \bar{R}$, then

$$(1)\ a^r \cdot a^s = a^{r+s} \qquad (4)\ (ab)^r = a^r b^r$$

$$(2)\ \frac{a^r}{a^s} = a^{r-s} \qquad (5)\ \left(\frac{a}{b}\right)^r = \frac{a^r}{b^r}$$

$$(3)\ (a^r)^s = a^{rs}$$

Proof:

(1) (a) If r and s are positive, apply Theorem 14(1).

(b) If either r or s is zero, the result is obvious.

(c) Suppose $r > 0$ and $s < 0$.

$$a^r \cdot a^s = a^r \cdot \frac{1}{a^{-s}} \qquad \text{Th. 24}$$

$$= \begin{cases} a^{r-(-s)} & \text{if } r > -s \\ 1 & \text{if } r = -s \\ \dfrac{1}{a^{-s-r}} & \text{if } r < -s \end{cases} \qquad \begin{array}{l}\text{Th. 14(2) applied to the posi-}\\ \text{tive exponents } r \text{ and } -s\end{array}$$

In the first case, i.e., $r > -s$, we have $a^{r-(-s)} = a^{r+s}$, and the result holds in this case.

If $r = -s$, then $a^{r+s} = 1$, since $a^{r+s} = a^{-s+s} = a^0 = 1$. Hence the result holds in this case.

In the final case,

$$\frac{1}{a^{-s-r}} = \frac{1}{a^{-(r+s)}} = a^{r+s}$$

(d) Suppose r and s are negative:

$$a^r \cdot a^s = \frac{1}{a^{-r}} \cdot \frac{1}{a^{-s}} \qquad \text{Th. 24}$$

$$= \frac{1}{a^{-r} \cdot a^{-s}}$$

$$= \frac{1}{a^{(-r)+(-s)}} \qquad \begin{array}{l}\text{Th. 14(1) applied to the posi-}\\ \text{tive exponents } -r \text{ and } -s\end{array}$$

$$= \frac{1}{a^{-(r+s)}}$$

$$= a^{r+s}$$

(2)
$$\frac{a^r}{a^s} = a^r \cdot \frac{1}{a^s}$$

$$= a^r \cdot a^{-s} \qquad \text{Th. 24}$$

$$= a^{r+(-s)} \qquad \text{Th. 30(1)}$$

$$= a^{r-s}$$

(3) If r and s are positive, apply Theorem 14(3). If r or s is 0, the result is obvious. Suppose $r > 0$ and $s < 0$.

$$(a^r)^s = \frac{1}{(a^r)^{-s}}$$

$$= \frac{1}{a^{r(-s)}} \qquad \text{Th. 14(3) applied to the positive exponents } r \text{ and } -s$$

$$= \frac{1}{a^{-rs}}$$

$$= a^{rs}$$

We leave the cases $r < 0$, $s > 0$ and $r < 0$, $s < 0$ as exercises.
(4) and (5): Exercises.

4.3   Some Consequences of the Main Theorem

In Chapter 8 we saw that if $a \in P$, then

(I) If $a > 1$, then $a^n > 1$ (8, 12)
(II) If $a = 1$, then $a^n = 1$ Example 3 of Chap. 8
(III) If $a < 1$, then $a^n < 1$ (8, 11)

where n is assumed to be a positive integer. We now consider a generalization of these results where we allow any rational exponents.

Theorem 31. Let $a \in P$ and $\alpha \in \bar{R}$.

(I) If $a > 1$, then
   (1) $a^\alpha > 1$ if and only if $\alpha > 0$
   (2) $a^\alpha = 1$ if and only if $\alpha = 0$
   (3) $a^\alpha < 1$ if and only if $\alpha < 0$
(II) If $a = 1$, then $a^\alpha = 1$.
(III) If $a < 1$, then
   (1) $a^\alpha < 1$ if and only if $\alpha > 0$
   (2) $a^\alpha = 1$ if and only if $\alpha = 0$
   (3) $a^\alpha > 1$ if and only if $\alpha < 0$

Proof: Let $\alpha = \dfrac{m}{n}$ for some $m \in J$ and $n \in N$.

(I) Assume $a > 1$.
   (1) $\alpha > 0$, so that $m > 0$: Since $(a^{1/n})^n = a$ and $a > 1$, by (8, 13b) it
   follows that $a^{1/n} > 1$. Hence by (8, 12), $(a^{1/n})^m > 1$ or $a^\alpha > 1$.
   (2) $\alpha = 0$: $a^\alpha = 1$ by Definition 3.
   (3) $\alpha < 0$: Then $-\alpha > 0$, and by part (1) of this proof, $a^{-\alpha} > 1$.
   Hence $a^\alpha \cdot a^{-\alpha} > a^\alpha \cdot 1$ or $1 > a^\alpha$.
   [**Remark:** Note we have proved only the "if" parts of (1), (2),
   and (3). Namely, we have shown if $\alpha > 0$, then $a^\alpha > 1$; if $\alpha = 0$,
   then $a^\alpha = 1$; if $\alpha < 0$, then $a^\alpha < 1$. But then the "only if" parts
   follow. For example, suppose $a^\alpha > 1$. Then we couldn't have
   $\alpha < 0$, since then $a^\alpha < 1$; and we couldn't have $\alpha = 0$, since
   then $a^\alpha = 1$. Hence $\alpha > 0$, etc.]
(II) Suppose $a = 1$. Then $a^\alpha = 1$ by Exercise 25.

(III) Suppose $a < 1$. Then $\dfrac{1}{a} > 1$.

  (1) $\alpha > 0$.

$$\left(\frac{1}{a}\right)^\alpha > 1 \qquad \text{(I, 1)}$$

$$\frac{1^\alpha}{a^\alpha} > 1 \qquad \text{Th. 30(5)}$$

$$1 > a^\alpha$$

  (2) If $\alpha = 0$, then $a^\alpha = 1$.
  (3) $\alpha < 0$. Then $-\alpha > 0$. Hence $a^{-\alpha} < 1$ [by (III, 1)] or $1 < a^\alpha$. (Why?)

The following theorem includes Theorem 31 as a special case (namely, when $\beta = 0$). However, we shall use Theorem 31 in the proof of Theorem 32.

Theorem 32. Let $a \,\epsilon\, P$ and $\alpha, \beta \,\epsilon\, \bar{R}$.

  (I) If $a > 1$, then
    (1) $a^\alpha > a^\beta$ if and only if $\alpha > \beta$
    (2) $a^\alpha = a^\beta$ if and only if $\alpha = \beta$
    (3) $a^\alpha < a^\beta$ if and only if $\alpha < \beta$
  (II) If $a = 1$, then $a^\alpha = a^\beta = 1$.
  (III) If $a < 1$, then
    (1) $a^\alpha < a^\beta$ if and only if $\alpha > \beta$
    (2) $a^\alpha = a^\beta$ if and only if $\alpha = \beta$
    (3) $a^\alpha > a^\beta$ if and only if $\alpha < \beta$

Proof: (I) Assume $a > 1$.

    (1) If $a^\alpha > a^\beta$, then $\dfrac{a^\alpha}{a^\beta} > 1$ or $a^{\alpha-\beta} > 1$. By Theorem 31, $\alpha - \beta > 0$ or $\alpha > \beta$.

    (2) If $a^\alpha = a^\beta$, then $\dfrac{a^\alpha}{a^\beta} = 1$ or $a^{\alpha-\beta} = 1$. By Theorem 31, $\alpha - \beta = 0$ or $\alpha = \beta$.

    (3) If $a^\alpha < a^\beta$, then $a^\beta > a^\alpha$ and by part (1), $\beta > \alpha$.
  (II) is a restatement of Theorem 31(II).
  (III) is proved similarly to (I).

Exercises

33. Prove the following.

  (a) $\sqrt{2} > 1$.
  (b) $\sqrt[3]{3} > 1$.
  (c) $5^{-7/4} < 1$.
  (d) $\sqrt{2} > \sqrt[3]{2}$.

  (e) $\sqrt{\frac{1}{2}} < \sqrt[3]{\frac{1}{2}}$.
  (f) $2 > \sqrt{2}$.
  (g) $\frac{3}{2} > \sqrt{2}$.
  (h) $\sqrt{3} > \sqrt{2}$.

  (i) $\sqrt[6]{5} < \sqrt{2}$.
  (j) $\sqrt[5]{5} < \sqrt{2} < \sqrt[4]{5}$.
  (k) $5 < 3^{3/2} < \frac{21}{4}$.

34. Theorem 3 tells us there is a rational number between 1 and $\sqrt{2}$. Exhibit such a number, and justify your contention.

35. Show that $|1 - \sqrt{2}| < \frac{1}{2}$.

36. Find a solution of the inequality $|x - \sqrt{3}| < \frac{1}{4}$, where x is a variable over R. Justify your answer.

37. Complete the proof of Theorem 30(3).

38. Prove Theorem 30(4).

39. Prove Theorem 30(5).

40. Let x be a variable over $\bar{R}$. Why is $\{3\}$ the solution set of $2^x = 8$?

41. If x is a variable over $\bar{R}$ and $a,b \in P$, can $a^x = b$ have more than one solution? Justify your answer.

42. Suppose $a \in R$ and $a > 1$. Let $S = \{a^x \in R/x \in \bar{R}, x \leq \sqrt{2}\}$. (That is, $a^r \in S$ if $r \in \bar{R}$ and $r \leq \sqrt{2}$.) Show that S is bounded above.

43. Let $a,b \in P$ and $\alpha \in \bar{R}$. Prove the following:

    (a) If $\alpha > 0$, then $a^\alpha > b^\alpha$ if and only if $a > b$.

    (b) If $\alpha = 0$, then $a^\alpha = b^\alpha$.

    (c) If $\alpha < 0$, then $a^\alpha > b^\alpha$ if and only if $a < b$.

[*Hint*: Consider $\left(\dfrac{a}{b}\right)^\alpha$ and apply Theorem 31.]

44. If $a_1, \ldots, a_n \in P$ and $\alpha \in \bar{R}$, prove that $(a_1 \cdots a_n)^\alpha = a_1^\alpha \cdots a_n^\alpha$.

45. If $a \in P$ and $\alpha_1, \ldots, \alpha_n \in \bar{R}$, prove that

$$a^{\alpha_1} a^{\alpha_2} \cdots a^{\alpha_n} = a^{\alpha_1 + \alpha_2 + \cdots + \alpha_n}$$

5. Irrational Numbers in R

Each of the equations $x^2 = 1, x^2 = 4, x^2 = 9, x^2 = 16, \ldots$ has a positive solution: $1, 2, 3, 4, \ldots$, respectively. Indeed, these solutions are positive integers. This is the case of $x^2 = a$, where a is the square (second power) of a natural number.

Definition 5. Let $a,n \in N$, $n > 1$, and suppose there exists $b \in N$ such that $b^n = a$. Then a is called a *perfect nth power*. In the case of $n = 2$, we also say a is a *perfect square;* for $n = 3$, a is also called a *perfect cube.*

Examples. Perfect squares are $1, 4, 9, 16, 25, 36, \ldots$.
              Perfect cubes are $1, 8, 27, 64, 125, 216, \ldots$.
              Perfect fourth powers are $1, 16, 81, 256, 625, 1296, \ldots$.

We shall now show that in the equations $x^2 = a$, where $a \in N$ and a is *not* a perfect square, the solution is irrational. That is, $\sqrt{2}, \sqrt{3}, \sqrt{5}, \sqrt{6}, \sqrt{7}, \sqrt{8}, \sqrt{10}, \ldots$ are irrational real numbers. For suppose $a \in N$ and $m,n \in N$, with

$$\left(\frac{m}{n}\right)^2 = a$$

Then $m^2 = an^2$. If one factors m into primes, one obtains a factorization of m^2 in which every prime appears an even number of times. Since $m^2 = an^2$, the same factors must occur in the factorization of an^2 (by the fundamental theorem of arithmetic). This means that every prime must appear an even number of times in the factorization of a, say

$$a = p_1{}^{2e_1}p_2{}^{2e_2} \cdots p_r{}^{2e_r}$$

But then $a = (p_1{}^{e_1} \cdots p_r{}^{e_r})^2$ (by Th. 30(3) and Ex. 44). Thus a is a perfect square.

We have shown if there exists a rational solution of $x^2 = a$, where $a \in N$, say $\dfrac{m}{n}$, then a must be a perfect square. Hence in the case where a is not a perfect square, the positive solution of $x^2 = a$ (which exists in R by Theorem 5) must be irrational.

The general result may be stated as follows:

Theorem 46. Let $a, t \in N$, $t > 1$. Then $x^t = a$ has a positive rational solution if and only if a is a perfect tth power (so that the positive rational solution is in fact a positive integer).

Examples. The above theorem would mean $\sqrt[5]{33}$ is irrational, as are $\sqrt[3]{7}$, $\sqrt[3]{2}$, $3^{1/3}$, etc.

Proof of Theorem. Suppose $x^t = a$ has a positive rational solution $\dfrac{m}{n}$, where $m, n \in N$. Then $\left(\dfrac{m}{n}\right)^t = a$. $m^t = an^t$. Factoring m into primes yields a factorization of m^t in which every prime appears a multiple of t times. Since $m^t = an^t$, the same must occur in the factorization of an^t, and hence in the factorization of a:

$$a = p_1{}^{e_1 t}p_2{}^{e_2 t} \cdots p_r{}^{e_r t}$$
$$= (p_1{}^{e_1} \cdots p_r{}^{e_r})^t$$

Thus a is a perfect tth power. Conversely if a is a perfect tth power, say $a = b^t$, where $b \in N$, then b is a solution of $x^t = a$. This completes the proof of the theorem.

Note that if r is rational and s is irrational, then $r \pm s$, rs, and $\dfrac{r}{s}$ are irrational. For example, if $r + s = t$ were rational, then $t - r$ (where t, r are rational) would be rational. But $t - r = s$ and s is irrational.

Thus $r + \sqrt{2}$, for example, is irrational for all $r \in \bar{R}$. Moreover, if $p \neq r$, then $p + \sqrt{2} \neq r + \sqrt{2}$. Thus for every rational number, say r, one may associate an irrational number, say $r + \sqrt{2}$. In a certain sense, therefore, there are at least as many real numbers which are irrational as there are those which are rational.

Theorem 3 states that between every two real numbers, there is a rational number. The fact is that there is also an irrational number. We can show this using the fact that we know that $\sqrt{2}$, say, is irrational.

Theorem 47. If $a,b \in R$ and $a < b$, there exists an irrational real number s such that $a < s < b$.

Proof: Since $a < b$, it follows that $\dfrac{a}{\sqrt{2}} < \dfrac{b}{\sqrt{2}}$. $\exists\, r \in \bar{R} \ni \dfrac{a}{\sqrt{2}} < r < \dfrac{b}{\sqrt{2}}$ by Theorem 3.

But then $a < r\sqrt{2} < b$. If we let $s = r\sqrt{2}$, then s is irrational and

$$a < s < b$$

Exercises

48. Tell whether each of the following is rational or irrational.

(a) 2.

(b) $1 + \sqrt{3}$.

(c) $\dfrac{2}{\sqrt{3}}$.

(d) 0.

(e) $\dfrac{\sqrt{2}}{\sqrt{3}}$. $\left(Hint: \dfrac{\sqrt{2}}{\sqrt{3}} = \dfrac{\sqrt{2}\sqrt{3}}{\sqrt{3}\sqrt{3}}.\right)$

(f) $\sqrt{2} - \sqrt{3}$.
(*Hint:* Let $r = \sqrt{2} - \sqrt{3}$ and assume r is rational. Then $\sqrt{2} = r + \sqrt{3}$. Square both sides.)

(g) $\sqrt[3]{2} - 1$.

(h) $\dfrac{1}{\sqrt{2} + 2}$.

(i) $\dfrac{1}{\sqrt{2} - \sqrt{3}}$.

(j) $(\sqrt[3]{2})^3$.

49. Theorem 47 states that between every two real numbers there is an irrational number. Find an irrational number between 5 and 6. Justify your contention.

50. Find a rational number and an irrational number between $\sqrt{2}$ and $\sqrt{3}$.

51. Let S be the set of Exercise 42, so that S is bounded above. Let u be the least upper bound of S. Find the solution set of $a^x = u$, where x is a variable over $\bar{R}$.

6. Examples

Example 1. Simplify $\sqrt[3]{48}$.
Solution: $48 = 2^4 \cdot 3$. Thus a perfect cube is a factor of 48, namely, 2^3. $48 = 2^3 \cdot 6$.
$\sqrt[3]{48} = \sqrt[3]{2^3 \cdot 6} = \sqrt[3]{2^3}\sqrt[3]{6}$ [by 30(4) since $(ab)^{1/3} = a^{1/3}b^{1/3}$]. Hence

$$\sqrt[3]{48} = 2\sqrt[3]{6}$$

By "simplify" in this example, then, we mean to remove as many factors as possible from under the "radical": $\sqrt[3]{\ }$.

Example 2. Find $\sqrt[5]{(32^4)}$.
Solution: $\sqrt[5]{(32^4)} = (\sqrt[5]{32})^4$. This follows from the fact that both $\sqrt[5]{(32^4)}$ and $(\sqrt[5]{32})^4$ are equal to $32^{4/5}$ (cf. Exercise 17). Thus $(\sqrt[5]{32})^4 = 2^4 = 16$.

Example 3. Show that $\dfrac{1}{\sqrt{2}} = \dfrac{\sqrt{2}}{2}\left(= \dfrac{1}{2}\sqrt{2}\right)$.

Solution: $\dfrac{1}{\sqrt{2}} = \dfrac{1}{\sqrt{2}} \cdot \dfrac{\sqrt{2}}{\sqrt{2}} = \dfrac{\sqrt{2}}{2}$

Example 4. Find $\dfrac{1}{\sqrt{2}} - \sqrt{2} + \dfrac{\sqrt[4]{4}}{2}$.

Solution: We have seen $\dfrac{1}{\sqrt{2}} = \dfrac{\sqrt{2}}{2}$.

Now $\sqrt[4]{4} = 4^{1/4} = (2^2)^{1/4} = 2^{1/2} = \sqrt{2}$.

Hence $\dfrac{1}{\sqrt{2}} - \sqrt{2} + \dfrac{\sqrt[4]{4}}{2} = \dfrac{\sqrt{2}}{2} - \sqrt{2} + \dfrac{\sqrt{2}}{2} = 0$.

Example 4 shows the use one can make of expressing $\dfrac{1}{\sqrt{2}}$ in a form with a rational denominator. Finding a name for $\dfrac{1}{\sqrt{2}}$ involving a rational denominator is called *rationalizing the denominator*.

Example 5. Express $\dfrac{a^2 b^{-1} - a^0 b}{ab^2 + a^{-2}b^{-2}}$ as an expression involving only positive exponents $(a,b \in P)$.

Solution: Multiply numerator and denominator by $a^2 b^2$ and use the theory of exponents.

$$\frac{a^2 b^{-1} - a^0 b}{ab^2 + a^{-2}b^{-2}} \cdot \frac{a^2 b^2}{a^2 b^2} = \frac{a^4 b - a^2 b^3}{a^3 b^4 + 1}$$

Example 6. Find: (a) $\sqrt{9}$; (b) $-\sqrt{9}$; (c) $16^{1/4}$; (d) $-16^{1/4}$; (e) $\sqrt{-9}$; (f) $(-16)^{1/4}$.
Solution: (a) 3; (b) -3; (c) 2; (d) -2. The designations in (e) and (f) have not been defined.

Example 7. Find: (a) $\sqrt[3]{8}$; (b) $-\sqrt[3]{8}$; (c) $\sqrt[3]{-8}$; (d) $27^{1/3}$; (e) $-27^{1/3}$; (f) $(-27)^{1/3}$.
Solution: (a) 2; (b) -2; (d) 3; (e) -3. The designations in (c) and (f) have not *yet* been defined. However, since $x^3 = -8$ and $x^3 = -27$ have unique solutions in R, namely, -2 and -3, respectively, it is customary to define $\sqrt[3]{-8}$ or $(-8)^{1/3}$ as -2 [since $(-2)^3 = -8$] and $\sqrt[3]{-27} = (-27)^{1/3}$ as -3 [since $(-3)^3 = -27$].

Definition 6. Let $a \in -P$ and n be a positive odd integer. Then $a^{1/n}$ or $\sqrt[n]{a}$ shall be the unique solution of $x^n = a$ (cf. Exercise 9e).

Thus

$$(-32)^{1/5} = -2 = -32^{1/5}$$
$$\sqrt[3]{-64} = -\sqrt[3]{64} = -4$$

One often sees designations such as $(-8)^{2/3}$, $(-27)^{4/3}$, $(-32)^{3/5}$, $(-8)^{-2/3}$, $(-27)^{-4/3}$, and $(-32)^{-3/5}$. These mean, respectively, $[(-8)^{1/3}]^2$, $[(-27)^{1/3}]^4$, $[(-32)^{1/5}]^3$, $[(-8)^{1/3}]^{-2}$, $[(-27)^{1/3}]^{-4}$, and $[(-32)^{1/5}]^{-3}$.

Definition 7. Let $a \in -P$ and $r \in R$. Write r as $\dfrac{m}{n}$, where $m \in J$ and $n \in N$ (this can always be done), and such that $\dfrac{m}{n}$ is in lowest terms. Then if n is odd, $a^{m/n}$ shall mean $(a^{1/n})^m$.

Definitions 6 and 7 define a^r where a is negative for certain rational exponents r. However, this is not in the main line of our development of the theory of exponents, because Theorem 30 does not apply. We should like to emphasize this fact.

Caution: **Theorem 30 does not apply when a is negative.**

For example,

$$[(-8)^{2/3}]^{1/2} = [((-8)^{1/3})^2]^{1/2} = [(-2)^2]^{1/2} = 4^{1/2} = 2$$

However, if the theory of exponents held, we should have

$$[(-8)^{2/3}]^{1/2} = (-8)^{2/3 \cdot 1/2} = (-8)^{1/3} = -2$$

Our first computation is the correct one, based on Definitions 6 and 7. The second one is incorrect, based upon the incorrect assumption that Theorem 30 can be applied.

Example 8. Solve $\sqrt{x^2 - 3x} = 2$, where x is a variable over R.

Solution: If a is a real number such that $\sqrt{a} = 2$, then $a = 4$. Conversely, if $a = 4$, then $\sqrt{a} = 2$. Hence $\sqrt{x^2 - 3x} = 2$ is equivalent to

$$x^2 - 3x = 4$$
$$x^2 - 3x - 4 = 0$$
$$(x - 4)(x + 1) = 0$$

Hence the solution set is $\{4, -1\}$.

Example 9. Solve $\sqrt{x^2 + 3x} = \sqrt{x}$, where x is a variable over R.

Solution: Any solution of $\sqrt{x^2 + 3x} = \sqrt{x}$ is also a solution of $x^2 + 3x = x$. But conversely, only those solutions of the latter equation which are nonnegative will yield solutions of the former one. For in R, $\sqrt{a}$ for $a \in -P$ is undefined. Solving $x^2 + 3x = x$, we obtain $x^2 + 2x = 0$, and solutions of this are 0 and -2. Hence the solution set of the given equation is $\{0\}$. The number -2 is often referred to as an *extraneous root*.

Extraneous roots arise in the following situation. One wishes to find the solution set S_A of equation A. In some manner he is able to find equations $B, C, \ldots, K$, with solution sets $S_B, S_C, \ldots, S_K$, respectively, such that

$$S_A \subseteq S_B \subseteq S_C \subseteq \cdots \subseteq S_K$$

If equality holds throughout, then this is the method of reducing A to an equivalent equation K from which the solution set is more easily derived. But if, as in this example, we may have proper inclusion, then one must check all elements of S_K in equation A. As S_K contains all the solutions of A, the elements of S_K which satisfy equation A yield the solution set S_A.

Example 10. Solve $\sqrt{x + 2} = x$. (Note that the left side is undefined for $x < -2$.)

Solution: "Squaring" both sides, one obtains

$$x + 2 = x^2$$
$$x^2 - x - 2 = 0$$
$$(x - 2)(x + 1) = 0$$

The solution set of this last equation is $\{2, -1\}$, and contains the solution set of our original equation. But -1 is an extraneous solution. Hence the solution set is $\{2\}$. (Observe that -1 is a solution of $-\sqrt{x + 2} = x$.)

Example 11. Solve: $\sqrt[3]{7x - 8} = x - 2$.

Solution:
$$(7x - 8)^{1/3} = x - 2$$
$$[(7x - 8)^{1/3}]^3 = (x - 2)^3$$
$$7x - 8 = x^3 - 6x^2 + 12x - 8$$
$$x^3 - 6x^2 + 5x = 0$$
$$x(x^2 - 6x + 5) = 0$$
$$x(x - 5)(x - 1) = 0$$

The solution set is $\{0, 1, 5\}$.

There can be no extraneous root, since if $a^3 = b^3$, then $a = b$ (why?). Hence all equations listed above are equivalent.

Example 12. Solve $\sqrt{x + 2} + \sqrt{3x - 2} = 4$.

Solution: Although one can "square both sides" of this equation, it is usually easier, if possible, to have one radical on each side before squaring. Thus we obtain

$$\sqrt{x + 2} = 4 - \sqrt{3x - 2}$$
$$x + 2 = (4 - \sqrt{3x - 2})^2$$
$$x + 2 = 16 - 8\sqrt{3x - 2} + (3x - 2)$$
$$8\sqrt{3x - 2} = 2x + 12$$
$$4\sqrt{3x - 2} = x + 6$$

Squaring again, we obtain

$$16(3x - 2) = x^2 + 12x + 36$$
$$48x - 32 = x^2 + 12x + 36$$
$$x^2 - 36x + 68 = 0$$
$$(x - 2)(x - 34) = 0$$

The solution set of this last equation is then $\{2, 34\}$. We see that 2 is a root of our original equation, and 34 is an extraneous root. Hence the solution set is $\{2\}$.

Exercises

52. In each of the following, remove as many factors from the radical as possible.

(a) $\sqrt{12}$.
(b) $\sqrt{200}$.
(c) $\sqrt{240}$.
(d) $\sqrt[3]{32}$.
(e) $\sqrt[5]{96}$.
(f) $\sqrt{a^4 b^3}$ (where $a^4 b^3 \geq 0$).
(g) $\sqrt{a^2}$. (*Answer:* $|a|$. Why?)
(h) $\sqrt[3]{81}$.
(i) $(162)^{1/3}$.
(j) $(2187)^{1/2}$.

53. In each of the following, rationalize the denominator.

(a) $\dfrac{1}{\sqrt{3}}$.   (b) $\dfrac{1}{\sqrt[3]{2}}$.

(c) $\dfrac{1}{2-\sqrt{3}}$. (*Hint:* Multiply numerator and denominator by $2+\sqrt{3}$.)

(d) $\dfrac{3}{4+\sqrt{2}}$.

(e) $\dfrac{1}{1-\sqrt[3]{2}}$. [*Hint:* In (c), one used the factorization of a^2-b^2. Here one uses a^3-b^3.]

(f) $\dfrac{1}{1+\sqrt[3]{2}}$.   (g) $\dfrac{2}{\sqrt{2}+\sqrt{3}}$.   (h) $\dfrac{1}{\sqrt{2}-\sqrt[3]{2}}$.

54. Find the value of the following:

(a) $7^{-1}\cdot 2^3 - \dfrac{1}{(\frac{1}{4})^{-1}} + \left(\dfrac{a^3b^2}{c}\right)^0$.   (e) $\sqrt[4]{9} - \dfrac{3}{\sqrt{3}}$. (*Answer:* 0.)

(b) $(125)^{-2/3} - 5^{-2}$.   (f) $(32)^7 \cdot 4^{-17} + \sqrt[3]{-8}$.

(c) $(2-\sqrt{2})(2+\sqrt{2})$.

(d) $\left(\sqrt[3]{\sqrt{2}}\right)^6$.

55. Simplify:

(a) $(a^0)^{50}$.

(e) $\left(\dfrac{a^{-1}b^{-1}}{a^{-2}+b^{-2}}-1\right)\cdot\dfrac{a^{-3}+b^{-3}}{a^{-1}b^{-1}}\cdot\dfrac{2^{-1}a+2^{-1}b}{3^{-1}a-3^{-1}b}$.

(b) $(a^{50})^0$.

(f) $2+\dfrac{2}{2+x^{-1}}$.

(c) $\sqrt[3]{\dfrac{a^{-6}b^9}{a^3b^{-3}}}$.

(g) $\dfrac{a^{-2}b^{1/2}c^{2/3}+ab^{3/2}c^{-1/3}}{a^{-2}b^{1/2}c^{-1/3}}$.

(d) $\sqrt[3]{(a^2-b^3+c)^3}$.

56. Solve the following, where x is a variable over R.

(a) $\sqrt{x}=3$.   (g) $x^{3/2}=8$.

(b) $-\sqrt{x}=3$.   (h) $x^{4/3}=(\sqrt[3]{x^2})^2$.

(c) $x^{1/3}=2$.   (i) $\sqrt{-x}=3$.

(d) $x^{1/3}=-2$.   (j) $\sqrt{-x^2}=9$.

(e) $\sqrt{2x^2-4x}=4$.   (k) $\sqrt{-x^2}=-9$.

(f) $\sqrt{x+7}-\sqrt{8-2x}=1$.   (l) $\sqrt{(-x)^2}=9$.

57. Solve the following, where x is a variable over R.

(a) $\sqrt{x-3}<2$.   (c) $\sqrt{x^2+1}>x-1$.

(b) $\sqrt{x-3}<x$.

58. Prove that all real numbers of the form $r+s\sqrt{2}$, where $r,s\in\bar{R}$ form a subfield of R [cf. Exercise (8, 25b)].

7. Real Exponents

7.1 *Motivation*

We are now ready to define a^α for $a \in P$ and $\alpha \in R$. For example, we wish to assign a meaning to the symbol '$3^{\sqrt{2}}$.'

According to Theorem 32, if $r,s \in \bar{R}$ and $r < \sqrt{2} < s$, then $3^r < 3^s$. For example, $\frac{1}{2} < \sqrt{2} < \frac{3}{2}$. Hence $3^{1/2} < 3^{3/2}$. In fact, $3^r < 3^{3/2}$ for any $r \in \bar{R}$

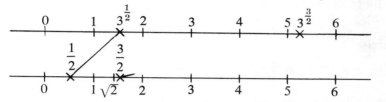

with $r < \sqrt{2}$. To have Theorem 30 hold for real exponents, it seems clear that one should not disturb this property expressed in Theorem 32. Thus since $\frac{1}{2} < \sqrt{2} < \frac{3}{2}$, we should have $3^{1/2} < 3^{\sqrt{2}} < 3^{3/2}$, or more generally $3^r < 3^{\sqrt{2}} < 3^s$ for any $r,s \in \bar{R}$ with $r < \sqrt{2} < s$.

One method that perhaps suggests itself is to consider the set of numbers 3^r for all $r \in \bar{R}$ with $r \le \sqrt{2}$. This set is bounded above (e.g., by $3^{3/2}$). Hence by postulate LUB, this set has a least upper bound. Define $3^{\sqrt{2}}$ to be this least upper bound. (Of course, the numbers r with $r \le \sqrt{2}$ are the same as those with $r < \sqrt{2}$ if $r \in \bar{R}$. However, we use '$\le$' to make it easier to see that the definition we are about to give assigns the same meaning to rational exponents as before.) Thus we have defined

$$3^{\sqrt{2}} = \text{lub } \{3^x \in R/x \le \sqrt{2}, x \in \bar{R}\}$$

Exercises

59. Suppose $a \in P$, $a > 1$, and $\alpha \in R$. Let $S = \{a^x \in R/x \le \alpha, x \in \bar{R}\}$. Prove that S is bounded above. (*Hint:* Use Theorems 2 and 32.)

60. Suppose $a \in P$, $a > 1$, and $\alpha \in \bar{R}$. Let S be as in Exercise 59. Prove that lub $S = a^\alpha$.

61. Suppose $a \in P$, $a < 1$, and $\alpha \in R$. Let $S = \{a^x \in R/x \ge \alpha, x \in \bar{R}\}$. Prove that S is bounded above.

62. Suppose $a \in P$, $a < 1$, and $\alpha \in \bar{R}$. Let S be as in Exercise 61. Prove that lub $S = a^\alpha$.

7.2 *Real Exponents Defined*

Definition 8. Let $a \in P$, $\alpha \in R$.
(1) If $a > 1$, $a^\alpha = \text{lub } \{a^x \in R/x \le \alpha, x \in \bar{R}\}$
(2) $1^\alpha = 1$
(3) If $a < 1$, $a^\alpha = \text{lub } \{a^x \in R/x \ge \alpha, x \in \bar{R}\}$

According to Exercises 59 and 61 the sets in (1) and (3) are bounded above, and hence have least upper bounds. According to Exercises 60 and 62 (and 25) if α is rational, Definition 8 agrees with the definitions previously given for rational exponents.

Our aim now becomes to prove that Theorems 30 to 32 remain true for real exponents. To give the student a chance to digest the theory of exponents as presented to this point, however, we shall defer the remaining and more difficult part of the theory to the chapter on exponential functions in Part III.

Exercise

63. If $a \in P$ and $\alpha \in R$, prove that $a^\alpha > 0$.

8. Notation for Positive Real Numbers

8.1 Decimal Expansions

We have seen how to represent any natural number in terms of a radix. We now turn to the representation of any positive real number. There is no essential difference in working with base ten or other bases, so we consider base ten here and develop the usual decimal notation.

When one writes 76.254 in decimal notation, he is referring to the number $7(10)^1 + 6(10)^0 + 2(10)^{-1} + 5(10)^{-2} + 4(10)^{-3}$. Note that we are giving the meaning of '76.254' in terms of concepts previously developed: notation for integers; addition and multiplication; and positive, zero, and negative integral exponents. The digits before the "decimal point" concern a natural number, in this case, 76. The ones after concern a real number between 0 and 1.

If we can show that every positive real number can be written as the sum of a nonnegative integer and some nonnegative real number less than 1, it will remain for us to establish the notation for real numbers between 0 and 1.

Theorem 64. Let $\alpha \in P$. Then there exists a nonnegative integer m and a real number t with $0 \le t < 1$ such that $\alpha = m + t$. (For example, if $\alpha = 76.254$, then $m = 76$ and $t = .254$; or if $\alpha = \frac{71}{3}$, then $m = 23$ and $t = \frac{2}{3}$; or if $\alpha = \frac{1}{2}$, then $m = 0$ and $t = \frac{1}{2}$.)

Proof: Let S be the set of natural numbers which are larger than α. S is nonempty by Theorem 2. Hence S has a least element, say n. Thus (1) $\alpha < n$; and (2) $n - 1 \le \alpha$. Let $m = n - 1$ so that either $m = 0$ (if $n = 1$) or $m \in N$. Let $t = \alpha - (n - 1)$. By (2), $t \ge 0$. Adding $1 - n$ to both sides of (1) shows that $\alpha - (n - 1) < 1$; i.e., $t < 1$. Hence $0 \le t < 1$. Finally

$$m + t = (n - 1) + [\alpha - (n - 1)] = \alpha$$

Now let us examine the notation for real numbers between 0 and 1.

.18 means $1(10)^{-1} + 8(10)^{-2}$

.4601 means $4(10)^{-1} + 6(10)^{-2} + 0(10)^{-3} + 1(10)^{-4}$

We shall write a_{-1} for the coefficient of 10^{-1}, a_{-2} for the coefficient of $10^{-2}, \ldots, a_{-n}$ for the coefficient of 10^{-n}.

In .4601, we have $a_{-1} = 4$, $a_{-2} = 6$, $a_{-3} = 0$, and $a_{-4} = 1$.

In general, we may define

$$.a_{-1}a_{-2} \cdots a_{-m}$$

to mean

$$a_{-1}(10)^{-1} + \cdots + a_{-m}(10)^{-m} \qquad (*)$$

where each of the coefficients a_{-i} is an integer satisfying $0 \leqq a_{-i} \leqq 9$.

Or we can further define

$$a_n a_{n-1} \cdots a_1 a_0.a_{-1}a_{-2} \cdots a_{-m}$$

where $a_n \neq 0$, to mean

$$a_n 10^n + \cdots + a_0 10^0 + a_{-1} 10^{-1} + \cdots + a_{-m} 10^{-m}$$

Thus in 732.18, $n = 2$ and $m = 2$. Also $a_2 = 7$, $a_1 = 3$, $a_0 = 2$, $a_{-1} = 1$, and $a_{-2} = 8$. For numbers of type $(*)$, we shall take n to be the subscript of the first number from $a_{-1}, a_{-2}, a_{-3}, \cdots$ which is distinct from 0. Thus in .18, $n = -1$ and $a_{-1} = 1$, $a_{-2} = 8$. In .0018, $n = -3$ and $a_{-3} = 1$, $a_{-4} = 8$; of course, $a_{-1} = a_{-2} = 0$.

There are two questions which may be raised:

(1) Is every number of the form $(*)$ a number between 0 and 1 (or possibly 0 if all coefficients are 0)?

(2) Conversely, is every real number between 0 and 1 obtained in this manner?

The first question may be answered in the affirmative. For

$$a_{-1} 10^{-1} + \cdots + a_{-m} 10^{-m}$$
$$\leqq 9 \cdot 10^{-1} + \cdots + 9 \cdot 10^{-m}$$
$$= 9(10^{-1} + \cdots + 10^{-m})$$

$$= 9 \cdot \frac{10^{-1} - 10^{-1}(10^{-1})^m}{1 - 10^{-1}} \qquad \left[\begin{array}{l} (8, 32) \text{ with } a = 10^{-1}, \\ \lambda = 10^{-1}, \, n = m - 1 \end{array} \right]$$

$$= 9 \cdot \frac{1 - 10^{-m}}{10 - 1} \qquad \left[\begin{array}{l} \text{multiplying numerator and denomi-} \\ \text{nator of the previous step by 10} \end{array} \right]$$

$$= 1 - 10^{-m}$$
$$< 1 \qquad \qquad \text{since } 10^{-m} > 0$$

The second question must be answered in the negative. As an example, let us consider $\frac{5}{7}$, which is between 0 and 1. Suppose we had

$$\tfrac{5}{7} = a_{-1}10^{-1} + \cdots + a_{-m}10^{-m}$$

Then multiplying both sides by 10^m we see that

$$\frac{5 \cdot 10^m}{7} = a_{-1}10^{m-1} + \cdots + a_{-m}10^0$$

so that $\dfrac{5 \cdot 10^m}{7}$ is a natural number, say q. But then

$$5 \cdot 10^m = 7q$$

and the right side has a factor 7, whereas the left side does not. By the fundamental theorem of arithmetic, this equality is impossible.

Thus dividing $5 \cdot 10^m$ by 7 can never yield a remainder of 0 for any m.

Dividing $5 \cdot 10^3 = 5000$ by 7, for example, yields the quotient 714 and remainder 7. Thus

$$\tfrac{5000}{7} = 714 + \tfrac{2}{7}$$

Let us translate this fact into information concerning $\tfrac{5}{7}$. Indeed, multiplying both sides by 10^{-3} yields

$$\begin{aligned}\tfrac{5}{7} &= 7(10)^{-1} + 1(10)^{-2} + 4(10)^{-3} + \tfrac{2}{7}(10)^{-3}\\ &= .714\tfrac{2}{7}\end{aligned}$$

where the $4\tfrac{2}{7}$ at the end represents $(4 + \tfrac{2}{7})10^{-3}$. Thus,

$$.714 < \tfrac{5}{7} < .715$$

In the same manner one sees that

$$\tfrac{5}{7} = .7142857142857142\tfrac{6}{7}$$

Since the remainders repeat after six steps, the digits appearing in the quotient will repeat in groups of six. Now certainly,

$$\tfrac{5}{7} \neq .7142857142857142$$

Indeed, the error is $\tfrac{6}{7} \cdot 10^{-16}$, or less than 10^{-16}. However, we see that if we consider the numbers: .7, .71, .714, .7142, .71428, . . . we get a number closer and closer to $\tfrac{5}{7}$. To be precise, we shall see that the least upper bound of this infinite set of numbers is exactly $\tfrac{5}{7}$. It is for this reason that we write

$$\tfrac{5}{7} = .714285714285 \ldots$$

That is, in decimal notation, $\tfrac{5}{7}$ is written as an infinite decimal. The meaning of saying that $\tfrac{5}{7} = .7142 \ldots$ is that $\tfrac{5}{7}$ is the least upper bound of the set consisting of

$7(10)^{-1}$, $7(10)^{-1} + 1(10)^{-2}$, $7(10)^{-1} + 1(10)^{-2} + 4(10)^{-3}$, . . .

One can similarly check that

$$\tfrac{2}{3} = .6666 \ldots$$
$$\tfrac{3}{4} = .7500 \ldots$$
$$\tfrac{5}{9} = .5555 \ldots$$
$$\tfrac{68}{165} = .412121212 \ldots$$

In each of these examples of representing rational numbers as an infinite decimal (sometimes an infinite number of zeros occurring, as in $\tfrac{3}{4} = .75000 \ldots$, which can also be written $\tfrac{3}{4} = .75$), we observe that repetitions occur. This will be true, as it was for $\tfrac{5}{7}$, for every rational number. For if we consider $\dfrac{p}{q}$, there can be at most q remainders (namely, $0, 1, \ldots , q - 1$). Hence if one gets, for example, a remainder at the eighth step repeating that at the third, one would obtain an expansion of the type

$$.abc\underbrace{defgh}\underbrace{defgh} \ldots$$

In this example we would get a decimal expansion which is called a *repeating decimal* of period 5. That is, after a certain point, the digits appearing repeat in groups of 5.

In general, if we say $\alpha = .a_{-1}a_{-2}a_{-3} \cdots$, we shall mean that α is the least upper bound of the set of numbers consisting of

$$a_{-1}10^{-1}, \; a_{-1}10^{-1} + a_{-2}10^{-2}, \; a_{-1}10^{-1} + a_{-2}10^{-2} + a_{-3}10^{-3}, \ldots$$

Since each number of this set is less than 1 (we are assuming $0 \leq a_{-i} \leq 9$ as before), this set is bounded above and has a least upper bound which is less than or equal to 1.

We shall see (Section 8.2) that the repeating decimal expansions designate rational numbers, the nonrepeating ones irrational numbers.

Finally, given two different infinite decimals, one may ask whether they might represent the same real number. We shall see (Section 8.2) that this can happen but only in the following situation. Namely, the decimals .75000 . . . and .749999 . . . have the same least upper bound, and therefore

$$.75000 \ldots = .74999 \ldots$$

Similarly,

$$.36792000 \ldots = .36791999 \ldots$$

Also

$$.9999 \ldots = 1.0000 \ldots$$

Exercises

65. Write the following in decimal notation:

(a) $\frac{2}{11}$. (b) $\frac{3}{8}$. (c) $\frac{4}{9}$. (d) $\frac{41}{3}$ (first write $\frac{41}{3}$ as the sum of an integer and a real number between 0 and 1).

66. Expand the above in the following bases: (a) 4. (b) 11. (c) 12. (d) 2.

67. Below are listed real numbers in decimal notation in the form

$$a_n a_{n-1} \cdots a_1 a_0.a_{-1}a_{-2} \cdots$$

State what n is, and then $a_n, a_{n-1}, \ldots$

(a) 732.0212121 . . . .   (d) 8.62.

(b) 732.0212121.   (e) .47861.

(c) .07321021321021 . . . .   (f) 876543210.12345678.

68. *Project:* Develop algorithms for addition, subtraction, multiplication, and division of finite decimals.

8.2   Underlying Theory of Decimal Expansions

Our aim in this section is to state and prove the theorems underlying the familiar notation for all positive real numbers. The remaining real numbers are the additive inverses of the positive ones, and zero. We thus obtain the decimal notation for all real numbers. This is a fitting conclusion to Part II.[3]

Theorem 69. Let $S \subseteq R$, $T \subseteq R$, and let

$$S + T = \{(x + y) \in R / x \in S, y \in T\}$$

Suppose S and T are bounded above. Then $S + T$ is bounded above. In fact, if $\alpha = \operatorname{lub} S$ and $\beta = \operatorname{lub} T$, then $\alpha + \beta = \operatorname{lub} (S + T)$.

Proof: If $s \in S$, $t \in T$, then $s \leq \alpha$, $t \leq \beta$, and $s + t \leq \alpha + \beta$. Hence $\alpha + \beta$ is an upper bound of $S + T$.

Suppose $\gamma < \alpha + \beta$, so that there exists $d \in P$ such that $\gamma + d = \alpha + \beta$. We shall show that γ cannot be an upper bound of $S + T$. Since $\alpha = \operatorname{lub} S$, $\alpha - \dfrac{d}{2}$ is not an upper bound of S. Hence there exists $s \in S$ with $\alpha - \dfrac{d}{2} < s$. Similarly, there exists $t \in T$ with $\beta - \dfrac{d}{2} < t$. Thus $\left(\alpha - \dfrac{d}{2}\right) + \left(\beta - \dfrac{d}{2}\right) < s + t$,

$$\alpha + \beta - d < s + t$$
$$\gamma < s + t$$

---

[3] The material in this section, which concludes the chapter, is rather technical and one may wish to omit it on a first reading. As with Section 2, however, the discussion is logically accessible to the student at this time, but requires slow and careful study.

But since $s + t \in S + T$, this means γ cannot be an upper bound of $S + T$. Hence $\alpha + \beta = \text{lub}\, (S + T)$.

Theorem 70. Let $S \subseteq P$, $T \subseteq P$, and let $ST = \{xy \in P / x \in S, y \in T\}$. Suppose S and T are bounded above. Then ST is bounded above; and if $\alpha = \text{lub}\, S$, $\beta = \text{lub}\, T$, then $\alpha\beta = \text{lub}\, ST$.

Proof: It is easy to see that $\alpha\beta$ is an upper bound of ST.

Suppose $0 < \gamma < \alpha\beta$. Then $1 < \dfrac{\alpha\beta}{\gamma}$. Let $r = \dfrac{\alpha\beta}{\gamma}$, so that $r > 1$. Then $\sqrt{r} > 1$.

Hence $\dfrac{\alpha}{\sqrt{r}} < \alpha$ and $\dfrac{\beta}{\sqrt{r}} < \beta$, and $\dfrac{\alpha}{\sqrt{r}}$ cannot be an upper bound of S, nor $\dfrac{\beta}{\sqrt{r}}$

of T. So there exists $s \in S$, $t \in T$ with $\dfrac{\alpha}{\sqrt{r}} < s$ and $\dfrac{\beta}{\sqrt{r}} < t$. Then $\dfrac{\alpha\beta}{\sqrt{r}\sqrt{r}} < st$, or

$\gamma < st$, and γ cannot be an upper bound of ST. Hence $\alpha\beta = \text{lub}\, ST$.

Exercises

71. State and prove a theorem similar to Theorem 69 for subsets S and T of R which are bounded below.
72. State and prove a theorem similar to Theorem 70 involving lower bounds T of P. (Of course, all nonempty subsets of P are bounded below.) (*Hint:* If α, β are both different from 0, follow the argument given in the proof of Theorem 70. If either $\alpha = 0$, $\beta = 0$, or both, choose any $\gamma > 0$. Then let $r \in R$ be any real number such that $r\sqrt{\gamma} > \beta$. Finally choose $s \in S$ with

$0 < s < \dfrac{\sqrt{\gamma}}{r}$, $t \in T$ with $\beta < t < r\sqrt{\gamma}$. Then $st < \gamma$.)

Theorem 73. Let $\alpha \in R$, $0 < \alpha < 1$. Let $S = \{1, \alpha, \alpha^2, \ldots, \alpha^n, \ldots\}$. Then glb $S = 0$. [In particular if $\gamma \in P$, there exists m such that $\alpha^m < \gamma$; for otherwise γ would be a lower bound of S.]

Proof: The set $\{\alpha\}$ certainly has glb α. Suppose $c = \text{glb}\, S$. Then $c\alpha = \text{glb}\, \{\{\alpha\} \cdot S\}$ by Exercise 72. But $\{\alpha\} \cdot S = \{\alpha, \alpha^2, \ldots, \alpha^{n+1}, \ldots\}$ and clearly has the same glb as S. Hence $c\alpha = c$ so that $c = 0$ (since $0 < \alpha < 1$).

Theorem 74. If $0 < \alpha < 1$, then $1 + \alpha + \alpha^2 + \cdots = \dfrac{1}{1 - \alpha}$. By this we

mean $\dfrac{1}{1 - \alpha} = \text{lub}\, \{1, 1 + \alpha, 1 + \alpha + \alpha^2, \ldots\}$.

Proof: $1 - \alpha^{n+1} = (1 - \alpha)(1 + \alpha + \cdots + \alpha^n)$. Hence

$$1 + \alpha + \cdots + \alpha^n = \frac{1 - \alpha^{n+1}}{1 - \alpha}$$

(a) $1 + \alpha + \cdots + \alpha^n = \dfrac{1}{1-\alpha} - \dfrac{\alpha^{n+1}}{1-\alpha}$

(b) $1 + \alpha + \cdots + \alpha^n < \dfrac{1}{1-\alpha}$

It follows from (b) that $\dfrac{1}{1-\alpha}$ is an upper bound of $1 + \alpha + \alpha^2 + \cdots$. Could

$\dfrac{1}{1-\alpha} - \beta$ be an upper bound, for $\beta \,\epsilon\, P$? By Theorem 73, since $\beta(1-\alpha) \,\epsilon\, P$,

we could choose m so that $\alpha^{m+1} < \beta(1-\alpha)$. Then

(c) $\dfrac{\alpha^{m+1}}{1-\alpha} < \beta$

Then

$$1 + \alpha + \cdots + \alpha^m = \dfrac{1}{1-\alpha} - \dfrac{\alpha^{m+1}}{1-\alpha} \qquad \text{by (a)}$$

$$> \dfrac{1}{1-\alpha} - \beta \qquad \text{by (c)}$$

and $\dfrac{1}{1-\alpha} - \beta$ is not an upper bound. Hence $\dfrac{1}{1-\alpha}$ is the lub, and Theorem

74 is proved.

Theorem 75. Let r be any positive integer greater than 1. If $a_{-1}, a_{-2}, \ldots$ are all integers satisfying $0 \leqq a_{-i} \leqq r - 1$, then

$$a_{-1}r^{-1} + a_{-2}r^{-2} + \cdots$$

is bounded above by 1. (That is, the set $\{a_{-1}r^{-1}, a_{-1}r^{-1} + a_{-2}r^{-2}, \ldots\}$ has 1 as *an* upper bound.)

Proof: Similar to that of base ten given in Section 8.1.

Definition 9. Let $\alpha = a_{-1}r^{-1} + a_{-2}r^{-2} + \cdots$. That is, $\alpha = \text{lub}$ $\{a_{-1}r^{-1}, a_{-1}r^{-1} + a_{-2}r^{-2}, \ldots\}$. Then we shall write $\alpha = (.a_{-1}a_{-2} \cdots)_r$. By Theorem 75, we have $0 \leqq \alpha \leqq 1$. Also $(a_n a_{n-1} \cdots a_0.a_{-1}a_{-2} \cdots)_r$ shall designate the nonnegative real number

$$(a_n a_{n-1} \cdots a_0)_r + (.a_{-1}a_{-2} \cdots)_r$$

In the case that $r = 10$, we shall omit the parentheses and the subscript.

We have seen that every positive real number can be written as a sum of a nonnegative integer and some nonnegative real number less than 1. We show next that *every* real number between 0 and 1 has a representation of the form given in Theorem 75.

Theorem 76. Let $\alpha \in R$, $0 \leq \alpha \leq 1$. Then there exist $a_{-1}, a_{-2}, \ldots$ in J with $0 \leq a_{-i} \leq r - 1$ such that $\alpha = (.a_{-1}a_{-2} \cdots)_r$.

Proof: If $\alpha = 0$, then $\alpha = 0r^{-1} + 0r^{-2} + \cdots$. Thus we may assume $\alpha > 0$. Let a_{-1} be the largest integer such that $a_{-1}r^{-1} < \alpha$. Certainly $0 \leq a_{-1} \leq r - 1$. For $rr^{-1} = 1 \geq \alpha$. Note that $a_{-1}r^{-1} < \alpha \leq (a_{-1} + 1)r^{-1}$. Let a_{-2} be the largest integer such that $a_{-1}r^{-1} + a_{-2}r^{-2} < \alpha$. Again $0 \leq a_{-2} \leq r - 1$. For if we had $a_{-2} \geq r$, then

$$a_{-1}r^{-1} + a_{-2}r^{-2} \geq a_{-1}r^{-1} + rr^{-2} = a_{-1}r^{-1} + r^{-1} = (a_{-1} + 1)r^{-1} \geq \alpha$$

This not being the case, $0 \leq a_{-2} \leq r - 1$ as asserted. Note that $a_{-1}r^{-1} + a_{-2}r^{-2} < \alpha \leq a_{-1}r^{-1} + (a_{-2} + 1)r^{-2}$. In particular

$$\alpha - (a_{-1}r^{-1} + a_{-2}r^{-2}) \leq r^{-2}$$

Assume one has defined a_{-n} with $0 \leq a_{-n} \leq r - 1$ such that $a_{-1}r^{-1} + \cdots + a_{-n}r_{-n} < \alpha \leq a_{-1}r^{-1} + \cdots + (a_{-n} + 1)r^{-n}$, so that

$$\alpha - (a_{-1}r^{-1} + \cdots + a_{-n}r^{-n}) \leq r^{-n}$$

Then choose $a_{-(n+1)}$ to be the largest integer such that $a_{-1}r^{-1} + \cdots + a_{-n}r^{-n} + a_{-(n+1)}r^{-(n+1)} < \alpha$. As before

$$\alpha - (a_{-1}r^{-1} + \cdots + a_{-(n+1)}r^{-(n+1)}) \leq r^{-(n+1)}$$

In this way we obtain

$$a_{-1}r^{-1} + a_{-2}r^{-2} + \cdots$$

The least upper bound is α. (How does this follow from Theorem 73?)

In the proof of Theorem 76, we showed that

$$\alpha - (a_{-1}r^{-1} + \cdots + a_{-n}r^{-n}) \leq r^{-n}$$

This was for the particular choice of $a_{-1}, a_{-2}, \ldots$ made in that proof. We next show that this condition holds for any decimal expansion of α.

Theorem 77. If $\alpha = .b_{-1}b_{-2} \cdots$, then

$$\alpha - (b_{-1}r^{-1} + \cdots + b_{-n}r^{-n}) \leq r^{-n}$$

Proof: We must show $\alpha \leq b_{-1}r^{-1} + \cdots + b_{-n}r^{-n} + r^{-n}$. But

$$\alpha = b_{-1}r^{-1} + \cdots + b_{-n}r^{-n} + b_{-(n+1)}r^{-(n+1)} + \cdots$$
$$\leq b_{-1}r^{-1} + \cdots + b_{-n}r^{-n} + (r - 1)r^{-(n+1)} + (r - 1)r^{-(n+2)} + \cdots$$

(For each number in the set being considered on the second line is equal to or larger than the corresponding number on the first line. Hence the lub of the second set is larger than or equal to that of the first.)

$$= b_{-1}r^{-1} + \cdots + b_{-n}r^{-n} + (r - 1)r^{-(n+1)} \cdot (1 + r^{-1} + r^{-2} + \cdots)$$

(For the numbers considered here are precisely the same as on the second line.)

$$= b_{-1}r^{-1} + \cdots + b_{-n}r^{-n} + (r-1)r^{-(n+1)} \cdot \frac{r}{r-1} \qquad \text{Th. 74}$$

$$= b_{-1}r^{-1} + \cdots + b_{-n}r^{-n} + r^{-n}$$

We now show that the representation of α as an infinite decimal is unique except for the finite (or "terminating") decimals, i.e., those with all zeros beyond a certain point. The terminating decimals, of course, represent rational numbers.

Theorem 78. If $\alpha \in R$, $0 \leq \alpha \leq 1$, then

$$\alpha = .a_{-1}a_{-2} \cdots \qquad (*)$$

and this representation is unique unless from a certain point on all co-efficients are $r-1$ or all coefficients are 0. In this case either $\alpha = 0$, or $\alpha = 1$, or α has precisely two representations of the type $(*)$:

(1) $.a_{-1}a_{-2} \cdots a_{-n}000 \cdots$ $(a_{-n} \neq 0)$

(2) $.a_{-1}a_{-2} \cdots a_{-(n-1)}(a_{-n}-1)sss \cdots$ $(s = r-1)$

Moreover the decimals (1) and (2) always represent the same real number (for all $a_{-1}, a_{-2}, \ldots, a_{-n}$).

Proof: Suppose $\alpha = a_{-1}r^{-1} + a_{-2}r^{-2} + \cdots = b_{-1}r^{-1} + b_{-1}r^{-2} + \cdots$. Then if n is the first place where $a_{-n} \neq b_{-n}$, say $a_{-n} > b_{-n}$. Since a_{-n} and b_{-n} are integers, $a_{-n} > b_{-n}$ means $a_{-n} \geq b_{-n} + 1$. Now $\alpha - (a_{-1}r^{-1} + \cdots + a_{-(n-1)} + a_{-n}) \geq 0$. By Theorem 77, $\alpha - (b_{-1}r^{-1} + \cdots + b_{-n}r^{-n}) \leq r^{-n}$. Adding $-r^{-n}$ to both sides yields

$$\alpha - (b_{-1}r^{-1} + \cdots + (b_{-n}+1)r^{-n}) \leq 0$$

Since $a_{-1} = b_{-1}, \ldots, a_{-(n-1)} = b_{-(n-1)}$, $a_{-n} \geq b_{-n} + 1$, we obtain

$$0 \leq \alpha - (a_{-1}r^{-1} + \cdots + a_{-n}r^{-n})$$
$$\leq \alpha - (b_{-1}r^{-1} + \cdots + (b_{-n}+1)r^{-n})$$
$$\leq 0$$

This means we must have all equalities. Hence

$$\alpha = a_{-1}r^{-1} + \cdots + a_{-n}r^{-n} \qquad \text{and} \qquad a_{-n} = b_{-n} + 1$$

It follows that $a_{-(n+1)} = 0$, $a_{-(n+2)} = 0, \ldots$. Also

$$\alpha = b_{-1}r^{-1} + \cdots + b_{-n}r^{-n} + r^{-n}$$
$$\leq b_{-1}r^{-1} + \cdots + b_{-n}r^{-n} + b_{-(n+1)}r^{-(n+1)} + \cdots + b_{-(n+m)}r^{-(n+m)} + r^{-(n+m)}$$

$$\text{Th. 77}$$

$$\leq b_{-1}r^{-1} + \cdots + b_{-n}r^{-n} + (r-1)(r^{-(n+1)} + \cdots + r^{-(n+m)}) + r^{-(n+m)}$$
$$= b_{-1}r^{-1} + \cdots + b_{-n}r^{-n} + (r-1)r^{-(n+m)}(r^{m-1} + r^{m-2} + \cdots + 1) + r^{-(n+m)}$$
$$= b_{-1}r^{-1} + \cdots + b_{-n}r^{-n} + (r-1)r^{-(n+m)} \cdot \frac{r^m - 1}{r-1} + r^{-(n+m)}$$
$$= b_{-1}r^{-1} + \cdots + b_{-n}r^{-n} + r^{-(n+m)}(r^m - 1 + 1)$$
$$= b_{-1}r^{-1} + \cdots + b_{-n}r^{-n} + r^{-n}$$
$$= \alpha$$

It follows that equality must have held throughout, and

$$b_{-(n+1)} = r - 1, \ldots, b_{-(n+m)} = r - 1$$

This is true for any $m \in N$.

That (1) and (2) always represent the same real number is left as an exercise. The only cases of repeating zeros or $(r - 1)$'s not covered in (1) and (2) are (1) all zeros; (2) all $(r - 1)$'s. The first yields the number 0, the second the number 1.

We have seen in Section 8.1 that every rational number yields a repeating decimal. We conclude now by showing that conversely every repeating decimal corresponds to a rational number.

Theorem 79. Let $\alpha \in R$, $0 < \alpha < 1$. Then the decimal expansion of α is a repeating decimal if and only if $\alpha \in \bar{R}$.

Proof: It remains to prove that if α has a repeating decimal expansion, then α is rational. We shall illustrate the proof with an example. Let

$$\alpha = .431\underbrace{524}\underbrace{652}\underbrace{465}\underbrace{246} \ldots$$

Then

$$\alpha = .431 + .0005246 + .00000005246 + \cdots$$

$$= .431 + 5246(10^{-3})(1 + 10^{-4} + (10^{-4})^2 + \cdots)$$

$$= .431 + 5246(10^{-3}) \cdot \frac{1}{1 - 10^{-4}} \qquad \text{Th. 74}$$

and this is a rational number.
In general one has

$$\alpha = .a_{-1} \cdots a_{-r}\underbrace{b_1 \cdots b_s}\, \underbrace{b_1 \cdots b_s} \cdots$$

$$= .a_{-1} \cdots a_{-r} + (b_1 \cdots b_s)10^{-r}(1 + 10^{-s} + (10^{-s})^2 + \cdots)$$

$$= .a_{-1} \cdots a_{-r} + (b_1 \cdots b_s)10^{-r}\frac{1}{1 - 10^{-s}}$$

9. Concluding Remarks

With this chapter we conclude the properties of the real numbers to be developed in this textbook. We have observed in our historical remarks how the natural numbers, the fractions, zero, negative numbers came into being. The exciting history of the development of notation for these numbers can be traced in the references we have given. We have also considered the introduction of the postulational approach in mathematics, we have presented one for the real-number system, and we have referred to the Peano postulates for the natural numbers. But what we have left unstated up to now is the history of the irrational numbers. For intuitively, it is not at all clear that irrational numbers are needed to measure lengths of line segments.

For example, consider a line segment of length 1: Mark off two equal

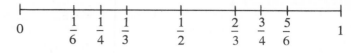

segments, thus obtaining $\frac{1}{2}$; then three equal segments, thus obtaining $\frac{1}{3}$, $\frac{2}{3}$; then four equal segments to obtain $\frac{1}{4}$, $\frac{2}{4} = \frac{1}{2}$, $\frac{3}{4}$; etc. In general one marks off $\frac{1}{n}$, $\frac{2}{n}$, $\frac{3}{n}$, $\cdots$, $\frac{n-1}{n}$. As n gets larger and larger, it seems as if one might cover all points on the line in the following sense: If any point between 0 and 1 is taken, then n can be taken large enough so that the process considered above would yield a number for this point. As this would be a rational number, every point between 0 and 1 could be represented by a rational number which would represent the length from 0 to that point.

The fact is, of course, that this process will not cover every point on the line. The same discussion applies to lines of length 2, 3, 4, etc.

The history of the recognition of the need for irrational numbers begins with Pythagoras. In Croton in the south of Italy, Pythagoras opened schools and would lecture to large and enthusiastic audiences (in the sixth century B.C.). His audiences were divided into two classes: the listeners and the mathematicians. The latter class formed a brotherhood, known as the Pythagoreans. The knowledge they discovered was shared among them, but it was forbidden to expose any of it to the outside world.[4]

As it was the custom to refer all results found within the society back to the founder, it is not known whether the theorem in geometry called

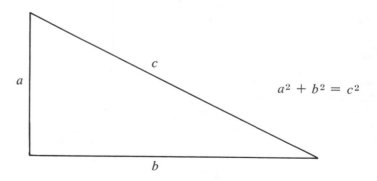

$$a^2 + b^2 = c^2$$

[4] W. W. R. Ball, *A Short Account of the History of Mathematics*, pp. 18–27, Macmillan, New York, 1888.

the "Pythagorean theorem" is actually due to Pythagoras. It states that in a right triangle, if a and b are the lengths of the sides adjacent to the right angle, and c the length of the hypotenuse, then $a^2 + b^2 = c^2$: Thus if $a = 1$ and $b = 1$, we have $c^2 = 1^2 + 1^2 = 2$. Therefore c is the length of a line segment and its square is 2. The discovery that c in this case is an irrational number is attributed to the Pythagoreans. To be the first to prove $\sqrt{2}$ is irrational is quite a feat, but to conceive the possibility of irrational numbers is really amazing. If the reader will imagine himself a Pythagorean, he will appreciate the dilemma. A new kind of number is needed, unless there really doesn't exist a length whose square is two. What kinds of numbers are these, where do we get them, and how do we explain them? It was a deep mystery to the Pythagoreans, and it is reported that the first one to leak this discovery of irrationals perished in a shipwreck.[5]

At any rate, a proof that $\sqrt{2}$ is irrational is contained in Euclid's elements. It is a proof which few, if any, mathematicians will fail to recognize as beautiful. Namely, suppose $\frac{p}{q}$ is a rational number expressed so that p and q have no common factors other than 1 or -1. Can we have $\left(\frac{p}{q}\right)^2 = 2$? If so, then

$$p^2 = 2q^2 \qquad\qquad (*)$$

Since the right side is even, so is the left. Thus p^2, and hence p, is even. *So q must be odd*, since otherwise p and q have the common factor 2.

Since p is even, we may write $p = 2r$. From $(*)$ we obtain

$$4r^2 = 2q^2$$
$$2r^2 = q^2$$

This proves q^2, and hence *q is even*.

We have therefore proved that q is odd and q is even, which is a contradiction. This was based upon the assumption that there existed a rational number whose square is 2. Hence no such number exists.

This proof is more than 2000 years old!

And more than 2000 years later, Richard Dedekind finally showed how to develop the real-number system from the rational numbers; and the existence of the irrational numbers now depends, therefore, upon the existence of the natural numbers. Thus $\sqrt{2}$ has the same stature as 3 and -8 in the real-number system. And the seas which wrecked the ships of ancient times have been tamed. But rather than follow the many eruptive tributaries, we shall conclude here.

[5] Florian Cajori, *A History of Mathematics*, pp. 69–70, Macmillan, New York, 1894.

a laboratory exercise

THE COMPLEX NUMBER SYSTEM

1. Introduction

One may, in an application, wish to know whether there is a natural number a for which $2a^2 - a - 1 = 0$; that is, is there a solution of

$$2x^2 - x - 1 = 0$$

where x is a variable over N?

Since $N \subset R$, one can solve the equation $2x^2 - x - 1 = 0$, where x is a variable over R, and look to see which, if any, of the solutions are natural numbers.

Thus one obtains $(x - 1)(2x + 1) = 0$ and the solution set over R is $\{1, -\frac{1}{2}\}$. Hence the solution set in N is $\{1\}$.

Now some expressions of the type $ax^2 + bx + c$, where $a,b,c \in R$ or even where $a,b,c \in J$, do not factor in R. This suggests the following question:

Suppose one could find a set C satisfying the following:

(1) $R \subset C$.
(2) Two binary operations $+$ and $\cdot$ are defined on C with respect to which C is a field.
(3) These two binary operations, when restricted to R, coincide with those of Chapter 5.
(4) Every expression of the type $ax^2 + bx + c$ (and hopefully others), where $a,b,c \in R$, can be factored into linear factors.

Would the theory of solving equations be simplified?

2. Getting Ideas

We now put aside our wishful thinking, and consider the problem of how to construct such a set C. The actual construction will be indicated in the next section, and most of the details will be left to the exercises there. But here we try to get ideas on how we should go about such a construction.

We could begin with a particular example of an expression of the type $ax^2 + bx + c$ (where $a,b,c \in R$), which cannot be factored in R. We could then *assume* that a set C exists satisfying (1), (2), and (3) of Section 1, and instead of (4) assume that this particular expression $ax^2 + bx + c$ factors in C into linear factors. We could then study the implications of these assumptions. Hopefully we could derive sufficient information to enable us to see how one might go about constructing such a set C.

Now if an expression $ax^2 + bx + c$ (where $a,b,c \in R$) could be factored into linear factors, then $ax^2 + bx + c = 0$ would have a solution in R by (5, 50). But $x^2 + 1 = 0$ has no solution in R. (Why?) So $x^2 + 1$ cannot be factored into linear factors in R.

Thus *suppose a set C exists* satisfying (1), (2), and (3) of Section 1, and such that there exists an element, say $i \in C$, satisfying $x^2 + 1 = 0$. Then $i^2 + 1 = 0$ or $i^2 = -1$.

Exercises

1. Show that $x^2 + 1$ factors into linear factors in C.
2. If $a,b \in R$, show that $a + bi \in C$.
3. Suppose $a,b,c,d \in R$. Show that $a + bi = c + di$ implies $(a - c)^2 = -(b - d)^2$.
4. Suppose $a,b,c,d \in R$. Show that $a + bi = c + di$ if and only if $a = c$ and $b = d$, i.e., if and only if $(a,b) = (c,d)$. (*Hint:* Use Exercise 3.)
5. If $a,b,c,d \in R$, show that
   (a) $(a + bi) + (c + di) = (a + c) + (b + d)i$.
   (b) $(a + bi)(c + di) = (ac - bd) + (ad + bc)i$.
6. Let $D = \{x + yi \in C / x,y \in R\}$. Show that D forms a subfield of C with respect to the binary operations $+$ and $\cdot$ restricted to D [cf. Exercises (8, 25b) and (10, 58)]. (*Hint:* If $a + bi \neq 0$, then $a^2 + b^2 \neq 0$, and the multiplicative inverse of $a + bi$ is $\dfrac{a}{a^2 + b^2} + \dfrac{-b}{a^2 + b^2} i$.)

We therefore see, from Exercise 6, that D itself possesses sufficient properties for which C was desired. Hence we may use D instead; i.e., we may assume $C = D$.

Thus if $C = \{x + yi / x \in R, y \in R\}$, and we assume C is a subset of a field, and $i^2 = -1$, then C itself is a field. One adds and multiplies elements of C according to Exercise 5.

The question arises, now, whether we can imitate the above observations in constructing a set together with two binary operations $+$ and $\cdot$ for which all the above hold.

3. Construction of C

According to Exercise 4, it seems clear that we should let

$$C = R \times R$$

We already have binary operations $+$ and $\cdot$ defined on R. In order not to confuse these with our new binary operations, we shall define binary operations $\oplus$ and $\otimes$ on C.

In our definition of $\oplus$ and $\otimes$, we should imitate Exercise 5.

Definition 1. If (a,b) and (c,d) are elements of C, we define

$$(a,b) \oplus (c,d) = (a + c, b + d)$$
$$(a,b) \otimes (c,d) = (ac - bd, ad + bc)$$

Note that the operations $\oplus$ and $\otimes$ on C are defined in terms of $+$ and $\cdot$ in R.

Exercises

7. Prove that C, with respect to $\oplus$ and $\otimes$, is a field.
8. Let R^* be the subset of C consisting of the elements $(a,0)$ for all $a \in R$.
   (a) Show that $a = b$ if and only if $(a,0) = (b,0)$.
   (b) Show that the addition table for R^* is the same as that for R in the following sense: Wherever 'a' appears in the table for R, '$(a,0)$' appears in R^*. [Thus, one must show $(a,0) \oplus (b,0) = (a + b,0)$.]
   (c) The same as (b) for multiplication. [One must show $(a,0) \otimes (b,0) = (ab,0)$.]

Exercise 8 shows that the system R^* with respect to $\oplus$ and $\otimes$ has tables which are not essentially different from the tables of R with respect to $+$ and $\cdot$.

If one gives the name 'a^*' to $(a,0)$, then we would have

In R:	
$+$	$\cdots\cdots b$
$\cdot$	
$\cdot$	
$\cdot$	
a	$a + b$

In R*:	
$\oplus$	$\cdots\cdots b^*$
$\cdot$	
$\cdot$	
a^*	$(a + b)^*$

Let $i = (0,1)$. (Think of $0 + 1 \cdot i$ in Section 2.)

Exercises

9. Show that $(a,b) = a^* \oplus [b^* \otimes i]$.
10. Show that $i \otimes i = (-1,0) = (-1)^*$.

Now we can call a^* positive in R^* if a is positive in R. Then all the theorems concerning R apply to R^*. Wherever one has a or b in R, one has a^* and b^* in R^*. For the tables—except for the asterisks appearing for R^*—are the same, as is the ordering.

But since we know the real numbers only by such properties, it follows that R^* is indistinguishable, in this sense, from R.

Thus in the set C, we can give the name 'a' to the element $a^* = (a,0)$. We can give the name 'R' to the subset R^*. If we work from now on only in C, then it remains true that we are not giving one name to two different elements.

With this notation, we have from Exercise 9 that

$$(a,b) = a \oplus bi$$

and from Exercise 10 that

$$i \otimes i = -1$$

For convenience, we now use the symbols '+' for '$\oplus$' and '·' for '$\otimes$'; as usual, we often omit the '·'. Then Exercises 9 and 10 become, respectively,

$$(a,b) = a + bi$$
$$i^2 = -1$$

and the results of Section 2 apply to C.

Even if we chose to maintain notational distinction between R and R^*, + and $\oplus$, etc., anything we prove in this new system could always be interpreted in the old, by the correspondence established in Exercise 8.

The elements of C will be called complex numbers. Thus the set of real numbers may be considered a subset of the complex numbers.

As $i^2 = -1$, one often writes $i = \sqrt{-1}$. However, the theory of exponents does not hold for C. In particular, it is not true that

$$\sqrt{-1} \ \sqrt{-1} = \sqrt{(-1)(-1)}.$$

Indeed $\sqrt{-1} \ \sqrt{-1} = i \cdot i = -1$.

On the other hand, the theory of natural number exponents does hold (since it holds in any field).

Thus $(a + bi)^m \cdot (a + bi)^n = (a + bi)^{m+n}$, etc., for $m, n \in N$.

Exercises

11. Show that $(x + i)(x - i) = x^2 + 1$ for all $x \in C$.
12. Solve $x^2 + 1 = 0$ in C.
13. Solve $x^2 = -\alpha$ in C, where $\alpha > 0$ in R. (*Solution:* $\{\sqrt{\alpha} \ i, -\sqrt{\alpha} \ i\}$.)

Definition 2. $\sqrt{-\alpha} = \sqrt{-1} \ \sqrt{\alpha} \ (= i\sqrt{\alpha})$ for $\alpha > 0$ in R.

Thus,

$$\sqrt{-16} = i\sqrt{16} = 4i$$
$$\sqrt{-32} = i\sqrt{32} = 4\sqrt{2} \ i$$
$$-\sqrt{-32} = -4\sqrt{2} \ i$$

Exercises

14. Write the multiplicative inverse of each of the following in the form $a + bi$ where $a, b \in R$.

(a) $2 - i$ $\left(\text{i.e., write } \dfrac{1}{2-i} \text{ in the form } a + bi\right)$.

(b) $1 + \sqrt{2}\, i$.

(c) -3.

(d) i.

(e) $3 + 2i$.

(f) $3 - 2i$.

15. Let n be a natural number.

(a) If n divided by 4 leaves a remainder of 0, show $i^n = 1$.

(b) If n divided by 4 leaves a remainder of 1, show $i^n = i$.

(c) If n divided by 4 leaves a remainder of 2, show $i^n = -1$.

(d) If n divided by 4 leaves a remainder of 3, show $i^n = -i$.

[*Hint*: If n divided by 4 has remainder 0, $n = 4q$, where $q \, \epsilon \, N$. Then $(i^{4q}) = (i^4)^q = 1^q = 1$. This uses the theory of exponents for N. If the remainder is 1, then $n = 4q + 1$; etc.]

In Exercise 14, to find the multiplicative inverse of $2 - i$, one uses $(2 + i) \cdot \dfrac{1}{5}$. More generally, the multiplicative inverse of $a + bi$ is $\dfrac{a - bi}{a^2 + b^2}$ $\left(\text{or } \dfrac{a}{a^2 + b^2} - \dfrac{b}{a^2 + b^2}\, i\right)$ if $a + bi \neq 0$.

Thus $(a + bi) \cdot \dfrac{a - bi}{a^2 + b^2} = 1$ or $(a + bi)(a - bi) = a^2 + b^2$.

Definition 3. If $z = a + bi$, then $\bar{z} = a - bi$ (or $\overline{a + bi} = a - bi$). We call $\bar{z}$ the *complex conjugate of z*.

If $z \, \epsilon \, R$, then $\bar{z} = z$. Note that $z\bar{z} = a^2 + b^2$ if $z = a + bi$.

Definition 4. If $z = a + bi$, then $\sqrt{a^2 + b^2}$ is called the *norm of z* or *modulus of z* or *absolute value of z*, and designated by $|z|$. Thus $|z| \, \epsilon \, R$. (If z is real, $|z|$ in this sense is the same as in the old sense.)

Thus we have

$$|z| = |\bar{z}| \qquad \text{and} \qquad z\bar{z} = |z|^2 = |\bar{z}|^2$$

The multiplicative inverse of z is then $\dfrac{\bar{z}}{|z|^2}$.

Definition 5. If $c \, \epsilon \, C$ and $c \notin R$, then c will be said to be *imaginary*. Thus the imaginary elements of C are the numbers $a + bi$, where $a,b \, \epsilon \, R$ and $b \neq 0$. An imaginary number $a + bi$ in which $a = 0$ (i.e., an imaginary number of the form bi, where $b \, \epsilon \, R$) is said to be a *pure imaginary number*.

We observe that C is the union of the set of real numbers and the set of imaginary numbers. Also, every imaginary number is the sum of a real number and a pure imaginary number.

Exercises

16. Find the complex conjugate and absolute value of the following:

(a) $2 - i$.   (e) 0.

(b) $2 + i$.   (f) $\sqrt{2} - \sqrt{3}\, i$.

(c) i.

(d) 3.   (g) $\dfrac{1 + i}{2}$.

17. If w and z are complex numbers, prove:

(a) $\overline{w + z} = \overline{w} + \overline{z}$.

(b) $\overline{wz} = \overline{w}\,\overline{z}$.

(Let $w = a + bi$, $z = c + di$.)

18. If $z_1, z_2, \ldots, z_n$ are complex numbers, prove:

(a) $\overline{z_1 + z_2 + \cdots + z_n} = \bar{z}_1 + \bar{z}_2 + \cdots + \bar{z}_n$.

(b) $\overline{z_1 z_2 \cdots z_n} = \bar{z}_1 \bar{z}_2 \cdots \bar{z}_n$.

19. How does it follow from Exercise 18 that if z is a complex number, then $\overline{(z^m)} = (\bar{z})^m$?

20. Let $a_0, a_1, \ldots, a_n \in R$ and $z \in C$, and suppose $a_0 z^n + a_1 z^{n-1} + \cdots + a_n = 0$. Prove that $a_0 \bar{z}^n + a_1 \bar{z}^{n-1} + \cdots + a_n = 0$.

21. Write $\dfrac{2 - 3i}{1 + 2i} - \dfrac{3 + i}{2 - i}$ in the form $a + bi$, where $a, b \in R$.

22. If $z \in C$, show that $z + \bar{z} \in R$.

23. If z is an imaginary number, show that $z - \bar{z}$ is pure imaginary.

24. If $w, z \in C$, show that $|wz| = |w|\,|z|$.

25. (a) If $z_1, z_2, \ldots, z_n \in C$, prove $|z_1 z_2 \cdots z_n| = |z_1| \cdot |z_2| \cdots |z_n|$.

(b) If $z \in C$, how does it follow from (a) that $|z^n| = |z|^n$?

4. Concluding Remarks

The question is often asked whether imaginary numbers exist, or are merely "figments of the imagination." Of course, all of mathematics is a "figment of the imagination." But aside from this, the complex-number system is the set $R \times R$ with certain binary operations defined on it. For historical reasons, we refer to the nonreal elements of C as imaginary numbers. But the number $2 + 3i$ is no more, but also no less, "imaginary" in the everyday sense of the word than is the number 3 or the number π.

C represented an extension of R in which $x^2 + 1 = 0$ had a solution. How about other equations of the type $ax^2 + bx + c = 0$, where $a, b, c \in R$? We shall see that C provides solutions to every such equation.

Then what about $ax^3 + bx^2 + cx + d = 0$?

The same result is true. The general result, often called the *Fundamental Theorem of Algebra* will be stated in Part III.

It is this theorem which Carl Friedrich Gauss considered in his doctoral dissertation (1799), where he presented the first rigorous proof.[1] Later Gauss gave two further proofs. Jean LeRond D'Alembert (1717–1783) had tried unsuccessfully to prove this theorem in 1746, and Albert Girard (ca. 1590–1633) had conjectured this result in 1629. In a treatise in 1831 Gauss included the algebra of complex numbers much as outlined in the foregoing pages, and the complex numbers were finally, in the words of E. T. Bell, "accepted as respectable members of mathematical society."

We should like to mention, to digress temporarily, that Gauss is often regarded as one of the three greatest mathematicians of all time. (Of course, the twentieth century cannot yet be evaluated.) Thus E. T. Bell writes: "Any list of the three 'greatest' mathematicians of all history would include Archimedes. The other two usually associated with him are Newton (1642–1727) and Gauss (1777–1855)." [2]

It was in the works of Heron of Alexandria in which the square root of a negative number [3] is first known to appear (ca. A.D. 50?). Here we find $\sqrt{81 - 144}$, which is then taken to be $\sqrt{144 - 81}$. (To be on the safe side, we make the hopefully unnecessary observation that this is incorrect.) Diophantus, in his attempt to solve the equation $336x^2 + 24 = 172x$, was the next known person to face the problem of square roots of negative numbers. Mahavira (ca. A.D. 850) stated that a negative number has no square root. Further confrontations with this difficulty were made, and then in 1545 Cardan was the first who used square roots of negative numbers in formal computational procedures. Thus he writes $5 + \sqrt{-15}$ and $5 - \sqrt{-15}$ as solutions of a particular equation. Gottfried Wilhelm Leibniz (1646–1716) showed in 1676 that

$$\sqrt{1 + \sqrt{-3}} + \sqrt{1 - \sqrt{-3}} = \sqrt{6}$$

and in 1702 that

$$x^4 + a^4 = (x + a\sqrt{-\sqrt{-1}})(x - a\sqrt{-\sqrt{-1}})(x + a\sqrt{\sqrt{-1}})(x - a\sqrt{\sqrt{-1}})$$

During the seventeenth and eighteenth century, most writers used the term "imaginary" for numbers of the form $a + b\sqrt{-1}$. As we have stated, these numbers are no longer regarded as imaginary in the everyday sense of the word, just as today one no longer looks for irrational numbers in mental institutions. The term "complex number" is due to Gauss, the use of i for $\sqrt{-1}$ to Leonard Euler (1707–1783), the name "conjugates" for $a + bi$ and $a - bi$ and "modulus" for $\sqrt{a^2 + b^2}$ to Augustin-Louis Cauchy

[1] D. J. Struik, *A Concise History of Mathematics,* Vol. II, p. 205, Dover, New York, 1948.

[2] E. T. Bell, *Men of Mathematics,* p. 20, Simon & Schuster, New York, 1937.

[3] Cf. D. E. Smith, *History of Mathematics,* Vol. II, pp. 261–267, Dover, New York, 1958, for what follows in this and the next paragraph.

(1789–1857), and the term "absolute value" and the notation $|a + bi|$ for $\sqrt{a^2 + b^2}$ to Karl Weierstrass (1815–1897).

Having provided a brief history of the development of the complex-number system, which contains all the numbers we shall make use of later, we are now ready to turn to an amazingly simple and exceedingly rich concept in the development of mathematics, that of *function*. This brings us to Part III, the concluding part of this textbook. Rather than continue our all too brief historical comments on this part of our subject, we should like to encourage the reader to consult the following works:

Ball, Walter W. Rouse, *A Short Account of the History of Mathematics*, Macmillan, New York, 1888.

Bell, E. T., *Development of Mathematics*, McGraw-Hill, New York, 1940.

Bell, E. T., *Men of Mathematics*, Simon & Schuster, New York, 1937.

Cajori, Florian, *A History of Mathematics*, Macmillan, New York, 1894.

Dantzig, Tobias, *Number, the Language of Science*, Doubleday (Anchor Books), New York, 1930.

Eves, Howard, *An Introduction to the History of Mathematics*, Holt, New York, 1953.

Eves, Howard, and C. V. Newsom, *An Introduction to the Foundations and Fundamental Concepts of Mathematics*, Holt, New York, 1965.

Newman, James R., *The World of Mathematics*, 4 vols., Simon & Schuster, New York, 1956.

Smith, D. E., *History of Mathematics*, Dover, New York, 1958.

Struik, Dirk J., *A Concise History of Mathematics*, Dover, New York, 1948.

Part III
FUNCTIONS

In Part II we considered the real-number system, a system which has many applications. For example, real numbers are used to measure time, or speed, or length, or area. But the applications involve not only time and distance, for example, but also relationships between time and distance. There is also a relationship between the number assigned as the area of a square, and the number assigned as the length of its side. There is a relationship between the number used for the area of a circle, and the number assigned as the length of its radius.

These examples of relationships lead to the idea of a *function*, and more generally to the idea of a *relation* of which a function is a special case.

Although the above examples involve associations between real numbers — between the *number* of seconds and the *number* of feet, for example — we shall generalize this idea to associations between elements of any two sets. This also occurs in applications. For example, if A is the set of automobiles registered in a particular state, and B the set of registration numbers, then with each car in A is associated a number in B. Or with each registered driver, to consider another example, is associated a driver's license number. Or with each individual, his fingerprints. Or with each college student, the college he is attending.

Our aim will be to abstract from these examples a concept which can be studied by itself, without reference to the particular application. After establishing the initial foundations, we shall concentrate on functions between two sets A and B where both A and B are sets of real (or complex) numbers. In particular, we shall consider polynomial, exponential, logarithmic, and circular (trigonometric) functions.

As one becomes more advanced in mathematics, his repertoire of known functions increases. His knowledge of their properties deepens. And all too soon, he encounters the unknown.

One of the great powers of the concept of function is the classification of functions in such a way that one can derive theorems valid for all functions of a particular class. Then in the future whenever one meets a new function of that class, he need not spend long hours, days, weeks, months, or even years, becoming acquainted with it; for it already shares the many properties of its family. Thus one can concentrate on its distinctly individual characteristics.

261

[The power of this idea can already be seen in elementary calculus. For those fortunate enough to study the calculus, the class of differentiable functions will provide a dramatic example. One will learn rules for differentiating sums, products, quotients, composite functions, which apply to all functions of this class. As his repertoire of new functions in this class increases with his advancement in mathematics, he will be able to apply all these old rules without further labor.]

There are still other uses made of the function concept. If one is interested in studying properties of a set A, he often considers functions from A into a set B, where B is a set with which he is more familiar. Information about B and the existence of functions (usually with some specified conditions) from A to B often gives one information about A. Or one even studies functions from A to A for this purpose.

Despite these varied applications, the idea of a function is itself strikingly simple; the power and beauty of this idea unfolds as one follows it throughout all of mathematics. We regret that the final part of this text can provide only a modest first step.

chapter xi

FUNCTIONS AND RELATIONS

1. A Function Defined on a Set

1.1 Function from A to B

Definition 1. Let A and B be two sets. Then a function from A to B is a *rule* which assigns to each element of A a unique element of B.

Example 1. Let A be the set of cities in the United States and B the set of states. We can define a function from A to B by assigning to each city the state in which it is located. Thus to Boston is assigned Massachusetts, to Los Angeles is assigned California. (For mathematical purposes, one would have to assign different names to distinct elements, e.g., Manchester-1 for the city in New Hampshire, Manchester-2 for the city in Connecticut, etc.)

It is convenient to label a function. Thus if we label the rule in Example 1 by 'f,' we may say f applied to Boston is Massachusetts; f applied to Los Angeles is California. This is further abbreviated to:

$$f(\text{Boston}) = \text{Massachusetts}$$
$$f(\text{Los Angeles}) = \text{California}$$

Example 2. Let A be the set of integers, B the set of nonnegative integers. (Thus $A = J$, $B = N \cup \{0\}$.) Let g be the rule assigning to each $a \in J$ the element $a^2 \in N \cup \{0\}$. Thus $g(-3) = 9$; $g(3) = 9$; $g(0) = 0$; $g(15) = 225$.

Example 3. Let $A = R$, $B = R$, f the rule assigning to each $r \in R$ the number $2^r \in R$. Thus $f(3) = 8$, $f(0) = 1$, $f(-1) = \frac{1}{2}$, $f(\frac{1}{2}) = \sqrt{2}$.

If we let x be a variable over J, the function of Example 2 may be written $g(x) = x^2$. Again x is a placeholder for $g(\ ) = (\ )^2$. Similarly in Example 3, $f(x) = 2^x$.

1.2 The Function Machine

A descriptive way of looking at a function is to regard it as a machine of the type shown in Figure 11.1. It is built to convert an element $a \in A$ to an element $b \in B$. The machine must be able to take *each* element of A into the input pipe, but *not every* element of B need come out of the output pipe. Thus in Example 2, place 3 into the machine. Then g grinds away at 3 and out comes 9. Or in Example 3, placing 2 into the machine produces 4 as the output. Or t is converted into 2^t; or t^2 into 2^{t^2}; or $a + 1$ into 2^{a+1}.

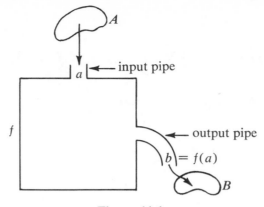

Figure 11.1

Example 4. Let $A = R$, $B = R$, $f(x) = 3x + 2$. Here $f(1) = 5$, $f(-2) = -4$.

Example 5. Let $A = R$, $B = R$, $f(x) = 3$. Here $f(2) = 3$; $f(-5) = 3$; $f(0) = 3$; $f(a^3) = 3$; $f(\pi) = 3$.

Example 6. Let $A = R$, $B = P$, $f(x) = 2^x$.

This example is essentially the same as Example 3. That is, the set A is the same in both examples, and the rule is the same. In Example 3 we said $B = R$ and here $B = P$. Nevertheless we regard these functions as identical. That is, they represent the same mathematical machine in the sense that in both cases the elements of A can be fed into the machine, and the effect on each element of A is the same for $B = R$ and for $B = P$.

Thus a function is defined once we know the set A and the rule associating to each element $a \in A$ an element $f(a)$. We can take B to be any set which includes the set $\{f(x)/x \in A\}$. This set $\{f(x)/x \in A\}$ is called the *range of f*, and A is called the *domain of f*.

1.3   Domain and Range of a Function

Definition 2. Let f be a function from A to B. Then $\{f(x)/x \in A\}$ is called the *range of f*. The set A is called the *domain of f*.

Note that the range of f is a subset of B. Elements going into the input pipe of the function machine are from the domain of f; the elements emitted from the output pipe are from the range of f.

In Example 1, the domain of the function is the set of cities in the United States, the range the set of states.

In Example 2, the domain is the set of integers, the range

$$\{0,1,4,9,16, \ldots ,n^2, \ldots\}$$

In Example 3 the domain is R, the range P.

In Example 4, the domain is R and the range is R.

In Example 5, the domain is R, the range is $\{3\}$.

In Example 6, the function is the same as in Example 3: same domain, same range, same rule.

Example 7. Let $A = R$, $B = R$, $f(x) = x$. Here $f(1) = 1$; $f(0) = 0$;

$$f(-2^{-3.01}) = -2^{-3.01}$$

Example 8. As a generalization of Example 7, we can take A to be any set, and $B = A$. Let $f(x) = x$. Thus if $a \in A$, $f(a) = a$.

The function of Example 8 is called the *identity function of A*. We shall denote it by I_A. Thus $I_A(a) = a$ for all $a \in A$.

In Example 7, then, the function is I_R. Thus $I_R(1) = 1$; $I_R(0) = 0$; $I_R(-2^{-3.01}) = -2^{-3.01}$. $I_J(\frac{1}{2})$ is undefined; $I_J(1) = 1$.

1.4   Function Defined on a Set

We have defined a "function from A to B" as involving a set A and a set B, and a rule. Actually the set A and the rule already determine the function, so that it is preferable to speak of a "function defined on a set A." With this terminology, a function from a set A to a set B is then a function *defined on A* whose range is a subset of B. Since the precise range of f is not always clear, we select B large enough to include the range of f.

In Example 2 we observe that $g(\frac{1}{2})$ is undefined. For g is defined only on J (i.e., g has domain J), and $\frac{1}{2} \notin J$. That is, throwing $\frac{1}{2}$ into the machine might very well break it.

Exercises

1. Let f be a function defined on R, where $f(x) = 2x - 3$. Find $f(2), f(-1), f(\frac{1}{2}), f(0)$, and $f(\sqrt{2})$.
2. Suppose $f(x) = 2x - 3$ and $g(x) = x + 5$, where x is a variable over R. Solve the equation $f(x) = g(x)$.
3. Let $f(x) = x^2 - x - 6$, where x is a variable over R. Solve $f(x) = 0$.
4. In Exercise 3, solve $f(x) = -4$.
5. In Exercise 3, if $a \in R$, find $f(a + 1), f(a^3), f(a^2 - a - 6), f(\sqrt{a})$, and $f(-\sqrt{a})$. (In the latter two cases, assume that a is nonnegative.)
6. Find $I_J(3), I_J(-3), I_R(3), I_N(-3), I_R(\frac{1}{2}), I_R(\sqrt{2})$, and $I_R(\sqrt{2})$.
7. (a) If $f(x) = 2x$, where x is a variable over N, what is the domain of f? The range?
   (b) If f is as in (a), solve $f(x) = 2, f(x) = -2, f(x) = \frac{1}{2}, f(2x) = 6$, and $f(x^4) = 2$.
8. Consider the following rules from R to R.
   (a) In each of the following, state whether the rule is a function, justifying your answer.
   (b) If the rule is not a function, suitably restrict the domain to make a function.
   (c) For each function in (a) or (b), indicate the domain and range.

(i) $f(x) = x - x.$

(ii) $f(x) = \sqrt{x}.$

(iii) $f(x) = \dfrac{1}{x}.$

(iv) $f(x) = \sqrt{x^2}.$

(v) $f(x) = |x - 2|.$

(vi) $f(x) = 2^x.$

(vii) $f(x) = |x|^3.$

(viii) $f(x) = |x^3|.$

2. Picturing a Function

2.1 A Function as a Converter

In Section 1.2 we gave one way of "picturing" a function — namely, as a converter. That is, a function converts an element of a set A into an element of a set B. Thus cities can be converted to states, numbers into other numbers, and people into wooden chairs. For example, let A be the set of people in a classroom, and B the set of chairs. Let g be the rule assigning to each person the chair in which he sits. (Of course, this example will soon be out of date when schools and especially mathematics classes will have standing room only.) In this example, drop a person into the machine, and out comes a wooden chair. Indeed, it is said that some professors lecture to the range of g rather than to the domain.

We now consider some other ways of picturing a function, not essentially different from the above.

2.2 A Function as a Mapping

We can regard a function as a "mapping" from a set A to a set B. The elements of A can be represented by points on a line, or in some subset of the plane, and similarly for the elements of B. If f is a function, then one connects the "point" $a \in A$ to the "point" $f(a)$, as in Figure 11.2. This can also be pictured with elements of A and B along lines, as in Figure 11.3.

One often writes

$$f \colon a \to r$$

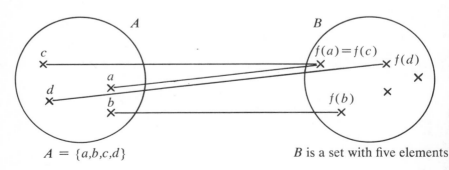

$A = \{a,b,c,d\}$ B is a set with five elements

Figure 11.2

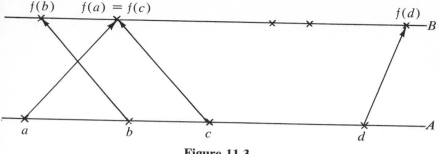

$f(b)$ $f(a) = f(c)$ $f(d)$

a b c d

Figure 11.3

or

$$a \underset{f}{\rightarrow} r$$

to mean that $r = f(a)$. Thus one can also write

$$f: a \rightarrow f(a)$$

or

$$a \underset{f}{\rightarrow} f(a)$$

or, in fact,

$$f: x \rightarrow f(x)$$

or

$$x \underset{f}{\rightarrow} f(x)$$

One says a is mapped onto r, or onto $f(a)$, or x is mapped onto $f(x)$.
In Example 1 (Section 1.1), we would have, in part, the result shown in
Figure 11.4.

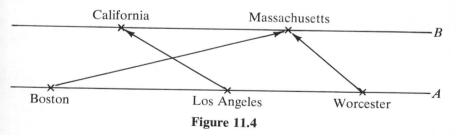

California   Massachusetts   B

Boston   Los Angeles   Worcester   A

Figure 11.4

If f is a mapping from A to A, i.e., if $f: A \rightarrow A$, we may pictorially represent this with arrows going from one element of A to another, or we can
draw two versions of A.

Example 9. Let $A = \{a,b,c\}$, and let $h: A \rightarrow A$, where h is defined as follows:
$h(a) = a$, $h(b) = c$, $h(c) = c$ (Figure 11.5).

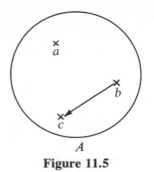

Figure 11.5

No arrows emanating from a or from c mean $h(a) = a$ and $h(c) = c$; that is, a and c are "not moved" by h. [Such elements are called *fixed points of h*. That is, if h is a mapping of a set into itself, the solutions of $h(x) = x$ are called *fixed points of h*, x being a variable over the set.]

We can also represent this mapping as shown in Figure 11.6. Or, as shown in Figure 11.7.

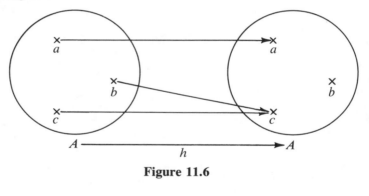

Figure 11.6

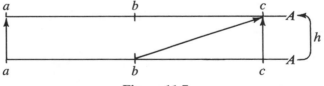

Figure 11.7

In Example 2 of Section 1.1, we could represent the elements of J and of $N \cup \{0\}$ on lines, as in Figure 11.8.

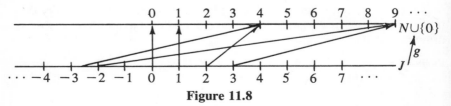

Figure 11.8

2.3 A Function as a Set

One will have observed that a function takes every element of a set, say *A*, and pairs with it some element of a set *B*. This observation suggests considering ordered pairs, that is, elements of $A \times B$. Thus, if $g(2) = 4$, then the ordered pair (2,4) will be regarded as an ordered pair of *g*. Other ordered pairs of *g* (in Example 2) are (0,0), (−1,1), (3,9), (−4,16), (12,144), (−12,144), etc.

In Example 1, some ordered pairs of *f* are (Boston, Massachusetts), (Los Angeles, California), (Worcester, Massachusetts), and (Deadwood, South Dakota).

In Example 3, some ordered pairs of *f* are (3,8), (0,1), $(-1, \frac{1}{2})$, and $(\frac{1}{2}, \sqrt{2})$.

In Example 9, ordered pairs of *f* are (*a*,*a*), (*b*,*c*), and (*c*,*c*).

Definition 3. If $f: A \rightarrow B$, then $(a, f(a))$ will be called an *ordered pair of f*.

Thus an element $(a,b) \in A \times B$ is an ordered pair of *f* if and only if $b = f(a)$.

Definition 4. If $f: A \rightarrow B$, the *graph of f* is the set of all ordered pairs of *f*.

Thus the graph of *f* is the solution set of $y = f(x)$ in the variables *x* over *A* and *y* over *B* (i.e., in the variable (*x*,*y*) over $A \times B$).[1]
Thus the graph of *f* is a subset of $A \times B$.
In Example 9, we have

$$\text{graph of } f = \{(a,a), (b,c), (c,c)\}$$

If we represent $A \times B$ pictorially as in Section 4.2 of Chapter 1, then we can also represent the graph of *f* as shown in Figure 11.9 (using Example 9 above for illustration). Above each point on the horizontal axis,

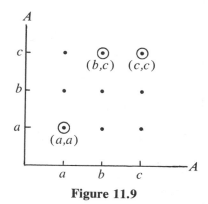

Figure 11.9

[1] It is advisable, at this point, to review Section 2.4 of Chapter 3; it might also be helpful to review Section 4.2 of Chapter 1.

there can be only one point of the graph. For $f(a)$ is uniquely determined. We cannot have $f(a) = a$ and also $f(a) = b$, for example. For then f would not be a function.

Now a function is completely determined if one knows its graph. *To say that two functions are the same means that their graphs are identical (i.e., consist of the same ordered pairs).*

Conversely, suppose S is a subset of $A \times B$ with the following properties:

(1) For each $a \in A$, $\exists^2 b \in B \ni (a,b) \in S$.

(2) If (a,b) and $(a,c) \in S$, then $b = c$.

The first requirement states that every element of A appears as a first member of an ordered pair in S. The second states that $a \in A$ uniquely determines the element $b \in B$ for which $(a,b) \in S$.

Given $S \subseteq A \times B$ with these properties, one may then define a function $k: A \rightarrow B$ as follows:

If $a \in A$, define $k(a) = b$, where b is the unique element of B for which $(a,b) \in S$.

Then k is a function from A to B.

One obtains such subsets S if above each point on the A-axis he selects one and only one point of $A \times B$, as in Figure 11.10.

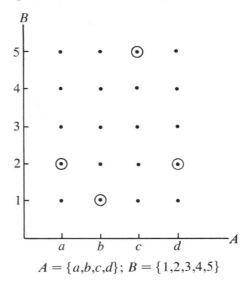

$A = \{a,b,c,d\}$; $B = \{1,2,3,4,5\}$

Figure 11.10

Above a we select $(a,2)$; above b, $(b,1)$; above c, $(c,5)$; above d, $(d,2)$. Thus $S = \{(a,2), (b,1), (c,5), (d,2)\}$.

---

² Recall that '∃' means "there exists"; '∋' means "such that."

Condition (1) is satisfied if there is *at least* one point above each element of A; condition (2) is satisfied if there is *at most* one point above each element of A.

Define k as follows:

$$k(a) = 2; \; k(b) = 1; \; k(c) = 5; \; k(d) = 2$$

Then k is a function from A to B and S is its graph.

Thus we see that given any function from A to B, there is associated its graph: a certain subset of $A \times B$ satisfying (1) and (2). Conversely, given a subset of $A \times B$ satisfying (1) and (2), there exists a function from A to B with this subset as its graph.

For this reason some authors choose to define a mapping (function) from A to B as a subset of $A \times B$ satisfying (1) and (2). This point of view certainly has merit, and makes clear the meaning of equality of functions: the same sets. In our development here, however, we shall maintain both points of view, by considering a function as a *rule* associating each point of A with a unique point of B, and also considering the *graph* of the function as a certain subset of $A \times B$: where the graph completely determines the function, and conversely the function determines the graph.

3. Examples

(a) Let $H = \{1,3,7,8\}$, $K = \{\alpha, \gamma\}$.

$f: H \to K$, where $f(x) = \alpha$ for all $x \in H$.

The graph of f is the solution set of $y = f(x)$ (or in this example, of $y = \alpha$). For this reason one often labels the horizontal axis as the x-axis, the vertical as the y-axis (Figure 11.11). Of course, if instead of '(x,y)' designating the variable over $H \times K$, one used '(s,t),' or '(u,v),' etc., then one would have the s-axis and t-axis, or the u-axis and v-axis.

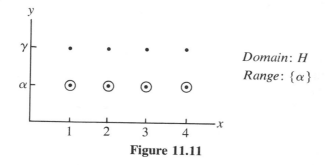

Domain: H
Range: $\{\alpha\}$

Figure 11.11

(b) Let H and K be as in (a). Can the subsets of $H \times K$ given in Figure 11.12 represent the graphs of functions?

In (i), there can be no corresponding function. For $(3,\alpha)$ and $(3,\gamma)$ are elements of this subset of $H \times K$. Hence if f were to be a corresponding

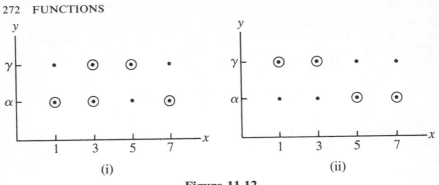

Figure 11.12

function, we would have $f(3) = \alpha$ and also $f(3) = \gamma$. But f must convert each element of H into a *unique* element of K.

In (ii), we can define a function. Namely,

$$1 \longrightarrow \gamma$$
$$3 \longrightarrow \gamma$$
$$5 \longrightarrow \alpha$$
$$7 \longrightarrow \alpha$$

(c) Let $f: J \to J$, where $f(x) = x$. This is, then, I_J.

We can represent this function by using two lines, as in Figure 11.13. It is clear that f has domain J and range J.

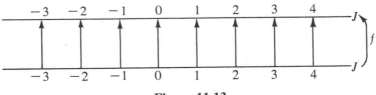

Figure 11.13

If we wish to imitate the method given in Section 2.3, and again in examples (a) and (b) of this section, we should like to give a pictorial representation of $J \times J$, and then indicate which points are on the graph of f. For this purpose, we draw one of the lines representing J as an x-axis, and the other perpendicular to the x-axis at 0 as a y-axis (Figure 11.14).

As in Chapter 1, we call the vertical line through the point labeled '1' on the x-axis the 1-vertical; similarly we have the 2-vertical, the -3-vertical, and the 0-vertical (which is the y-axis), etc. We also have the -1-horizontal, the 2-horizontal, and the 0-horizontal (which is the x-axis).

The element (a,b) of $J \times J$ will then be represented by the point which is the intersection of the a-vertical and the b-horizontal. The points representing $(-3,2)$ and $(2,-1)$ are indicated in Figure 11.15.

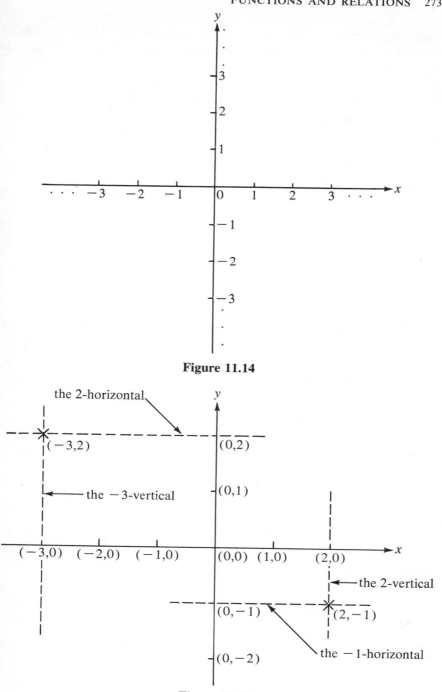

Figure 11.14

Figure 11.15

The points on the x-axis are all on the 0-horizontal, and therefore represent elements of the type $(a,0)$ in $J \times J$; those on the y-axis $(0,b)$. Thus the points on the x-axis are labeled $(1,0)$, $(2,0)$, $(0,0)$, $(-1,0)$, rather than 1, 2, 0, -1, respectively. Similarly, points on the y-axis are $(0,1)$, $(0,2)$, $(0,0)$, $(0,-1)$, rather than 1, 2, 0, -1, respectively.

The graph of $y = x$ [i.e., $f(x) = x$] is shown in Figure 11.16.

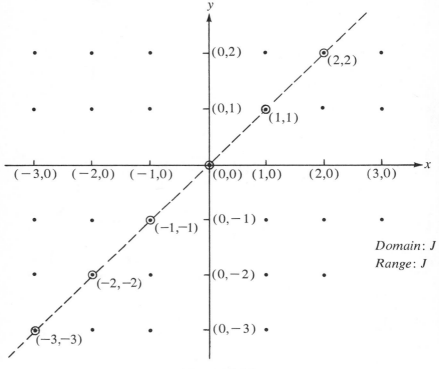

Figure 11.16

(d) Let $g: R \rightarrow R$, where $g(x) = x$. This is, then, I_R.

We may picture $R \times R$ as we did $J \times J$, now allowing elements such as $(\sqrt{5},0)$ and $(0,-\sqrt{2})$ as well as $(-1,1)$, etc. (Figure 11.17). Every point on the graph of the line passing through the points of Example (c) is a point of the graph of g.

(e) Let $f: N \rightarrow N$, where $f(n) = 2n$. The graph of f is represented in Figure 11.18.

(f) Let $A = \{x \in N/x \leq 10\}$, $B = \{0,1\}$. Let

$$f(x) = \begin{cases} 0 & \text{if } x \neq 2,3 \\ 1 & \text{if } x = 2,3 \end{cases}$$

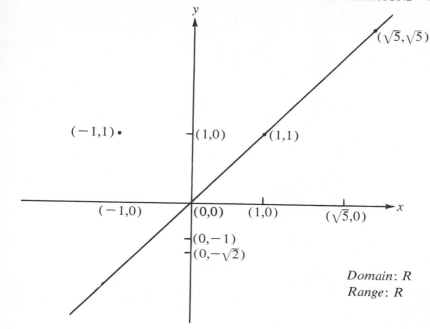

Domain: R
Range: R

Figure 11.17

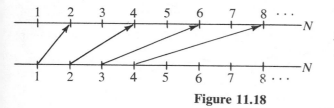

Domain: N
Range: {2,4,6, ...}

Figure 11.18

By this we mean that f applied to an element of A produces 0 if that element is not 2 or 3, and otherwise produces 1. The graph of f is represented in Figure 11.19.

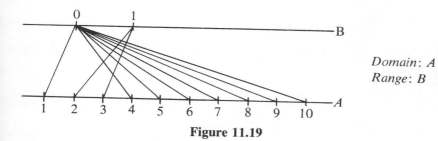

Domain: A
Range: B

Figure 11.19

(g) Let $A = \{a,b\}$ and $B = [A]$; i.e., B is the power set of A. $f: A \to B$, where $f(x) = \{x\}$. Thus $f(a) = \{a\}, f(b) = \{b\}$ (Figure 11.20).

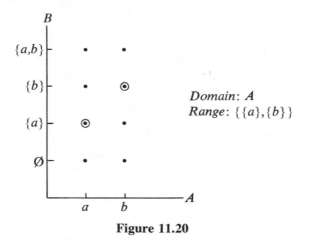

Domain: A
Range: $\{\{a\},\{b\}\}$

Figure 11.20

(h) Let $p: R \to R$, where $p(x) = x^2$. To get an idea of how to draw the graph, one may select values for x; corresponding to each value for x is the value for $p(x)$ below:

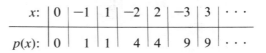

x:	0	−1	1	−2	2	−3	3	$\cdots$
$p(x)$:	0	1	1	4	4	9	9	$\cdots$

Thus $(0,0)$, $(-1,1)$, $(1,1)$, $(-2,4)$, $(2,4)$, $(-3,9)$, and $(3,9)$ are some elements of the graph of p (Figure 11.21).

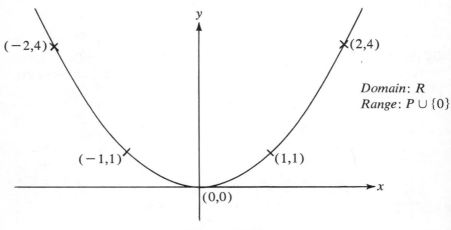

Domain: R
Range: $P \cup \{0\}$

Figure 11.21

(i)   Let $A = \{a,b,c\}$ and $B = \{0,1,2,3\}$. Let $f: A \times A \to B$ as follows: $f(x,a) = 0, f(x,b) = 1$, and $f(x,c) = 2$ (Figure 11.22). To each ordered pair of A is assigned an element of B. Hence this is another way of describing

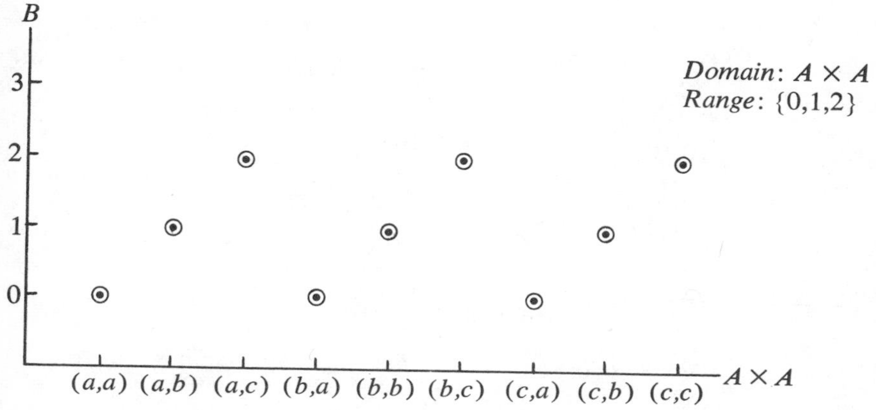

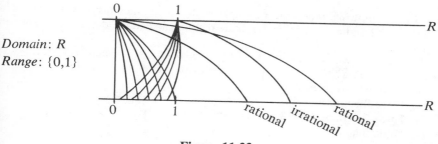

Figure 11.22

a *binary operation* on A. That is, a binary operation on a set A is a function from $A \times A$ to some set B. In this language, the set A is closed with respect to this binary operation if the range of f is a subset of A.

(j) $f: R \to R$, where $f(x) = \begin{cases} 0 & \text{if } x \text{ is rational} \\ 1 & \text{if } x \text{ is irrational} \end{cases}$

Here $f(\frac{1}{2}) = 0, f(\sqrt{2}) = 1, f(.532) = 0, f(-101.1) = 0$, and $f(2 + \sqrt{3}) = 1$. Of course, the graph can be only partially indicated in this representation (Figure 11.23).

Domain: R
Range: {0,1}

Figure 11.23

(k) $f: R \to J$. The rule for f is as follows: Let $r \in R$, and suppose r is between the consecutive integers n and $n + 1$ as follows: $n < r \leq n + 1$. Then $f(r) = 5(n + 1)$.

Thus $f(\frac{1}{2}) = 5$, $f(2) = 10$, $f(\sqrt{2}) = 10$, and $f(-\frac{3}{2}) = -5$. This graph is represented in Figure 11.24. The two axes have not been drawn to the same scale (for the sake of space).

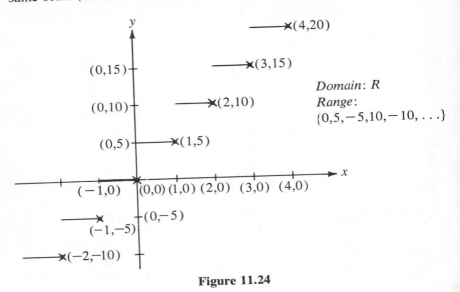

Figure 11.24

This is the so-called *postage-stamp function*. For if (a,b) is an element of the graph, and if $a \geq 0$, then for a ounces of mail one pays b cents postage. Thus $(0,0)$ is on the graph: One pays 0 cents for 0 ounces mail. Similarly, $(\frac{1}{2},5)$ is on the graph: One pays 5 cents for $\frac{1}{2}$ ounce of mail. (This application of the postage stamp function is based on 1966 rates!)

Exercises

In the following, represent the graphs of the given functions in two ways, as in Section 2.2 and as in Section 2.3. State the domain and the range of the function in each case.

9. $f: A \to B$, where $A = \{1,2,3,4,5,6\}$, $B = \{0,2,4,6, \ldots\}$, and $f(x) = 2x$.

10. $g: S \to T$, where $S = \{1,2\}$, $T = \{5, \text{Boston}\}$, and $g(1) = \text{Boston}$, $g(2) = 5$.

11. All functions from A to A, where $A = \{1,2\}$.

12. Three functions from $A \times A$ to B, where $A = \{1,2\}$, $B = \{2,3,4\}$.

13. Three functions from A to $[A]$, where $A = \{1,2\}$.

14. Three functions from $[A]$ to A, where $A = \{1,2\}$.

15. I_A, where $A = \{1,2\}$.

16. $f: x \to -5x + 3$, where x is a variable over R.

17. $y = x^2 + 1$, where x is a variable over R. [That is, $f(x) = x^2 + 1$. Recall that the graph of this function is the solution set of $y = f(x)$.]

18. $f: R \to R$, where $f(x) = \begin{cases} x & \text{if } x \geq 0, \\ 0 & \text{if } x < 0. \end{cases}$

19. $g: R \rightarrow R$, where $g(x) = \begin{cases} x & \text{if } x < 0, \\ 0 & \text{if } x \geq 0. \end{cases}$

20. $h: R \rightarrow R$, where $h(x) = \begin{cases} -x & \text{if } x > 0, \\ 0 & \text{if } x \leq 0. \end{cases}$

21. $f: R \rightarrow R$, where $f(x) = \begin{cases} x^2 & \text{if } x > 0, \\ -2 & \text{if } x \leq 0. \end{cases}$

22. $g: R \rightarrow R$, where $g(x) = \begin{cases} x & \text{if } x \geq 0, \\ -x & \text{if } x < 0. \end{cases}$

23. $h: R \rightarrow R$, where $h(x) = |x|$.

24. $k: R \rightarrow R$, where $k(x) = |x + 1|$.

25. $p: R \rightarrow R$, where $p(x) = |x - 2|$.

26. $f: J \rightarrow J$, where $f(x) = x^3$.

27. $g: R \rightarrow R$, where $f(x) = x^3$.

28. $h: R \rightarrow R$, where $h(x) = |x^3|$.

29. $f: A \rightarrow R$, where $A = \{x \in R / x \neq 2\}$ and $f(x) = x + 1$.

30. A as in Exercise 29. I_A.

4. Composite Functions

Suppose f is a function defined on a set A, and g a function defined on a set B. Furthermore, suppose that the range of f is a subset of B (Figure 11.25). We may then regard f as a function from A to B, and g as a function, say, from B to C.

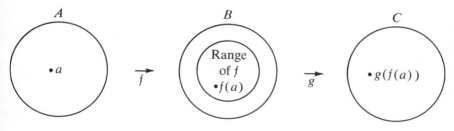

Figure 11.25

If $a \in A$, then f maps a onto an element $f(a)$ of B. Now since $f(a) \in B$, g maps $f(a)$ onto an element of C, namely $g(f(a))$.

$$a \underset{f}{\rightarrow} f(a) \underset{g}{\rightarrow} g(f(a))$$

That is, if one writes $a \underset{f}{\rightarrow} b \underset{g}{\rightarrow} c$, then $b = f(a)$ and $c = g(b) = g(f(a))$.

This gives us a procedure for defining a new function h from A to C from the given functions $f: A \rightarrow B$, and $g: B \rightarrow C$. Namely, if $a \in A$, define $h(a) = g(f(a))$. This function h from A to C is usually designated by '$g \circ f$' or also 'gf,' and is called the *composite* of f and g.

Definition 5. Let f be a function defined on a set A, and g a function defined on a set containing the range of f. Say $f\colon A \to B$ and $g\colon B \to C$. Then the *composite* of f and g, denoted by '$g \circ f$' or 'gf' is the function from A to C defined as follows:

$$gf\colon a \to g(f(a))$$

In machine terms, the composite function gf may be thought of as building a new machine with the machines of f and g as component parts (Figure 11.26).

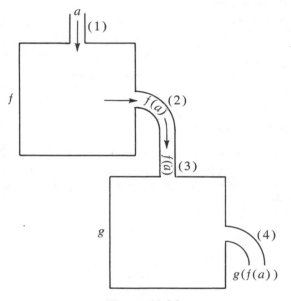

Figure 11.26

Into pipe (1) can go any element of A. At (2), although no longer visible to the observer, elements from the range of f come out. Since these latter elements are all in B, the component for g can accept these elements and convert them at (4) into elements of C. This is then a machine which has the same effect as gf.

Now there may be other machines which accomplish the same result. One may have

$$A \xrightarrow[h_1]{} D_1 \xrightarrow[h_2]{} D_2 \xrightarrow[h_3]{} D_3 \xrightarrow[h_4]{} C$$

Here one puts together four components to obtain a composite function from A to C:

$$k(a) = h_4(h_3(h_2(h_1(a))))$$

If it should happen that $k(a) = gf(a)$ for each $a \in A$, then the functions are the same even though their representation is different. (We have seen this before with numbers: $8 = 7 + 1$, but also $8 = 1 + 1 + 1 + 2 + 2 + 1$.)

In engineering it may happen that a certain set of simple components is at hand, or can be built, and one has to consider composites of these components in order to represent a given function, say f. One solution may occupy a building, whereas another is the size of a matchbox. But, mathematically, as long as each operates on elements of the same set and has the same effect on each element of that set, these functions are equal.

Example 10. Let $A = \{a,b,c\}$, $B = \{b,c,d\}$, $C = \{1,2,3,4\}$. Let $f: A \rightarrow B$ such that $a \rightarrow b$, $b \rightarrow c$, $c \rightarrow b$ and $g: B \rightarrow C$ such that $b \rightarrow 1$, $c \rightarrow 3$, $d \rightarrow 3$. Then

$$gf(a) = g(f(a)) = g(b) = 1$$
$$gf(b) = g(f(b)) = g(c) = 3$$
$$gf(c) = g(f(c)) = g(b) = 1$$

Hence gf is the function from A to C: $a \rightarrow 1$, $b \rightarrow 3$, $c \rightarrow 1$ (Figure 11.27).

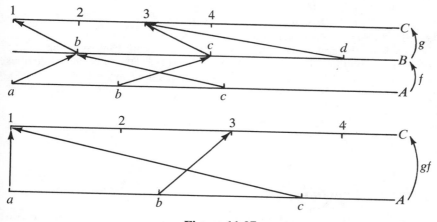

Figure 11.27

Example 11. $f: R \rightarrow R$, $g: R \rightarrow R$, where $f(x) = x + 1$, $g(x) = x^2$.

$$x \underset{f}{\rightarrow} x + 1 \underset{g}{\rightarrow} (x + 1)^2$$

Hence $gf(x) = (x + 1)^2$.

Example 12. f and g as above. Then $fg(x) = x^2 + 1$.

Now is gf equal to or different from fg? To say $gf = fg$ means that gf and fg have the same effect on every element of R. To say they are unequal means they have a different effect on at least *one* element of R.

$$gf(1) = 4$$
$$fg(1) = 2$$

Hence $gf \neq fg$.

Observe that in Example 10, fg has no meaning, as $g: B \to C$ cannot be followed by $f: A \to B$, since the range of g is not a subset of A, which is the domain of f.

Example 13. $f: R \to P$, $g: P \to P$, where $f(x) = x^2 + 1$, $g(x) = \sqrt{x}$.
  Then $gf(x) = \sqrt{x^2 + 1}$, where $gf: R \to P$.

Exercises

In each of the following:
  (a) Give the composite gf of f and g.
  (b) Sketch the graph of f, of g, and of gf in two ways (cf. Section 3).
  (c) Tell whether fg is defined.
  (d) If the answer to (c) is yes, determine whether or not $gf = fg$.
31. $A = \{0,1,2,3,4\}$, $B = \{0,2,4,6,8,10\}$, $C = \{0,1,2,3,4,5,6\}$. $f: A \to B$, where $f(n) = 2n$. $g: B \to C$, where $g(u) = \frac{1}{2}u + 1$.
32. $f: N \to N$; $g: N \to P$, where $f(n) = n^2$ and $g(w) = \sqrt{w}$.
33. $f: R \to R$; $g: R \to R$, where $f(x) = |x|$; $g(x) = x + 1$.
34. $f: R \to R$; $g: R \to R$, where $f(x) = x^3$; $g(x) = x^2$.
35. $f: P \to P$; $g: P \to P$, where $f(x) = x^2$; $g(x) = \sqrt{x}$.
  In each of the following, find a way of representing each function as the composite of two functions. For example, $f(x) = (x^2 + 1)^3$ can be represented as hg, where $g(x) = x^2 + 1$ and $h(x) = x^3$. All functions are from R to R.
36. $f(x) = (x + 1)^{50}$.
37. $g(x) = \sqrt{x^2 + 2}$.
38. $f(x) = |x - x^2|$.
39. $h(x) = (x - 3)^3$.
40. $f(x) = x^3 - 3$.

5. Inverse Functions

Consider a function $f: A \to B$ in which the range of f is B. Thus, given $b \in B$, $\exists\, a \in A \ni f(a) = b$. In this case we say that f is a mapping (function) of A *onto* B.

Definition 6. If $f: A \to B$ and $B = $ range of f, then f is said to map A *onto* B. This means that for every $b \in B$, $\exists\, a \in A \ni f(a) = b$. [Or also, the solution set of $f(x) = b$ is nonempty for every $b \in B$.]

Consider the examples of Section 3. In Example (a), f is not onto, since there is no element of H mapped onto γ in K. However, in Example (b, ii), we have an *onto* mapping.

Examples (c) and (d) are onto.

Example (e) is not. Nothing is mapped onto $1 \in N$.

Example (f) is onto; (g), (h), and (i) are not.

According to Definition 6, $f: A \to B$ is *onto* if and only if *range* $f = B$. Thus f is *not onto* if and only if *range* $f \subset B$. Of course, we always have range $f \subseteq B$.

Now suppose f is a mapping of a set A *onto* a set B. Then we can imagine a machine associated with f converting elements of A into elements of B. If one uses up all elements of A, one gets out all elements of B. Can we now construct a machine to carry out the reverse procedure? That is, can we construct a machine to convert any element b of B back to the element(s) which were converted into b by f?

The trouble is that, in general, this reverse procedure is not a function. For if $f(a) = b$ and also $f(\bar{a}) = b$, then one would have to convert b, in the reverse procedure, into both a and $\bar{a}$. Unless, of course, whenever $a \neq \bar{a}$, we had $f(a) \neq f(\bar{a})$. That is, unless there were at most one element of A mapped onto any given element of B. Functions with this property (including functions which are not onto) are said to be *one-to-one*, abbreviated '1-1.'

Definition 7. Let $f: A \to B$ (not necessarily onto). We say f is a 1-1 mapping of A into B if whenever a and $\bar{a}$ are distinct elements in A, $f(a)$ and $f(\bar{a})$ are distinct elements of B. [Thus if $a \neq \bar{a}$, then $f(a) \neq f(\bar{a})$. An equivalent statement is: If $f(a) = f(\bar{a})$, then $a = \bar{a}$.]

Example 14. $A = \{a,b,c\}$, $B = \{1,2,3,4\}$, $f: A \to B$, where $f(a) = 1$, $f(b) = 3$, $f(c) = 4$. Then f is 1-1, since distinct elements are mapped onto distinct elements. This mapping is not onto.

Example 15. $f: N \to \{2,4,6, \ldots\}$; $f(x) = 2x$. This mapping is 1-1 and onto.

Example 16. $f: R \to R$, where $f(x) = 3$. This mapping is neither 1-1 nor onto.

Example 17. $f: R \to \{3\}$, where $f(x) = 3$. This mapping is onto but not 1-1.

For mappings $f: A \to B$ which are both 1-1 and onto, the machine producing the reverse conversion is a function. In fact, for such mappings f we define a mapping $f^{-1}: B \to A$, called the *inverse* of f, as follows:

Let $b \in B$. We must give the rule telling onto which element of A the function f^{-1} maps b.

Since f is onto, $\exists\, a \in A \ni f(a) = b$.

Since f is 1-1, a is uniquely determined by b; that is, if $f(\bar{a}) = b$, then $a = \bar{a}$.

Let $f^{-1}(b)$ be this unique element $a \in A$ for which $f(a) = b$.

Then f^{-1} is a function from B to A.

Definition 8. Let $f: A \to B$ be 1-1 and onto. Then $f^{-1}: B \to A$ is defined as follows: $f^{-1}(b) = a$ if and only if $f(a) = b$. We call f^{-1} the *inverse func-*

tion of f. [Note that (a,b) is in the graph of f if and only if (b,a) is in the graph of f^{-1}.]

Suppose we have that f is 1-1 and onto. Is f^{-1} also 1-1 and onto? This is in fact the case, and for emphasis we state this as a theorem.

Theorem 1. Let $f: A \rightarrow B$ be 1-1 and onto. Then $f^{-1}: B \rightarrow A$ is 1-1 and onto. Moreover, $f^{-1}f = I_A$ and $ff^{-1} = I_B$.

Proof:

(1) We first show f^{-1} is onto. Suppose $a \in A$. Let $f(a) = b$. Then $f^{-1}(b) = a$ by Definition 8 [since $f(a) = b$]. Hence for each $a \in A$, $\exists b \in B \ni f^{-1}(b) = a$, and hence f^{-1} is onto.

(2) We show f^{-1} is 1-1. Suppose $f^{-1}(b) = f^{-1}(\bar{b})$. We must show $b = \bar{b}$. Let $f^{-1}(b) = a$. Then $f(a) = b$. But $f^{-1}(\bar{b}) = f^{-1}(b)$, so that $f^{-1}(\bar{b}) = a$ and $f(a) = \bar{b}$. Since f is a function, $f(a) = b$ and $f(a) = \bar{b}$ means $b = \bar{b}$.

(3) We have: $A \xrightarrow[f]{} B \xrightarrow[f^{-1}]{} A$. If $f(a) = b$, then by Definition 8, $f^{-1}(b) = a$. Thus $f^{-1}f(a) = f^{-1}(f(a)) = f^{-1}(b) = a$. So $f^{-1}f(a) = a$ for each $a \in A$. But $I_A(a) = a$ for each $a \in A$. Hence $f^{-1}f = I_A$.

(4) Similarly: $A \xrightarrow[f^{-1}]{} B \xrightarrow[f]{} B$. If $b \in B$, then say $f^{-1}(b) = a$. This means

$$f(a) = b$$

Hence $ff^{-1}(b) = f(f^{-1}(b)) = f(a) = b$. So $ff^{-1} = I_B$.

Example 18. $f: P \rightarrow P$, where $f(x) = x^2$. Then f is 1-1 and onto: If $c \in P$, there exists a unique solution to $x^2 = c$. The inverse function is $f^{-1}(x) = \sqrt{x}$.

Example 19. $f: R \rightarrow R$, where $f(x) = 2x$. The inverse is $g(x) = \frac{1}{2}x$. Thus $gf(x) = x$; ie., $gf = I_R$.

Observe that $f: A \rightarrow B$ is 1-1 and onto means that for each $b \in B$, the solution set of $f(x) = b$ consists of precisely one element.

Exercises

In the following, tell whether the given function falls under case (a), (b), (c), or (d). For those which fall under (d), give the inverse function.

(a) Neither 1-1 nor onto. (c) Not 1-1, but onto.
(b) 1-1, but not onto. (d) 1-1 and onto.

41. $f: A \rightarrow B$, where $A = \{0,1\}$, $B = \{a,b\}$, and $f(0) = a$, $f(1) = b$.
42. A and B as in Exercise 41. $g(0) = b$; $g(1) = a$.
43. A and B as in Exercise 41. $h(0) = a$; $h(1) = a$.
44. $f: R \rightarrow R$, where $f(x) = |x|$.
45. $f: R \rightarrow P \cup \{0\}$, where $f(x) = |x|$.
46. $f: R \rightarrow R$, where $f(x) = 2x + 1$.
47. $f: R \rightarrow P$, where $f(x) = x^2 + 1$.
48. $g: P \rightarrow P$, where $g(x) = x^2 + 1$.

49. $h: R \rightarrow R$, where $h(x) = x^3$.
50. $f: N \rightarrow \{2,4,6, \ldots\}$, where $f(x) = 2x$.
51. $f: J \rightarrow J$, where $f(x) = 2x$.
52. $f: P \rightarrow P$, where $f(x) = \sqrt{x}$.

6. Relations from a Set A to a Set B

6.1   Definition

Up to now we have considered mappings of a set A into a set B. A more general concept is that of a relation. We first illustrate this idea.

Example 20. Let A be the set of people in the United States, and B the set of colleges. If $a \in A$ and $b \in B$, we shall say a stands in the relation T to b if a attends b; we write aTb. This is an example of a relation from A to B. The graph of the relation T is the set of all elements (a,b) of $A \times B$ such that a attends b

Example 21. Another example is the relation L from R to R defined as follows: if $r,s \in R$, then rLs if $r \leqq s$. Thus $3L5$, $4L5$, $\sqrt{2} L5$, $\sqrt{2} L6$, and $-1L6$; also 7 is not in the relation L to 4, written $7\rlap{/}{L}4$. Of course, it is more customary to use '$\leqq$' for 'L' and '$\not\leqq$' for '$\rlap{/}{L}$.' The graph is $\{(r,s) \in R \times R / r \leqq s\}$.

Example 22. Let A and B be any sets, and let V be a subset of $A \times B$. Define aSb if $(a,b) \in V$.

Example 23. Let f be a mapping of a set A into a set B. Define the relation W as follows:

$$aWb \qquad \text{if } b = f(a)$$

Definition 9. Let A and B be any sets, and S be a rule assigning to each element of A one or more or possibly no elements of B. Then S is said to be a *relation* from A to B. If S associates $a \in A$ and $b \in B$, then we write aSb and say a is in the relation S to b.

Example 22 gives the essential idea of a relation. Any subset of $A \times B$ can be used to define a relation. What counts in a relation is the rule of assignment, not how it is described. Thus

$$aSb \text{ if } a < b \text{ and } aTb \text{ if } a - 1 < b - 1$$

is the same relation. That is, they describe the same rule of assignment.

We described how a function from A to B (Definition 1) may be regarded as a certain type of subset of $A \times B$ [satisfying conditions (1) and (2) of Section 2.3]. A relation, then, is regarded as any subset of $A \times B$, this being an alternative view of Definition 9.

It is for this reason that one often writes $(a,b) \in S$ to mean aSb; i.e., one thinks of S as a subset of $A \times B$. This subset is called the *graph* of S. Similarly, if f is a mapping from A to B, one writes $(a,b) \in f$ to mean $b = f(a)$.

Definition 10. Let S be a relation from A to B. Let

$$A_0 = \{a \in A/(a,b) \in S \text{ for some } b \in B\}$$
$$B_0 = \{b \in B/(a,b) \in S \text{ for some } a \in A\}$$

Then A_0 is called the *domain* of S and B_0 the *range*. In particular, if S is a function, the domain of S is A.

Example 24. Let $A = \{a,b,c,d\} = B$. Define the relation S as $\{(a,b), (a,c), (d,c)\}$. Figure 11.28 is (a representation of) the graph of S. It is customary to omit the words in parentheses and allow the term "graph of S" to refer also to its representation. The domain of S is $\{a,d\}$, i.e., the subset of A having points

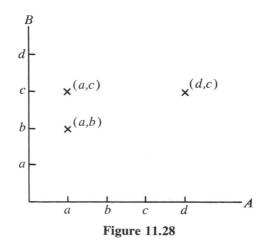

Figure 11.28

above them on the graph. The range is $\{b,c\}$, the subset of B having points to the right on the graph. One can also indicate the graph as shown in Figure 11.29.

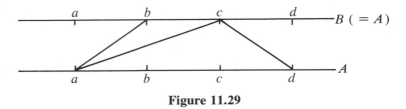

Figure 11.29

Let A_0 be the domain of a relation S from A to B. If for each $a \in A_0$ there is a unique $b \in B \ni aSb$, then we may define a function $f: A_0 \to B$ as $f(a) = b$. Under this condition, we say that S itself is a function. By this we mean, then, that S defines a function on its domain.

6.2 Branch Functions of a Relation

Example 25. Let S be the relation from R to R such that xSy if $y^2 = x$ (Figure 11.30). The domain of S is $P \cup \{0\}$; the range is R. Note that S is not a function since, for example, $(9,3) \epsilon S$ and $(9,-3) \epsilon S$.

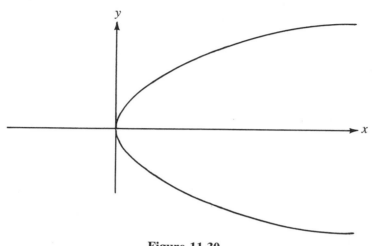

Figure 11.30

One can write S as a union of two subsets S_1 and S_2 such that S_1 and S_2 represent functions; namely, take S_1 as the upper half and S_2 as the lower half of the above graph of S. Indeed for S_1 we have the function $y = \sqrt{x}$, and for S_2 we have $y = -\sqrt{x}$. These are called the *branch functions* of $y^2 = x$.

There are other ways of subdividing S into branch functions, but usually one specifies a particularly convenient subdivision (in this example the one we have given is the usual one taken), and refers to the branches of this subdivision as *the* branches of the relation.

Example 26. Let U be the relation from R to R defined by the graph on the left in Figure 11.31. Then the graph on the right indicates a suitable subdivision into (infinitely many) branch functions.

Example 27. In Example 24 there is no subdivision of S into branch functions which seems most natural. One can either choose $\{(a,b), (d,c)\}$, and $\{(a,c)\}$ as branch functions, or $\{(a,c), (d,c)\}$, and $\{(a,b)\}$ as branch functions.

This last example points up the fact that the branch functions do not necessarily have the same domain as the original relation, but in any case the domain of the former is always a subset of that of the latter.

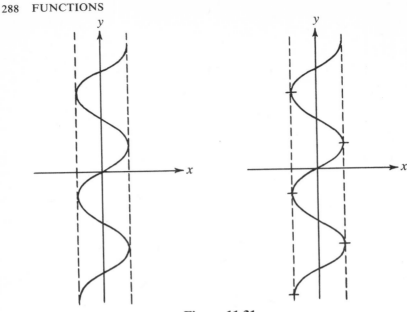

Figure 11.31

6.3   Inverse Relations

We have seen that if f is a function from A to B, then in certain cases f may have an inverse function f^{-1} from B to A; namely, if f is 1-1 and onto. In the case of relations, however, we shall define the inverse for every relation.

Definition 11. Let S be a relation from A to B. Then we define the *inverse relation* S^{-1} from B to A as follows: $bS^{-1}a$ shall mean aSb; i.e., $(b,a) \in S^{-1}$ if and only if $(a,b) \in S$.

Example 28. Let $K = \{1,2,3\}$ and $L = \{a,b,c,d\}$. Let U be the relation from K to L consisting of $\{(1,b), (1,c), (3,b)\}$. Thus $1Ub, 1Uc, 3Ub$. Then U^{-1} is the relation $\{(b,1), (c,1), (b,3)\}$ from L to K. Thus $bU^{-1}1, cU^{-1}1$, and $bU^{-1}3$ (Figure 11.32).

Assuming equal scales are used, the picture for U^{-1} on the right is obtained by reflecting as in a mirror the entire diagram on the left in the line we have marked 'mirror.' Similarly, one can pass from the figure on the right to the one on the left. That is,

$$(U^{-1})^{-1} = U$$

Example 29. If S is the relation xSy, where $y^2 = x$, then S^{-1} is the relation $xS^{-1}y$, where $x^2 = y$, these being relations from R to R.

Now one could have written: "$yS^{-1}x$ means $y^2 = x$" if one wished to use y to range over the domain and x the range. But if one wishes, in a given dis-

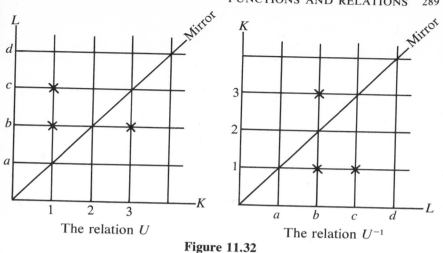

The relation U The relation U^{-1}

Figure 11.32

cussion, to have the same letter used for the domain for all relations considered—it makes for easier reading—then $xS^{-1}y$ becomes $x^2 = y$ as stated.

Thus $(9,3)$, $(9,-3)$ ϵ S and $(3,9)$, $(-3,9)$ ϵ S^{-1}. Note that $y^2 = x$ is trans-
formed into $x^2 = y$ by interchanging x and y. The graphs are given in Figure
11.33.

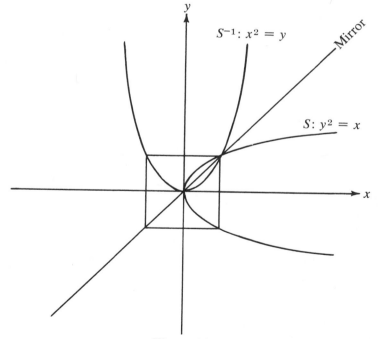

Figure 11.33

Note that $y = \sqrt{x}$ (the upper half of $y^2 = x$) is a function, as previously stated. In fact it is 1-1 and onto from $P \cup \{0\}$ to $P \cup \{0\}$. Its inverse function is the right half of $x^2 = y$. Similarly, the inverse function of $y = -\sqrt{x}$, a function from P to $-P$ (if we agree to take 0 in the domain of $y = \sqrt{x}$), is the left half of $x^2 = y$, excluding $(0,0)$.

Also observe that S^{-1} is a function, although S is not.

Example 30. Let S be the relation from R to R given by the function $y = f(x)$ with the graph as shown in Figure 11.34. Then S^{-1} is given by taking the mirror image as in Example 29. We obtain the graph of Figure 11.35. We observe that S^{-1} is not a function.

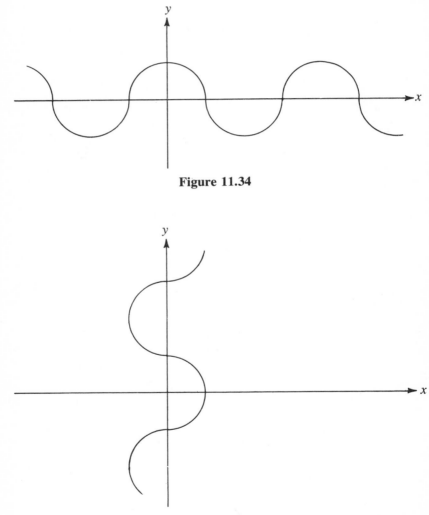

Figure 11.34

Figure 11.35

Exercises

53. Let S be the relation from R to R defined by xSy if $x^2 + y^2 = 25$.
    (a) Which of the following hold: $3S4$, $-3S4$, $\sqrt{5}\,S20$, $-\sqrt{5}\,S2\sqrt{5}$?
    (b) How is S^{-1} defined?
54. Let T be the relation from A to B given by $\{(a,1), (a,2), (c,2), (c,3)\}$, where
    $A = \{a,b,c,d,e\}$, $B = \{1,2,3\}$.
    (a) What is the domain of T? The range?
    (b) Draw the graph of T.
    (c) The same for T^{-1}.
    (d) Is T a function from its domain A_0 to B? Justify your answer.
    (e) Give one example of selecting branch functions of T.
55. Let S be the relation from R to R given by uSv, where $u = v + 1$.
    (a) Draw the graph of S and S^{-1} on the same coordinate system.
    (b) Define $uS^{-1}v$.
    (c) Is either S or S^{-1} a function?
56. Following are shown relations from R to R. Sketch the inverse relation, and
    determine which of the given relations and their inverses are functions (de-
    fined on the domain of the relation).

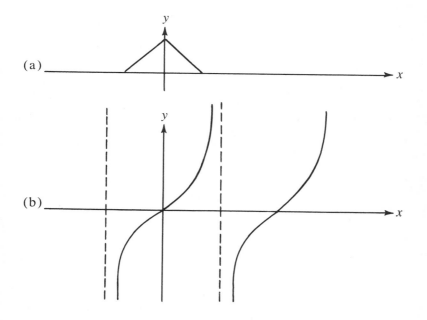

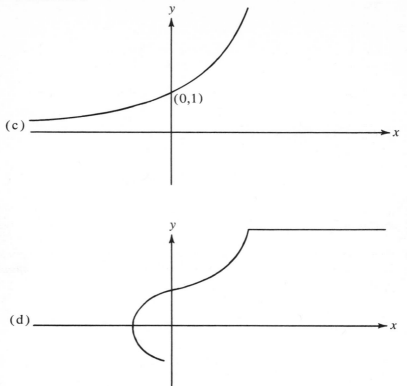

(c)

(0,1)

(d)

57. In each of the relations of Exercise 56, and their inverses, give a subdivision into branch functions for those relations which are not already functions.

chapter xii

POLYNOMIAL FUNCTIONS

In this chapter we consider polynomial functions from C to C, where C is the field of complex numbers. That is, the functions f we consider are of the type

$$f(x) = a_n x^n + a_{n-1} x^{n-1} + \cdots + a_0$$

where $a_n, a_{n-1}, \ldots, a_0$ are complex numbers called the *coefficients of the polynomial*. More generally, we consider polynomial functions with coefficients in any subfield F of C (this includes the case $F = C$). A discussion of factoring such polynomials in F is provided, and in particular the fundamental theorem of arithmetic for polynomials is proved. Solution of polynomial equations is given in special cases, and the solution of the quadratic equation is given in full. The chapter closes with restricted applications to maximum-minimum problems.

1. Definitions

Let F be any subfield of the field C of complex numbers. That is, F is a subset of C such that when the addition and multiplication of C are restricted to F, then F becomes a field. For example, F may be C, or R, or $\bar{R}$; or F may be the set of all numbers of the type $a + b\sqrt{2}$, where $a, b \in \bar{R}$; etc.

Definition 1. We shall say $f(x)$ is a *polynomial function* with coefficients in F (or also a polynomial) if

$$f(x) = a_n x^n + a_{n-1} x^{n-1} + \cdots + a_0$$

where $a_n, a_{n-1}, \ldots, a_0 \in F$. If $a_n \neq 0$, we call n the *degree* of the polynomial function.[1] (The variable x may range over F or any field containing F.) If all coefficients are zero, we say the polynomial function has no degree.

If x is a variable over C, then f is a function from C to C; similarly, if x is a variable over R or $\bar{R}$ and the coefficients are from R or $\bar{R}$, then f is a function from R to R or $\bar{R}$ to $\bar{R}$, respectively.

---

[1] Suppose $g(x) = b_m x^m + b_{m-1} x^{m-1} + \cdots + b_0$, with $b_m \neq 0$. The question arises as to whether $f(x)$ and $g(x)$ can be the same functions without having $m = n$ and corresponding coefficients equal. We shall see in Section 5 that for subfields of C, this cannot occur.

Example 1. $f(x) = 3x^4 + \frac{1}{3}x^2 - 2$, where $F = \bar{R}$. Here $n = 4$; $a_4 = 3, a_3 = 0, a_2 = \frac{1}{3}$, $a_1 = 0, a_0 = -2$.

$$f(i) = 3 - \frac{1}{3} - 2 = \frac{2}{3}$$

$$f(\sqrt[4]{2}) = 6 + \frac{1}{3}\sqrt{2} - 2 = 4 + \frac{\sqrt{2}}{3}$$

Definition 2. If $f(x)$ and $g(x)$ are two polynomial functions, $f(x) + g(x)$, $f(x) - g(x)$, and $f(x) \cdot g(x)$ shall refer to the polynomial functions obtained by adding, subtracting, and multiplying the polynomials as in Section 7 of Chapter 9.

If $f(x)$ is the zero polynomial, one often writes $f(x) = 0$ [or similarly if $f(x)$ is not the zero polynomial, one writes $f(x) \neq 0$]. However, one may also write $f(x) = 0$ to mean a polynomial equation in x. Similarly

$$f(x) = g(x)$$

may mean two polynomials are the same, or may represent the problem of finding the values for which they are equal. These meanings have to be determined from the context.

2. The Remainder Theorem

Example 2. If $f(x) = 5x^4 - x^3 + x - 1$, find $f(2)$.
Solution 1:
$$\begin{aligned} f(2) &= 5(2)^4 - (2)^3 + 2 - 1 \\ &= 80 - 8 + 2 - 1 \\ &= 73 \end{aligned}$$
Solution 2: Divide $5x^4 - x^3 + x - 1$ by $x - 2$ according to the division algorithm:

$$f(x) = 5x^4 - x^3 + x - 1 = (x - 2)(5x^3 + 9x^2 + 18x + 37) + 73$$

This is true for all values of x, in particular for $x = 2$. Thus

$$f(2) = (2 - 2)[5(2)^3 + 9(2)^2 + 18(2) + 37] + 73$$

$$= 73$$

Example 3. If $f(x) = 5x^4 - x^3 + x - 1$, find $f(-3)$.
Solution 1:
$$\begin{aligned} f(-3) &= 5(-3)^4 - (-3)^3 + (-3) - 1 \\ &= 405 - (-27) + (-3) - 1 \\ &= 428 \end{aligned}$$
Solution 2: Divide $5x^4 - x^3 + x - 1$ by $x + 3$ according to the division algorithm:

$$f(x) = 5x^4 - x^3 + x - 1 = (x + 3)(5x^3 - 16x^2 + 48x - 143) + 428$$

Hence

$$f(-3) = (3 - 3)(\cdots) + 428$$
$$= 428$$

Except for simple cases, the method given in the second solutions to Examples 2 and 3 is the more economical one. We formalize this method in Theorem 2. For this purpose we state:

Theorem 1 (Division Algorithm). Let $f(x)$ and $g(x)$ be polynomial functions with coefficients in any subfield F of the complex numbers, and assume that $g(x)$ is not the zero polynomial. Then there exist polynomial functions $q(x)$ and $r(x)$ with coefficients in F such that

$$f(x) = g(x) \cdot q(x) + r(x)$$

and where either the degree of $r(x)$ is less than that of $g(x)$, or $r(x)$ is the zero polynomial.

Proof: The proof is given in Theorem 3 of Chapter 9. One sees in that proof that we could have assumed the coefficients to have come from any field.

Theorem 2 (Remainder Theorem). Let $f(x)$ be a polynomial of positive degree with coefficients in a subfield F of the complex numbers, and let $\alpha \in F$. Then if upon dividing $f(x)$ by $x - \alpha$ one obtains the remainder r [i.e., $f(x) = (x - \alpha)q(x) + r$], then $f(\alpha) = r$.

Proof: Note that by Theorem 1, $f(x) = (x - \alpha)q(x) + r(x)$, where the degree of $r(x)$ is less than that of $x - \alpha$, or else $r(x) = 0$. Thus $r(x)$ is either of degree 0 or else $r(x) = 0$. Thus we may set $r(x) = r \in F$. It follows that

$$f(\alpha) = (\alpha - \alpha)q(\alpha) + r$$

so that $f(\alpha) = r$.

Theorem 2 offers a method for finding $f(\alpha)$, where $f(x)$ is a polynomial. Namely, divide $f(x)$ by $x - \alpha$. The remainder r is $f(\alpha)$.

Example 4. If $f(x) = -x^3 + 2x^2 + 2$, find $f(-\frac{1}{2})$.
Solution: Divide $-x^3 + 2x^2 + 2$ by $x - (-\frac{1}{2})$, i.e., by $x + \frac{1}{2}$.

$$
\begin{array}{r}
-x^2 + \frac{5}{2}x \quad - \frac{5}{4} \\
x + \frac{1}{2} \overline{) -x^3 + 2x^2 + 0 \cdot x + 2} \\
\underline{-x^3 - \frac{1}{2}x^2} \\
\frac{5}{2}x^2 + 0 \cdot x \\
\underline{\frac{5}{2}x^2 + \frac{5}{4}x} \\
- \frac{5}{4}x \quad + 2 \\
\underline{- \frac{5}{4}x \quad - \frac{5}{8}} \\
\boxed{\frac{21}{8}} = r
\end{array}
$$

Hence $f(-\frac{1}{2}) = \frac{21}{8}$.

Definition 3. If $f(x)$ and $g(x)$ are polynomials with coefficients in a field F, we say $g(x)$ is a *divisor* of $f(x)$ (over F) if $\exists$ a polynomial $h(x)$ with coefficients in $F \ni f(x) = g(x)h(x)$. [One also calls $g(x)$ a *factor* of $f(x)$, or also $f(x)$ is a *multiple* of $g(x)$; or also, one says $g(x)$ *divides* $f(x)$.]

Theorem 3 (Factor Theorem). If $f(x)$ is a polynomial with coefficients in a subfield F of the complex numbers, and $\alpha \in F$, then $x - \alpha$ is divisor of $f(x)$ if and only if $f(\alpha) = 0$ [i.e., if and only if α is a root of $f(x)$.]

Proof: (a) If $x - \alpha$ is a factor of $f(x)$, then $f(x) = (x - \alpha)q(x)$. Hence

$$f(\alpha) = (\alpha - \alpha)q(\alpha) = 0$$

(b) Conversely, suppose $f(\alpha) = 0$. Divide $f(x)$ by $x - \alpha$ to obtain

$$f(x) = (x - \alpha)q(x) + r$$

By the remainder theorem, $f(\alpha) = r$, so that $r = 0$. Hence

$$f(x) = (x - \alpha)q(x)$$

and $x - \alpha$ is a factor of $f(x)$.

Example 5. Is $x - 1$ a factor of $x^5 + x^4 - x^2 - 1$?
Solution: If $f(x) = x^5 + x^4 - x^2 - 1$, then $f(1) = 1^5 + 1^4 - 1^2 - 1 = 0$. Hence $x - 1$ is a factor.

Exercises

1. If $f(x) = x^5 - 3x^3 + x - 2$ find the following by means of Theorem 2:
   (a) $f(1)$. (c) $f(\frac{3}{2})$.
   (b) $f(-1)$. (d) $f(-3)$.
2. Determine whether $x - 2$ is a factor of:
   (a) $x^2 - 4x + 4$. (d) $x^4 - 16$.
   (b) $x^3 - 3x + 2$. (e) $2x^4 - 3x^3 + x + 8$.
   (c) $x^3 - 2x^2 + x - 2$.

3. Synthetic Division

Using the remainder theorem, or the factor theorem, involves dividing a polynomial $f(x)$ by $x - \alpha$. This occurs so frequently that a "synthetic" form of this division has been devised, which we now describe.

Suppose we wish to divide $a_n x^n + a_{n-1}x^{n-1} + \cdots + a_0$ by $x - \alpha$. We obtain, by the division algorithm, something of the form:

$$a_n x^n + \cdots + a_0 = (x - \alpha)(b_{n-1}x^{n-1} + \cdots + b_0) + r \qquad (*)$$

The quotient is $b_{n-1}x^{n-1} + \cdots + b_0$, the remainder r. Note that r is a constant, since its degree must be less than that of $x - \alpha$ or else $r = 0$. The process would look as follows:

$$\begin{array}{r} b_{n-1}x^{n-1} \quad + b_{n-2}x^{n-2} \\ \hline x-\alpha\,)\,a_nx^n \quad + a_{n-1}x^{n-1} \quad + a_{n-2}x^{n-2} + \cdots + a_0 \\ b_{n-1}x^n - b_{n-1}\alpha x^{n-1} \\ \hline (a_{n-1}+b_{n-1}\alpha)x^{n-1} + a_{n-2}x^{n-2} \\ b_{n-2}x^{n-1} - b_{n-2}\alpha x^{n-2} \\ \hline (a_{n-2}+b_{n-2}\alpha)x^{n-2} \\ \cdots \end{array}$$

Of course, $b_{n-1}=a_n$, $b_{n-2}=a_{n-1}+b_{n-1}\alpha$, etc.

The work can be shortened as follows:

Write the coefficients of $x^n, x^{n-1}, \ldots$ in order, and place α to the right:

$$\begin{array}{ccccccc} a_n & a_{n-1} & a_{n-2} & \cdots & a_1 & a_0 & \underline{|\alpha} \\ & a_n\alpha & b_{n-2}\alpha & \cdots & & & \\ \hline b_{n-1}=a_n & b_{n-2} & b_{n-3} & \cdots & b_0 & r & \end{array}$$

Carry down the a_n. Multiply a_n by α and add the result to a_{n-1}. This is b_{n-2}. Multiply b_{n-2} by α and add the result to a_{n-2}. This is b_{n-3}. Continue this process.

Note that if the dividend has degree n, the quotient has degree $n-1$.

Example 6. Divide $3x^4 - 2x^3 + x - 2$ by $x+1$ [i.e., by $x-(-1)$].
Solution:
$$\begin{array}{rrrrr} 3 & -2 & 0 & 1 & -2 \quad \underline{|-1} \\ & -3 & 5 & -5 & 4 \\ \hline 3 & -5 & 5 & -4 & 2 \end{array}$$

quotient remainder

The quotient is $3x^3 - 5x^2 + 5x - 4$, the remainder 2. That is,

$$3x^4 - 2x^3 + x - 2 = (3x^3 - 5x^2 + 5x - 4)(x+1)+2$$

Example 7. If $g(x)=6x^6 - 3x^4 + x^3 - 2$, find $g(2)$.
Solution: We divide $g(x)$ by $x-2$ by means of synthetic division. The remainder is the answer:

$$\begin{array}{rrrrrrr} 6 & 0 & -3 & 1 & 0 & 0 & -2 \quad \underline{|2} \\ & 12 & 24 & 42 & 86 & 172 & 344 \\ \hline 6 & 12 & 21 & 43 & 86 & 172 & \boxed{342} \end{array}$$

Hence $g(2)=342$.

Example 8. Determine whether $4x+2$ is a divisor of $2x^3 - 3x^2 + 4x + 3$.
Solution: Since $4x+2=4(x+\frac{1}{2})$, if $4x+2$ is a divisor of $2x^3-3x^2+4x+3$, so is $x+\frac{1}{2}$. We therefore determine the remainder upon dividing $2x^3-3x^2+4x+3$ by $x-(-\frac{1}{2})$; we use synthetic division.

$$\begin{array}{rrrr} 2 & -3 & 4 & 3 \quad \underline{|-\frac{1}{2}} \\ & -1 & 2 & -3 \\ \hline 2 & -4 & 6 & 0 \end{array}$$

remainder

Since the remainder is 0, by the factor theorem, $x + \frac{1}{2}$ is a factor. In fact,

$$2x^3 - 3x^2 + 4x + 3 = (x + \tfrac{1}{2})(2x^2 - 4x + 6)$$
$$= (4x + 2)\left(\frac{x^2}{2} - x + \frac{3}{2}\right)$$

Exercises

3. Find the remainder when
   (a) $x^2 - 2x + 5$ is divided by $x + 1$.
   (b) $2x^2 - x + 6$ is divided by $x - \frac{1}{3}$.
   (c) $6x^3 + 5x^2 - 19x + 3$ is divided by $x - \frac{1}{6}$.
   (d) $x^4 + 3x^2 - 2x + 1$ is divided by $x + 2$.
4. In each of the parts of Exercise 3, what is the quotient?
5. In each of the following, determine whether the first polynomial is a divisor of the second. When it is, give the second polynomial in factored form.

   (a) $x - 2$; $x^2 + x + 1$.   (d) $x - 3$; $2x^4 - x^2 + x - 6$.
   (b) $x + \frac{1}{2}$; $2x^2 - x - 1$.   (e) $x + 3$; $x^3 + 3$.
   (c) $2x + 1$; $2x^2 - x - 1$.   (f) $x - 2$; $2x^4 + x^3 - 8x^2 - 4x - 4$.

4. The Fundamental Theorem of Algebra

The field C of complex numbers contains the subfield R, and also an element i satisfying the polynomial equation $x^2 + 1 = 0$. In R, the polynomial $x^2 + 1$ does not have a root, since $x^2 + 1 > 0$ is satisfied by every element of R.

We may ask whether there exists a polynomial $f(x)$ of positive degree with coefficients in R such that $f(x)$ has no root in C. The answer is in the negative according to the following:

Theorem 4 (The Fundamental Theorem of Algebra). Let $f(x)$ be a polynomial with coefficients in R having positive degree. Then

$$\exists \alpha \in C \ni f(\alpha) = 0.$$

Or equivalently, if n is the degree of $f(x)$, $\exists \alpha \in C \ni f(x) = (x - \alpha)g(x)$, where $g(x)$ has coefficients in C and is of degree $n - 1$.

There are many known proofs of this theorem, and in most introductory texts on the Theory of Functions of a Complex Variable, one can find several proofs given. Unfortunately, to develop the tools necessary for even the most elementary known proof will have to be regarded as beyond the scope of this text. However, the reader will be glad to know that the theorems we develop below are not needed to prove the fundamental theorem, so that we are not involving ourselves in circular reasoning.

It is a corollary of the fundamental theorem that if $f(x)$ is a polynomial of positive degree with *coefficients in C*, then $\exists \alpha \in C \ni f(\alpha) = 0$.

Exercise

6. Suppose $f(x)$ is a polynomial with coefficients in $\bar{R}$. Does there exist a root of $f(x)$ in C? Justify your answer.

5. The Roots of a Polynomial

Using the fundamental theorem of algebra and the factor theorem, one can prove the following:

Theorem 5. Let $f(x)$ be a polynomial with coefficients in C of degree $n > 0$. Let a_n be the leading coefficient of $f(x)$. Then $\exists \alpha_1, \alpha_2, \ldots, \alpha_n$ (not necessarily distinct) in $C \ni$

$$f(x) = a_n(x - \alpha_1)(x - \alpha_2) \cdots (x - \alpha_n) \qquad (*)$$

In particular, $f(x)$ has at most n solutions in C (and hence, a fortiori, at most n solutions in any subfield of C); namely, $f(\beta) = 0$ if and only if β is one of the $\alpha_i (i = 1, 2, \ldots, n)$.

Proof: We use induction on the degree n of $f(x)$ to prove that $f(x)$ can be written as in (*). If $n = 1$, we have $f(x) = a_1x + a_0$. Since $a_1 \neq 0$, we may write

$$f(x) = a_1 \left(x + \frac{a_0}{a_1} \right)$$

and the result is true for $n = 1$. Assume the result is true for $n - 1$. Let $f(x) = a_nx^n + a_{n-1}x^{n-1} + \cdots + a_0$, where $a_n \neq 0$, $n > 1$. By the fundamental theorem, $\exists \alpha_1 \ni f(\alpha_1) = 0$. By the factor theorem, $x - \alpha_1$ is a factor of $f(x)$. The method used in synthetic division shows that one can determine $g(x)$ *of degree* $n - 1$ and leading coefficient a_n such that

$$f(x) = (x - \alpha_1)g(x)$$

By our inductive hypothesis, $g(x) = a_n(x - \alpha_2) \cdots (x - \alpha_n)$; hence

$$f(x) = a_n(x - \alpha_1)(x - \alpha_2) \cdots (x - \alpha_n)$$

This establishes (*). By (*), β is a root of $f(x)$ if and only if

$$a_n(\beta - \alpha_1)(\beta - \alpha_2) \cdots (\beta - \alpha_n) = 0$$

which in turn holds if and only if $\beta - \alpha_i = 0$ for some i with $1 \leq i \leq n$. This completes the proof of the theorem.

Example 9. Find a polynomial with coefficients in C having the roots 1 and -1, and no others.

Solution: $(x - 1)(x + 1)$ or $x^2 - 1$ is one such. Another is $3(x^2 - 1)$. Still another is $(x - 1)^2(x + 1)$; i.e., $x^3 - x^2 - x + 1$.

Example 10. Find a polynomial with coefficients in C having the roots i and $2 - 3i$ and no others.

Solution: $(x - i)(x - (2 - 3i))$; i.e.,

$$x^2 - (2 - 2i)x + (3 + 2i)$$

To check that i is a root, we may use synthetic division:

$$
\begin{array}{ccc}
1 & -(2 - 2i) & 3 + 2i \quad \underline{|i} \\
 & i & -3 - 2i \\
\hline
1 & -2 + 3i & 0
\end{array}
$$

Similarly, one may check that $2 - 3i$ is a root.

We have avoided the following question up to this point. Suppose $f(x)$ and $g(x)$ are polynomials with coefficients in C, say where

$$f(x) = a_n x^n + a_{n-1} x^{n-1} + \cdots + a_0$$

and $g(x) = b_m x^m + b_{m-1} x^{m-1} + \cdots + b_0$. Under what circumstances can f and g be the same functions? That is, under what circumstances can $f(x) = g(x)$ be an identity in the variable x over C? Let

$$
\begin{aligned}
f(x) &= a_n x^n + a_{n-1} x^{n-1} + \cdots + a_0 \\
g(x) &= b_m x^m + b_{m-1} x^{m-1} + \cdots + b_0
\end{aligned}
$$

If, say, $n \geqq m$, we may write

$$g(x) = b_n x^n + \cdots + b_m x^m + b_{m-1} x^{m-1} + \cdots + b_0$$

where the coefficients preceding b_m (if $n > m$) are all 0. Then

$$f(x) - g(x) = (a_n - b_n)x^n + (a_{n-1} - b_{n-1})x^{n-1} + \cdots + (a_0 - b_0)$$

Suppose $f(x) - g(x)$ is 0 for all $x \in C$.

Then, in particular, $f(x) - g(x)$ is 0 on $n + 1$ distinct elements, e.g., $1, 2, \ldots, n, n + 1$. According to Theorem 5, this is impossible, unless $f(x) - g(x)$ is the zero polynomial. That is, $a_n - b_n = 0$, $a_{n-1} - b_{n-1} = 0$, $\ldots$, $a_0 - b_0 = 0$, so that the degree of $f(x)$ and $g(x)$ are the same and so are the coefficients. This yields the following:

Theorem 6. If $f(x) = a_n x^n + \cdots + a_0$ and $g(x) = b_m x^m + \cdots + b_0$, where $a_n, b_m \neq 0$, and $f(x) = g(x)$ for all $x \in C$, then $m = n$ and

$$a_n = b_n,\ a_{n-1} = b_{n-1},\ \ldots,\ a_0 = b_0$$

We used the fact here that C had as many elements as we needed. For Theorem 6 to hold for all m and n, we need to know that C has infinitely many elements. For finite fields Theorem 6 is false.

Thus, let $F = \{0, 1\}$ be the field defined by Tables 12.1.

Tables 12.1

+	0 1	·	0 1
0	0 1	0	0 0
1	1 0	1	0 1

Let $f(x) = x^3 + x^2 + x + 1$, $g(x) = x + 1$. Then $f(0) = g(0) = 1$,

$$f(1) = g(1) = 0$$

Hence $f(x) = g(x)$ for all $x \in F$, and f and g are the same functions.

We say $x^3 + x^2 + x + 1$ and $x + 1$ are two representations of the same function—in this case two different representations. One representation is as a polynomial of degree 3, the other of degree 1. To distinguish the forms of these representations of the function, we say that $x^3 + x^2 + x + 1$ and $x + 1$ are distinct *polynomial forms*, although they represent the same function.

Theorem 6 may be stated that distinct polynomial forms yield distinct polynomial functions over C. The proof shows that the result remains true if C is replaced by any infinite subset of C. If F is any subfield of C, we shall see that F must be infinite. Hence C may be replaced by F in Theorem 6.

To see that any subfield F of C is infinite, we show that N must be a subset of F. For if $M = \{m \in N / m \in F\}$, then we see that $1 \in M$; and if $n \in M$, then $n + 1 \in M$, since F is closed under $+$. Hence (cf. Theorem 1(c) of Chapter 8) $M = N$, so that $N \subseteq F$.

In fact, one can now see that $\bar{R} \subseteq F$. For since every element of F has an additive inverse in F, it follows that $J \subseteq F$. And, finally, if $q \in J$ and $q \neq 0$, then $\dfrac{1}{q} \in F$, so that $p \cdot \dfrac{1}{q} = \dfrac{p}{q} \in F$ for any $p \in J$.

In defining the degree of a polynomial, we are really referring to the degree of a polynomial form. However, for polynomials with complex coefficients, we may also regard this as the (unique) degree of the polynomial function.

A useful remark is the following:

$$\text{degree } (f(x) \cdot g(x)) = \text{degree } f(x) + \text{degree } g(x)$$

For if $f(x)$ has degree m and leading coefficient a_m, and $g(x)$ degree n with leading coefficient b_n, then

$$f(x)g(x) = a_m b_n x^{m+n} + \cdots$$

and $f(x)g(x)$ has degree $m + n$.

We can use this remark to prove the following:

Theorem 7. Let $f(x)$ and $g(x)$ be polynomials with coefficients in C. Then $f(x)g(x) = 0$ if and only if either $f(x) = 0$ or $g(x) = 0$.

Proof: If either $f(x)$ or $g(x) = 0$, then certainly $f(x)g(x) = 0$.
Conversely suppose $f(x)g(x) = 0$. If both $f(x)$ and $g(x)$ are not 0, then degree $f(x)g(x) = $ degree $f(x) + $ degree $g(x)$, so that we could not have (by Theorem 6) that $f(x)g(x) = 0$. This is a contradiction, so that we must have had $f(x)$ or $g(x)$ is the zero polynomial.

Corollary: If $a(x)$, $b(x)$, $c(x)$ are polynomials with coefficients in C and $a(x) \neq 0$, then $a(x)b(x) = a(x)c(x)$ if and only if $b(x) = c(x)$.

Proof: $a(x)b(x) = a(x)c(x)$ if and only if $a(x)(b(x) - c(x)) = 0$. Since $a(x) \neq 0$, this latter equality holds if and only if $b(x) - c(x) = 0$ or $b(x) = c(x)$.

Exercise

7. Determine at least two polynomials having precisely the prescribed roots:

(a) 1.   (e) 1,i.   (i) 1,0,1 + i.
(b) 0.   (f) i,$-i$.   (j) $\sqrt{2}$,1.
(c) -1,1.   (g) 1 + i, 1 $-$ i. (k) 2 + $\sqrt{2}$,2 $-$ $\sqrt{2}$.
(d) -1,0.   (h) 1,2,-1.

6. Theory of Factorization

We have seen that every polynomial $f(x)$ with coefficients in C can be factored into a product of linear factors and a constant. This factorization is not quite unique. For example,

$$2x^2 + 3x - 2 = (2x - 1)(x + 2) = 2(x - \tfrac{1}{2})(x + 2) = \tfrac{2}{3}(x - \tfrac{1}{2})(3x + 6)$$

and so on. The problem is that we can always modify a factor by a constant. For if $f(x) = g(x)h(x)$, then $f(x) = [ag(x)][a^{-1}h(x)]$, where a is any nonzero element in C. Thus a different factorization is $f(x) = s(x)t(x)$, where $s(x) = ag(x)$ and $t(x) = a^{-1}h(x)$.

In the factorization theory for polynomials, therefore, the nonzero elements of C play the same role as did the integers 1 and -1 in the factorization of integers.

One often wishes to restrict the factors to have coefficients in some sub-field of the complex numbers. For example, $x^2 + 1$ (apart from constant factors) cannot be factored into factors (of lower degree) with real co-efficients, but with complex coefficients we have $x^2 + 1 = (x - i)(x + i)$. Similarly, $x^2 - 2$ cannot be factored over the field of rational numbers, but in the reals we have $x^2 - 2 = (x + \sqrt{2})(x - \sqrt{2})$.

We shall therefore present the theory of factorization over any subfield F of the complex numbers.

Definition 4. Let F be a subfield of the complex numbers. Let $\mathscr{P}$ denote the set of all polynomials in x with coefficients in F. The nonzero constant polynomials (i.e., the polynomials of degree 0) in $\mathscr{P}$ will be called the *units* of $\mathscr{P}$. If $f(x)$, $g(x) \in \mathscr{P}$, we shall say that $f(x)$ is *associated* to $g(x)$ if $\exists a \neq 0$ in $F \ni f(x) = ag(x)$. In this case, $g(x)$ is associated to $f(x)$, since $g(x) = a^{-1}f(x)$. We therefore call $f(x)$ and $g(x)$ *associates*.

Definition 5. Let F and $\mathscr{P}$ be as above, and $f(x) \in \mathscr{P}$. We say $f(x)$ is *irreducible* over F if $f(x)$ has positive degree and its only factors are ele-ments of $\mathscr{P}$ which are associates or units. Otherwise $f(x)$ is said to be *reducible*.

Example 11. $x^2 + 1$ is irreducible over the field R of real numbers. We can factor $x^2 + 1$ as

$$
\begin{aligned}
x^2 + 1 &= 3(\tfrac{1}{3}x^2 + \tfrac{1}{3}) \\
&= \tfrac{1}{4}(4x^2 + 4) \\
&= a(a^{-1}x^2 + a^{-1}) \qquad \text{where } a \neq 0 \text{ in } R \\
&= 4 \cdot \tfrac{1}{2} \cdot \tfrac{1}{2} \cdot (x^2 + 1)
\end{aligned}
$$

but in each factorization, the factors are either units, or associates of $x^2 + 1$.

Definition 6. If $f(x)$ is a polynomial with leading coefficient 1, then $f(x)$ is said to be *monic*.

Let $f(x) = a_n x^n + \cdots + a_0$, where $a_n \neq 0$. Then we may write

$$f(x) = a_n g(x)$$

where $g(x)$ is a monic polynomial. Namely,

$$g(x) = x^n + b_{n-1}x^{n-1} + \cdots + b_0$$

where $b_i = a_i/a_n$ for $i = 0, 1, \ldots, n - 1$. In fact it is clear that $g(x)$ is the *unique monic* polynomial associated to $f(x)$.

The fundamental theorem pertaining to factorization of polynomials in F states that *every $f(x) \in \mathscr{P}$ can be factored uniquely into a product of a unit and monic irreducible polynomials of $\mathscr{P}$, except possibly for the order in which the factors are written.*

We prove this result (Theorem 15) in Section 9 after developing the necessary tools.[2]

Exercise

8. In each of the following, write the given polynomial as a product of a unit and the unique associated monic polynomial. For example, $2x^2 - 3x$ would be written as $2(x^2 - \frac{3}{2}x)$ or $x^3 - x^2 + 1$ as $1 \cdot (x^3 - x^2 + 1)$.

(a) $3x^3 - x^2 + 6x - 1$.   (d) $-\frac{2}{3}x^5 + 3x^3 + \frac{1}{2}x - 2$.

(b) $2x^4 - \frac{1}{3}x^2 + \sqrt{2}$.   (e) $-x^4 + 5x^2$.

(c) $\frac{1}{4}x^2 - 2x$.   (f) $ax^7 + bx^5 - 3x^3 + \frac{1}{2}x - \frac{11}{3}$ where $a \neq 0$.

*7. Euclidean Algorithm

In this section F is a subfield of C, and $\mathcal{P}$ the set of polynomials in the variable x with coefficients in F.

Theorem 8. Suppose $a(x)$ and $b(x) \in \mathcal{P}$.
(1) If $b(x)$ is a factor of $a(x)$, then so is every associate of $b(x)$.
(2) If $b(x)$ is a factor of $a(x)$, then $b(x)$ is a factor of every associate of $a(x)$.
(3) If $b(x)$ is a factor of $a(x)$, and $a(x)$ a factor of $b(x)$, then $a(x)$ and $b(x)$ are associates.

Proof: (1) Suppose $a(x) = b(x)q(x)$. Let $c(x)$ be an associate of $b(x)$. Then $b(x) = kc(x)$ for some $k \neq 0$ in F. Hence

$$a(x) = kc(x)q(x)$$
$$= c(x)s(x) \qquad \text{where } s(x) = kq(x)$$

So $c(x)$ is a factor of $a(x)$.
(2) Cf. Exercise 10.
(3) Since $b(x)$ is a factor of $a(x)$, we have
    (i) $a(x) = b(x)q(x)$
Since $a(x)$ is a factor of $b(x)$, we have
    (ii) $b(x) = a(x)s(x)$
Substituting (ii) in (i), we obtain
    (iii) $a(x) = a(x)s(x)q(x)$

[If $a(x) = 0$, then by (ii), $b(x) = 0$; if $b(x) = 0$, then by (i), $a(x) = 0$. Thus it remains to consider the case $a(x)$ and $b(x)$ not zero.] By (iii),

$$\text{degree } a(x) = \text{degree } a(x)s(x)q(x)$$
$$= \text{degree } a(x) + \text{degree } s(x) + \text{degree } q(x)$$

---

[2] The reader who wishes to defer reading the proof of Theorem 15 may proceed to Section 10. He should then carefully read, however, the statement *italicized* in the preceding sentence of the text; and he should also review Definitions 4, 5, and 6 of this section.

It follows that degree $s(x) =$ degree $q(x) = 0$, and $s(x)$ and $q(x)$ are non-zero elements of F. Thus by either (i) or (ii), $a(x)$ and $b(x)$ are associates.

Theorem 9. Let $a(x), b(x) \in \mathscr{P}$, and suppose $b(x)$ is a divisor of $a(x)$. Then the common factors of $a(x)$ and $b(x)$ are precisely the factors of $b(x)$.

Proof: (1) Suppose $c(x)$ is a divisor of $a(x)$ and $b(x)$. Then in particular $c(x)$ is a divisor of $b(x)$.

(2) Conversely, suppose $c(x)$ is a divisor of $b(x)$. Then $b(x) = c(x)s(x)$ for some $s(x) \in \mathscr{P}$. By hypothesis,

$$\begin{aligned} a(x) &= b(x)t(x) \qquad \text{for some } t(x) \in \mathscr{P} \\ &= (c(x)s(x))t(x) \\ &= c(x) \cdot (s(x)t(x)) \end{aligned}$$

Hence $c(x)$ is a divisor of $a(x)$, and hence a common divisor of $a(x)$ and $b(x)$.

Theorem 10. Suppose $a(x), b(x), q(x), r(x) \in \mathscr{P}$ and $a(x) = b(x)q(x) + r(x)$. Then the common factors of $a(x)$ and $b(x)$ are precisely the same as the common factors of $b(x)$ and $r(x)$.

Proof: (1) Suppose $c(x)$ is a factor of $a(x)$ and of $b(x)$. Say $a(x) = c(x)s(x)$, $b(x) = c(x)t(x)$. Then

$$\begin{aligned} r(x) &= a(x) - b(x)q(x) \\ &= c(x)s(x) - (c(x)t(x))q(x) \\ &= c(x)s(x) - c(x)(t(x)q(x)) \\ &= c(x)[s(x) - t(x)q(x)] \end{aligned}$$

So $c(x)$ divides $r(x)$. Hence $c(x)$ divides $b(x)$ and $r(x)$.

(2) It remains to prove that if $c(x)$ divides $b(x)$ and $r(x)$, then $c(x)$ divides $a(x)$ and $b(x)$. This is left as an exercise (cf. Exercise 11).

We consider next the question of determining the common factors of two nonzero elements $a(x)$ and $b(x)$ of $\mathscr{P}$. Theorem 10 suggests a procedure for reducing this problem to that of determining common factors of polynomials of smaller degree. This procedure is known as the *Euclidean algorithm*, which we now set forth.

Say degree $a(x) \geqq$ degree $b(x)$. Apply the division algorithm to $a(x)$ and $b(x)$ to obtain

(1) $a(x) = b(x)q_1(x) + r_1(x)$ degree $r_1(x) <$ degree $b(x)$ or $r_1(x) = 0$
If $r_1(x) \neq 0$, apply the division algorithm to $b(x)$ and $r_1(x)$:
(2) $b(x) = r_1(x)q_2(x) + r_2(x)$ degree $r_2(x) <$ degree $r_1(x)$ or $r_2(x) = 0$
If $r_2(x) \neq 0$, apply the division algorithm to $r_1(x)$ and $r_2(x)$:
(3) $r_1(x) = r_2(x)q_3(x) + r_3(x)$ degree $r_3(x) <$ degree $r_2(x)$ or $r_3(x) = 0$
As degree $b(x) >$ degree $r_1(x) >$ degree $r_2(x) >$ degree $r_3(x) > \cdots$

we must reach a point, say $r_n(x)$, such that $r_{n+1}(x) = 0$. Thus we have

(n) $r_{n-2}(x) = r_{n-1}(x)q_n(x) + r_n(x)$ degree $r_n(x)$ < degree $r_{n-1}(x)$

$(n+1)$ $r_{n-1}(x) = r_n(x)q_{n+1}(x)$

If $r_1(x)$ is already 0, then we shall take n to be 0; i.e., line $n + 1$ is to be regarded as line 1.

Now we apply Theorem 10 to see that the common divisors of $a(x)$ and $b(x)$ are the same as those of $b(x)$ and $r_1(x)$ (Theorem 10 applied to line 1), which in turn are the same as those of $r_1(x)$ and $r_2(x)$ (Theorem 10 applied to line 2), which in turn are the same as those of $r_2(x)$ and $r_3(x)$ (Theorem 10 applied to line 3), . . . , which in turn are those of $r_{n-1}(x)$ and $r_n(x)$ (Theorem 10 applied to line n). Now apply Theorem 9 to line $n + 1$ to obtain that the common divisors of $r_{n-1}(x)$ and $r_n(x)$ are precisely the divisors of $r_n(x)$.

In summary: The common divisors of $a(x)$ and $b(x)$ are precisely the divisors of $r_n(x)$, which includes $r_n(x)$ itself.

Example 12. We take $a(x) = x^4 - 1$, $b(x) = 2x^3 + x^2 - 5x + 2$, and apply the Euclidean algorithm:

(1) $x^4 - 1 = (2x^3 + x^2 - 5x + 2)(\frac{1}{2}x - \frac{1}{4}) + (\frac{11}{4}x^2 - \frac{9}{4}x - \frac{1}{2})$

(2) $2x^3 + x^2 - 5x + 2 = (\frac{11}{4}x^2 - \frac{9}{4}x - \frac{1}{2})(\frac{8}{11}x + \frac{116}{121}) + (-\frac{300}{121}x + \frac{300}{121})$

(3) $\frac{11}{4}x^2 - \frac{9}{4}x - \frac{1}{2} = (-\frac{300}{121}x + \frac{300}{121})(-\frac{113}{1200}x - \frac{121}{600})$

Thus $n = 2$, and $r_n(x) = -\frac{300}{121}x + \frac{300}{121}$.

Hence the divisors of $a(x)$ and $b(x)$ are the divisors of $-\frac{300}{121}x + \frac{300}{121}$. Of course, the same statement holds, by Theorem 8(2), if we replace $r_n(x)$ by any associate, for example, $-\frac{121}{300}r_n(x)$. In this case we obtain $x - 1$. But $x - 1$ is clearly irreducible.[3] Hence, except for units and associates, $x - 1$ is the only common factor of $x^4 - 1$ and $2x^3 + x^2 - 5x + 2$. Note that here $x - 1$ is irreducible already over C, and hence a fortiori over any subfield of C.

Perhaps one will observe that $r_n(x)$ is analogous, with respect to $a(x)$ and $b(x)$, to the greatest common divisor (g.c.d.) of two integers (cf. Chapter 6).

Indeed, what the Euclidean algorithm shows is the following:

Theorem 11. Let $a(x)$ and $b(x)$ be two nonzero elements of $\mathscr{P}$. Then $\exists d(x) \in \mathscr{P}$ such that

(a) $d(x)$ is a common divisor of $a(x)$ and $b(x)$.

(b) If $c(x)$ is a common divisor of $a(x)$ and $b(x)$, then $c(x)$ is a divisor of $d(x)$.

Moreover, $d(x)$ is uniquely determined up to associates. That is, $e(x) \in \mathscr{P}$ satisfies (a) and (b) if and only if $e(x)$ is an associate of $d(x)$.

[3] $r_n(x)$ does not always turn out to be irreducible.

Proof: The Euclidean algorithm shows that we may take $d(x)$ to be $r_n(x)$, and (a) and (b) hold.

Let $e(x)$ be any associate of $d(x)$. By Theorem 8(1), $e(x)$ satisfies (a); by Theorem 8(2), $e(x)$ satisfies (b).

Conversely, suppose $e(x)$ satisfies (a) and (b). Then $e(x)$ divides $a(x)$ and $b(x)$ and hence by (b) applied to $d(x)$, $e(x)$ divides $d(x)$. But also $d(x)$ divides $a(x)$ and $b(x)$ and by (b) applied to $e(x)$, $d(x)$ divides $e(x)$. By Theorem 8(3), $d(x)$ and $e(x)$ are associates.

The g.c.d. of two integers was also uniquely determined up to associates. For example, 10 and 15 have greatest common divisors 5 and -5. Of course we made the convention that when referring to *the* g.c.d. of 10 and 15, we would choose 5.

Definition 7. If $a(x)$ and $b(x)$ are nonzero elements of $\mathscr{P}$, any element $d(x) \in \mathscr{P}$ satisfying conditions (a) and (b) of Theorem 11 will be called a *greatest common divisor* (g.c.d.) or also *highest common factor* (h.c.f.) of $a(x)$ and $b(x)$. When referring to *the* g.c.d. of $a(x)$ and $b(x)$, we shall mean the one having leading coefficient 1, and this particular g.c.d. will be denoted by $(a(x),b(x))$.

In Example 12 we found $(x^4 - 1, 2x^3 + x^2 - 5x + 2) = x - 1$.

Note that in the Euclidean algorithm we have a sequence of polynomials $a(x)$, $b(x)$, $r_1(x)$, . . . , $r_n(x)$. If any of these are replaced by associates (for example, to avoid the appearance of fractions) in any of the lines of the algorithm, then the last line will yield an associate of $r_n(x)$, and hence again a greatest common divisor.

The Euclidean algorithm applies to two polynomials $a(x)$ and $b(x)$ with coefficients in a field F. Actually we work in the smallest field containing the coefficients of the polynomials to determine $r_n(x)$. If c is the leading coefficient of $r_n(x)$, then $(a(x),b(x)) = c^{-1}r_n(x)$, and *the* g.c.d. still has coefficients in this smallest field of the coefficients. Working in any larger subfield of the complex numbers does not change $(a(x),b(x))$, but it does introduce more associates.

Definition 8. If $(a(x),b(x)) = 1$, we say $a(x)$ and $b(x)$ are *relatively prime*. [In this case, all the nonzero elements of F yield all the g.c.d.'s of $a(x)$ and $b(x)$.]

Exercises

9. Find the following:
   (a) $(x^5 - x^4 + x^3 + 1, x^4 - 2x^3 + x^2 + x - 1)$.
   (b) $(2x^5 - 2x^4 - 11x^3 - x^2 - 6x, x^3 + x^2 - 8x - 12)$.
   (c) $(\sqrt{2}\, x^2 - x + 1, x + 2)$. (What is the smallest subfield of C containing the coefficients of these polynomials?)

    (d) $(2x^2 - 3x + 1, 4x^2 + 2x - 2)$.
    (e) $(2x^5 - 2, x^4 + x^3 + x^2 + x + 1)$.
10. Prove Theorem 8(2).
11. Prove Theorem 10(2).

*8. $d(x) = s(x)a(x) + t(x)b(x)$

The following theorem is of great importance in the further study of polynomials.

Theorem 12. Let $a(x)$ and $b(x)$ be two nonzero elements of $\mathscr{P}$, and $d(x)$ any g.c.d. of $a(x)$ and $b(x)$. Then $\exists$ polynomials $s(x)$ and $t(x)$ $\ni$

    (1) $d(x) = s(x)a(x) + t(x)b(x)$

$a(x)$ and $b(x)$ are relatively prime if and only if (1) holds with $d(x) = 1$, i.e.,

    (2) $1 = s(x)a(x) + t(x)b(x)$

Proof: In the Euclidean algorithm, $r_n(x)$ is determined in line n. We use induction on n.

    (α) If $n = 1$, then $a(x) = b(x)q_1(x) + r_1(x)$, and $r_1(x)$ is a g.c.d. Then

$$r_1(x) = a(x) + b(x)(-q_1(x))$$

    If $d(x)$ is any g.c.d., $d(x) = cr_1(x)$ for some $c \neq 0$ in F. Then

$$d(x) = cr_1(x) = ca(x) + b(x)(-cq_1(x))$$

    and (1) holds with $s(x) = c$, $t(x) = -cq_1(x)$.
    (β) Assume that (1) holds for polynomials in which the Euclidean algorithm yields a g.c.d. in the kth line. Now suppose for $a(x)$ and $b(x)$ that a g.c.d. $r_{k+1}(x)$ appears on line $k + 1$.

$$
\left.
\begin{array}{lll}
(1) & a(x) & = b(x)q_1(x) + r_1(x) \\
(2) & b(x) & = r_1(x)q_2(x) + r_2(x) \\
& \cdot \\
& \cdot \\
& \cdot \\
(k+1) & r_{k-1}(x) = r_k(x)q_{k+1}(x) + r_{k+1}(x) \\
(k+2) & r_k(x) & = r_{k+1}(x)q_{k+2}(x)
\end{array}
\right\} \quad (*)
$$

Then the Euclidean algorithm needs k lines to determine a g.c.d. for $b(x)$ and $r_1(x)$. Namely, one begins with line (2) in (*). By our inductive assumption, $\exists u(x)$ and $v(x)$ $\ni$

$$r_{k+1}(x) = u(x)b(x) + v(x)r_1(x)$$

But by line (1) of (*), $r_1(x) = a(x) - b(x)q_1(x)$. Hence

$$
\begin{aligned}
r_{k+1}(x) &= u(x)b(x) + v(x)(a(x) - b(x)q_1(x)) \\
&= v(x)a(x) + (u(x) - q_1(x)v(x))b(x)
\end{aligned}
$$

Again if $cr_{k+1}(x)$ is any associate of $r_{k+1}(x)$, then (1) holds with

$$s(x) = cv(x), \ t(x) = cu(x) - cq_1(x)v(x)$$

This proves (1). In particular, if $(a(x), b(x)) = 1$, then (2) holds. Conversely, suppose (2) holds. Then if $f(x)$ is a divisor of $a(x)$ and $b(x)$, say $a(x) = a_1(x)f(x)$, $b(x) = b_1(x)f(x)$, we have by (2)

$$1 = s(x)a_1(x)f(x) + t(x)b_1(x)f(x)$$

or

$$1 = (s(x)a_1(x) + t(x)b_1(x))f(x)$$

Hence $f(x)$ is a divisor of 1. So 1 satisfies condition (b) of Theorem 11. Condition (a) of Theorem 11 is clearly satisfied, and hence $(a(x), b(x)) = 1$.

Example 13. Suppose the Euclidean algorithm applied to $a(x)$ and $b(x)$ revealed $r_4(x)$ as a g.c.d. of $a(x)$ and $b(x)$. Show how you would determine $s(x)$ and $t(x)$ of Theorem 12.

Solution: We have:

(1) $a(x) = b(x)q_1(x) + r_1(x)$
(2) $b(x) = r_1(x)q_2(x) + r_2(x)$
(3) $r_1(x) = r_2(x)q_3(x) + r_3(x)$
(4) $r_2(x) = r_3(x)q_4(x) + r_4(x)$
(5) $r_3(x) = r_4(x)q_5(x)$

By (4), we determine $r_4(x)$ in terms of $r_2(x)$ and $r_3(x)$:

(6) $r_4(x) = r_2(x) - r_3(x)q_4(x)$

But (3) gives $r_3(x)$ in terms of $r_1(x)$ and $r_2(x)$:

(7) $r_3(x) = r_1(x) - r_2(x)q_3(x)$

Substituting (7) in (6) gives $r_4(x)$ in terms of $r_1(x)$ and $r_2(x)$:

$$r_4(x) = r_2(x) - (r_1(x) - r_2(x)q_3(x))q_4(x)$$

(8) $r_4(x) = (-q_4(x))r_1(x) + (q_3(x)q_4(x) + 1)r_2(x)$

Now use (2) to get $r_2(x)$ in terms of $b(x)$ and $r_1(x)$:

(9) $r_2(x) = b(x) - r_1(x)q_2(x)$

Substitute (9) in (8) to obtain $r_4(x)$ in terms of $b(x)$ and $r_1(x)$:

$$r_4(x) = (-q_4(x))r_1(x) + (q_3(x)q_4(x) + 1)(b(x) - r_1(x)q_2(x))$$

(10) $r_4(x) = (q_3(x)q_4(x) + 1)b(x) + [(-q_3(x)q_4(x) + 1)q_2(x) - q_4(x)]r_1(x)$

Use (1) to obtain $r_1(x)$ in terms of $a(x)$ and $b(x)$:

(11) $r_1(x) = a(x) - b(x)q_1(x)$

Finally substitute (11) in (10) to obtain $r_4(x)$ in terms of $a(x)$ and $b(x)$:

$$r_4(x) = (q_3(x)q_4(x) + 1)b(x) + [(-q_3(x)q_4(x) + 1)q_2(x) - q_4(x)](a(x) - b(x)q_1(x))$$

(12) $r_4(x) = s(x)a(x) + t(x)b(x)$

where

$$s(x) = (-q_3(x)q_4(x) + 1)q_2(x) - q_4(x)$$
$$t(x) = q_3(x)q_4(x) + 1 - q_1(x)[(-q_3(x)q_4(x) + 1)q_2(x) - q_4(x)]$$

Needless to say, in any particular example one does not memorize formulas for $s(x)$ and $t(x)$, but rather carries out the above procedure.

Exercise

12. In each part of Exercise 9, express the g.c.d. of the given polynomials according to formula (1) of Theorem 12.

*9. The Fundamental Theorem

Theorem 13. Suppose $a(x)$, $b(x)$, $c(x)$ are nonzero elements of $\mathscr{P}$, $a(x)$ divides the product $b(x)c(x)$, and $(a(x),b(x)) = 1$. Then $a(x)$ divides $c(x)$.

Proof: Since $(a(x), b(x)) = 1$, by Theorem 12, $\exists s(x),t(x) \in \mathscr{P} \ni$

(1) $1 = s(x)a(x) + t(x)b(x)$

Multiply through by $c(x)$:

(2) $c(x) = s(x)a(x)c(x) + t(x)b(x)c(x)$

Since $a(x)$ divides $b(x)c(x)$ we have $b(x)c(x) = a(x)d(x)$ for some $d(x) \in \mathscr{P}$. Then by (2),

$$c(x) = s(x)a(x)c(x) + t(x)a(x)d(x)$$
$$= a(x)[s(x)c(x) + t(x)d(x)]$$

and $a(x)$ divides $c(x)$.

Theorem 14. Suppose $a(x),b_1(x),b_2(x), \ldots ,b_r(x)$ are monic irreducible polynomials in $\mathscr{P}$, and suppose $a(x)$ divides the product

$$b_1(x)b_2(x) \cdots b_r(x)$$

Then $a(x) = b_i(x)$ for some i with $1 \leq i \leq r$.

Proof: If $r = 1$, we have $a(x)$ divides $b_1(x)$. Both being monic and irreducible, we must have $a(x) = b_1(x)$. Assume the result for $r = k$. Now suppose $a(x)$ divides $b_1(x)b_2(x) \cdots b_{k+1}(x)$, where $k \geq 1$. Then $a(x)$ divides

$$[b_1(x) \cdots b_k(x)]b_{k+1}(x)$$

If $a(x)$ divides $b_{k+1}(x)$, then as before we have $a(x) = b_{k+1}(x)$. If $a(x)$ does not divide $b_{k+1}(x)$, then $(a(x),b_{k+1}(x)) = 1$, and by Theorem 13 we have $a(x)$ divides $b_1(x) \cdots b_k(x)$. By our inductive hypothesis, $a(x)$ divides $b_i(x)$ for some i with $1 \leq i \leq k$.

Theorem 15. The Fundamental Theorem of Arithmetic for Polynomials.
Let $f(x)$ be any nonzero element of $\mathscr{P}$. Then $f(x)$ can be written as a
product of a unit c and monic irreducible polynomials:

(1) $f(x) = cp_1(x)p_2(x) \cdots p_r(x)$

[The polynomials $p_1(x), p_2(x), \ldots, p_r(x)$ need not be distinct.]
    Moreover the representation of $f(x)$ as such a product (1) is unique
(except possibly for the order in which the factors are written).

Proof: Let $f(x)$ be a nonzero element of $\mathscr{P}$, and let $g(x)$ be its associated monic
polynomial: $f(x) = cg(x)$. Then every representation (1) must clearly have c
appearing as the unit, and $g(x) = p_1(x)p_2(x) \cdots p_r(x)$. The theorem will be
proved, therefore, if we can prove it for monic polynomials $f(x)$ and where
$c = 1$ in (1). Assume, then, that $f(x)$ is a monic polynomial of degree n. We
first show that $f(x)$ can be written as in (1). We use induction on n. If $n = 0$,
then $f(x) = 1$, and (1) holds with $c = 1$ and $r = 0$.
    Assume the result for degree $\leq k$, and suppose $f(x)$ has degree $k + 1$.
If $f(x)$ is already irreducible, then (1) holds with $c = 1$, $r = 1$. If $f(x)$ is reducible, $f(x) = a(x)b(x)$, where $a(x), b(x)$ have lower degree than $f(x)$. We
may assume $a(x)$ and $b(x)$ are monic. By our inductive hypothesis, $a(x)$ and
$b(x)$ have representations as in (1), and this yields a representation for $f(x)$.
    It remains to prove uniqueness. Thus suppose

$$f(x) = p_1(x)p_2(x) \cdots p_r(x) = q_1(x)q_2(x) \cdots q_s(x)$$

where $p_i(x)$ and $q_j(x)$ are monic irreducible polynomials.
    We prove $r = s$, and for a suitable rearrangement of the $q_j(x)$,

$$p_1(x) = q_1(x), \ p_2(x) = q_2(x), \ldots, p_r(x) = q_r(x)$$

We use induction on r.
    If $r = 1$, we have $p_1(x) = q_1(x)q_2(x) \cdots q_s(x)$. Since $p_1(x)$ is irreducible, we
must have $s = 1$.
    Now assume $p_1(x)p_2(x) \cdots p_r(x) = q_1(x)q_2(x) \cdots q_s(x)$. Since $p_1(x)$ is a
factor of the left side, it is a factor of the right side (which is the same polynomial). By Theorem 14, $p_1(x) = q_i(x)$ for some i. For a suitable rearrangement of the $q_j(x)$ we may assume $p_1(x) = q_1(x)$. By the corollary to Theorem
7, it follows that

$$p_2(x) \cdots p_r(x) = q_2(x) \cdots q_s(x)$$

Hence by induction $r - 1 = s - 1$ (so that $r = s$), and for a suitable rearrangement of $q_2(x), \ldots, q_r(x)$ we have $p_2(x) = q_2(x), \ldots, p_r(x) = q_r(x)$.
    This completes the proof.

Exercises

13. The factorization theory developed here for polynomials could also be given
    for integers, and thus a proof of the fundamental theorem of arithmetic (for
    integers) alternative to that given in Part II would result. In particular, the

Euclidean algorithm could be developed for integers. The student is invited to develop this theory on his own, where he may use the above theory of polynomials as a guide.

14. Let $a(x), b(x)$ be two nonzero elements of $\mathscr{P}$, and suppose $(a(x), b(x)) = d(x)$. Say $a(x) = a_1(x)d(x)$, $b(x) = b_1(x)d(x)$, and let $m(x) = a_1(x)b_1(x)d(x)$. Prove that $m(x)$ satisfies the following:

(a) $m(x)$ is a multiple of $a(x)$ and of $b(x)$.

(b) If $\ell(x)$ is a multiple of $a(x)$ and $b(x)$, then $\ell(x)$ is a multiple of $m(x)$.

Furthermore, show that if $n(x)$ satisfies (a) and (b), then $n(x)$ is an associate of $m(x)$.

Definition 9. Any polynomial satisfying conditions (a) and (b) of Exercise 14 is called a *least common multiple* (l.c.m.) of $a(x)$ and $b(x)$. The unique monic l.c.m. of $a(x)$ and $b(x)$ is denoted by $[a(x), b(x)]$.

Exercise

15. Referring to Exercise 14, and the above definition, find the l.c.m. of the polynomials given in Exercise 9.

10. Multiplicity of Roots

We have now seen that every nonzero polynomial $f(x)$ with coefficients in a subfield F of C can be written uniquely as a product of a unit and irreducible polynomials. These irreducible factors need not be distinct. If $p_1(x), p_2(x), \ldots, p_t(x)$ are the distinct ones appearing in the factorization, then

$$f(x) = cp_1(x)^{e_1} p_2(x)^{e_2} \cdots p_t(x)^{e_t}$$

where $p_1(x)$ appears e_1 times, $p_2(x)$ appears e_2 times, $\ldots, p_t(x)$ appears e_t times. We say that $p_i(x)$ is a factor of $f(x)$ of multiplicity e_i, $i = 1,2, \ldots ,t$. An irreducible polynomial which is not a factor of $f(x)$ is said to be a *factor of multiplicity* 0 of $f(x)$.

If one of the monic irreducible factors of $f(x)$ is of first degree, say $x - \alpha$, where $\alpha \in F$, and $x - \alpha$ has multiplicity e, we say α is a root of $f(x)$ of multiplicity e.

Definition 10. Let $f(x)$ be a nonzero polynomial with coefficients in F, and suppose $\alpha \in F$. If e is the multiplicity of $x - \alpha$ as an irreducible factor of $f(x)$, then α is said to be a *root of $f(x)$ of multiplicity e*. Note that if $e \geq 1$, α is a root of $f(x)$; if $e = 0$, α is not a root of $f(x)$.

With this terminology, we may state the second part of Theorem 5 as follows:

Theorem 16. If $f(x)$ is a polynomial with coefficients in C of degree $n > 0$, then $f(x)$ has precisely n roots providing multiplicities are counted. (That is, if α is root of multiplicity e, then α is to be counted as e roots.)

Proof: According to Theorem 5, all the irreducible factors of $f(x)$ are of first degree. So

$$f(x) = c(x - \alpha_1)^{e_1}(x - \alpha_2)^{e_2} \cdots (x - \alpha_t)^{e_t}$$

where $e_1 + e_2 + \cdots + e_t = n$ is the degree of $f(x)$. Thus if α_1 counts as e_1 roots, α_2 as e_2 roots, . . . ,α_t as e_t roots, the number of roots is exactly n.

Corollary. If $f(x)$ is a polynomial with coefficients in a subfield F of C, then $f(x)$ has at most n roots counting multiplicities.

Example 14. Determine the multiplicity of 1 as a root of $x^4 - 5x^2 + 6x - 2$.
Solution: We divide $x - 1$ into $x^4 - 5x^2 + 6x - 2$ synthetically:

$$
\begin{array}{rrrrr|l}
1 & 0 & -5 & 6 & -2 & \underline{1} \\
  & 1 & 1 & -4 & 2 & \\
\hline
1 & 1 & -4 & 2 & 0 &
\end{array}
$$

Hence $x^4 - 5x^2 + 6x - 2 = (x - 1)(x^3 + x^2 - 4x + 2)$. We now divide $x - 1$ into $x^3 + x^2 - 4x + 2$. If 1 is again a root, we continue the process:

$$
\begin{array}{rrrr|l}
1 & 1 & -4 & 2 & \underline{1} \\
  & 1 & 2 & -2 & \\
\hline
1 & 2 & -2 & 0 & \\
  & 1 & 3 & & \\
\hline
1 & 3 & \boxed{1} & &
\end{array}
$$

Thus $x^4 - 5x^2 + 6x - 2 = (x - 1)^2(x^2 + 2x - 2)$, and 1 is not a root of

$$x^2 + 2x - 2$$

The multiplicity is 2.

Example 15. Determine the multiplicity of -2 as a root of

$$x^3 + 5x^2 - 7x - 5$$

Solution:
$$
\begin{array}{rrrr|l}
1 & 5 & -7 & -5 & \underline{-2} \\
  & -2 & -6 & 26 & \\
\hline
1 & 3 & -13 & 21 &
\end{array}
$$

The multiplicity is 0 since -2 is not a root.

Exercises

16. Determine the multiplicity of -1 as a root of each of the following:
(a) $2x^3 + 2x^2 - x - 1$.
(b) $x^4 + 4x^3 + 6x^2 + 4x + 1$.
(c) $x^{531} - x^{27} + 10$.
(d) $\sqrt[3]{3}\, x^2 + (\sqrt[3]{3} + \sqrt{2})x + \sqrt{2}$.
(e) $3x^5 - x^4 + 72x^2 + 1$.

17. Determine the multiplicity of $x - 2$ as a factor of each of the following:

(a) $x^3 + 5x - 8$.

(b) $2x^6 - 8x^5 + 8x^4 + 2x^2 - 8x + 8$.

(c) x^{7284}.

(d) $(x - 2)^4(x^2 - x - 2)$.

(e) $(x - 2)(x^2 + 1)(x^3 + 5x - 8)x^{7284}(x^2 - 2x)$.

(f) $ix^2 - 5ix + 6i$.

18. Construct a polynomial having the following roots and no others:

(a) 1 with multiplicity 1; 0 with multiplicity 2.

(b) -3 with multiplicity 2; i with multiplicity 1.

(c) $\sqrt{2}$ and $i - 2$ each with multiplicity 1.

(d) 0 with multiplicity 52.

11. Coefficients and Roots of a Polynomial

If

$$f(x) = a_n x^n + a_{n-1} x^{n-1} + \cdots + a_0 = a_n(x - \alpha_1)(x - \alpha_2) \cdots (x - \alpha_n)$$

then upon multiplying out the right side we obtain

$$f(x) = a_n x^n - (\alpha_1 + \alpha_2 + \cdots + \alpha_n) a_n x^{n-1} +$$

$$(\alpha_1 \alpha_2 + \alpha_1 \alpha_3 + \cdots + \alpha_{n-1} \alpha_n) a_n x^{n-2} + \cdots + (-1)^n \alpha_1 \alpha_2 \cdots \alpha_n a_n$$

Hence, upon equating coefficients we obtain:

$$\left.\begin{aligned}
a_n &= a_n \\
a_{n-1} &= -(\alpha_1 + \alpha_2 + \cdots + \alpha_n) a_n \\
a_{n-2} &= (\alpha_1 \alpha_2 + \cdots + \alpha_{n-1} \alpha_n) a_n \\
&\cdots\cdots\cdots\cdots\cdots\cdots\cdots \\
a_0 &= (-1)^n \alpha_1 \alpha_2 \cdots \alpha_n a_n
\end{aligned}\right\} \tag{*}$$

We therefore obtain:

Theorem 17. If $f(x) = a_n x^n + a_{n-1} x^{n-1} + \cdots + a_0$ is a polynomial with coefficients in C of degree n, and $\alpha_1, \alpha_2, \ldots, \alpha_n$ are the (not necessarily distinct) roots of $f(x)$, then

$$\alpha_1 + \alpha_2 + \cdots + \alpha_n = -\frac{a_{n-1}}{a_n}$$

$$\alpha_1 \alpha_2 + \alpha_1 \alpha_3 + \cdots + \alpha_{n-1} \alpha_n = \frac{a_{n-2}}{a_n}$$

$$\alpha_1 \alpha_2 \alpha_3 + \alpha_1 \alpha_2 \alpha_4 + \cdots + \alpha_{n-2} \alpha_{n-1} \alpha_n = -\frac{a_{n-3}}{a_n}$$

$$\cdots\cdots\cdots\cdots\cdots\cdots\cdots\cdots\cdots\cdots\cdots\cdots$$

$$\alpha_1 \alpha_2 \cdots \alpha_n = (-1)^n \frac{a_0}{a_n}$$

Proof: A careful proof would proceed by induction on the degree of $f(x)$. One checks the result for $n = 1$; then assuming $(x - \alpha_1) \cdots (x - \alpha_{n-1})$ yields a polynomial with coefficients of the form (*), one multiplies this polynomial by $x - \alpha_n$. We leave the details to Exercise 21.

Example 16. Find the sum and product of the roots in C of $3x^3 - 2x^2 + 5x + 1$.

Solution: Here $a_3 = 3$, $a_2 = -2$, $a_1 = 5$, $a_0 = 1$. The sum of the roots is $-\dfrac{a_2}{a_3} = \dfrac{2}{3}$.

The product of the roots is $-\dfrac{a_0}{a_3} = \dfrac{1}{3}$.

Example 17. Find the sum and product of the roots in C of $2x^2 - ix + 5$.

Solution: The sum is $\dfrac{i}{2}$, the product $\dfrac{5}{2}$.

Exercises

19. Find the sum and the product of the roots in C of each of the following:

(a) $x^2 + 1$.

(b) $x^{20} - 5$.

(c) $3x^3 + 2x + 2 - 3i$.

(d) $5x^6 - 2x^4 + 3x^2 + 5x$.

(e) $2x^2 - 5x - 7$.

(f) $(i - 2)x^2 + ix - \sqrt{2} + 2$.

20. Prove Theorem 17 for $n = 2$, $n = 3$, $n = 4$, and $n = 5$.

21. Prove Theorem 17.

12. Polynomials with Coefficients in R

In this section we consider polynomials with coefficients in the field R of real numbers. Concerning their roots in the field of complex numbers we have the following result from Exercise 20 in the Laboratory Exercises on the Complex Number System:

Theorem 18. Let $a_n x^n + \cdots + a_0 = 0$ be an equation with coefficients in R, and variable x over the field C of complex numbers. Then if $p + qi$ (where $p, q \in R$) is a solution, so is $p - qi$.

Example 18. Suppose $f(x)$ is a monic [4] polynomial of second degree with real coefficients having a root $2 - 3i$ in C. Determine $f(x)$.

Solution: By Theorem 18, the other root must be $2 + 3i$ and

$$f(x) = (x - (2 - 3i))(x - (2 + 3i))$$
$$= x^2 - 4x + 13$$

Corollary 1. If $f(x)$ is a polynomial with coefficients in R, and $p + qi$ is a root in C, then the multiplicity of $p - qi$ as a root is the same as that for $p + qi$.

[4] Cf. Definition 6.

Proof: We use induction on the degree of $f(x)$.

If $f(x)$ is of degree 1, say $f(x) = a_1x + a_0$, then the only root is $-\dfrac{a_0}{a_1}$. Here $p = -\dfrac{a_0}{a_1}$, $q = 0$ so that $p + qi = p - qi$ has multiplicity 1.

Assume the result for polynomials of degree less than n, and now suppose $f(x)$ of degree $n \geq 2$. Since $p + qi$ is a root, by Theorem 18, so is $p - qi$. If $q = 0$, $p + qi = p - qi$ and there is nothing to prove. Otherwise

$$f(x) = (x - (p - qi))(x - (p + qi))g(x)$$

where $g(x)$ has degree $n - 2$. Assuming the result for $g(x)$ clearly yields the result for $f(x)$.

Example 19. Suppose $f(x)$ is a polynomial of degree 3 with real coefficients. Can $f(x)$ be irreducible in R?

Solution: If $f(x)$ has a real root α, then $x - \alpha$ is a factor in R, and $f(x)$ cannot be irreducible. But in fact $f(x)$ must have a real root. For by Corollary 1, the number of nonreal complex roots is even. Thus $f(x)$ is reducible.

Example 20. Suppose $f(x)$ is a polynomial of degree 4 with real coefficients. Can $f(x)$ be irreducible in R?

Solution: Again the answer is no. For if $f(x)$ has a real root α, then

$$f(x) = (x - \alpha)g(x)$$

[Recall that $g(x)$ has coefficients in R according to Theorem 3.] Thus $f(x)$ is not irreducible in this case.

If none of the roots is real, the roots are of the type: $p + qi$, $p - qi$, $s + ti$, $s - ti$. Then

$$f(x) = c(x - (p - qi))(x - (p + qi))(x - (s + ti))(x - (s - ti))$$

But $(x - (p - qi))(x - (p + qi)) = x^2 - 2px + (p^2 + q^2)$ is a polynomial with coefficients in R. We have

$$f(x) = c(x^2 - 2px + (p^2 + q^2))(x^2 - 2sx + (s^2 + t^2))$$

and hence again $f(x)$ is reducible.

Corollary 2. Suppose $f(x)$ is a polynomial with coefficients in R of degree $n > 1$. Then the irreducible factors of $f(x)$ are of degree at most 2.

Proof: (a) If α is a real root of $f(x)$, then $(x - \alpha)$ is a factor of $f(x)$.

(b) If $p + qi$ is a complex, nonreal root of $f(x)$, then so is $p - qi$. As in Example 20, we see that $x^2 - 2px + (p^2 + q^2)$ is a factor of $f(x)$. Such a factor is obtained for every pair of conjugate complex roots.

The sum of the degrees of the factors appearing in (a) and (b) is the degree of $f(x)$. Hence all irreducible factors are obtained.

Exercise

22. Let $f(x)$ be a polynomial with coefficients in R of odd degree. Prove that $\exists \alpha \in R \ni f(\alpha) = 0$. [That is, $f(x) = 0$ as an equation in the variable x over R has a nonempty solution set.]

13. The Quadratic Equation

Let $f(x)$ be a polynomial with real coefficients, and suppose we wish to solve the equation $f(x) = 0$ in R or in C. If one knew the irreducible factors in R of $f(x)$, say $f(x) = cp_1(x)p_2(x) \cdots p_r(x)$, then the solution set of $f(x) = 0$ would be the union of the solution sets for

$$p_1(x) = 0, p_2(x) = 0, \ldots, p_r(x) = 0$$

By Corollary 2 of Theorem 18, each of these latter equations is of degree 1 or degree 2. The solution of a first degree equation $ax + b = 0$ is $-\dfrac{b}{a}$. We now turn to equations of second degree, called *quadratic equations*, with coefficients in R.

Thus we shall consider the equation

$$ax^2 + bx + c = 0 \tag{1}$$

where $a, b, c \in R$ and $a \neq 0$. We shall solve (1) in C, as this includes the solutions in R.

We know that (1) has two solutions, counting multiplicity. It may have two distinct real roots, a repeated real root (i.e., a real root of multiplicity 2), or two nonreal complex roots $p + qi$ and $p - qi$.

If $b = 0$, there is no difficulty in solving (1). We have

$$ax^2 + c = 0$$

$$x^2 = -\frac{c}{a}$$

$$x = \pm\sqrt{-\frac{c}{a}}$$

Example 21. Solve $2x^2 - 3 = 0$ in C.
Solution: $x^2 = \frac{3}{2}$
$$x = \pm\sqrt{\tfrac{3}{2}}$$

The solution set is $\left\{ \dfrac{\sqrt{3}}{2}, -\dfrac{\sqrt{3}}{2} \right\}$.

Example 22. Solve $2x^2 + 3 = 0$ in C.
Solution: $x^2 = -\frac{3}{2}$
$$x = \pm\sqrt{-\tfrac{3}{2}}$$
$$x = \pm i\sqrt{\tfrac{3}{2}}$$
The solution set is $\{ i\sqrt{\tfrac{3}{2}}, -i\sqrt{\tfrac{3}{2}} \}$.

This method can be extended as in the following examples.

Example 23. Solve $2(x - 1)^2 - 3 = 0$ in C.

Solution: Multiplied out, this equation would be $2x^2 - 4x - 1 = 0$, but it is easier to solve it in the form given. Namely,

$$(x - 1)^2 = \tfrac{3}{2}$$
$$x - 1 = \pm\sqrt{\tfrac{3}{2}}$$
$$x = 1 \pm \sqrt{\tfrac{3}{2}}$$

The solution set is $\{1 + \sqrt{\tfrac{3}{2}}, 1 - \sqrt{\tfrac{3}{2}}\}$, or $\left\{\dfrac{2 + \sqrt{6}}{2}, \dfrac{2 - \sqrt{6}}{2}\right\}$.

Example 24. Solve $2(x - 1)^2 + 3 = 0$ (i.e., $2x^2 - 4x + 5 = 0$) in C.

Solution: $(x - 1)^2 = -\tfrac{3}{2}$

$$x - 1 = \pm\sqrt{-\tfrac{3}{2}}$$
$$x = 1 \pm \sqrt{\tfrac{3}{2}}\, i$$

The solution set is $\{1 + \sqrt{\tfrac{3}{2}}\, i, 1 - \sqrt{\tfrac{3}{2}}\, i\}$, or $\left\{\dfrac{2 + \sqrt{6}\, i}{2}, \dfrac{2 - \sqrt{6}\, i}{2}\right\}$.

In the general case, we attempt to imitate the above examples. That is, if $f(x) = ax^2 + bx + c$, we attempt to write $f(x)$ in the form

$$f(x) = a(x + r)^2 + s \tag{2}$$

Actually, this can always be done.

For if $f(x) = ax^2 + bx + c$, we may write

$$f(x) = a\left(x^2 + \frac{b}{a}x\right) + c$$

The problem now is to add something to $x^2 + \dfrac{b}{a}x$ so that it becomes "a perfect square," i.e., of the form $(x + r)^2$. If α is any real number, we can always write

$$f(x) = a\left(x^2 + \frac{b}{a}x + \alpha\right) - a\alpha + c$$

Thus it remains to choose α appropriately, i.e., so that

$$x^2 + \frac{b}{a}x + \alpha = (x + r)^2 \qquad \text{for some } r$$

or

$$x^2 + \frac{b}{a}x + \alpha = x^2 + 2rx + r^2$$

Here we see that we must have $r = \dfrac{b}{2a}$, so that $\alpha = r^2 = \dfrac{b^2}{4a^2}$. Hence

$$f(x) = a\left(x^2 + \frac{b}{a}x + \frac{b^2}{4a^2}\right) - a \cdot \frac{b^2}{4a^2} + c$$

or

$$f(x) = a\left(x + \frac{b}{2a}\right)^2 - \frac{b^2}{4a} + c \tag{3}$$

Example 25. If $f(x) = 3x^2 + 2x - 5$, we have $\dfrac{b}{2a} = \dfrac{1}{3}$. Hence $3x^2 + 2x - 5 =$ $3(x + \tfrac{1}{3})^2 + ($ $)$. To find what must go in parentheses, we observe that

$$3(x + \tfrac{1}{3})^2 = 3x^2 + 2x + \tfrac{1}{3}$$

So $3x^2 + 2x - 5 = 3(x + \tfrac{1}{3})^2 - \tfrac{1}{3} - 5 = 3(x + \tfrac{1}{3})^2 - \tfrac{16}{3}$. It is now easy to solve $3x^2 + 2x - 5 = 0$. We have

$$3(x + \tfrac{1}{3})^2 - \tfrac{16}{3} = 0$$
$$(x + \tfrac{1}{3})^2 = \tfrac{16}{9}$$
$$x + \tfrac{1}{3} = \pm \sqrt{\tfrac{16}{9}}$$
$$x = -\tfrac{1}{3} \pm \tfrac{4}{3}$$

The solution set is $\{-\tfrac{1}{3} + \tfrac{4}{3}, -\tfrac{1}{3} - \tfrac{4}{3}\}$, or $\{1, -\tfrac{5}{3}\}$.

Example 26. Solve $2x^2 + x + 1 = 0$ in C.

Solution: $2x^2 + x + 1 = 0$
$2(x + \tfrac{1}{4})^2 - \tfrac{1}{8} + 1 = 0$
$(x + \tfrac{1}{4})^2 = -\tfrac{7}{16}$

$$x + \frac{1}{4} = \pm \frac{\sqrt{7}}{4} i$$

$$x = -\frac{1}{4} \pm \frac{\sqrt{7}}{4} i$$

The solution set is $\left\{-\dfrac{1}{4} + \dfrac{\sqrt{7}}{4} i, -\dfrac{1}{4} - \dfrac{\sqrt{7}}{4} i\right\}$.

The method we have used to solve quadratic equations in Examples 25 and 26 is known as "completing the square." That is, one writes

$$ax^2 + bx + c = a\left(x^2 + \frac{b}{a}x + \right) - \left(\right) + c$$

By inserting $\dfrac{b^2}{4a^2}$ in the first parentheses $\left(\text{and } \dfrac{b^2}{4a} \text{ in the second}\right)$, one makes the first parentheses a square: $\left(x + \dfrac{b}{2a}\right)^2$.

By applying this procedure to the general case, one can derive a formula for the roots of (1) in terms of the coefficients.

Namely, one may write (3) as

$$f(x) = a\left[\left(x + \frac{b}{2a}\right)^2 - \frac{b^2 - 4ac}{4a^2}\right] \tag{4}$$

To solve $ax^2 + bx + c = 0$, one need only solve

$$\left(x + \frac{b}{2a}\right)^2 - \frac{b^2 - 4ac}{4a^2} = 0$$

so that

$$\left(x + \frac{b}{2a}\right)^2 = \frac{b^2 - 4ac}{4a^2}$$

$$x + \frac{b}{2a} = \frac{\pm \sqrt{b^2 - 4ac}}{2a}$$

$$x = \frac{-b \pm \sqrt{b^2 - 4ac}}{2a}$$

Theorem 19. The solution set of $ax^2 + bx + c = 0$, where $a,b,c \in R$ and $a \neq 0$ is

$$\left\{ \frac{-b + \sqrt{b^2 - 4ac}}{2a}, \frac{-b - \sqrt{b^2 - 4ac}}{2a} \right\}$$

Example 27. Solve $2x^2 + 3x - 1 = 0$.

Solution: $a = 2$, $b = 3$, $c = -1$. By Theorem 19, the solutions are $\dfrac{-3 \pm \sqrt{17}}{4}$.

Corollary. The roots of $ax^2 + bx + c = 0$ are real if and only if

$$b^2 - 4ac \geq 0$$

The roots are equal (i.e., repeated) if and only if $b^2 - 4ac = 0$.

Definition 11. $b^2 - 4ac$ is called the *discriminant* of the polynomial $ax^2 + bx + c$ (or also of the equation $ax^2 + bx + c = 0$).

Example 28. How many real roots does $2x^2 - 5x + 1$ have?
Solution: The discriminant is 17. Hence the roots are unequal and real. There are 2 real roots.
Example 29. The discriminant of $x^2 - 2\sqrt{2}\,x + 2$ is 0. Hence we have one real root, or to better indicate the situation we might say we have two equal real roots.

In summary, then, we may use three methods to solve $ax^2 + bx + c = 0$:
(1) Complete the square.
(2) Use the formula derived by method (1).
(3) Factoring.
The third method is quickest if one can see how to factor $ax^2 + bx + c$ into two first-degree factors. This method was used in Chapter 6.

Exercises

23. Solve each of the following (i) by completing the square; (ii) by using Theorem 19; (iii) in parts (a), (c), (e), (h) by factoring.

(a) $x^2 - 2x - 3 = 0.$ (f) $\sqrt{2}\, x^2 - x - 2 = 0.$

(b) $x^2 - 2x - 2 = 0.$ (g) $2x^2 - ax + \sqrt{2} + 1 = 0.$

(c) $6x^2 - x - 1 = 0.$ (h) $3x = 5x^2 - 2.$

(d) $3x^2 - x + 6 = 0.$ (i) $(2x + 1)^2 = -x^2 - 3.$

(e) $4x^2 + 4x + 1 = 0.$ (j) $5x^2 + 2 = 0.$

24. In each of the following use the discriminant to tell whether the roots are real or imaginary. If real, tell whether the roots are equal or unequal.

(a) $2x^2 + 2x + 1 = 0.$ (e) $3x^2 - 5 = 0.$

(b) $3x^2 - 4\sqrt{3}\, x + 4 = 0.$ (f) $2x^2 + \sqrt{2}\, x + \sqrt{3} = 0.$

(c) $x^2 - 5x - 6 = 0.$ (g) $2x^2 - \sqrt{2}\, x = \sqrt{3}.$

(d) $x^2 + 6 = 5x.$

25. In each part of Exercise 23, use the roots (say r_1 and r_2) to give the left side of the equation in factored form: $a(x - r_1)(x - r_2).$

26. In Exercise 24 determine, without solving, the sum and the product of the roots of each of the equations.

14. Polynomials with Coefficients in $\bar{R}$

In this section we consider polynomials with coefficients in the field $\bar{R}$ of rational numbers. All such polynomials have roots in C, but we wish to consider their roots, if any, in $\bar{R}$. This is equivalent, of course, to the determination of factors $x - \alpha$, where $\alpha \in \bar{R}$.

The roots of any polynomial are the same as for all its associated polynomials. Thus a polynomial with rational coefficients may be replaced by one with integral coefficients. For example,

$$\tfrac{2}{3}x^4 + \tfrac{1}{4}x^3 + \tfrac{5}{6}x^2 - \tfrac{1}{12}x - 3$$

may be multiplied by the l.c.m. (which is 12) of the denominators of the coefficients to obtain the associated polynomial

$$8x^4 + 3x^3 + 10x^2 - x - 36$$

We may therefore consider polynomials with coefficients in the set J of integers. Thus we consider polynomials

$$a_n x^n + a_{n-1} x^{n-1} + \cdots + a_0$$

with coefficients $a_n, a_{n-1}, \ldots, a_0$ in J, and $a_n \neq 0$. Actually we may assume $a_0 \neq 0$. For if we had a polynomial with $a_0 = 0$ (e.g., $8x^6 + 3x^5 + 10x^4 - x^3 - 36x^2$), we could factor out a power of x [in our example, factor out x^2 to obtain $x^2(8x^4 + 3x^3 + 10x^2 - x - 36)$, and the problem is reduced to determining the roots in $\bar{R}$ of x^2 — which are 0 — and of $8x^4 + 3x^3 + 10x^2 - x - 36$].

Theorem 20. Let $a_n x^n + a_{n-1} x^{n-1} + \cdots + a_0 = 0$ be an equation with coefficients in J in the variable x over $\bar{R}$, and with $a_n \neq 0$, $a_0 \neq 0$. Then if $\alpha \in \bar{R}$ is a solution, and $\alpha = \dfrac{r}{s}$, where $r, s \in J$ and $(r,s) = 1$ $\left(\text{i.e.}, \dfrac{r}{s} \text{ is in low-est terms} \right)$, then r is a factor of a_0 and s is a factor of a_n.

Proof: Substituting $\dfrac{r}{s}$ in the given equation yields

$$a_n \left(\frac{r}{s}\right)^n + a_{n-1} \left(\frac{r}{s}\right)^{n-1} + \cdots + a_1 \left(\frac{r}{s}\right) + a_0 = 0 \qquad (1)$$

Multiply both sides by s^n; and transpose the last term:

$$a_n r^n + a_{n-1} r^{n-1} s + \cdots + a_1 r s^{n-1} = -a_0 s^n \qquad (2)$$

Since r is a factor of the left side of this equation, r is a factor of $a_0 s^n$. But $(r,s) = 1$. Hence r is a factor of a_0.

Now transpose all terms of (2) except $a_n r^n$ to the right:

$$a_n r^n = -a_{n-1} r^{n-1} s - \cdots - a_1 r s^{n-1} - a_0 s^n \qquad (3)$$

Since s is a factor of the right, s is a factor of $a_n r^n$. As before we obtain s is a factor of a_n.

Corollary. If $x^n + a_{n-1} x^{n-1} + \cdots + a_0 = 0$ is an equation with coefficients in J, then all rational roots are in fact integral.

Proof: If $\dfrac{r}{s}$ is a rational root in lowest terms, s must be a factor of 1 by Theorem 20, since in this case $a_n = 1$. Thus $s = \pm 1$. (Of course, this proof is valid only if $a_0 \neq 0$. We leave it to the student to consider the case $a_0 = 0$.)

Example 30. Determine the rational roots of $2x^4 - x^3 + x^2 - x - 1$.
Solution: According to Theorem 20, the possible solutions are $1, -1, \frac{1}{2}, -\frac{1}{2}$.
We try 1, using synthetic division:

	2	−1	1	−1	−1	$\underline{\lfloor 1}$
		2	1	2	1	
	2	1	2	1	0	

Hence 1 is a root, and

$$2x^4 - x^3 + x^2 - x - 1 = (x - 1)(2x^3 + x^2 + 2x + 1)$$

We now consider $2x^3 + x^2 + 2x + 1$. The possible rational roots are again $1, -1, \frac{1}{2}, -\frac{1}{2}$.

	2	1	2	1	$\underline{\lfloor 1}$
		2	3	5	
	2	3	5	6	

Hence 1 is not a repeated root. We could have seen this by inspection, as all terms are positive.

$$\begin{array}{rrrr} 2 & 1 & 2 & 1 \\ & -2 & 1 & -3 \\ \hline 2 & -1 & 3 & -2 \end{array} \quad \underline{|-1}$$

Hence -1 is not a root.
$\frac{1}{2}$ is not a root by inspection.

$$\begin{array}{rrrr} 2 & 1 & 2 & 1 \\ & -1 & 0 & -1 \\ \hline 2 & 0 & 2 & 0 \end{array} \quad \underline{|-\frac{1}{2}}$$

Thus $-\frac{1}{2}$ is a root. We therefore have factors, so far, $x - 1, x + \frac{1}{2}, 2x^2 + 2$. As $2x^2 + 2$ has only imaginary roots, the solution set in $\bar{R}$ is $\{1, -\frac{1}{2}\}$. The solution set in R is again $\{1, -\frac{1}{2}\}$. The solution set in C is $\{1, -\frac{1}{2}, i, -i\}$.

We may ask when the roots of a quadratic equation are rational, if the coefficients are integers. We have seen the roots are $\dfrac{-b + \sqrt{b^2 - 4ac}}{2a}$. Hence the roots are rational if and only if $\sqrt{b^2 - 4ac}$ (a, b, and c are here assumed to be integers) is rational. But we have seen as an application of the fundamental theorem of arithmetic that this is so if and only if $b^2 - 4ac$ is a perfect square: $0, 1, 4, 9, 16, 25, 36, \ldots$.

Example 31. Using the discriminant, tell whether (a) $x^2 - 2x + 1 = 0$; (b) $x^2 - 2x - 1 = 0$ have rational roots.
Solution: In (a), the discriminant is 0; hence the roots are rational (and equal). In (b), the discriminant is 8; hence the roots are real and irrational (and distinct).

Exercises

27. Determine the rational roots, if any, of the following equations:
    (a) $x^3 + x^2 - 2 = 0$.
    (b) $4x^4 + 4x^3 - 3x^2 - 2x + 1 = 0$.
    (c) $6x^3 + x^2 - 5x = 0$.
    (d) $x^4 + x^3 + x^2 + x + 1 = 0$.
    (e) $2x^4 - 3x^3 + 6x^2 - 3x + 4 = 0$.
    (f) $4x^6 - 21x^5 - 10x^4 - 42x^3 - 32x^2 - 21x - 18 = 0$.
    (g) $x^5 + x^4 - 2x^2 = 0$.
    (h) $6x^4 + x^3 - 5x^2 = 0$.
    (i) $2x^9 - 3x^8 + 6x^7 - 3x^6 + 4x^5 = 0$.
28. Solve the following equations in the field C of complex numbers:
    (a) $x^3 - 2x^2 + x - 2 = 0$.
    (b) $4x^4 + 2x^3 + 7x^2 - 3x + 2 = 0$.
    (c) $2x^5 + x^4 - 15x^3 - 19x^2 + x + 6 = 0$.
    (d) $x^4 - 1 = 0$.
    (e) $4x^7 + 2x^6 + 7x^5 - 3x^4 + 2x^3 = 0$.
    (f) $x^{100} - x^{96} = 0$.

29. Give an example of a third-degree polynomial, with integral coefficients, which is irreducible in $\bar{R}$. Justify your contention that it is irreducible. (Hence Corollary 2 to Theorem 18 does not apply to $\bar{R}$.)

30. The following quadratic equations have integral coefficients. Use the discriminant to tell the "nature of the roots": i.e., tell whether they are real or imaginary; and if they are real tell whether they are equal or unequal, rational or irrational.

(a) $2x^2 + 3x - 5 = 0$.   (d) $6x^2 + x - 2 = 0$.
(b) $3x^2 + x + 2 = 0$.   (e) $3x^2 - 2 = 0$.
(c) $49x^2 - 14x + 1 = 0$.   (f) $x^2 = 0$.

15. Real Roots of Polynomials with Coefficients in R [5]

Up to now we have been considering polynomial equations $f(x) = 0$ with coefficients in a subfield of C. In most applications, the equation has coefficients in R and the variable ranges over R.

[Of course, if one can factor $f(x)$ into irreducible factors, finding the real roots explicitly is no problem according to Corollary 2 of Theorem 18 and Theorem 19.]

To solve such an equation in R, one may consider the equation

$$y = f(x)$$

in the variables x and y. The problem of solving $f(x) = 0$ is then equivalent to finding the values for x such that y [i.e., $f(x)$] is 0. If one draws the graph of $y = f(x)$ in the plane, this means we must find where, if anywhere, the graph crosses the x-axis.

For example, if $y = f(x)$ has the graph of Figure 12.1, we would know there are three distinct real solutions of $f(x) = 0$: one between -3 and -2, one between -1 and 0, and 2.

The problem arises, however, as to the accuracy of such a picture. For small-degree polynomials, the methods of curve tracing studied in the calculus offer complete information on this question; and in any case they offer more information than can be obtained from plotting sample points.

A theorem of importance in this connection is the *Intermediate Value Theorem for Polynomials:*

> Let $f(x)$ be a polynomial. Then if $a,b \in R$ with $a < b$, and if γ is any real number between $f(a)$ and $f(b)$, then $\exists c \in R$ between a and $b \ni f(c) = \gamma$. That is, as x ranges over $[a,b]$,[6] $f(x)$ assumes all (intermediate) values between $f(a)$ and $f(b)$.

[5] The remainder of the chapter may be omitted without disturbing the continuity of the text. Also this section is not used in Sections 16 and 17.
[6] $[a,b]$ means $\{x \in R/a \leq x \leq b\}$. Similarly, (a,b) means $\{x \in R/a < x < b\}$; $[a,b) = \{x \in R/a \leq x < b\}$; $(a,b] = \{x \in R/a < x \leq b\}$. This use of brackets and parentheses is not to be confused with the same notation used for g.c.d. and l.c.m.; actually, the context will always make it clear as to which particular meaning is desired.

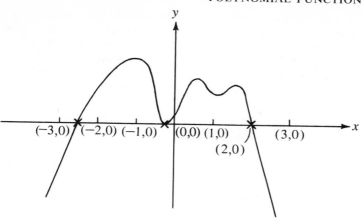

Figure 12.1

This theorem is proved for the set of all functions *continuous on the interval* [a,b]. This concept (of continuity) is definable in terms of our previous development. One then shows that the set of polynomials (over R in the real variable x over R) is a subset of the set of continuous functions. It then follows that the intermediate value theorem applies to polynomials.

Hence in particular, if $f(a) > 0$ and $f(b) < 0$ [or $f(a) < 0$ and $f(b) > 0$], then ∃ *at least one root of* $f(x)$ *between a and b;* i.e., the graph of $y = f(x)$ crosses the x-axis between $(a,0)$ and $(b,0)$.

We shall not undertake systematic methods for determining the real roots. In texts on the Theory of Equations it is shown how to find intervals $[a,b]$ containing single real roots (not counting multiplicity) of $f(x) = 0$. This is known as *isolating* the roots. (For example, the intervals $[-3,-2]$, $[-1,0]$, $[1.6,2.1]$ isolate the roots in our example above.) Then methods can be given to determine the real roots to any desired degree of approximation (e.g., to the nearest hundredth, or nearest ten-thousandth, etc.). We indicate a most primitive method in Exercises 31 and 32 below. Of course we have seen instances in which the roots can be determined precisely.

Exercises

31. Let $f(x) = x^3 - 6x^2 + 3x + 1$.
    (a) Find $f(-1), f(0), f(1)$, and $f(6)$.
    (b) Using part (a), the intermediate value theorem, and Theorem 16, show that $f(x) = 0$ has precisely three real roots.
    (c) Find the real root between 0 and 1 to the nearest tenth as follows: (i) Observe $f(0) > 0$ and $f(1) < 0$; (ii) find $f(.1), f(.2), \ldots$ until you get a negative result.[7] Say $f(.8) > 0$ and $f(.9) < 0$ for example. (iii) Conclude the

[7] If among $f(.1), f(.2), \ldots$ one obtains 0, then of course one has found the root precisely, and no approximation is necessary.

root is between .8 and .9. (iv) See whether $f(.85) > 0$ or $f(.85) < 0$. (v) Use part (iv) to determine whether the answer is .8 or .9.

32. Discuss how you would find the root in Exercise 31c to the nearest hundredth.

33. Suppose $f(x)$ is a polynomial with real coefficients having a single root in the interval $[-1,2]$, where $f(-1) < 0$ and $f(2) > 0$. Describe a procedure for finding this root to any degree of approximation desired (cf. Exercises 31 and 32).

16. Graph of $y = ax^2 + bx + c$

In the case of second-degree polynomials with real coefficients, we have seen that the real roots, if any, can be determined precisely. Here $f(x) = ax^2 + bx + c$ with $a,b,c \in R$ and $a \neq 0$. We consider the equation $y = f(x)$, that is,

(1) $y = ax^2 + bx + c$.

By equation (4) of Section 13, we may write (1) in the form

(2) $y = a\left[\left(x + \dfrac{b}{2a}\right)^2 - \dfrac{b^2 - 4ac}{4a^2}\right]$.

Note that for every $\alpha \in R$, $f\left(-\dfrac{b}{2a} + \alpha\right) = a\left[\alpha^2 - \dfrac{b^2 - 4ac}{4a^2}\right]$.

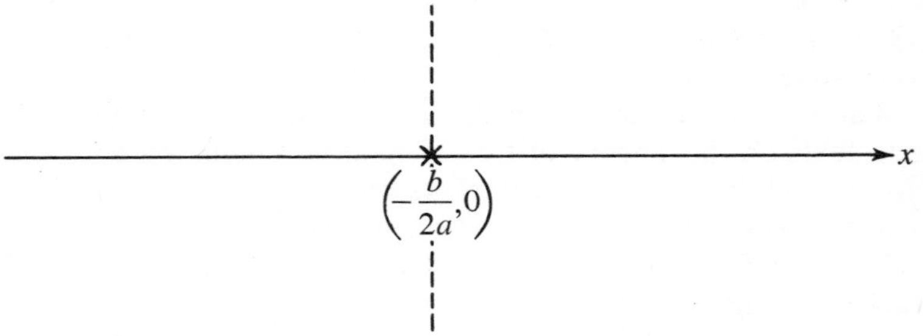

Figure 12.2

In drawing the graph, therefore, we have the situation shown in Figure 12.2. Whatever appears on one side of the indicated dotted line above appears as a mirror image on the other side. The curve cuts the dotted line at the point $\left(-\dfrac{b}{2a}, -\dfrac{b^2 - 4ac}{4a}\right)$. It is readily seen that this point is the lowest point of the curve if $a > 0$; moreover, it is the highest point if $a < 0$. For $\left(x + \dfrac{b}{2a}\right)^2$ is never negative; it is 0 if and only if $x = -\dfrac{b}{2a}$. Consequently, $\left(x + \dfrac{b}{2a}\right)^2 - \dfrac{b^2 - 4ac}{4a^2}$ assumes its smallest value at $-\dfrac{b}{2a}$. Thus if $a > 0$, $f(x)$ assumes its smallest value and if $a < 0$, $f(x)$ assumes its largest value at $x = -\dfrac{b}{2a}$.

Case I: a > 0

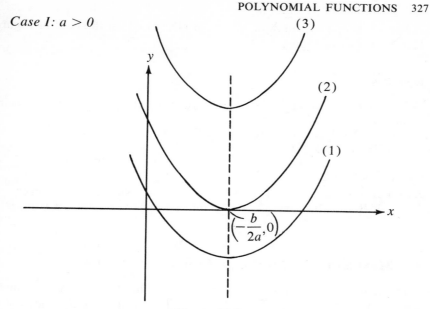

Figure 12.3

In Figure 12.3 above, (1) represents a curve where the discriminant of $ax^2 + bx + c$ is positive, thus yielding 2 unequal real roots; (2) represents discriminant 0, a repeated real root; (3) represents negative discriminant, 2 imaginary roots.

Case II: a < 0

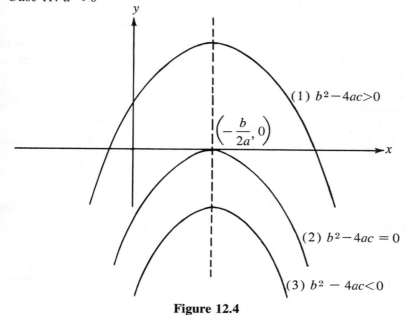

Figure 12.4

The same analysis may be given for (1), (2), (3) in the case of Figure 12.4 as in that of Figure 12.3.

Exercises

34. Sketch the graphs of the following. Give the coordinates of the highest point (maximum) or lowest point (minimum):

(a) $y = 2x^2 - 3x + 1$.   (e) $y = -2x^2 + 3x + 2$.
(b) $y = -2x^2 + x - 3$.   (f) $y = -9x^2 + 12x - 4$.
(c) $y = x^2 - 2x + 1$.   (g) $y = 3x^2 + 6x + 4$.
(d) $y = 2x^2 - 3x - 2$.

35. (a) If $f(x) = 2x^2 - 3x + 1$, what is the minimum value $f(x)$ can assume?
(b) If $f(x) = -2x^2 + 3x - 2$, what is the maximum value $f(x)$ can assume?

17. **Maximum and Minimum Problems**

In the previous section we showed how to find the maximum (or minimum) value of a function $f(x) = ax^2 + bx + c$. In some applications, it is desired to find the maximum value of such a function on some interval.

For example, suppose we have 100 feet of fencing, and wish to use it to enclose a rectangular portion of a field. Figure 12.5 gives some examples of the rectangles we can form with 100 feet of fencing. By the *perimeter* of a rectangle we shall mean the sum of the lengths of its sides. Thus we have, in Figure 12.5, three rectangles of perimeter 100 feet.

By the area of a rectangle we mean the product of the lengths of two of its adjacent sides. This tells us the number of square feet (i.e., squares 1 foot by 1 foot) which "fit" into the rectangle. Accordingly if "foot" is the unit for length, "square foot" or "ft²" is the unit for area. In (a) of Figure 12.5 the area is 625 ft²; in (b), it is 525 ft²; in (c), it is 600 ft².

If one were interested in having a rectangle of ground of as much area as possible (to grow something, for example), then of the three rectangles below he would choose the first.

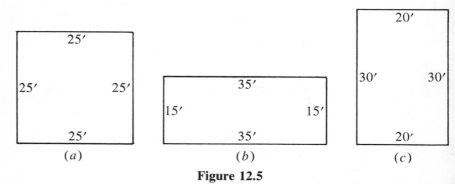

Figure 12.5

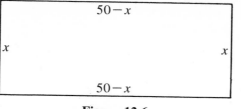

Figure 12.6

The natural question is: *What is the rectangle* (i.e., *what are its dimensions, for example*) *of perimeter 100 having the maximum possible area?*

We may vary one of the sides of the rectangle; the others are then determined: If one side is 20, the adjacent side is 30; if one is 35, the adjacent one is 15; etc. Accordingly, we may use a variable x as ranging over the *number* of feet comprising the length of one side; then $50 - x$ will be the number of feet in the adjacent side (Figure 12.6). For purposes of this problem, we allow x to range over real numbers between 0 and 50. The area $A(x)$ will be $x(50 - x)$:

$$A(x) = x(50 - x)$$

For which real number x is $A(x)$ maximum where $0 < x < 50$?

We can attack this problem by the methods of the previous section. Thus

$$A(x) = -x^2 + 50x$$

and we may, as in Figure 12.7, graph x against $A(x)$ [or, if one prefers, x against y where $y = A(x)$]. In this case, $a = -1$, $b = 50$, $c = 0$; so

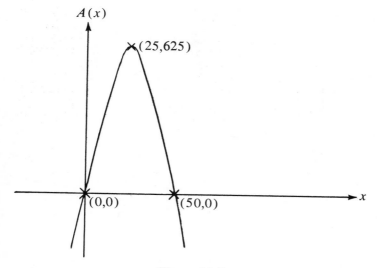

Figure 12.7

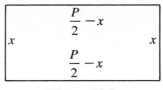

Figure 12.8

$-\dfrac{b}{2a} = 25$. As $a < 0$ $(a = -1)$, we obtain a maximum at $x = 25$. We can find $A(25)$ as:

$$A(25) = 25(50 - 25) = 625$$

Hence the rectangle of largest area is the one 25 ft by 25 ft. The corresponding area is 625 ft².

One can generalize this to show that the rectangle of fixed perimeter P having largest area is the square (of perimeter P). Namely (Figure 12.8),

$$A(x) = x\left(\frac{P}{2} - x\right)$$
$$= -x^2 + \frac{P}{2}x$$

Here $a = -1$, $b = \dfrac{P}{2}$, $c = 0$; so $-\dfrac{b}{2a} = \dfrac{P}{4}$ (Figure 12.9).

The maximum occurs at $x = \dfrac{P}{4}$, so that the dimensions are $\dfrac{P}{4}$ by $\dfrac{P}{4}$. Note

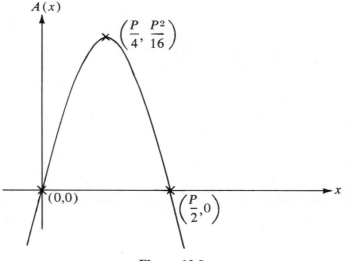

Figure 12.9

that it is important to observe which letters designate variables, and which constants.

As a second example, suppose the sum of two *positive* real numbers is 50. How can we select two such numbers in such a way that their product is maximum?

Possible selections would be:

(1) 20 and 30
(2) $\frac{50}{3}$ and $\frac{100}{3}$
(3) 2 and 48

The respective products are 600, $\frac{5000}{9}$, and 96.

Again we can vary one of the numbers, and then the other is determined. If we let x represent one of the numbers, $50 - x$ will represent the other. The product is then given by

$$P(x) = x(50 - x)$$
$$= -x^2 + 50x$$

and one proceeds as in the previous problem.

For a third example, we determine two real numbers whose difference is 10 and whose product is minimum.

Solution: Let x be the first number, $x - 10$ the second. Let y be the product:

$$y = x(x - 10)$$
$$y = x^2 - 10x$$

We have $-\dfrac{b}{2a} = 5$ (Figure 12.10). Thus the two numbers are 5 and -5.

It is clear that we are considering very special "maximum-minimum" problems, namely those in which second-degree polynomials arise. For

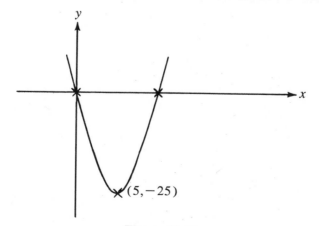

Figure 12.10

applications involving a greater variety of functions, the student must await the sharper methods of the calculus.

Exercises

36. Suppose one wishes to enclose a rectangular lot with 96 feet of fencing on three sides, leaving the fourth side open:

What should be the dimensions to obtain the maximum area? (Indicate which dimension, in your answer, refers to the side opposite the opening.)

37. Generalize Exercise 36.

38. What two real numbers whose sum is 20 yield the maximum product?

39. What two real numbers whose sum is S yield the maximum product?

40. Suppose one wishes to enclose a rectangular lot with a single partition parallel to one of the sides with 288 ft of fencing. What should be the dimensions to obtain the maximum area?

41. The same as Exercise 40 with two parallel partitions.

42. The same as Exercise 40 with P feet of fencing.

43. The same as Exercise 41 with P feet of fencing.

44. The same as Exercise 43 with n partitions.

chapter xiii

ELEMENTS OF
ANALYTIC GEOMETRY

In this chapter we introduce the methods of analytic geometry, methods which bring together geometry and algebra. However, nearly the first half of the chapter is devoted to a survey of Euclidean geometry (Section 2). Included in this part is the idea of a directed angle (not used in Euclidean geometry), and its measure. The measure of Euclidean angles is then also given.

In Section 3 analytic geometry is first introduced in one dimension: the line; and then in two dimensions: the plane. In Section 4 we develop the point of division and midpoint formulas, and in Section 5 the conditions for parallel and perpendicular lines. We conclude the chapter with a discussion of analytic methods applied to the proofs of theorems of Euclidean geometry. Further methods will be considered in Chapter 14.

1. Introduction

Our program up to now has been to display a structure at an introductory level within which the various parts of elementary mathematics may be placed, and upon which the most advanced parts may be built. As our foundation we have used postulates for the real-number system. For intuition and guides we have used pictures of graphs, but geometry has not played an essential role.

Euclid developed (about 300 B.C.) an axiomatic foundation for geometry, and despite the imperfections revealed under today's deeper vision of mathematical foundations, the influence of Euclid's axiomatic development remains a profound and beautiful one.

The axiomatic development of arithmetic and algebra was not undertaken until the nineteenth century, more than two hundred years after *analytic geometry* was invented by Descartes in 1637. This connection which Descartes provided between algebra and geometry is often deemed to be the beginning of modern mathematics. Approximately thirty years after Descartes' invention, the calculus was developed by Newton and Leibniz independently of each other. But a rigorous development again had to await the nineteenth century, and in one's mathematical training today such rigor is offered in courses in advanced calculus and functions of a real variable, and a taste is given here and there in elementary calculus. (And for questions deeper within the foundations of our subject one studies mathematical logic.) In such a rigorous formulation, our presentation to now will serve as good preparation.

In this formulation, a study of analytic geometry is made in one, two, and three dimensions, and in fact in n dimensions for any positive integer n. Although it is tempting to consider such a development here, the purpose of an introductory text is probably better served by providing a more intuitive approach. For one thing such a background would make the more rigorous discussion a more natural one. Second, it would better suit the preparation called upon in one's first view of the calculus. And finally, a knowledge of the concepts of the calculus would enrich one's view of n-dimensional geometry.

Accordingly, we shall make use of one's intuitive view of points, lines, angles, and circles; and we shall also use some of the ideas and results given in high-school courses in plane geometry. For the reader's convenience, however, or for those who managed to miss such a course, we shall outline the needed background in the next section before proceeding to analytic geometry. The treatment is by no means axiomatic, and theorems are not necessarily listed in the order in which they can be proved.

2. Plane Euclidean Geometry

2.1 Points, Lines, Segments, and Rays

We assume the reader to be familiar with the notion of a point, straight line, and circle drawn in the plane.

A line is regarded as extending indefinitely in both directions. If one considers that part of a line between two distinct points, say P and Q, one has a *line segment, PQ* (Figure 13.1). If P and Q are to be included, one

Figure 13.1

has a *closed* line segment; if they are excluded, one has an *open* line segment. If one considers the line segment drawn from P to Q in that order, then we have a *directed* line segment, written $\overrightarrow{PQ}$; similarly, one may consider $\overrightarrow{QP}$ (Figure 13.2).

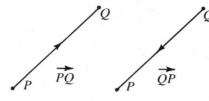

Figure 13.2

If the line segment PQ is extended indefinitely beyond Q, we obtain what we call a *ray* (or half-line) from P in the direction Q (Figure 13.3). If R is any other point on this ray distinct from P, then the ray from P through R is the same as that from P through Q.

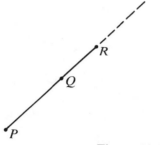

Figure 13.3

2.2 Polygons

Let $P_0, P_1, \ldots, P_n$ be $n + 1$ points in the plane for which each pair of adjacent points are distinct. Then the figure obtained by joining P_0 to P_1, P_1 to $P_2, \ldots, P_{n-1}$ to P_n by line segments is called a *polygon* of n sides (Figure 13.4). If in this polygon, $P_0 = P_n$, then the figure obtained is called a *closed polygon* (Figure 13.5). In Figure 13.5 we have $P_4 = P_0$, and a closed polygon of four sides.

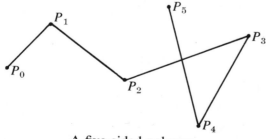

A five-sided polygon.

Figure 13.4

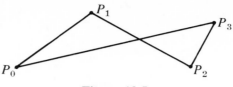

Figure 13.5

The points $P_0, P_1, \ldots, P_n$ are called the *vertices* of the polygon. Each of these points is called a *vertex*.

A polygon is said to be *simple* if none of its segments intersect any of the other segments except possibly that $P_0 = P_n$ (Figure 13.6).

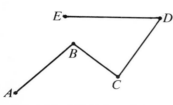

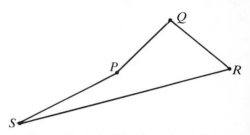

four-sided simple polygon   four-sided simple closed polygon

Figure 13.6

The *simple closed* polygons of 3, 4, 5, 6, 7, and 8 sides, respectively, are given the following names: (3) *triangle* (Figure 13.7), (4) *quadrilateral*, (5) *pentagon* (Figure 13.7), (6) *hexagon*, (7) *heptagon*, and (8) *octagon*.

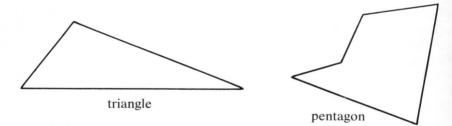

triangle   pentagon

Figure 13.7

2.3 Congruence. Length

The notion of one geometric figure being congruent to a second as given by Euclid is the following: If α and β are the two figures, then α is *congruent* to β if α can be taken by a rigid motion through space and placed upon β in such a way that all parts of α and all parts of β coincide, i.e., if α can be superimposed upon β.

Although this definition of congruence is clarified today by the use of further axioms, we shall regard it as sufficient for our purposes.

Two congruent line segments are said to have "the same length." We assume a number has been assigned to each line segment as a measure of its length, congruent line segments having the same measure assigned. We call this assigned number the *length* of the given segment. Today we know precisely which numbers are being referred to—the positive real numbers.

Let a line segment AB be divided by a point P:

Then the real number assigned as the measure of AB is assumed to be the sum of the numbers assigned to AP and PB. If we use $|AP|, |PB|, |AB|$ to denote the lengths of AP, PB, AB, respectively, we have

$$|AP| + |PB| = |AB|$$

If we have AB subdivided into n parts by $P_1, P_2, \ldots, P_{n-1}$, then we have

$$|AB| = |AP_1| + |P_1P_2| + \cdots + |P_{n-1}B|$$

This follows from the previous paragraph by induction.

The sum of the lengths of the sides of a simple closed polygon is called the *perimeter* of the polygon.

If A and B are two points, the length of AB is also called the *distance* between the points A and B.

2.4 Circles

A circle is a set of points whose distance from a fixed point, say O, is constant. We call O the *center* of the circle (Figure 13.8). If P is any point on the circle, OP is said to be a *radius* of the circle. If P and Q are any two points on the circle, PQ is said to be a *chord* of the circle. A chord passing through the center of the circle is called a *diameter*.

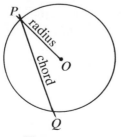

Figure 13.8

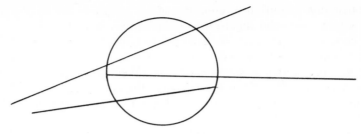

Figure 13.9

A *secant* of the circle is any line, ray, or line segment which is not a chord and which meets the circle in two distinct points. Figure 13.9 shows an example of three secants of the circle.

Let P be a fixed point on a circle (Figure 13.10). One can consider a point R moving along the circumference toward P, reaching P, and going beyond P on the other side. For each position of R, consider the secant line passing through P and R. As R moves, this secant line may be viewed as rotating about P. In this rotation, one line is missed—when R reaches P. This line may be thought of as the limiting case of the secant lines through P. It meets the circle in only one point—namely P. We call this line the *tangent* line to the circle *at P*.

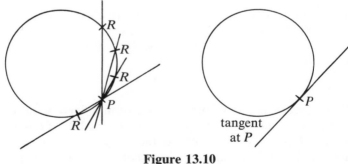

Figure 13.10

We present the tangent to the circle at P as the limiting case of the secant lines through P because this better generalizes to curves other than circles. For we could also have defined a tangent line to a circle as being a line meeting the circle in precisely one point. But the curves of Figure 13.11 show that this would not be the case in more general situations. On the left we have a tangent line to the curve at P meeting the curve elsewhere in another point. On the right we have a line meeting the curve in a single point, but it is not a tangent line.

If α is a circle, the length of α is denoted by $|\alpha|$ and is called the *circumference* of α.

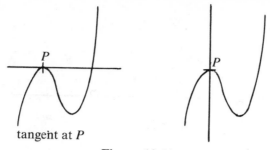

tangent at P

Figure 13.11

If r is the length of a radius of the circle, then $2r$ is the length of a diameter. One often loosely refers to r being *the* radius and $2r$ *the* diameter. The words in italic type indicate that all radii have the same lengths, as do all diameters. Thus the words 'radius' and 'diameter' are used interchangeably to mean certain line segments and lengths of those line segments.

It is shown in elementary geometry (also in the calculus) that the ratio of the circumference to the diameter of a circle is always the same, no matter which circle is taken. That is, if we let $C = |\alpha|$, $\dfrac{C}{2r}$ is always the same, for all circles α. This real number giving the ratio of the circumference to the diameter of all circles is usually written 'π,' the Greek letter "pi." There are several proofs of the fact that π *is an irrational number*. It is a number between 3 and 4 and to the nearest hundredth is 3.14. The rational number $\dfrac{22}{7}$, which to the nearest hundredth is also 3.14, is often used as a rational approximation to π; as is, also, the number 3.14. Thus the statements that $\pi = \dfrac{22}{7}$, or that $\pi = 3.14$ are incorrect.

We have $\dfrac{C}{2r} = \pi$, where C is the circumference of any circle and r the radius of that circle. This formula often appears as

$$\boxed{C = 2\pi r}$$

2.5 Directed Angles

We shall regard a *directed angle* as being given by a rotation of a ray to a second (not necessarily distinct) ray. In Figure 13.12 we have the ray PR (i.e., the ray from P through R) moving counterclockwise to the ray PQ. The ray PR is called the *initial side,* and the ray PQ the *terminal side* of the directed angle. One can start with the same initial side and rotate an entire revolution about P and then rotate further to the terminal side PQ (Figure 13.13).

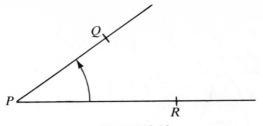

Figure 13.12

Although the initial and terminal sides may be the same, then, the directed angles involved can be different. In Figures 13.12 and 13.13 we rotated counterclockwise. We may also rotate clockwise (Figure 13.14). In Figure 13.14, we have two further directed angles with PR as initial side and PQ as terminal side.

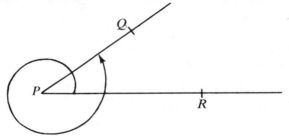

Figure 13.13

In all the illustrations above, P is said to be the *vertex* of the angle.

Of course one can also pass through 2 or 3 or n revolutions before passing to the terminal side. In Figure 13.15, PQ is the initial side and PR the terminal side.

We come now to the question of measuring a directed angle. Let us consider first directed angles which are rotations in the counterclockwise direction.

One method of measuring such angles is by the number of revolutions. Examples are shown in Figure 13.16.

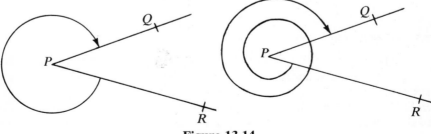

Figure 13.14

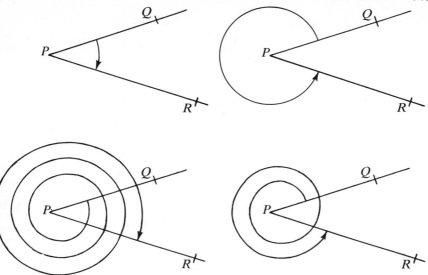

Figure 13.15

As a matter of fact, we could assign any positive real number, say r, as a measure of 1 revolution. Then in the above examples of Figure 13.15, the measure of $\frac{1}{4}$ revolution would be $\frac{r}{4}$, that of the second $\frac{5r}{8}$, that of the third $2r$.

For example, if $r = 360$, then the measures of these three angles would be 90, 225, and 720, respectively.

The two measures most frequently used for 1 revolution are 360 and 2π. In the first case, we call the measure the number of *degrees* in the angle, in the second the number of *radians*. Thus an angle of $\frac{1}{4}$ revolution has $\frac{1}{4} \cdot 360 = 90$ degrees or $\frac{1}{4} \cdot 2\pi = \frac{\pi}{2}$ radians.

In general we have

$$\text{number of revolutions} = \frac{\text{number of degrees}}{360} = \frac{\text{number of radians}}{2\pi}$$

Or, if one prefers, one obtains, using the second equality,

$$\frac{\text{number of degrees}}{180} = \frac{\text{number of radians}}{\pi}$$

As 2π is the circumference of a circle of radius 1 (called a *unit circle*), one may look upon the number of radians in an angle as being the length of the arc which is traversed in going along a unit circle, with center at the

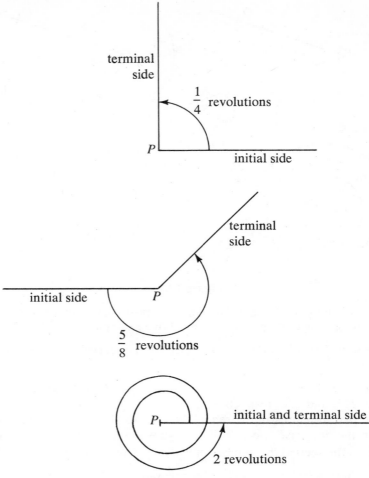

Figure 13.16

vertex, from the initial side to the terminal side (Figure 13.17). Note that we use 135° and 180°, which is the standard notation for 135 degrees and 180 degrees.

If instead of a unit circle, one used a circle of radius a, then the arc length s from the initial side to the terminal side would satisfy the formula

$$\text{number of revolutions} = \frac{s}{2\pi a} = \frac{\text{number of radians}}{2\pi}$$

so that

$$\boxed{s = a\alpha}$$

where α is the number of radians (Figure 13.18).

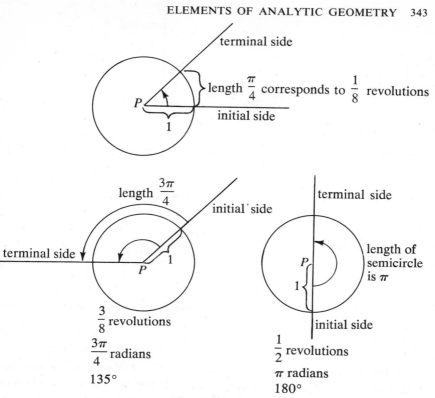

Figure 13.17

For clockwise rotations, one takes the *negative* of the number of revolutions for the measure (Figure 13.19). As in the examples, the same convention is used for the number of radians or degrees. We also include an angle of 0 revolutions, or 0 radians, or 0 degrees.

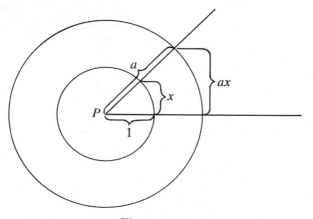

Figure 13.18

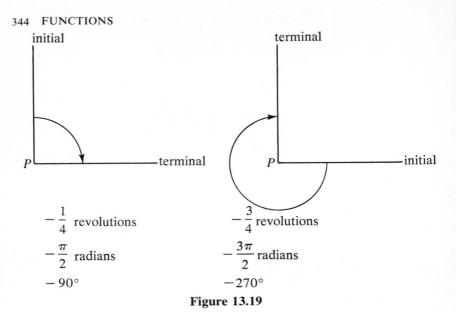

$-\dfrac{1}{4}$ revolutions

$-\dfrac{\pi}{2}$ radians

$-90°$

$-\dfrac{3}{4}$ revolutions

$-\dfrac{3\pi}{2}$ radians

$-270°$

Figure 13.19

Thus, whichever measure one is using for directed angles, the entire real-number system is involved.

2.6   Euclidean Angles

In Euclidean geometry, an angle can be defined as a pair of rays emanating from the same point P (Figure 13.20). If one selects a point Q on one of the rays and a point R on the other, both distinct from P, then we may denote this angle by

$$\text{‘} \measuredangle QPR \text{’} \qquad \text{or} \qquad \text{‘} \measuredangle RPQ \text{’}$$

In this view, an angle is assigned a measure between 0 and 180 (if measured in degrees). Namely one may consider the measures of the two directed angles: (1) Initial side PR rotated counterclockwise to PQ without exceeding one revolution; (2) the same with PQ initial side and PR terminal side. These are between 0 and 360, one between 0 and 180, the other between 180 and 360. One then assigns the number between 0 and 180.

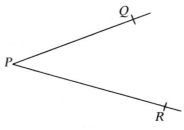

Figure 13.20

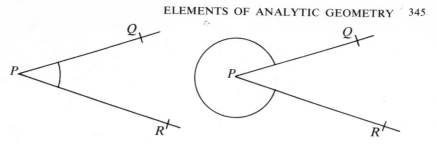

between 0 and 180   between 180 and 360

Figure 13.21

A second point of view is to regard the rays PQ and PR as determining two angles, as marked in Figure 13.21. The one is assigned the measure of (1) above, the other the measure of (2).

We shall adopt the latter point of view in what follows, thereby allowing us to state Theorem 28 on page 355 in its customary form. But the former point of view is being widely adopted today, and in any case either definition may be incorporated into a rigorous development of plane Euclidean geometry.

In the first view, two angles are congruent if and only if their measures are equal. In the second view this may also be said to be true if one regards an angle as the portion of the plane covered in the rotations mentioned in (1) and (2) above.

In what follows, when we speak of *the* angle determined by two rays, we shall mean the one between 0 and 180 degrees.

It is customary to call angles equal if their measures are equal.

An angle of 90° is called a *right* angle; an angle of 180° is called a *straight* angle. Two angles whose sum (i.e., of their measures in degrees) is 90° are said to be *complementary*; two angles whose sum is 180° are said to be *supplementary*. An angle less than 90° is called an *acute* angle, between 90° and 180° an *obtuse* angle.

An angle formed by two adjacent sides of a simple closed polygon is called an *interior* angle of the polygon. An angle formed by a side of a polygon and the ray in the opposite direction of the adjacent side is called an *exterior* angle of the polygon. In Figure 13.22, (1) AC and AB are adjacent sides forming interior angle BAC. (2) AB and BC are adjacent sides; BD is the ray in the opposite direction to BC. AB and BD determine an exterior angle. (3) BE and BC determine an exterior angle.

The interior angles of the polygon are called the *angles of the polygon*.

If two lines intersect at a point, four angles are formed by considering adjacent pairs of rays (Figure 13.23). The nonadjacent angles are called *vertical* angles. Thus angles 1 and 3 are vertical angles; and angles 2 and 4 are vertical angles.

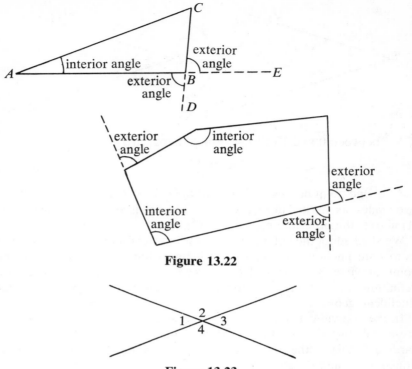

Figure 13.22

Figure 13.23

2.7   Theorems and Further Definitions from Euclidean Geometry

We list some theorems and definitions from Euclidean geometry in the plane. Some of these we shall use later, others are given because they are useful for handling illustrative exercises in the calculus.

(1) Two angles complementary to the same angle are equal.

(2) Two angles supplementary to the same angle are equal.

(3) Vertical angles are equal.

We shall next list theorems [in (4) through (8)] giving conditions under which one can conclude that two triangles are congruent. The following terminology is useful.

Figure 13.24 shows the triangle ABC. We have labeled side AB as c, BC as a, AC as b. We shall label the (interior) angles of the triangle as $\angle A$, $\angle B$, $\angle C$. Now AB appears as a side of two of the angles—$\angle A$ and $\angle B$. We call $\angle A$ and $\angle B$ angles *adjacent* to the side AB; we call $\angle C$ the angle *opposite* to AB, and similarly side AB is *opposite* $\angle C$. Also $\angle A$ is said to be the *included* angle between sides AB and AC.

Thus the opposites are A and a, B and b, and C and c. (A and a are written briefly to mean the angle A and side a.)

C is included between a and b, B between c and a, A between c and b.

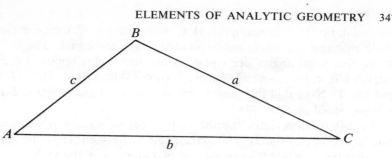

Figure 13.24

A and *B* are adjacent to *c*, *B* and *C* adjacent to *a*, and *C* and *A* adjacent to *b*.

A triangle is said to be a *right triangle* if one of its angles is a right angle. The sides forming the right angle are said to be *perpendicular*. More generally, any two line segments, rays, lines, or combination thereof are said to be perpendicular if they meet at right angles (Figure 13.25).

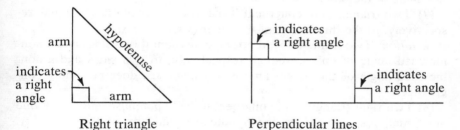

Right triangle   Perpendicular lines

Figure 13.25

If *l* and *m* are two perpendicular line segments, rays, lines, or combination thereof, *l* ⊥ *m* means *l* is perpendicular to *m*.

In a right triangle, the side opposite the right angle is called the *hypotenuse* of the right triangle; the sides adjacent to the right angle are called the *arms* (or *legs*) of the right triangle.

(4) Two triangles are congruent if a side and two adjacent angles of one are equal, respectively, to a side and two adjacent angles of the other. Thus in Figure 13.26, if one knows that *AC* = *DE* (meaning their lengths

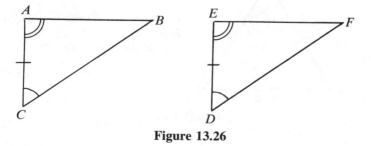

Figure 13.26

are equal, i.e., they are congruent), $C = D$, and $A = E$, then one can con-clude that the remaining corresponding parts are equal: The sides op-posite the equal angles are equal, as are the angles opposite the equal sides. Thus in the above we conclude from (4) that $BC = DF$, $AB = EF$, and $B = F$. Note that the same marks on the sides and angles are used to indicate equal parts.

One often abbreviates the theorem in (4) to $a.s.a. = a.s.a.$ and says "angle-side-angle equals angle-side-angle." This conveys the informa-tion that one is using the equality of two angles and the included side of one triangle to similar parts, respectively, of a second triangle to conclude congruence.

(5) Two triangles are congruent if two sides and the included angle of one are equal, respectively, to two sides and the included angle of the other ($s.a.s. = s.a.s.$).

(6) Two triangles are congruent if a side, adjacent angle, and opposite angle of one are equal, respectively, to a side, adjacent angle, and oppo-site angle of the other ($s.a.a. = s.a.a.$).

(7) Two triangles are congruent if the three sides of one are equal, re-spectively, to the three sides of the other ($s.s.s. = s.s.s.$).

(*Caution*: Two triangles need not be congruent if two sides and a non-included angle of one are equal, respectively, to two sides and a non-included angle of the other. That is, $a.s.s. = a.s.s.$ does not imply con-gruence.)

(8) Two right triangles are congruent if the hypotenuse and arm of one are equal, respectively, to the hypotenuse and arm of the other (*hy. arm = hy. arm*).

A triangle is said to be *isosceles* if two of its sides are equal. The third side of an isosceles triangle is called its *base*, and the angles opposite the equal sides the *base angles* (Figure 13.27). The vertex opposite the base is called *the vertex* of the isosceles triangle, and the angle at the vertex is called *the vertex angle*.

A triangle is *equilateral* if its three sides are equal. It follows that an

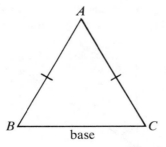

Base angles: B and C
Base: BC
Equal sides: AB and AC

Figure 13.27

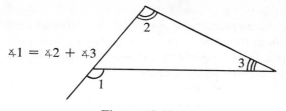

$$\angle 1 = \angle 2 + \angle 3$$

Figure 13.28

equilateral triangle is isosceles. A triangle is *equiangular* if its three angles
are equal.

(9) The base angles of an isosceles triangle are equal. Conversely if two
angles of a triangle are equal, the sides opposite are equal.

(10) A triangle is equilateral if and only if it is equiangular.

(11) The sum of the angles of any triangle is 180°. In particular, every
angle of an equilateral triangle is 60°, and the acute angles of a right triangle are complementary.

(12) An exterior angle of a triangle is equal to the sum of the two re-
mote interior angles (Figure 13.28).

A line cutting a number of other lines is said to be a *transversal* of
those lines.

Let *l* and *m* be two lines, and *q* a transversal of *l* and *m*. In Figure
13.29, angles 1, 2, 3, 4, 5, 6, 7, and 8 are called the angles of the two lines
l and *m* cut by the transversal *q*. Angles 1, 2, 7, and 8 are called the *exterior angles;* angles 3, 4, 5, and 6 the *interior angles.* Angles 1, 3, 5, and 7
are said to be *alternate* to 2, 4, 6, and 8 (and vice versa). Angles 1 and 8
are called *alternate exterior angles;* also angles 2 and 7. Angles 3 and 6
are called *alternate interior angles;* also angles 4 and 5. Angles 1 and 5

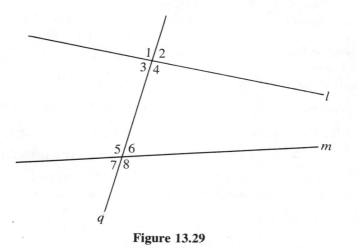

Figure 13.29

are called *corresponding angles;* also 3 and 7; also 2 and 6; also 4 and 8. The lines *l* and *m* are said to be *parallel* if they have no points in common. We write *l* ∥ *m* in this case.

(13) Let two lines be cut by a transversal. Then any one of the following conditions implies all the others:

(a) The lines are parallel.

(b) A pair of alternate exterior angles are equal.

(c) A pair of alternate interior angles are equal.

(d) A pair of corresponding angles are equal.

We are not giving an axiomatic treatment of Euclidean geometry, but perhaps we should observe the important fifth postulate of Euclid—that through any point not on a given line, ∃ one and only one line through the point parallel to the given line. For it was the attempt to show that this postulate could be deduced as a theorem from the other postulates that led to non-Euclidean geometries.

(14) Let ABC be a triangle with sides a, b, c opposite the vertices A, B, C, respectively. Then $\angle A > \angle B$ if and only if $a > b$. In particular, the hypotenuse of the right triangle is the largest side of that triangle. Finally, $a + b > c$ and $|a - b| < c$.

(15) Let l be a line and P a point not on l. Then there exists one and only one line through P perpendicular to l. Of all line segments drawn from P to a point of l, the one perpendicular to l is the shortest. Its length is called the *distance* between P and l.

(16) *Pythagorean theorem:* Let ABC be a right triangle with sides a, b, c, where c is the hypotenuse. Then $c^2 = a^2 + b^2$. Conversely, if ABC is a triangle with sides a, b, c such that $c^2 = a^2 + b^2$, then it is a right triangle with hypotenuse c.

A generalization of the idea of congruence of two geometric figures is that of similarity. Intuitively speaking, two figures are *similar* if one of them is a photographic enlargement of the other. That is, all parts of one are in the same proportion to the corresponding parts of the other, and all corresponding angles involved are equal. For triangles we may state this as follows:

Let ABC and DEF be two triangles with $\angle A = \angle D$, $\angle B = \angle E$, $\angle C = \angle F$, and suppose $\dfrac{BC}{EF} = \dfrac{CA}{FD} = \dfrac{AB}{DE}$. Then the triangles are said to be *similar*. [It will be seen below (Cf. (17)) that it is only necessary to assume $\dfrac{BC}{EF} = \dfrac{CA}{FD} = \dfrac{AB}{DE}$. For it then follows as a consequence that $\angle A = \angle D$, $\angle B = \angle E$, and $\angle C = \angle F$.] Thus in Figure 13.30 the angles are equal as marked and the sides corresponding to the equal angles (i.e., opposite them) are in the same proportion. In fact, $\dfrac{BC}{EF} = \dfrac{12}{8}$, $\dfrac{CA}{FD} = \dfrac{15}{10}$, $\dfrac{AB}{DE} = \dfrac{9}{6}$, which in all cases is $\dfrac{3}{2}$. Hence these triangles are similar.

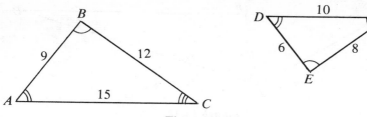

Figure 13.30

In (17) to (19) we list theorems giving conditions under which one can conclude two triangles are similar.

(17) If in two triangles ABC and DEF we have $\dfrac{BC}{EF} = \dfrac{CA}{FD} = \dfrac{AB}{DE}$, then $\angle A = \angle D$, $\angle B = \angle E$, $\angle C = \angle F$, so that the triangles are similar.

(18) If two angles of one triangle are equal, respectively, to two angles of a second, then the triangles are similar.

(19) If two sides of one triangle are proportional, respectively, to two sides of a second, and the included angles are equal, then the third sides have the same proportion, so that the triangles are similar.

We next give definitions of the perpendicular bisectors, angle bisectors, medians, and altitudes of a triangle.

If AB is a line segment, then a point C on AB is said to *bisect AB* if $AC = CB$. The line perpendicular to AB at C is called the *perpendicular bisector* of AB (Figure 13.31).

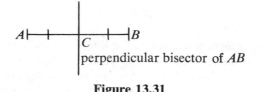

perpendicular bisector of AB

Figure 13.31

If AP, AQ, AR are rays from the point A, AQ is said to *bisect* angle PAR if $\angle PAQ = \angle QAR$ (Figure 13.32).

Now let A, B, C be three noncollinear points (i.e., points not on the same line), so that they determine a triangle (Figure 13.33). The *angle bisector* of the triangle at A is the line segment from A to the side BC

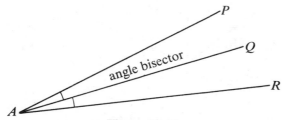

angle bisector

Figure 13.32

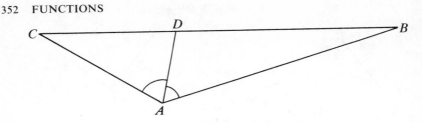

Figure 13.33

bisecting ⊀*CAB*. In our diagram, *AD* is the angle bisector at *A*. Thus a triangle has 3 angle bisectors.

A *median* of the triangle is a line segment drawn from a vertex to the midpoint of the opposite side.

The *perpendicular bisectors* of a triangle are the perpendicular bisectors of the sides of the triangles (Figure 13.34).

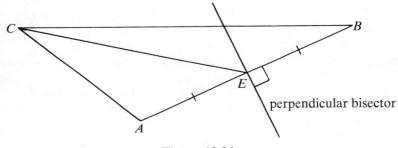

perpendicular bisector

Figure 13.34

Finally an *altitude* of a triangle is the line segment from a vertex to the opposite side (extended, if necessary) which is perpendicular to that side. In Figure 13.35, the point *F* is called the *foot* of the altitude from *C* to *AB*, and *G* the foot of the altitude from *A* to *BC*. The side to which the altitude is drawn is called the *base corresponding to that altitude*, or, vice versa, the altitude is the altitude corresponding to that base. When

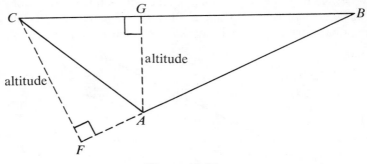

Figure 13.35

one refers to the base and altitude of a triangle, he means any altitude and its *corresponding* base. We have the following:

(20) If h is an altitude, b the corresponding base, and A the area of a triangle, then $A = \frac{1}{2}bh$. This is often stated: The area is one-half the base times the altitude.

Two nonadjacent sides (angles) of a quadrilateral are called *opposite* sides (angles).

A quadrilateral in which one pair of opposite sides are parallel sides and one pair are not is called a *trapezoid*. If the nonparallel sides are equal, it is called an *isosceles trapezoid*. A line segment from one of the parallel sides to the other (extended, if necessary) meeting both at right angles is called an *altitude* of the trapezoid; the parallel sides are called the *bases*.

A quadrilateral in which *both pairs* of opposite sides are parallel is called a *parallelogram*. In this case an altitude can be taken between either pair of parallel sides. If an altitude is taken between a given pair of parallel sides (extended, if necessary), the sides are said to be the *bases corresponding to the altitude*.

A parallelogram in which two adjacent sides are equal is called a *rhombus*.

A parallelogram in which one of the angles is a right angle is called a *rectangle*.

A *square* is a rectangle in which two adjacent sides are equal.

The line segments joining the opposite vertices of a quadrilateral are called the *diagonals* of the quadrilateral.

(21) If b_1 and b_2 are the bases, h the altitude, and A the area of a trapezoid, $A = \frac{1}{2}h(b_1 + b_2)$.

(22) If b is a side and h a *corresponding* altitude of a parallelogram, and A the area, then $A = bh$ ("area is base times altitude").

(23) A quadrilateral is a parallelogram if and only if both pairs of opposite angles are equal.

We next list some theorems for circles.

(24) Let α be a circle with center O, and let AB be a chord of α not passing through O. Then a point D on AB bisects AB if and only if $OD \perp AB$ (Figure 13.36).

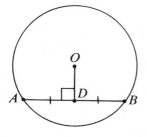

$OD \perp AB$ if and only if $AD = DB$

Figure 13.36

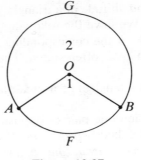

Figure 13.37

Let α be a circle with center O, and A, B any points on the circle (Figure 13.37). There are two arcs determined by A and B, one from A to B proceeding counterclockwise, the other clockwise. The former we can label arc AFB, the latter AGB, the F and G being marked on the figure to make this distinction. The chord AB is called the chord of the arc AFB (or AGB). The angle 1 is called the angle subtended by the arc AFB at O, the angle 2 is called the angle subtended by the arc AGB at O. Angles subtended by arcs at the center of a circle are called *central angles*.

If E is a point on the arc AGB, then the angle AEB is said to be *inscribed* in the arc AFB. Similarly, if K is a point on the arc AFB, the angle AKB is said to be inscribed in the arc AGB. All such angles are called *inscribed angles* (Figure 13.38). Each arc determines a single central angle (between 0° and 360°), but many inscribed angles (between 0° and 180°).

(25) In equal circles (i.e., congruent circles—the circles need not be distinct), two arcs subtend equal central angles if and only if the arcs are equal (i.e., congruent, or have equal lengths); furthermore, two equal arcs determine equal chords.

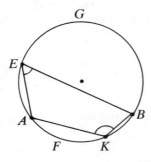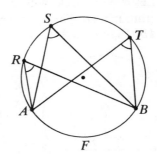

Figure 13.38

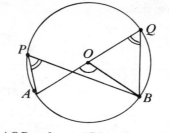

$$\sphericalangle AOB = 2 \cdot \sphericalangle APB = 2 \cdot \sphericalangle AQB$$

Figure 13.39

(26) In equal circles, two chords are equidistant (i.e., have the same distance) from the centers if and only if they are equal.

(27) The tangent at any point P of a circle (center at O) and the radius OP are perpendicular to one another.

(28) The central angle subtended by an arc of a circle is twice that of any inscribed angle subtended by the same arc (Figure 13.39).

(29) An angle inscribed in a semicircle is a right angle (Figure 13.40).

(30) If r is the radius of a circle, its area A is $A = \pi r^2$.

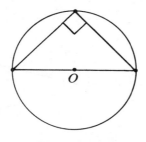

Figure 13.40

Exercises

1. Suppose a directed angle has the measure indicated. Give 3 positive and 3 negative measures of angles having the same initial and terminal sides. The same for the initial and terminal sides reversed.

   (a) 60°.

   (b) $\frac{2}{3}$ revolution.

   (c) $-\frac{3\pi}{2}$ radians.

   (d) 1 radian.

   (e) −820°.

   (f) $\sqrt{2}$ revolutions.

   (g) $-\frac{5\pi}{4}$ radians.

   (h) 7π radians.

   (i) 6°.

   (j) 0°.

2. Complete the following table:

No. revolutions		$\frac{1}{12}$	$\frac{1}{8}$	$\frac{1}{6}$		$\frac{1}{3}$			$\frac{1}{2}$		$\frac{5}{8}$					$\frac{11}{12}$	
No. degrees	0	30	45					150				240	270		315		360
No. radians		$\frac{\pi}{6}$		$\frac{\pi}{3}$	$\frac{\pi}{2}$		$\frac{3\pi}{4}$			$\frac{7\pi}{6}$				$\frac{5\pi}{3}$			

3. In Exercise 1, convert the given measures of angles to revolutions, degrees, radians — whichever do not appear.

4. Suppose an arc of a circle subtends a central angle of $\frac{\pi}{8}$ radians.

    (a) If the circle has radius 1, what is the length of the arc?
    (b) The same for radius 2.
    (c) Radius 3.
    (d) Radius a.

5. Answer the same question as in Exercise 4 for each of the angles of Exercise 2.

6. In the following diagram, $\angle ACB$ is a right angle. $\angle ABC = 30°$, $\angle BDE =$

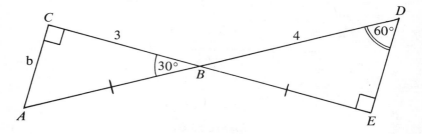

60°, $BC = 3$, $BD = 4$, $AB = BE$. Answer the following, giving reasons from Section 2.7.

    (a) How many degrees in $\angle DBE$?   (d) What is the length of BE?
    (b) $\angle CBD$?   (e) Of AC?
    (c) $\angle CAB$?

7. (a) What is the sum of the (interior) angles of a quadrilateral? Justify your answer.

    (b) What is the sum of a pair of adjacent angles of a parallelogram?
    (c) Show that all angles in a rectangle are right angles.

8. In parallelogram $ABCD$ below, why are triangles ADB and BCD congruent? (*Hint:* DB is a transversal to two parallel lines.) Use this to show that the opposite sides of a parallelogram are equal. (It follows that all sides of a rhombus and square are equal.)

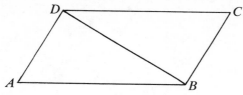

9. State and prove the converse of Exercise 8.
10. Show that the altitude from the vertex of an isosceles triangle is also a median and an angle bisector.
11. Suppose the hypotenuse of an isosceles right triangle has length a. Show that each arm has length $\frac{a}{2}\sqrt{2}$.
12. How many degrees are there in each of the three angles of an equilateral triangle? Why?
13. Let a triangle have angles 30°, 60°, 90°. Suppose the hypotenuse has length a. Show that the side opposite the 30° angle has length $\frac{a}{2}$, and the side opposite the 60° angle length $\frac{a}{2}\sqrt{3}$. (*Hint:* Consider the diagram below.)

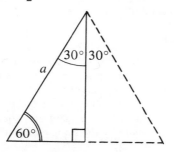

14. In the following, $AB \parallel DE$, angles ABC and DEF are right angles. Prove that triangles ABC and DEF are similar.

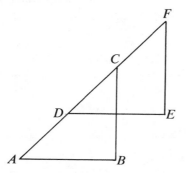

15. In the following, $BC \parallel DE$. Prove that triangle ABC is similar to triangle ADE. Hence show that $\frac{AB}{AD} = \frac{AC}{AE} = \frac{BC}{DE}$.

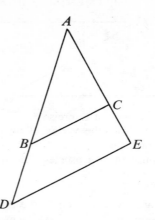

16. Using Exercise 15, show that if ADE is an isosceles triangle with equal sides AD and AE, B is the midpoint of AD, and C is the midpoint of AE, then BC is parallel to DE, and $DE = 2BC$.

17. What is the length of the other arm of a right triangle if an arm and the hypotenuse have lengths given?

(a) 3,5.   (d) 12,13.
(b) 8,10.   (e) 10,26.
(c) 7,25.   (f) $4a,5a$.

18. Why is it impossible for a triangle to have sides of lengths 1, 5, and 7?

19. Suppose that in a circle a chord of length 10 is at a distance 3 from the center. Find the circumference and area of the circle.

20. What is the area of an isosceles triangle inscribed in a semicircle of radius 6?

21. Show that the angle inscribed by a tangent and chord of a circle is one-half of the central angle subtended by the same chord. That is, show that $\alpha = 2\gamma$.

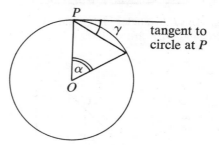

tangent to
circle at P

3. Coordinate Systems

3.1   Coordinates on the Line

Descartes' idea was to unite geometry and algebra by associating points with numbers. We have introduced his idea in Parts I and II, and again in

Chapter 11, but shall attempt to partially expose its greater scope in the remainder of this chapter.

For the geometry of the line, the system R of real numbers is used; for the geometry of the plane, $R \times R$ is used; and for the geometry of space, $R \times R \times R$ is used.

Definition 1. For the geometry of the line (we have seen that) we choose an arbitrary point O on the line as origin, associating the "coordinate" 0 to this point, and a second point U is labeled '1.' We then associate with every point P on the same side of O as U the positive number giving the length of OP. For points Q on the other side of O we use the additive inverse of the length of OQ:

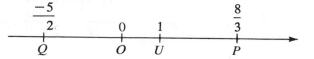

In this way with each point on the line is associated a unique real number, and every real number is associated to some point.

If P has coordinate $\frac{8}{3}$, we shall often write $P(\frac{8}{3})$; similarly $O(0)$, $Q(-\frac{5}{2})$, $U(1)$, etc.

If $R(r)$ and $S(s)$ are two distinct points on the line, then we say that the direction from R to S is positive if $s > r$, and negative if $s < r$.

Thus the direction from $U(1)$ to $Q(-\frac{5}{2})$ is negative since $-\frac{5}{2} < 1$; the direction from $P(\frac{8}{3})$ to $U(1)$ is negative; from $U(1)$ to $P(\frac{8}{3})$ is positive; from $O(0)$ to $U(1)$ is positive.

Definition 2. The *directed distance* from $R(r)$ to $S(s)$ is defined to be:

(a) The length of RS if the direction from R to S is positive.
(b) 0 if $R = S$.
(c) The additive inverse of the length of RS if the direction from R to S is negative.

The directed distance from $R(r)$ to $S(s)$ is also called the *component* or *directed length* of $\overrightarrow{RS}$.

Example 1. Take $R(2)$ and $S(5)$. The directed distance from R to S is 3, from S to R is -3:

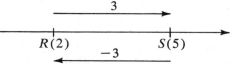

Example 2. Take $R(3)$ and $S(-4)$:

The component of $\overrightarrow{RS}$ is -7, of $\overrightarrow{SR}$ is 7.

Example 3. If $P(p)$ is any point on the line, the directed distance from $O(0)$ to $P(p)$ is p. Thus the coordinate of a point P is also the directed distance from the origin to that point, or the directed length of $\overrightarrow{OP}$.

Theorem 1. If $P_1(x_1)$ and $P_2(x_2)$ are two points on the line, the directed distance from P_1 to P_2, or component of $\overrightarrow{P_1P_2}$, is $x_2 - x_1$.

Proof: *Case 1:* Assume P_1 and P_2 are both on the positive side of O, and distinct:

or

In (a), $P_1P_2 = OP_2 - OP_1$, where by this, as in Section 2, we mean P_1P_2 as the length of the segment P_1P_2, etc.[1] Thus $P_1P_2 = x_2 - x_1$ by Definition 1 of the coordinate of a point. Since the direction from P_1 to P_2 is positive, this length gives the directed distance from P_1 to P_2 by Definition 2(a).

In (b), the length of P_2P_1 (or P_1P_2 for that matter) is $x_1 - x_2$ by a similar argument. But the direction from P_1 to P_2 is negative, so that by Definition 2(c), the directed distance from P_1 to P_2 is $-(x_1 - x_2)$, which again is $x_2 - x_1$.

Case 2: Assume P_1 and P_2 are on opposite sides of O:

or

In (a), $P_1P_2 = P_1O + OP_2$. But P_1O has length $-x_1$ (so that $-(-x_1)$ is the coordinate of P_1), and OP_2 length x_2. So $P_1P_2 = -x_1 + x_2 = x_2 - x_1$. As the direction from P_1 to P_2 is positive, the directed distance from P_1 to P_2 is also $x_2 - x_1$.

In (b),

$$P_2P_1 = P_2O + OP_1$$
$$= -x_2 + x_1$$
$$= x_1 - x_2$$

---

[1] Strictly speaking, one should write $|P_1P_2| = |OP_2| - |OP_1|$. However, as indicated earlier, we shall simply write $P_1P_2 = OP_2 - OP_1$ when it is clear from the context that we are discussing lengths.

Since the direction from P_1 to P_2 is negative, the directed distance from P_1 to P_2 is $-(x_1 - x_2)$ or $x_2 - x_1$.

Case 3: P_1 and P_2 both on the negative side of O and distinct (cf. Exercise 24).

Case 4: $P_1 = P_2$. Then $x_2 - x_1 = 0$, and the result holds in this case by Definition 2(b).

Case 5: Either $P_1 = O$ or $P_2 = O$ (cf. Exercise 24).

Example 4. Suppose P and Q are points on the line, and $\overrightarrow{PQ}$ has component 3. If P has coordinate 2, what is the coordinate of Q?

Solution: Let Q have coordinate b so that we have $P(2)$ and $Q(b)$. By Definition 2 and Theorem 1, $\overrightarrow{PQ}$ has component $b - 2$, so that $b - 2 = 3$ and $b = 5$:

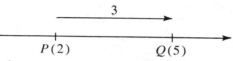

$$P(2) \qquad\qquad Q(5)$$

Example 5. Suppose A and B are points on the line, and $\overrightarrow{AB}$ has component -3. If A has coordinate 1, what is the coordinate of B?

Solution: If $A(1)$ and $B(b)$, $b - 1 = -3$ and $b = -2$:

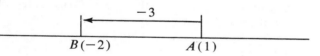

$$B(-2) \qquad\qquad A(1)$$

The above examples illustrate the fact that if one knows the component of a directed line segment, then starting from an initial point the component will tell him how to reach the terminal point, i.e., in what direction and how far he must go.

Definition 3. The (undirected) *distance* from P_1 to P_2 is defined to be the length of P_1P_2.

It follows from Definition 2 that the distance from $P_1(x_1)$ to $P_2(x_2)$ is the absolute value of the directed distance from P_1 to P_2 (or also from P_2 to P_1). By Theorem 1, we therefore have:

Corollary 1. The (undirected) distance from $P_1(x_1)$ to $P_2(x_2)$ is $|x_2 - x_1|$ (which is equal to $|x_1 - x_2|$).

Corollary 2. If $P_1(x_1)$, $P_2(x_2)$, $P_3(x_3)$ are 3 points on the line,

$$\overrightarrow{P_1P_3} = \overrightarrow{P_1P_2} + \overrightarrow{P_2P_3}$$

(Again, this is shorthand for: the directed length of $\overrightarrow{P_1P_3}$ is the sum of the directed lengths of $\overrightarrow{P_1P_2}$ and $\overrightarrow{P_2P_3}$.)

Proof: $\qquad \overrightarrow{P_1P_3} = x_3 - x_1$

$$\overrightarrow{P_1P_2} + \overrightarrow{P_2P_3} = (x_2 - x_1) + (x_3 - x_2) = x_3 - x_1$$

Corollary 3. If $P_1(x_1)$, $P_2(x_2)$, . . . , $P_n(x_n)$ are n points on the line,

$$\overrightarrow{P_1P_n} = \overrightarrow{P_1P_2} + \overrightarrow{P_2P_3} + \cdots + \overrightarrow{P_{n-1}P_n}.$$

Proof: Induction.

Exercises

22. In each of the following, P and Q are points on the line with the coordinates given. Find the component of $\overrightarrow{PQ}$ and the distance between P and Q.

   (a) $P(0)$, $Q(3)$.   (h) $P(a - \sqrt{2})$, $Q(\sqrt{2})$.
   (b) $P(0)$, $Q(-3)$.   (i) $P(s)$, $Q(t)$.
   (c) $P(3)$, $Q(0)$.   (j) $P(s - t)$, $Q(s + t)$.
   (d) $P(\sqrt{2})$, $Q(-1)$.   (k) $P(|\,s\,|)$, $Q(0)$.
   (e) $P(1)$, $Q(\pi)$.   (l) $P(x_2)$, $Q(x_1)$.
   (f) $P(-1)$, $Q(-3)$.   (m) $P(t_5)$, $Q(t_7)$.
   (g) $P(-3)$, $Q(-2)$.

23. If $\overrightarrow{AB}$ has the component given, give the length of AB and tell whether B is in a positive or negative direction from A.

   (a) 2.   (e) $-\sqrt{2}$.
   (b) 1.   (f) $\sqrt[3]{5}$.
   (c) $-\pi$.   (g) $1 - \sqrt{2}$.
   (d) 0.   (h) $\sqrt{3} - 2$.

24. (a) Carry out the proof of Case 3 of Theorem 1.
   (b) Case 5.

25. (a) Suppose $\overrightarrow{AB}$ has component 2, $\overrightarrow{BC}$ component -3, $\overrightarrow{CD}$ component 4. What is the component of $\overrightarrow{AC}$? Of $\overrightarrow{AD}$? Of $\overrightarrow{DB}$?
   (b) Suppose in part (a) that A has the coordinate $\frac{1}{2}$. Find the coordinate of D.
   (c) If $\overrightarrow{AB} + \overrightarrow{BC} + \overrightarrow{CD} + \overrightarrow{DE} + \overrightarrow{EF} = 0$, what is the relation between A and F?

3.2 Coordinates in the Plane [2]

We now turn to the plane. For this purpose, we take any two perpendicular lines in the plane intersecting, say, at the point O (Figure 13.41). We regard each line marked with numbers as in Section 3.1, with O as the origin of both lines. (These are not the numbers we shall asso-

---

[2] In Section 3 of Chapter 11 a brief introduction to coordinates in the plane was given in Examples (c) and (d). However, we make no use of this previous discussion in our present development.

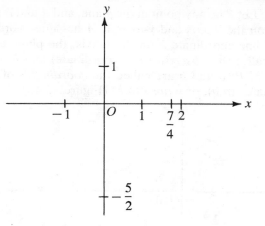

Figure 13.41

ciate with these points when regarded as part of the plane, since we shall use ordered pairs of real numbers — as will be seen.)

We shall call one of the lines (say the horizontal one as presented here) the *axis of abscissas,* and the other the *axis of ordinates;* the two lines are called the *coordinate axes.* As before, O is called the origin. We may use letters to designate each of the axes, and often one uses the *x-axis* for the axis of abscissas, and *y-axis* for axis of ordinates. But we could just as well have the u- and v-axes, or s- and t-axes, or α- and β-axes, or whatever one's pleasure or the writer's pleasure may be.

One then writes x and y at the positive sides of their respective axes.

Definition 4. Let P be any point in the plane, and l any line. If P is not on l, draw a line m through P and perpendicular to l. The point of intersection of l and m is called the *projection of P on l.* If P is on l, then we call P itself the projection of P on l (Figure 13.42).

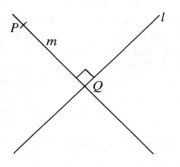

Q is the projection of P on l.
Q is also the projection on l of
any point on m.

Figure 13.42

Definition 5. Let P be any point in the plane, and A and B its projections, respectively, on the x-axis and y-axis. If A has line-coordinate a on the x-axis, and B line-coordinate b on the y-axis, the plane coordinate of P is (a,b). We call a the *abscissa* (or x-coordinate) and b the *ordinate* (or y-coordinate) of P; a and b are called the *coordinates* of P, and we say P has coordinates (a,b), or write $P(a,b)$ (Figure 13.43).

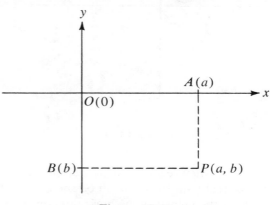

Figure 13.43

According to Definition 5, the plane coordinate of A is $(a,0)$ and of B is $(0,b)$ and of O is $(0,0)$. Accordingly, we have Figure 13.44. Thus associated with each point in the plane is a unique element of $R \times R$. Conversely, given any element (a,b) of $R \times R$, there exists a unique $A(a)$ on the x-axis and $B(b)$ on the y-axis. It is easily seen how to uniquely determine $P(a,b)$.

For convenience, we shall speak of lines parallel to the x-axis as being *horizontal* lines, and those parallel to the y-axis as *vertical* lines; also the positive x-direction as *right*, the negative *left*; and the positive y-direction *up*, the negative *down*.

Let $P_1(x_1,y_1)$ and $P_2(x_2,y_2)$ be two distinct points. We consider the significance of the numbers $x_2 - x_1$ and $y_2 - y_1$ (Figure 13.45). Let $A_1(x_1,0)$ and $A_2(x_2,0)$ be as indicated in the diagram. Then from our development in Section 3.1, $x_2 - x_1$ represents the directed distance from A_1 to A_2 on the line. This is a measure of how far P_2 is from P_1 in the x-direction. That is, knowing $x_2 - x_1$ and P_1 tells where R is. It is in a horizontal direction from P_1, to the right if $x_2 - x_1 > 0$, to the left if $x_2 - x_1 < 0$. The number of units to the right or left is $|x_2 - x_1|$. Similarly, $y_2 - y_1$ tells where S is. It is in a vertical direction from P_1, up if $y_2 - y_1$ is positive, down if $y_2 - y_1$ is negative. The number of units up or down is $|y_2 - y_1|$.

Hence knowing P_1, $x_2 - x_1$, and $y_2 - y_1$ tells what the point P_2 is. It is $x_2 - x_1$ units along the horizontal and $y_2 - y_1$ units along the vertical. And the length of RP_1 (and P_2S) is $|x_2 - x_1|$, and of RP_2 (and P_1S) is $|y_2 - y_1|$. This is valid whether P_2 is to the right or to the left of, above or below P_1.

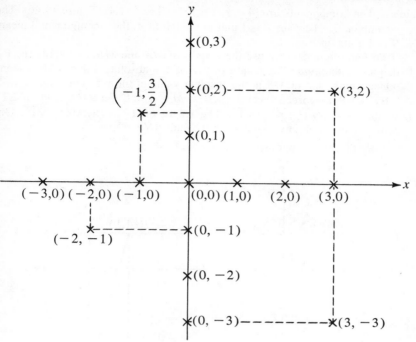

Figure 13.44

Definition 6. Let $P_1(x_1,y_1)$ and $P_2(x_2,y_2)$ be two points in the plane. Then $x_2 - x_1$ is called the *x-component* (or horizontal component), and $y_2 - y_1$ the *y-component* (or vertical component) of $\overrightarrow{P_1P_2}$. We say $\overrightarrow{P_1P_2}$ has components $[x_2 - x_1, y_2 - y_1]$.

Example 6. Suppose $A(5,-3)$, $B(4,1)$. What are the components of $\overrightarrow{AB}$? What is the length of AB?

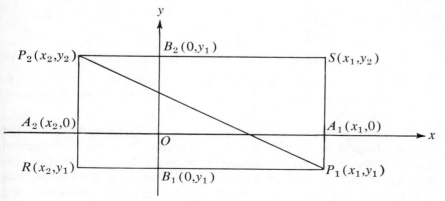

Figure 13.45

Solution: The components are [4 − 5, 1 − (−3)], i.e., [−1,4] (Figure 13.46). The x-component −1 means B is 1 unit to the left of A, the y-component 4 means B is 4 units up from A.

To find the length, we use the lengths of MA and MB, and apply the Pythagorean theorem. The length of MA is the absolute value of the x-component, or 1; that of MB is the absolute value of the y-component, or 4.

By the Pythagorean theorem, $\overline{AB^2} = \overline{MA^2} + \overline{MB^2}$ [cf. (16), Section 2.7], so that $AB = \sqrt{1^2 + 4^2} = \sqrt{17}$. The length of AB is therefore $\sqrt{17}$. One could equally well have used sides AN and BN.

Note that the components of $\overrightarrow{BA}$ are [1,−4].

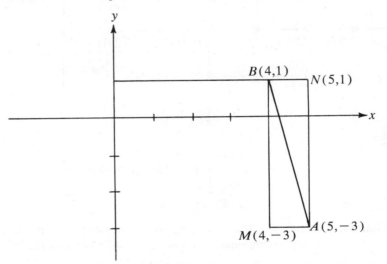

Figure 13.46

Example 7. Suppose $\overrightarrow{CD}$ has components [−2,−3], and C has coordinates (−2,1). Find D, and the length of CD.

Solution: Let D have coordinates (a,b). Then since C(−2,1), D(a,b), the components of $\overrightarrow{CD}$ are [a − (−2), b − 1] = [−2,−3]. Hence a + 2 = −2 and

$$b − 1 = −3$$

or a = −4, b = −2 and D(−4,−2). We have the diagram of Figure 13.47. As $\overrightarrow{CD}$ has horizontal component −2, DR has length 2 (= |−2|); and as $\overrightarrow{CD}$ has vertical component −3, RC has length 3 (= |−3|). By the Pythagorean theorem, CD has length $\sqrt{13}$.

Of course, where actual numbers are given, one can determine the various lengths or components by inspection and the Pythagorean theorem. But we are trying to provide methods which can lead to general theorems, and as an example of this we have the distance formula between two points. As before, the distance between two points is the length of the line segment joining them.

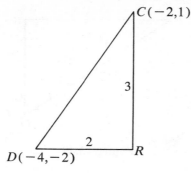

Figure 13.47

Theorem 2. Distance Formula. Let $P_1(x_1,y_1)$ and $P_2(x_2,y_2)$ be two points in the plane. Then the distance from P_1 to P_2, denoted by '$d(P_1,P_2)$' is

$$d(P_1,P_2) = \sqrt{(x_2 - x_1)^2 + (y_2 - y_1)^2}$$

Proof: We have, regardless of where the axes are, Figure 13.48. The length of P_1A is $|x_2 - x_1|$, of P_2A is $|y_2 - y_1|$. By the Pythagorean theorem,

$$d(P_1,P_2) = \sqrt{|x_2 - x_1|^2 + |y_2 - y_1|^2}$$

As $|x_2 - x_1|^2 = (x_2 - x_1)^2$, $|y_2 - y_1|^2 = (y_2 - y_1)^2$, this proves the theorem, except when $P_1 = P_2$. But in that case, $x_1 = x_2$, $y_1 = y_2$, and the formula still holds.

The Pythagorean theorem could also have been applied to triangle P_1BP_2.

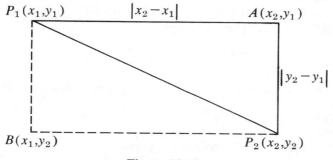

Figure 13.48

Of course, $(x_2 - x_1)^2 = (x_1 - x_2)^2$ and $(y_2 - y_1)^2 = (y_1 - y_2)^2$, so that the order of the points does not matter in computing distance.

If one knows the components $[a,b]$ of a directed line segment, one knows its length, namely $\sqrt{a^2 + b^2}$, by the distance formula, and also its direction. For example, if $\overrightarrow{PQ}$ has components $[3,-2]$, then we have

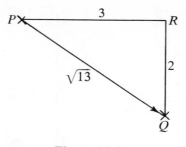

Figure 13.49

Figure 13.49. We do not know, however, the exact position of P. Once this is given, Q is determined.

   In summary, the analogue of Definition 1 for line analytic geometry is Definition 5 for plane geometry. The component of a line segment for line geometry is extended to the plane in Definition 6. A knowledge of the components of directed line segments in both cases leads one to a knowledge of their directions and lengths. We spoke of "directed lengths" and "directed distances" in Definition 2. In the plane, however, we shall not speak of the directed length of a line segment, or directed distance between two points. We may, however, speak of the directed horizontal and vertical lengths or distances, these being the components of the directed line segments. The distance between two points, as given in Definition 3, is defined similarly in the plane — as the length of the line segment connecting them. In Corollary 1 of Theorem 1 the formula for the line is given, in Theorem 2 for the plane. If in Theorem 2 one takes $y_1 = y_2$, one obtains the result in Corollary 1 of Theorem 1, $\sqrt{(x_2 - x_1)^2}$, which of course is equal to $|x_2 - x_1|$. Or, similarly, if one takes $x_1 = x_2$, one obtains $|y_2 - y_1|$ [i.e., $\sqrt{(y_2 - y_1)^2}$].

Exercises

26. Plot on a coordinate system the points having the following coordinates:
    (a) $(2,-1)$.
    (b) $(5,0)$.
    (c) $(5,1)$.
    (d) Three points having coordinates of the form $(a,-2)$.
    (e) Three points having coordinates of the form $(1,b)$.
    (f) $(-3,-4), (-3,-1)$, and $(-3,2)$.
    (g) $(0,0), (-3,0)$, and $(0,3)$.
27. In each of the following, find the components of $\overrightarrow{AB}$, and $d(A,B)$:
    (a) $A(2,1), B(-1,0)$.   (d) $A(a,0), B(0,-b)$.
    (b) $A(-3,0), B(1,-5)$.   (e) $A(7,-6), B(4,1)$.
    (c) $A(x_2,y_2), B(x_1,y_1)$.   (f) $A(-3,-4), B(x_1,0)$.

28. In each of the following, give two examples of directed line segments (i.e., specify the points) having the given components. Find their lengths. Draw a diagram.
    (a) $[3,-1]$.   (d) $[-2,-3]$.
    (b) $[2,0]$.   (e) $[4,-3]$.
    (c) $[0,-3]$.

29. Let $A(-1,4)$, $B(3,8)$, and $C(-4,11)$ be the vertices of triangle ABC. Prove that the triangle is isosceles.

30. Suppose $\overrightarrow{AB}$ is a directed line segment, and $A(1,-2)$. If $\overrightarrow{AB}$ has components as given in each of the parts of Exercise 28, find B.

31. Suppose $\overrightarrow{BA}$ is a directed line segment, and $A(1,-2)$. If $\overrightarrow{BA}$ has components as given in each of the parts of Exercise 28, find B.

32. Prove that the points (having coordinates) $(3,1)$, $(1,-3)$, and $(7,-1)$ form the vertices of a right triangle [cf. (16) of Section 2.7].

33. In each of the following, tell whether the three given points lie on a line. Justify your answer [cf. the last sentence of (14), Section 2.7].
    (a) $(1,2)$, $(\frac{1}{3},1)$, $(3,5)$.   (c) $(-2,-4)$, $(1,0)$, $(4,3)$.
    (b) $(-4,1)$, $(0,-3)$, $(2,3)$.   (d) $(-1,2)$, $(3,0)$, $(5,-1)$.

4. Point of Division and Midpoint Formulas

We next consider the following problem. Suppose P_1 and P_2 are two distinct points in the plane whose coordinates are known, and suppose one wishes to find a point Q on the segment P_1P_2 such that Q divides the segment P_1P_2 in a specified manner. For example, one may wish to find Q such that P_1Q and QP_2 are in the ratio 3 to 2, or 2 to 3, or 5 to 1, or more generally in the ratio r_1 to r_2 (Figure 13.50).

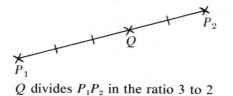

Q divides P_1P_2 in the ratio 3 to 2

Figure 13.50

Theorem 3. Let $P_1(x_1,y_1)$ and $P_2(x_2,y_2)$ be two distinct points in the plane, and suppose $Q(x_0,y_0)$ is a point of the line segment P_1P_2 such that Q divides P_1P_2 in the ratio r_1 to r_2; i.e., $\dfrac{P_1Q}{QP_2} = \dfrac{r_1}{r_2}$. Then:

(1) $x_0 = \dfrac{r_1x_2 + r_2x_1}{r_1 + r_2}$

(2) $y_0 = \dfrac{r_1y_2 + r_2y_1}{r_1 + r_2}$

Proof: (a) Suppose the segment P_1P_2 is parallel to the x-axis, so that $y_1 = y_2$. Then certainly $y_0 = y_1 = y_2$, and this checks with (2), since then

$$\frac{r_1y_2 + r_2y_1}{r_1 + r_2} = \frac{(r_1 + r_2)y_1}{r_1 + r_2} = y_1$$

$$\overline{\quad\underset{P_1(x_1,y_1)}{+}\qquad\quad\underset{Q(x_0,y_1)}{+}\qquad\qquad\qquad\qquad\qquad\underset{P_2(x_2,y_1)}{+}\quad}$$

The component of $\overrightarrow{P_1Q}$ is $x_0 - x_1$ and of $\overrightarrow{QP_2}$ is $x_2 - x_0$. Either $x_0 - x_1$ and $x_2 - x_0$ are both positive (P_2 to the right of P_1) or both negative (P_2 to the left of P_1). In either case $\dfrac{x_0 - x_1}{x_2 - x_0}$ is positive. Hence

$$\frac{x_0 - x_1}{x_2 - x_0} = \frac{|x_0 - x_1|}{|x_2 - x_0|} = \frac{P_1Q}{QP_2} = \frac{r_1}{r_2}$$

$$\frac{x_0 - x_1}{x_2 - x_0} = \frac{r_1}{r_2}$$

$$r_2x_0 - r_2x_1 = r_1x_2 - r_1x_0$$

$$(r_1 + r_2)x_0 = r_1x_2 + r_2x_1$$

$$x_0 = \frac{r_1x_2 + r_2x_1}{r_1 + r_2}$$

(b) If P_1P_2 is parallel to the y-axis, the argument is similar (cf. Exercise 34b).

(c) Hence suppose P_1P_2 is neither horizontal nor vertical (Figure 13.51).

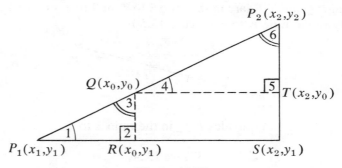

Figure 13.51

(3) $\dfrac{P_1R}{RS} = \dfrac{x_0 - x_1}{x_2 - x_0}$, as proved in part (a).

(4) $\dfrac{ST}{TP_2} = \dfrac{y_0 - y_1}{y_2 - y_0}$, as one would prove in part (b).

(5) $\dfrac{RQ}{TP_2} = \dfrac{y_0 - y_1}{y_2 - y_0}$, since $RQ = ST$.

Now triangles P_1RQ and QTP_2 are similar. One can see this, for example, by observing that $\angle 1$ and $\angle 4$ are corresponding angles (parallel lines P_1R and QT, transversal P_1P_2), and hence are equal [cf. (13) and (18), Section 2.7]. And $\angle 2$ and $\angle 5$ are right angles, and hence equal.

So the corresponding sides are in proportion:

(6) $$\frac{P_1R}{QT} = \frac{RQ}{TP_2} = \frac{P_1Q}{QP_2}$$

Since $QT = RS$ and $RQ = ST$, we obtain

(7) $$\frac{P_1R}{RS} = \frac{ST}{TP_2} = \frac{P_1Q}{QP_2}$$

But $\dfrac{P_1Q}{QP_2} = \dfrac{r_1}{r_2}$ by hypothesis.

So from (7), $\dfrac{P_1R}{RS} = \dfrac{r_1}{r_2}$ and $\dfrac{ST}{TP_2} = \dfrac{r_1}{r_2}$, or by (3) and (4),

$$\frac{x_0 - x_1}{x_2 - x_0} = \frac{r_1}{r_2}$$

$$\frac{y_0 - y_1}{y_2 - y_0} = \frac{r_1}{r_2}$$

Solving these for x_0 and y_0 yields (1) and (2).

Corollary (Midpoint Formula). If $Q(x_0, y_0)$ is the midpoint of $P_1(x_1, y_1)$ and $P_2(x_2, y_2)$, then

$$x_0 = \frac{x_1 + x_2}{2}$$

$$y_0 = \frac{y_1 + y_2}{2}$$

Proof: Take $r_1 = r_2 = r$ in Theorem 3.

$$x_0 = \frac{rx_2 + rx_1}{r + r} = \frac{r(x_1 + x_2)}{2r} = \frac{x_1 + x_2}{2}$$

Similarly, $y_0 = \dfrac{y_1 + y_2}{2}$.

Example 8. Let $A(1,-2)$, $B(3,1)$, and $C(5,-3)$ be the vertices of a triangle. Show that the medians intersect in a point M, where AM, BM, CM are each two-thirds of the lengths of the medians, respectively, of which they are part (Figure 13.52).

Solution: Let D be the midpoint of BC. By the midpoint formula, D has coordinates $\left(\dfrac{5 + 3}{2}, \dfrac{-3 + 1}{2}\right)$ or $(4,-1)$. We next determine a point M on AD such

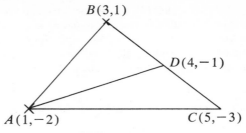

Figure 13.52

that $\dfrac{AM}{AD} = \dfrac{2}{3}$, which is the same as saying AM is in the ratio 2 to 1 to MD; i.e.,

$\dfrac{AM}{MD} = \dfrac{2}{1}$. By the point-of-division formula, M has coordinates

$$\left(\frac{2(4) + 1(1)}{2 + 1}, \frac{2(-1) + 1(-2)}{2 + 1}\right) \text{ or } \left(3, -\frac{4}{3}\right).$$

Now if we can show that the point on the median from B to AC which is $\frac{2}{3}$ of the way to the opposite side is also $(3, -\frac{4}{3})$, and again for the median from C, this will prove $(3, -\frac{4}{3})$ is on each of the medians and at the same time divides each in the ratio 2 to 1. We leave the completion of this example to Exercise 34.

One might ask whether this result holds for any triangle. It does, and its proof in Euclidean geometry is tricky. We shall see that the methods of analytic geometry provide a direct method of proof.

Exercises

34. (a) Complete the example of this section.
(b) Complete part (b) of the proof of Theorem 3.

35. Let $A(2,3)$, $B(-1,2)$. Find the point P on the segment AB such that:

(a) $\dfrac{AP}{PB} = 3$. (d) $\dfrac{BP}{AP} = \dfrac{2}{5}$.

(b) $\dfrac{AP}{PB} = \dfrac{4}{3}$. (e) $\dfrac{BP}{AB} = \dfrac{3}{4}$.

(c) $\dfrac{AP}{AB} = \dfrac{1}{3}$. (f) P is the midpoint of AB.

36. Let $A(-2,1)$, $B(0,4)$, $C(5,2)$, $D(1,-3)$ be the vertices of a quadrilateral. Prove that the lines joining the midpoints of the opposite sides bisect each other.

37. Suppose M is the midpoint of the segment AB, where $A(-1,-3)$ and $M(3,3)$. Find B.

38. Suppose C is a point on the y-axis which is equidistant from the points $(2,1)$ and $(-1,-4)$. Find C. [*Hint:* C has coordinates of form $(0,c)$. Find c.]

5. Direction of a Straight Line

5.1 *Direction Numbers of a Line*

Definition 7. Let l be any line in the plane, and A and B any two distinct points on l. Then AB is called a line segment of l, and $\overrightarrow{AB}$ a directed line segment of l. The components $[a,b]$ of any directed line segment of l are called *a set of direction numbers* of l (Figure 13.53).

$\overrightarrow{AB}, \overrightarrow{BC}, \overrightarrow{DA}, \overrightarrow{AD}$, etc., are examples of directed line segments of l.

Thus if $A(x_1,y_1)$ and $B(x_2,y_2)$ are two points of l, a set of direction numbers of l is $[x_2 - x_1, \; y_2 - y_1]$ arising from the directed line segment $\overrightarrow{AB}$, or also $[x_1 - x_2, y_1 - y_2]$ arising from $\overrightarrow{BA}$.

Different sets of points A, B on l may lead to different sets of direction numbers of l, but we now show their ratio remains unchanged.

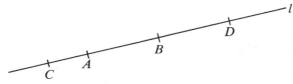

Figure 13.53

Theorem 4. Let l be any *nonvertical* line in the plane. Then if $P_1(x_1,y_1)$ and $P_2(x_2,y_2)$ are two distinct points on l, $\dfrac{y_2 - y_1}{x_2 - x_1}$ is independent of the two points selected. That is, if $A(a_1,b_1)$ and $B(a_2,b_2)$ are any two distinct points on l,

$$\frac{y_2 - y_1}{x_2 - x_1} = \frac{b_2 - b_1}{a_2 - a_1}$$

If l is a vertical line, $\dfrac{y_2 - y_1}{x_2 - x_1}$ is undefined, no matter which two points P_1 and P_2 on l are selected.

Proof: (a) If l is a horizontal line, $y_2 = y_1$ and $x_1 \neq x_2$. Hence $\dfrac{y_2 - y_1}{x_2 - x_1} = 0$. It is clear that one obtains 0 for any two distinct points selected, and the result holds in this case.

   (b) If l is a vertical line, $x_2 = x_1$ and one obtains $\dfrac{y_2 - y_1}{x_2 - x_1} = \dfrac{y_2 - y_1}{0}$. This is undefined.

   (c) We now assume l is neither horizontal nor vertical (Figure 13.54).

We choose any two distinct points $A(a_1,b_1)$, $B(a_2,b_2)$ on l. As $\dfrac{b_2 - b_1}{a_2 - a_1} =$

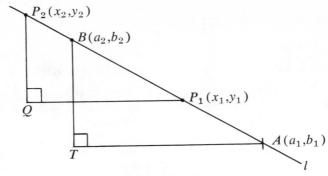

Figure 13.54

$\dfrac{b_1 - b_2}{a_1 - a_2}$, we may assume A and B are so chosen that $b_2 - b_1$ is positive if $y_2 - y_1$ is positive, and otherwise negative.

Triangles P_1QP_2 and ATB are similar, so that $\dfrac{QP_2}{TB} = \dfrac{QP_1}{TA}$, or $\dfrac{QP_2}{QP_1} = \dfrac{TB}{TA}$;

i.e., $\dfrac{|\,y_2 - y_1\,|}{|\,x_2 - x_1\,|} = \dfrac{|\,b_2 - b_1\,|}{|\,a_2 - a_1\,|}$.

If $y_2 - y_1$ and $b_2 - b_1$ are positive, then one must go *up* from P_1 to P_2 and from A to B. Hence one must either go to the left in both cases ($x_2 - x_1$ and $a_2 - a_1$ negative), or to the right ($x_2 - x_1$ and $a_2 - a_1$ positive). It follows that

$\dfrac{y_2 - y_1}{x_2 - x_1} = \dfrac{b_2 - b_1}{a_2 - a_1}$, and similarly if $y_2 - y_1$ and $b_2 - b_1$ are both negative.

5.2   Slope of a Line. Parallel Lines

Definition 8. Let l be any nonvertical line in the plane. Then the number of Theorem 3, i.e., $\dfrac{y_2 - y_1}{x_2 - x_1}$, where $P_1(x_1,y_1)$ and $P_2(x_2,y_2)$ are any two distinct points of l, is called the *slope* of l.

The slope of a vertical line is undefined. (Some say the slope of a vertical line is infinite. We shall soon see why.)

Example 9. In Figure 13.55, the slope of the line is $\frac{2}{3}$, as $y_2 - y_1 = 4$ and $x_2 - x_1 = 6$ (or $y_1 - y_2 = -4$ and $x_1 - x_2 = -6$).

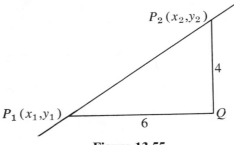

Figure 13.55

Example 10. In Figure 13.56, $b_2 - b_1 = -4$ and $a_2 - a_1 = -6$, so that the slope of the line is $-\frac{2}{3}$.

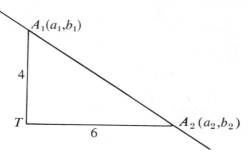

Figure 13.56

Example 11. The slope of a horizontal line is 0; conversely, if the slope of a line is 0, it is horizontal.

The same connection can be made between vertical lines and undefined slopes by Definition 8.

The slope of a line is a measure of its direction in the following sense:

Theorem 5. Let l_1 and l_2 be any two lines in the plane. Then l_1 and l_2 are parallel or coincident if and only if their slopes are equal, or both undefined.

Proof: If l_1 and l_2 are horizontal, their slopes are 0; and conversely. If l_1 and l_2 are vertical, their slopes are undefined; and conversely. In both these cases then, the result holds.

Assume l_1 and l_2 are neither horizontal nor vertical.
(a) Suppose $l_1 \parallel l_2$ or $l_1 = l_2$ (Figure 13.57). Let $A(a,b)$ and $B(c,d)$ be any two distinct points on l_1 with $d > b$. Also choose $R(m,n)$ and $S(u,v)$ on l_2 with $v > n$. The argument using similar triangles in the proof of Theorem 4 carries over here to prove that $\dfrac{v - n}{u - m} = \dfrac{d - b}{c - a}$, and the slopes are equal.

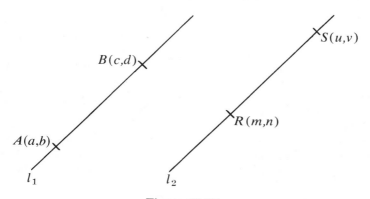

Figure 13.57

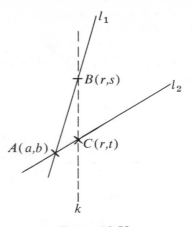

Figure 13.58

(b) Suppose the slopes of l_1 and l_2 are equal.

If l_1 and l_2 are neither parallel nor coincide, they intersect in a single point, say $A(a,b)$ (Figure 13.58). Let k be any vertical line not passing through A. It must intersect l_1 and l_2 in points B and C, respectively, distinct from A. Now B and C have the same x-coordinate, say r, so that $B(r,s)$ and $C(r,t)$. Here $s \neq t$, since otherwise we would have $B = C$ and $l_1 = l_2$.

Compute the slope of l_1 using A and B: $\dfrac{s-b}{r-a}$.

Compute the slope of l_2 using A and C: $\dfrac{t-b}{r-a}$.

By hypothesis, $\dfrac{s-b}{r-a} = \dfrac{t-b}{r-a}$, so that $s = t$. This contradicts the fact that $s \neq t$. Hence $l_1 \parallel l_2$ or $l_1 = l_2$.

Take P to be any point in the plane, A one unit to the left and B one unit to the right. Draw verticals through A and B; call them a and b, respectively (Figure 13.59). If a line through P is neither vertical nor horizontal, it intersects one of the lines a and b above the segment AB. If it intersects b at the point R, the slope of the line is $\dfrac{BR}{1}$, or the length of BR. If it intersects a in Q, the slope of the line is $\dfrac{AQ}{-1}$, or the negative of the length of AQ.

The slope of a horizontal line is 0. As it rotates through angles between $0°$ and $90°$, the length BR becomes larger and larger, and hence so do the slopes of the lines. At $90°$, the slope is undefined. Between $90°$ and $180°$, the length AQ ranges from very large to smaller numbers, and finally at $180°$ is 0. The slopes therefore range through the negatives of these numbers.

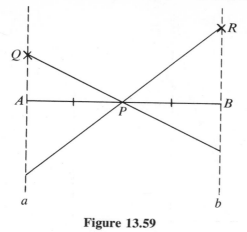

Figure 13.59

If one were to graph the slopes m of lines against the angles θ they make with the horizontal $(0 \leq \theta \leq 180)$, one would obtain something like Figure 13.60 (not using the same scale on both axes).

Example 12. Show that $(1,2)$, $(\frac{1}{3},1)$, and $(3,5)$ lie on the same straight line.
Solution: One method was suggested in Exercise 33. Another is to find the slopes of the lines passing through $(1,2)$, $(\frac{1}{3},1)$, and through $(1,2)$ and $(3,5)$, and show that they are equal. One then concludes that the lines are parallel or coincide. But since they have the point $(1,2)$ in common, they must coincide.

The line through $(1,2)$, $\left(\frac{1}{3},1\right)$ has slope $\dfrac{1-2}{(1/3)-1} = \dfrac{3}{2}$.

The line through $(1,2)$ and $(3,5)$ has slope $\dfrac{5-2}{3-1} = \dfrac{3}{2}$.

Example 13. Let $A(-4,-2)$, $B(-1,3)$, $C(3,-1)$, and $D(2,-5)$ be the vertices of a quadrilateral. Show that the midpoints of the sides are vertices of a parallelogram.

Solution (Figure 13.61): The midpoint E of AB is $\left(\dfrac{-4+(-1)}{2}, \dfrac{-2+3}{2}\right)$ or $(-\frac{5}{2},\frac{1}{2})$. Similarly one computes the midpoints $F(1,1)$ of BC, $G(\frac{5}{2},-3)$ of CD, and $H(-1,-\frac{7}{2})$ of AD.

To show $EF \parallel HG$, we compute the slopes of the lines through E and F, and through H and G, respectively.

$$EF:\ \text{slope}\ \frac{1-\frac{1}{2}}{1-(-\frac{5}{2})}\ \text{or}\ \frac{1}{7}$$

$$HG:\ \text{slope}\ \frac{-3-(-\frac{7}{2})}{\frac{5}{2}-(-1)}\ \text{or}\ \frac{1}{7}$$

Hence $EF \parallel HG$.

Similarly the lines through E and H, and F and G, both have slope $-\frac{8}{3}$. Hence $EH \parallel FG$.

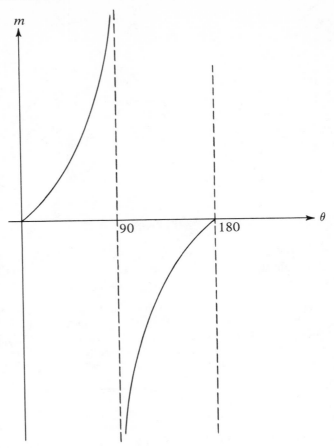

Figure 13.60

As the opposite sides of $EFGH$ are parallel, this quadrilateral is a parallelogram.

Example 14. Suppose a line l passes through $A(-2,3)$ and has slope 2. Find a set of direction numbers. Draw the line on a coordinate system.

Solution: Choose any point $P(a,b)$ such that $\dfrac{b-3}{a-(-2)} = 2$. Then P lies on the given line. For the slope of the line through A and P is 2 by the choice of P, and since A is on this line and also is on l, by Theorem 5, these lines coincide.

Thus one can choose $b-3 = 2$ and $a+2 = 1$, or $b-3 = 4$ and $a+2 = 2$, or $b-3 = 2k$ and $a+2 = k$ for any real number $k \neq 0$, as in all these cases $\dfrac{b-3}{a+2} = 2$, and the point $P(a,b)$ is on the line l.

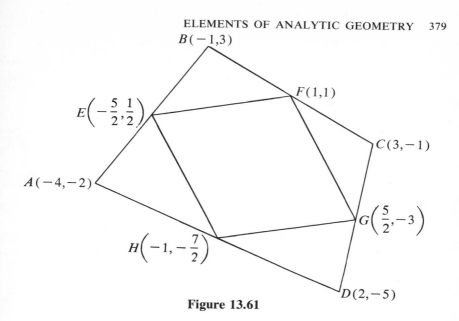

$B(-1,3)$

$F(1,1)$

$E\left(-\dfrac{5}{2},\dfrac{1}{2}\right)$

$C(3,-1)$

$A(-4,-2)$

$G\left(\dfrac{5}{2},-3\right)$

$H\left(-1,-\dfrac{7}{2}\right)$

$D(2,-5)$

Figure 13.61

All·possible direction numbers, then, are $[k,2k]$, where $k \neq 0$. For example, $[1,2]$, $[\tfrac{3}{2},3]$, $[-1,-2]$ are obtained for $k = 1, \tfrac{3}{2}, -1$, respectively.

To draw the line, one can determine $P(a,b)$ and use the two points A and P. Or one can use the point $A(-2,3)$ and any set of direction numbers, say $[-1,-2]$. This means a second point is obtained by going 1 unit to the left and 2 units down (Figure 13.62). Or using $[\tfrac{3}{2},3]$, one could go to the right $\tfrac{3}{2}$, and up 3 units.

Example 15. A line with slope $-\tfrac{3}{2}$ yields direction numbers of the form $[2k,-3k]$. It makes no difference which component is taken with a minus sign, as k can take any nonzero real number—positive or negative.

Thus a line with slope $-\tfrac{3}{2}$ means that beginning at a point, one obtains a second point by going 2 to the right and 3 down (direction numbers $[2,-3]$), or another by going 4 to the right and 6 down ($[4,-6]$), or another by going 2 to the left and 3 up ($[-2,3]$), etc., (Figure 13.63). The slope therefore gives the direction of the line. That is, a line of slope $-\tfrac{3}{2}$ is parallel to (or coincident with) the one we have drawn. Given a point on the line would then uniquely determine the line.

Any set of direction numbers of a line also gives its direction. In fact, a knowledge of a set of direction numbers is equivalent to a knowledge of the slope of the line. In a sense, therefore, it seems unnecessary to introduce both. However, in one's study of analytic geometry in 3-space or higher-dimensional space, he will find direction numbers used to determine direction, and there is no concept of slope. He will see that if a line in 3-space has a set of direction numbers $[a,b,c]$, then any line having a set of direction numbers $[ka,kb,kc]$, and only such lines, are parallel to or coincident with the given line.

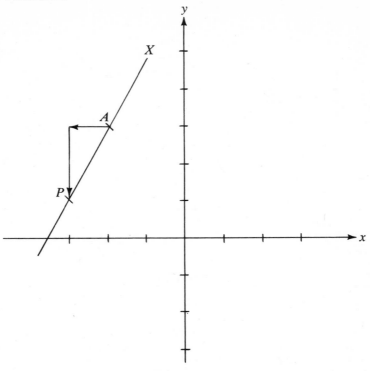

Figure 13.62

5.3   Perpendicular Lines

Horizontal and vertical lines are, of course, perpendicular to each other. The one has slope 0, the other has "no slope." We ask for the relation between the slopes of perpendicular lines in all other cases.

Theorem 6. Suppose l_1 and l_2 are lines having slopes m_1 and m_2, respectively, and suppose they are neither horizontal nor vertical lines. Then $l_1 \perp l_2$ if and only if $m_1 m_2 = -1$.

Proof: As parallel lines have the same slope, we may prove this result for lines l_1 and l_2 passing through the origin (Figure 13.64).
  (a) Suppose $l_1 \perp l_2$. Choose any point $P_1(x_1, y_1)$ distinct from O on l_1, and $P_2(x_2, y_2)$ distinct from O on l_2. Then

$$m_1 = \frac{y_1 - 0}{x_1 - 0} = \frac{y_1}{x_1}$$

$$m_2 = \frac{y_2}{x_2}$$

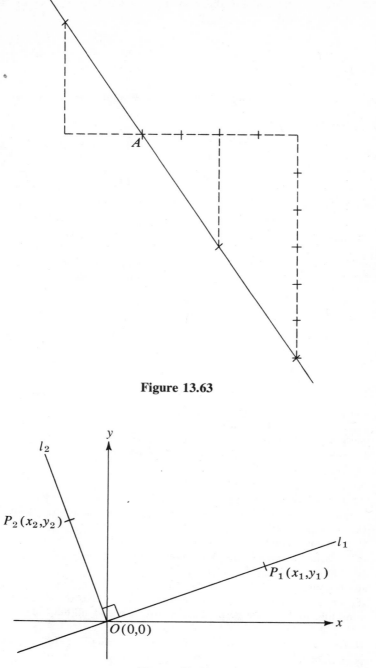

Figure 13.63

Figure 13.64

By the Pythagorean theorem, $\overline{P_1P_2}^2 = \overline{OP_1}^2 + \overline{OP_2}^2$, or by the distance formula,

$$(x_2 - x_1)^2 + (y_2 - y_1)^2 = [(x_1 - 0)^2 + (y_1 - 0)^2] + [(x_2 - 0)^2 + (y_2 - 0)^2]$$
$$x_2{}^2 - 2x_1x_2 + x_1{}^2 + y_2{}^2 - 2y_1y_2 + y_1{}^2 = x_1{}^2 + y_1{}^2 + x_2{}^2 + y_2{}^2$$
$$x_1x_2 + y_1y_2 = 0$$

As both $x_1 \neq 0$ and $x_2 \neq 0$, we may multiply both sides by $\dfrac{1}{x_1x_2}$ to obtain

$$1 + \frac{y_1}{x_1}\frac{y_2}{x_2} = 0$$

or

$$m_1\,m_2 = -1$$

(b) Suppose l_1 and l_2 intersect at the origin, and have slopes m_1 and m_2, respectively, with $m_1m_2 = -1$. We could try to work backward in (a), and show $\overline{P_1P_2}^2 = \overline{OP_1}^2 + \overline{OP_2}^2$. Instead, however, we reason as follows:

Suppose l_2 is not perpendicular to l_1. Then draw l_3 perpendicular to l_1 at O. Say l_3 has slope m_3. By part (a), $m_1m_3 = -1$. But $m_1m_2 = -1$, by hypothesis. As $m_1 \neq 0$ (since l_1 is not horizontal), we obtain

$$m_2 = m_3 = -\frac{1}{m_1}$$

But then, since l_2 and l_3 have O in common, by Theorem 5 we see that l_2 and l_3 coincide. Contradiction. Hence $l_2 \perp l_1$.

Exercises

39. Let l be the line passing through $(2,-1)$ and $(1,5)$.
  (a) Find a set of direction numbers of l.
  (b) Find two other sets of direction numbers of l.
  (c) What is the form of all direction numbers of l?
  (d) Find the slope of l.
  (e) Determine two other points on l.
  (f) Draw l on a coordinate system.
40. Answer the same questions as in Exercise 39 for the following lines:
  (a) Passing through $(0,-1)$ and $(-2,3)$.
  (b) Passing through $(-2,3)$ and having slope -3.
  (c) Passing through $(-2,3)$ and having slope $\frac{5}{3}$.
  (d) Passing through $(1,3)$ and $(1,-5)$.
  (e) Passing through $(7,-2)$ and $(-100,-2)$.
  (f) Passing through $(-2,3)$ and perpendicular to lines of slope $-\frac{3}{2}$.
41. Find the slopes of the perpendicular bisectors and altitudes of triangle ABC, where $A(1,-3)$, $B(3,7)$, and $C(-2,-10)$.
42. In Exercise 32, you proved that $(3,1)$, $(1,-3)$, and $(7,-1)$ formed the vertices of a right triangle by using the Pythagorean theorem. Give an alternative proof, using Theorem 6.

43. Let $O(0,0)$, $A(a,0)$, $B(a,a)$, and $C(0,a)$ be the vertices of a square, where $a \neq 0$. Prove that the diagonals bisect each other at right angles.

44. Let $O(0,0)$, $A(a,0)$, $B(b,c)$, and $C(d,e)$ be the vertices of a quadrilateral. Prove that the quadrilateral joining their midpoints is a parallelogram.

6. Applications to Euclidean Geometry

Exercise 43 suggests the idea that one may be able to prove *analytically* that the diagonals of a square bisect each other at right angles. Indeed, suppose one is given any square in the plane, say having a side of length a (Figure 13.65). One can then choose the axes as one wishes: for example,

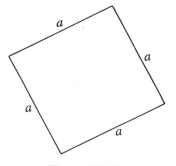

Figure 13.65

one of the axes along one side, and another along an adjacent side. If one moves around appropriately, or else moves the page, the picture is viewed as in Figure 13.66. (Alternatively, one can think of the axes as fixed, moving the square "rigidly" to the position indicated.)

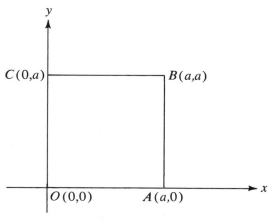

Figure 13.66

Thus proving this result with the axes selected as above proves the result for all squares.

The proof is now quite direct. The midpoint of OB is $\left(\frac{a}{2}, \frac{a}{2}\right)$, and so is the midpoint of AC — by the midpoint formula. Hence the diagonals bisect each other.

The slope of OB is $\frac{a-0}{a-0}$, or 1; the slope of AC is $\frac{0-a}{a-0}$, or -1. The product of these slopes is -1, and by Theorem 6, $OB \perp AC$. Q.E.D.

Similarly, Exercise 44 refers to the general theorem that the midpoints of the sides of any quadrilateral form the vertices of a parallelogram. We may choose the x-axis so that one vertex of the quadrilateral is at $O(0,0)$, and another on the x-axis in the positive direction, say, from O. We may choose the positive direction of the y-axis (this is not essential), so that the opposite side of the quadrilateral is above the x-axis.

Finally, as we know we are going to take midpoints, we use $(2a,0)$ for the coordinates of A, and $B(2b,2c)$, $C(2d,2e)$. This is no restriction. The midpoints are indicated D, E, F, and G in Figure 13.67.

The slope of DG is $\frac{e}{d-a}$, of EF is $\frac{e}{d-a}$ if $d-a \neq 0$. Otherwise $d = a$, and DG is vertical, as is EF. Thus $DG \parallel EF$. Similarly, $GF \parallel DE$.

A remark is in order here. According to the way we have labeled our coordinates, there is no reason why our diagram could not have looked as shown in Figure 13.68. In this situation some of the midpoints may coincide, or three of them might lie on a line, or both. In the cases where GF, FE, ED, and DG represent four distinct sides, our argument proves the result for this diagram.

We return to the example of Section 4. The general theorem states that

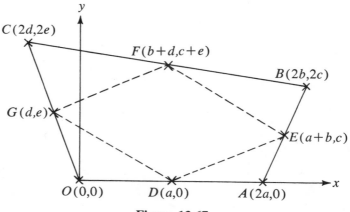

Figure 13.67

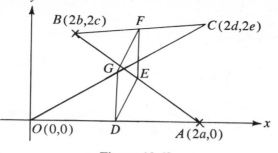

Figure 13.68

the medians of any triangle intersect at a point dividing each median in the ratio 2 to 1, the point being further from each vertex than from the midpoint of the opposite side.

Again we can take one of the vertices to be at O, but we shall give an alternative placement of the axes (Figure 13.69).

The idea is to make the algebra as painless as possible. We know we are going to deal with midpoints. So we choose the y-axis to be the perpendicular bisector of one of the sides. Also we use coordinates $A(-2a,0)$, $B(2a,0)$, and $C(2b,2c)$, to avoid fractions. The midpoint of AC is $(b - a,c)$, of AB is $(0,0)$, and of BC is $(b + a,c)$.

By the point of division formula, the coordinates of the point dividing the median AE in the ratio 2 to 1 are

$$\left(\frac{2(b + a) + 1(-2a)}{2 + 1}, \frac{2c + 1(0)}{2 + 1}\right) \quad \text{or} \quad \left(\frac{2b}{3}, \frac{2c}{3}\right)$$

Similarly, the coordinates of the point dividing the median BD in the ratio 2 to 1 are

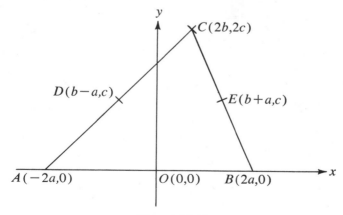

Figure 13.69

$$\left(\frac{2(b-a)+1(2a)}{2+1}, \frac{2(c)+1(0)}{2+1}\right) \qquad \text{or} \qquad \left(\frac{2b}{3}, \frac{2c}{3}\right)$$

Finally, for the median CO we have

$$\left(\frac{2(0)+1(2b)}{2+1}, \frac{2(0)+1(2c)}{2+1}\right) \qquad \text{or} \qquad \left(\frac{2b}{3}, \frac{2c}{3}\right)$$

This proves the theorem.

As a final example, we prove the theorem that a quadrilateral is a parallelogram if and only if its opposite sides are equal.

Proof: (a) Assume that the quadrilateral is a parallelogram. We choose the coordinates (i.e., coordinate axes) as indicated in Figure 13.70. In assigning the same y-coordinate to C and B, we have used the fact that $CB \parallel OA$. But we have not yet made use of the fact that $OC \parallel AB$. This means that the slope $\frac{c-0}{b-0}$ of OC is equal to the slope $\frac{c-0}{d-a}$ of AB, or $\frac{c}{b} = \frac{c}{d-a}$ (unless $b=0$ or $d-a=0$). This means that $b = d - a$. If $b = 0$, then $d = a$ and $d - a = b$ holds again. Thus $d = a + b$ in any case. [Hence whenever using the above coordinate system in working with any parallelogram, one can use (b,c) and $(a+b,c)$ as the coordinates of C and B.]

Now by the distance formula,

$$\begin{aligned}
OC &= \sqrt{(b-0)^2 + (c-0)^2} \\
&= \sqrt{b^2 + c^2} \\
AB &= \sqrt{(a+b-a)^2 + (c-0)^2} \\
&= \sqrt{b^2 + c^2} \\
OA &= \sqrt{a^2} = a \\
CB &= \sqrt{a^2} = a
\end{aligned}$$

Hence $OC = AB$ and $OA = CB$.

(b) Conversely, suppose a quadrilateral has opposite sides equal (Figure 13.71). $OC = AB$ means $d^2 + e^2 = (a-b)^2 + c^2 = a^2 - 2ab + b^2 + c^2$. $OA = CB$ means $a^2 = (b-d)^2 + (c-e)^2 = b^2 - 2bd + d^2 + c^2 - 2ce + e^2$.

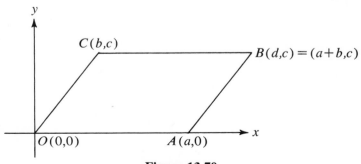

Figure 13.70

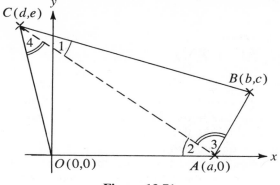

Figure 13.71

At this point, we are stuck. The trouble is again that in our diagram, according to the way the coordinates are labeled, we may have AB and OC intersecting, and we would not have a parallelogram.

For completeness, then, we give the usual *synthetic* proof, as opposed to an *analytic* one, namely, draw the diagonal AC. Since $OC = AB$ and $OA = CB$, and CA is a common side, triangles COA and ABC are congruent ($s.s.s. = s.s.s.$). Hence $\angle 1 = \angle 2$, $\angle 3 = \angle 4$. The first equality yields $CB \parallel OA$, the second, $OC \parallel AB$, by (13) of Section 2.7.

Exercises

45. Prove (analytically) that the lines joining the midpoints of the opposite sides of a quadrilateral bisect each other.

46. Prove that the diagonals of a rhombus are perpendicular.

47. Prove that in any right triangle, the midpoint of the hypotenuse is equidistant from the vertices.

48. Prove: If two medians of a triangle are equal, then the triangle is isosceles.

49. Show that if the diagonals of a parallelogram are equal, then the parallelogram is a rectangle.

50. Prove that if the diagonals of a parallelogram are perpendicular, then the parallelogram is a rhombus.

chapter xiv

STRAIGHT LINE AND CIRCLE

In this chapter we derive the equations which are represented by the straight lines and circles in the plane. The class of equations $ax + by + c = 0$ are represented by the lines, and every line arises in this way. Every circle represents an equation of the type $ax^2 + ay^2 + dx + ey + f = 0$, but not all such equations are obtained. This analysis is given in full. We show how further geometrical theorems can be proved analytically. And the formula giving the distance from a point to a line is proved. This chapter essentially concludes our development of analytic geometry, because this subject has now become a traditional part of introductory courses in the calculus.

We also consider the solution of simultaneous equations in this chapter. Although this topic could have been treated in Part II (and more generally in Part I) by purely algebraic methods, an additional view of the subject is provided with the presentation of the corresponding geometric situation.

1. Introduction

1.1 Two Important Problems of Analytic Geometry

We have seen in previous chapters that given a relation or function from R to R, one can trace its graph in the plane. Indeed this indicates one of the important problems of analytic geometry: Given a relation in two real variables x and y (i.e., a relation xSy from R to R), what does its graph look like in the plane? For example, if xSy means $x^2y^3 + 2y^2x - 3x^2 + 2 = 0$, what does the set $\{(x,y) \in R \times R / x^2y^3 + 2y^2x - 3x^2 + 2 = 0\}$ look like when plotted in the plane? In Chapter 12 we worked with relations (functions) of the form $y = a_nx^n + \cdots + a_1x + a_0$, i.e., polynomial functions in x. Already, difficulty was seen. And if one considers polynomial relations in x and y as in the previous example, the problem is further complicated.

> Here we have a polynomial relation $x^2y^3 + 2y^2x - 3x^2 + 2 = 0$. The left side of this equation is said to be a polynomial in x and y of degree 5. To determine the degree, one considers the degree of each term first. The degree of x^2y^3 is 5 because the variables x and y appear five times together: $xxyyy$. Thus the degree of a term is the sum of the powers of

the variables appearing, and the degree of the polynomial is the highest degree of all terms appearing with nonzero co-efficient.

One can approach this problem by beginning with first-degree poly-nomial relations in x and y, i.e., relations of the form

(1) $ax + by + c = 0$ $(a,b,c \in R)$

where not both a and b are zero, and study their graphs. If successful, one can then proceed to second-degree polynomial relations:

(2) $ax^2 + bxy + cy^2 + dx + ey + f = 0$ $(a,b,c,d,e,f \in R)$

where a, b, c are not all zero. Etc.

It happens that in the two classes (1) and (2) of the relations given above, one can classify their geometric counterparts. But one does this by a simultaneous consideration of the second important problem of analytic geometry: Given a curve of some sort in the plane, what is the relation (i.e., a workable description thereof) it represents? For example, we may consider all lines in the plane, or circles, or other classes of curves, and attempt to find equations — or other suitable descriptions of relations — representing these curves. Let us consider some examples.

1.2   Examples

Example 1 (Figure 14.1). A point is on this line if and only if its x-coordinate is equal to its y-coordinate; i.e., if and only if its x- and y-coordinates satisfy the equation $y = x$. We may state this as follows: A point $P(x,y)$ is on l if

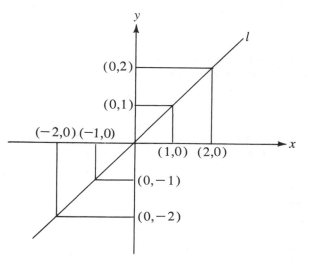

Figure 14.1

and only if $y = x$. Another way this is often stated is: A necessary and sufficient condition that $P(x,y)$ be on l is that $y = x$.

In general, Y is a *necessary* condition for Z means that if Y is not true, then neither is Z; or equivalently Z implies Y. To say Y is a *sufficient* condition for Z means Y implies Z. Thus $x < 7$ is a necessary condition on x for $x < 5$ to hold. It is not sufficient. Of course, Y is *necessary and sufficient* for Z therefore means Y holds if and only if Z does.

Example 2 (Figure 14.2). A point $P(x,y)$ is on l if and only if $y = -\frac{3}{2}$, i.e., if and only if its second coordinate is $-\frac{3}{2}$. Thus $(5,-\frac{3}{2})$, $(-1001,-\frac{3}{2})$, $(t,-\frac{3}{2})$, and $(\sqrt{22},-\frac{3}{2})$ are all points of l.

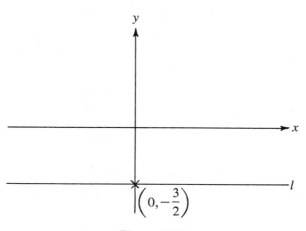

Figure 14.2

$y = x$ is said to be the equation of l in Example 1, $y = -\frac{3}{2}$ in Example 2. We may write these equations as:

(3) $x - y = 0$
(4) $2y + 3 = 0$

Thus, these are both instances of (1). Of course, equivalent equations can also be used, such as (3') $\frac{1}{2}(x - y) = 0$ and (4') $8y + 12 = 0$, respectively
Other examples follow:

Example 3 (Figure 14.3). The equations of these lines are:

$$l_1: x = -3 \quad \text{or} \quad x + 3 = 0$$
$$l_2: x = -1 \quad \text{or} \quad x + 1 = 0$$
$$l_3: x = \tfrac{1}{2} \quad \text{or} \quad 2x - 1 = 0$$
$$l_4: x = 2 \quad \text{or} \quad x - 2 = 0$$
$$l_5: x = 3 \quad \text{or} \quad x - 3 = 0$$

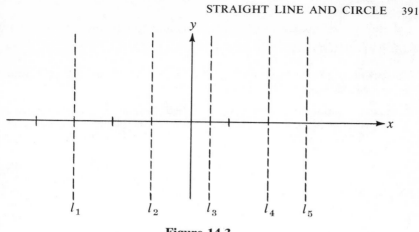

Figure 14.3

Example 4. The equation of the y-axis is $x = 0$, that of the x-axis is $y = 0$.
Example 5 (Figure 14.4). The relations are

$$\begin{cases} x = -1 & \text{if } y \geq 1 \\ y = 1 & \text{if } x \geq -1 \end{cases}$$

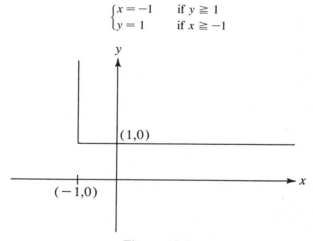

Figure 14.4

In Example 3, we see that all the equations of the vertical lines given (as well as any other one) have the form (1) where $b = 0$; i.e., are of the form

(5) $ax + c = 0$

where $a, c \in R$ and $a \neq 0$. Conversely, suppose we have an equation in x and y of the form (5). This is equivalent to

(6) $x = -\dfrac{c}{a}$

and this is represented in the plane by a vertical line passing through $\left(-\frac{c}{a},0\right)$ $\left(\text{or also } \left(-\frac{c}{a},2\right) \text{ or } \left(-\frac{c}{a},-\sqrt{2}\right), \text{ etc.}\right)$. Hence we have solved the first problem posed (Section 1.1) for equations of the type (5), and the second problem for vertical lines.

Example 6. Consider the line l passing through the point $(2,-1)$ and having slope $-\frac{3}{2}$ (Figure 14.5). Let $P(x,y)$ be any point in the plane. What is a necessary and sufficient condition that it be on the line? If P is not the point $(2,-1)$, such

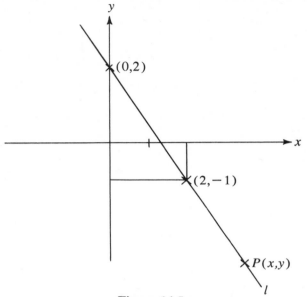

Figure 14.5

a condition is that the slope of the line through P and $(2,-1)$ be equal to $-\frac{3}{2}$, i.e., that

(7) $\dfrac{y-(-1)}{x-2} = -\dfrac{3}{2}$

A point distinct from $(2,-1)$ is on l if and only if (7) holds. For all such points, (7) is equivalent to

(8) $y - (-1) = -\frac{3}{2}(x-2)$

But furthermore, $(2,-1)$ satisfies (8). Thus all points of l satisfy (8), and only such points. We may write (8) as an equivalent equation:

(9) $3x + 2y - 4 = 0$

Example 7. What is the set of points in the plane satisfying $x^2 + y^2 = -3$?
Solution: The empty set. For the left side is nonnegative for all values of x and y.
Example 8. What is the set of points in the plane satisfying $(x-3)^2 + (y+2)^2 = -1$?

Solution: As in Example 7, the empty set.

Example 9. The same for $x^2 + y^2 = 0$.

Solution: The point $(0,0)$.

Example 10. The same for $(x - 3)^2 + (y + 2)^2 = 0$.

Solution: Only the point $(3,-2)$ will make the left side of the equation 0. For all other points, the left side is positive.

Example 11. Give equations representing the points (a) $(2,-1)$, (b) $(3,0)$, (c) $(-1,-2)$, (d) $(0,-5)$, and (e) (h,k).

Solution: Using Examples 9 and 10 as guides, we obtain:

    (a) $(x - 2)^2 + (y + 1)^2 = 0$
    (b) $(x - 3)^2 + (y - 0)^2 = 0$
    (c) $(x + 1)^2 + (y + 2)^2 = 0$
    (d) $x^2 + (y + 5)^2 = 0$
    (e) $(x - h)^2 + (y - k)^2 = 0$

Of course these are not the only descriptions of these relations. For example, for (a) we could also have

    (a$_1$) $|x - 2| + |y + 1| = 0$

or

    (a$_2$) $[(x - 2)^2 + (y + 1)^2](x^2 + 1) = 0$

or

    (a$_3$) $3(x - 2)^2 + 4(y + 1)^2 = 0$

Nevertheless, in (e), for example, we arrive at one class of equations representing points, and every point has such a representation.

Example 12. $xy = 0$ represents the x- and y-axes. For the product of the coordinates of a point is 0 if and only if one of the coordinates is 0.

Example 13. $(3x + 2y - 4)(2y + 3) = 0$ represents the union of those points satisfying $3x + 2y - 4 = 0$ (Example 6), and $2y + 3 = 0$ (Example 2), as shown by Figure 14.6.

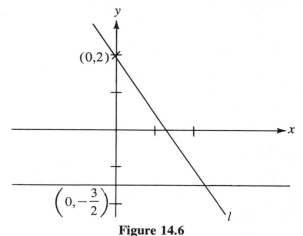

Figure 14.6

Exercises

1. Write an equation for the following:
   (a) A horizontal line passing through $(3,-2)$.
   (b) A horizontal line passing through $(-1,-2)$.
   (c) The union of (a) and (b).
   (d) A vertical line passing through $(0,1)$.
   (e) A vertical line passing through $(1,0)$.
   (f) The union of (c) and (e).
   (g) A horizontal line passing through $(t,2)$.
   (h) A horizontal line passing through (r,s).
   (i) A vertical line passing through (α,β).

2. Write an equation for the following:
   (a) The point $(1,-2)$.
   (b) The point $(-6,0)$.
   (c) The point $(2,2)$.
   (d) The point $(-2,-3)$.
   (e) The origin.
   (f) The union of $(0,-1)$ and the y-axis.
   (g) The union of $(3,-1)$, $(1,-3)$, and the x-axis.
   (h) The intersection of the lines whose equations are $x = 1$ and $y = -2$.

3. Draw the graph of the following:
   (a) $x = -5$.
   (b) $y = 2$.
   (c) $2x + 3 = 0$.
   (d) $7y - 2 = 0$.
   (e) $(2x + 3)(7y - 2) = 0$.
   (f) $x^2 + y^2 = -1$.
   (g) $(x - 7)^2 + (y + 2)^2 = 0$.
   (h) $[(x + 1)^2 + y^2]x = 0$.
   (i) $x + y = 0$.
   (j) $|x| = 0$.
   (k) $|y| = 0$.
   (l) $|x| = 1$.
   (m) $|y| = -1$.

4. Write an equation for the following, and draw the graph:
   (a) A line passing through $(3,-1)$ having slope 2.
   (b) A line passing through $(-1,2)$ having slope -1.
   (c) A line passing through $(0,0)$ and having slope 3.
   (d) A line passing through $(0,0)$ and having slope 2.
   (e) A line passing through the points $(2,3)$ and $(-1,2)$.
   (f) A line passing through the points $(-2,0)$ and $(3,4)$.
   (g) A line passing through $(-2,3)$ and $(1,3)$.
   (h) A line passing through $(-2,4)$ and $(-2,-22)$.

2. The Straight Line

2.1 Equation of the Straight Line

We use Example 6 as a guide in determining the equation of any straight line in the plane.

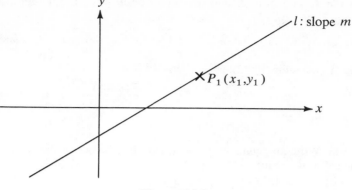

Figure 14.7

All vertical lines have been treated in Example 3.[1] Our treatment here will hold for all other lines.

Thus let l be any nonvertical line passing through the point $P_1(x_1,y_1)$ and having slope m (Figure 14.7). If $P(x,y)$ is any point distinct from $P_1(x_1,y_1)$, a necessary and sufficient condition that P be on the line l through P_1 is that the slope of the line through P and P_1 be m (Figure 14.8). For if P is on l, this is the case; and conversely if the slope of said

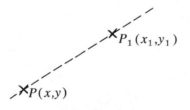

Figure 14.8

line PP_1 is m, then PP_1 must coincide with l, since it has the point P_1 in common with l (Theorem 5 of Chapter 13). Hence the necessary and sufficient condition is

(1) $\dfrac{y - y_1}{x - x_1} = m$

For all points $P(x,y)$ distinct from $P_1(x_1,y_1)$, this is equivalent to

(2) $y - y_1 = m(x - x_1)$

But $P_1(x_1,y_1)$ also satisfies (2), and hence (2) is an equation of the line.

[1] Cf. the discussion following Example 5.

Theorem 1. The nonvertical line of slope m passing through the point (x_1, y_1) has Equation (2), and conversely.

Example 14. Write an equation of the line passing through $(-3, 5)$ and having slope $-\frac{3}{4}$.

Solution: An equation, by (2), is

$$y - 5 = -\tfrac{3}{4}(x + 3)$$

or

$$3x + 4y - 11 = 0$$

Example 15. Write an equation of the straight line perpendicular to that of Example 1 at the point $(-3, 5)$.

Solution: By Theorem 6 of Chapter 13, the slope of this line is $\frac{4}{3}$. As it goes through the point $(-3, 5)$, the equation—by (2)—is

$$y - 5 = \tfrac{4}{3}(x + 3)$$
$$4x - 3y + 27 = 0$$

Now we can write (2) in the form $ax + by + c = 0$ since (2) yields

(3) $mx - y + y_1 - mx_1 = 0$

where $a = m$, $b = -1$, and $c = y_1 - mx_1$. Note that $b \neq 0$.
Now conversely, suppose we have an equation

(4) $ax + by + c = 0$

where $b \neq 0$. We attempt to reach an equivalent equation of the form (3). Thus let (x_1, y_1) be a point satisfying (4). $\left[\left(0, -\dfrac{c}{b}\right)\right.$ is such a point, for example.$\Big]$ Then

$$ax_1 + by_1 + c = 0$$

or

(5) $c = -ax_1 - by_1$

Use this expression for c in (4):

$$ax + by - ax_1 - by_1 = 0$$
$$a(x - x_1) + b(y - y_1) = 0$$

(6) $y - y_1 = -\dfrac{a}{b}(x - x_1)$

But by (2), this is an equation of the line passing through (x_1, y_1) and having slope $-\dfrac{a}{b}$ (so that the line is not vertical).

Thus we see that a nonvertical straight line represents an equation of the form (4) with $b \neq 0$, and such an equation represents a nonvertical straight line. Since (4) represents vertical lines when $b = 0$, and conversely, we have the following:

Theorem 2. Every equation of the form $ax + by + c = 0$,[2] where not both a and b are zero, represents a straight line; conversely every line has such an equation. The line is vertical if and only if $b = 0$. If $b \neq 0$, the line has slope $-\dfrac{a}{b}$.

Example 16. What are the slopes of the following lines?
  (a) $2x + 4y - 1 = 0$
  (b) $3x + 5 = 0$
  (c) $2y - 3 = 0$

Solution: In (a), we have $-\dfrac{a}{b} = -\dfrac{1}{2}$ so that the slope is $-\dfrac{1}{2}$. In (b), we have $b = 0$ and the line is vertical. In (c), the line is horizontal, so that the slope is 0. This also follows from the fact that $-\dfrac{a}{b} = 0$.

Example 17. Find an equation of the line passing through $(-3,5)$ and having slope $-\tfrac{3}{4}$.

Solution: This is identical to Example 1, where a solution has been given. We give an alternative solution here. $3x + 4y + c = 0$ represents various straight lines having slope $-\tfrac{3}{4}$, depending upon the value of c. Choose c so that $(-3,5)$ satisfies the equation

$$3(-3) + 4(5) + c = 0$$
$$c = -11$$

Hence $3x + 4y - 11 = 0$ is an equation of slope $-\tfrac{3}{4}$ passing through $(-3,5)$. Other values of c give lines parallel to this one.

Example 18. Prove that the perpendicular bisectors of a triangle meet in a point.

Solution: Choose the coordinate system as indicated in Figure 14.9. The perpendicular bisector of AB is the y-axis. Hence it remains to prove that the perpendicular bisectors of AC and BC intersect on the y-axis.

The slope of the line AC is $\dfrac{c}{b + a}$, where $c \neq 0$ and $b + a \neq 0$. The slope of any perpendicular is therefore $\dfrac{-(b + a)}{c}$. Hence an equation of the line perpendicular to AC at $D(b - a, c)$ is, by Theorem 1,

$$y - c = \frac{-(b + a)}{c}(x - (b - a))$$

To find where it intersects the y-axis, let $x = 0$ to obtain $y = c + \dfrac{b^2 - a^2}{c}$.

Thus it intersects the y-axis at $\left(0, c + \dfrac{b^2 - a^2}{c}\right)$.

---

[2] An equation of this form is called a *linear* equation (in 2 variables).

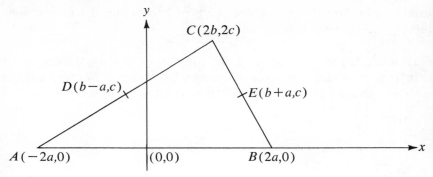

Figure 14.9

The slope [3] of the line BC is $\dfrac{c}{b-a}$, and hence of the perpendicular bisector is $\dfrac{-(b-a)}{c}$. The equation of the perpendicular bisector of BC is

$$y - c = \frac{-(b-a)}{c}(x - (b+a))$$

Letting $x = 0$ yields $y = c + \dfrac{b^2 - a^2}{c}$ and the point $\left(0, c + \dfrac{b^2 - a^2}{c}\right)$ is on this line.

Hence the perpendicular bisectors all meet in a point, namely the point

$$\left(0, c + \frac{b^2 - a^2}{c}\right).$$

2.2   Simultaneous Linear Equations

We have now seen that the set of solutions of an equation of the type

(1) $ax + by + c = 0$

can be represented in the plane as the points of a straight line, say l_1. (Here x and y are variables over R and $a,b,c \in R$.) One therefore sees clearly that the solution set is infinite.

If one has a second such equation

(2) $dx + ey + f = 0$

then again the solution set is infinite: one for each point on a line l_2.

How many solutions do (1) and (2) have in common? The answer depends upon whether $l_1 \parallel l_2$ (no solutions in common), $l_1 = l_2$ (infinitely

---

[3] If $b = a$, the slope of BC is undefined and BC is perpendicular to the x-axis. But then the perpendicular bisector is parallel to the x-axis and therefore has slope 0, which is again $\dfrac{-(b-a)}{c}$.

many solutions in common: the equations are equivalent), or l_1 and l_2 are neither parallel nor coincident. In the latter case, since l_1 and l_2 would intersect in precisely one point, there would be precisely one solution in common.

Example 19. How many solutions are there in common to the equations
    (a) $2x - y + 1 = 0$
    (b) $x + 2y - 3 = 0$
Solution: The slope of the line representing (a) is 2; that representing (b) is $-\frac{1}{2}$. The lines therefore are neither parallel nor coincident, so that (a) and (b) have one solution in common.

Example 20. How many solutions are there in common to the equations
    (a) $x + y - 3 = 0$
    (b) $-2x - 2y + 1 = 0$
Solution: The slopes of the corresponding lines are both 1. Hence either these equations are equivalent, or else they have no solutions in common. Consider any solution of (a), say (0,3). If (a) and (b) were equivalent, (0,3) would have to be a solution of (b). Since it is not, (a) and (b) have no solutions in common.

When one is concerned with finding the solutions common to a set of equations, one calls the set of equations a *simultaneous system of equations*. Thus in examples (1) and (2) we are concerned with systems of two simultaneous equations in two variables. To solve a simultaneous system of equations means to find the set of solutions common to each equation in the system.

Example 21. Solve the simultaneous system of equations
    (a) $2x - 3y + 1 = 0$
    (b) $3x + 5y - 27 = 0$

Before solving this system, we note that this is a special instance of solving a simultaneous system

(a*) $u(x,y) = 0$
(b*) $v(x,y) = 0$

Multiplying (a*) and (b*) by nonzero constants, say, α and β, respectively, replaces them by equivalent equations, and hence also their common solutions remain unchanged:

(c*) $\alpha u(x,y) = 0$
(d*) $\beta v(x,y) = 0$

Now we shall show that

(c*) $\alpha u(x,y) = 0$
(e*) $\alpha u(x,y) \pm \beta v(x,y) = 0$

is equivalent to (c*) and (d*). [Or also (d*) and (e*) is equivalent to (c*) and (d*).]

For if (x_0, y_0) is a solution of both (c*) and (d*), then $\alpha u(x_0, y_0) = 0$ and $\beta v(x_0, y_0) = 0$, so that $\alpha u(x_0, y_0) \pm \beta v(x_0, y_0) = 0$; i.e., (x_0, y_0) is a solution of (e*). Conversely if (x_0, y_0) is a solution of (c*) and (e*), then $\alpha u(x_0, y_0) \pm \beta v(x_0, y_0) = 0$ by (e*); and setting $u(x_0, y_0) = 0$ by (c*) yields $\pm \beta v(x_0, y_0) = 0$. Thus (x_0, y_0) is a solution of (d*).

Solution of Example 21:

Applying the above method, multiply (a) by 5 and (b) by 3:

(c) $10x - 15y + 5 = 0$
(d) $9x + 15y - 81 = 0$

Adding (c) and (d) yields

$$19x - 76 = 0$$

which is equivalent to

(e) $x = 4$

Thus (c) and (e) are equivalent to (a) and (b).

Now, since any common solution of (c) and (e) must have x-coordinate 4, we may replace x by 4 in (c) to obtain

$$40 - 15y + 5 = 0$$

which is equivalent to

(f) $y = 3$

Hence (e) and (f) are equivalent to (a) and (b). But from (e) and (f) the solution set is seen to be $\{(4,3)\}$.

The situation, graphically, is as shown in Figure 14.10. Thus, graphically, we have replaced the problem of determining where two lines intersect [(a) and (b)], to that of determining where two other lines intersect [(e) and (f)], the point of intersection being the same in both cases.

The method used in the above solution is called *elimination*. In this case we "eliminated" the variable y.

A second method is called the method of *substitution*:

We begin again with (a) and (b). We replace (a) by the equivalent equation

(g) $y = \frac{2}{3}x + \frac{1}{3}$

Now we "substitute" (g) in (b); that is, we replace y in (b) by $\frac{2}{3}x + \frac{1}{3}$:

(h) $3x + 5(\frac{2}{3}x + \frac{1}{3}) - 27 = 0$

The student may check that the systems (g) and (h), (a) and (h), and (b) and (h) are all equivalent. That is, the solutions of one system are precisely the solutions of the others.

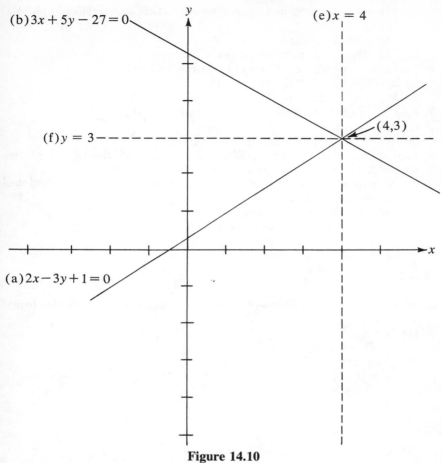

(b) $3x + 5y - 27 = 0$

(e) $x = 4$

(4,3)

(f) $y = 3$

(a) $2x - 3y + 1 = 0$

Figure 14.10

Now (h) yields

$$3x + \tfrac{10}{3}x + \tfrac{5}{3} - 27 = 0$$
$$19x - 76 = 0$$
$$x = 4$$

One obtains $y = 3$, as before.

Exercises

5. Find the equations of the following lines:
  (a) Passing through $(-1,2)$ and having slope $\tfrac{7}{3}$.
  (b) Passing through $(7,1)$ and perpendicular to the line $3x - 2y = 6$.
  (c) Passing through the points $(1,-2)$ and $(3,4)$.
  (d) The altitudes of the triangle with vertices $A(1,2)$, $B(7,-1)$, and $C(4,-3)$.

   (e) The diagonals of the quadrilateral whose vertices are $(1,-1)$, $(3,5)$, $(4,-4)$, and $(2,-3)$.
   (f) The sides of the triangle in (d).
   (g) The sides of the quadrilateral in (e).

6. Find two points on the following lines. Draw each line.
   (a) $2x - y + 1 = 0$.   (c) $2x - 1 = 0$.
   (b) $3x + y + 5 = 0$.   (d) $2x = 5 - 3y$.

7. Find a point and the slope of the following lines, and draw them:
   (a) $2x + 3y - 2 = 0$.   (c) $y - 2 = 3x$.
   (b) $5x = 7y + 2$.   (d) $3 - 2x = \sqrt{2}$.

8. Find the equation of a line parallel, and one perpendicular to each of the lines of Exercises 6 and 7 and passing through the origin.

9. (a) Suppose a line has slope m and passes through the point $(0,\beta)$. Find the equation of the line.
   (b) Suppose a line passes through the points $(\alpha,0)$ and $(0,\beta)$, where $\alpha,\beta \neq 0$. Show that an equation of the line is

$$\frac{x}{\alpha} + \frac{y}{\beta} = 1$$

10. Solve the following systems of simultaneous equations, all variables being over R.
   (a) $2x - y = 7$
       $x + 2y = 6$
   (b) $3x + 2y - 6 = 0$
       $2x - 7y + 21 = 0$
   (c) $x + 4y = -7$
       $3x + 12y + 8 = 0$
   (d) $-2x + y - 5 = 0$
       $4x - 2y = -10$
   (e) $2x - y = 7$
       $x + 2y = 6$
       $x = 3$
   (f) $2x - y - 2z = 4$
       $-3x + 2y - 3z = -6$
       $4x - 3y + 5z = -1$

   (*Hint:* Eliminate a variable from a pair of the equations, and the same variable from a different pair of the equations. This reduces the problem to solving two equations in two variables.)

11. (a) Show that the three lines $2x - y - 4 = 0$, $x + 3y + 5 = 0$, and

$$3x - 2y - 7 = 0$$

   pass through a point.
   (b) The same for $x + 3y - 1 = 0$, $2x - 3y - 11 = 0$, and $x = 4$.

12. Show that in any trapezoid, the diagonals and the line joining the midpoints of the parallel sides meet in a point.

13. (a) Show that the lines $a_1x + b_1y + c_1 = 0$ and $a_2x + b_2y + c_2 = 0$ have the same slope if and only if $\dfrac{a_1}{a_2} = \dfrac{b_1}{b_2}$, or $a_1 = a_2 = 0$, or $b_1 = b_2 = 0$; hence if and only if $a_1b_2 - a_2b_1 = 0$.

(b) Show that the two given equations are equivalent if and only if $\dfrac{a_1}{a_2} = \dfrac{b_1}{b_2} = \dfrac{c_1}{c_2}$ [or where any numerator (denominator) is 0, then the corresponding denominator (numerator) is 0]; i.e., if and only if $a_1b_2 - a_2b_1 = 0$, $b_1c_2 - b_2c_1 = 0$, and $a_1c_2 - a_2c_1 = 0$.

14. Use Exercise 13 to show the following: The simultaneous system

$$a_1x + b_1y + c_1 = 0$$
$$a_2x + b_2y + c_2 = 0$$

of equations in two variables has:
  (i) One solution if $a_1b_2 - a_2b_1 \neq 0$.
  (ii) No solution if $a_1b_2 - a_2b_1 = 0$ and either $b_1c_2 - b_2c_1 \neq 0$ or $a_1c_2 - a_2c_1 \neq 0$.
  (iii) Infinitely many solutions if $a_1b_2 - a_2b_1 = b_1c_2 - b_2c_1 = a_1c_2 - a_2c_1 = 0$.

15. How many solutions do the following systems of simultaneous equations in two variables have:

(a) $2x + y - 5 = 0$
  $x = 3y - 11$

(b) $3x + 6 = y$
  $2y = 6x - 1$

(c) $3x - 3y + 6 = 0$
  $-2y + 2x = -4$

(d) $4y + 1 = 2x$
  $3x - y = 1$

16. Show that the altitudes of any triangle meet in a point. Use the coordinate system of Example 18 (Figure 14.9).

17. Prove that the medians of a triangle meet in a point by a method alternative to that given in Chapter 13. Use the same coordinate system (Figure 13.69).

18. In the following, use the coordinate system which places the triangle at $(a,0)$, $(b,0)$, $(0,c)$.

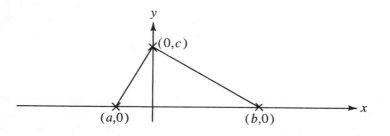

(a) Prove that the perpendicular bisectors of a triangle meet in a point (using the above coordinate system).
(b) Same for the medians.
(c) Same for the altitudes.

19. The points obtained in parts (a), (b), and (c) of Exercise 18 are

(a) $\left(\dfrac{a+b}{2}, \dfrac{ab+c^2}{2c}\right)$; (b) $\left(\dfrac{a+b}{3}, \dfrac{c}{3}\right)$; (c) $\left(0, -\dfrac{ab}{c}\right)$. Use this to show that

these three points—namely the intersection of the perpendicular bisectors, of the medians, of the altitudes of any triangle—lie on the same straight line.

20. Show that an equation of the line perpendicular to $ax + by + c = 0$ and passing through the origin is $bx - ay = 0$.

2.3   Intercepts

Definition 1. Let l be a line. If l intersects the x-axis, say at $(\alpha,0)$, then α is called an *x-intercept* of l; similarly if l intersects the y-axis, say at $(0,\beta)$, then β is called a *y-intercept* of l.

Example 22. $3x - 2y + 4 = 0$ has the x-intercept $-\frac{4}{3}$. This is determined by setting $y = 0$ and finding the corresponding value of x. The y-intercept is 2.
Example 23. $x = 4$ has x-intercept 4 and no y-intercept.
Example 24. $3y = 2x$ has x-intercept 0 and y-intercept 0.
Example 25. $x = 0$ has x-intercept 0; every number is a y-intercept.

Remark: Definition 1 applies to any curve.

If a line l intersects the x-axis and y-axis in points distinct from the origin, then its x-intercept α and y-intercept β are uniquely determined, and $\alpha,\beta \neq 0$. In this case one can show (cf. Exercise 9b) that an equation of l is

(1) $\quad \dfrac{x}{\alpha} + \dfrac{y}{\beta} = 1$

This is called the *intercept form* of the equation of l. The equation of Theorem 1 is called the *point-slope form*, that of Theorem 2 the *general form*.

We remark that if one has an equation of the form (1), it is the equation of a line with x-intercept α and y-intercept β.

A fourth type of equation which is used is the *slope-intercept form*. This applies to all nonvertical lines (as does the point-slope form). Namely, if m is the *slope* and β the *y-intercept* of l, then an equation of l is

(2) $\quad y = mx + \beta$

Simply apply the point-slope form using $(0,\beta)$ as the point. Conversely if an equation is of the form (2), one may write it as $y - \beta = m(x - 0)$, and hence it is an equation of a line of slope m passing through $(0,\beta)$ by Theorem 1.

2.4   Distance from a Point to a Line

Theorem 3. Let $ax + by + c = 0$ be the equation of a line. Then the distance from the origin to the line is

$$\frac{|c|}{\sqrt{a^2 + b^2}}$$

Proof: By Exercise 20, an equation of the line perpendicular to

(1) $ax + by + c = 0$

and passing through $(0,0)$ is

(2) $bx - ay = 0$

Solving (1) and (2) simultaneously yields the point of intersection

$$P_0 \left(\frac{-ac}{a^2 + b^2}, \frac{-bc}{a^2 + b^2} \right)$$

The distance from $O(0,0)$ to the line (1) is then the distance from O to P_0. By the distance formula, this is

$$\sqrt{\frac{a^2c^2}{(a^2 + b^2)^2} + \frac{b^2c^2}{(a^2 + b^2)^2}} = \sqrt{\frac{(a^2 + b^2)c^2}{(a^2 + b^2)^2}}$$

$$= \frac{|c|}{\sqrt{a^2 + b^2}}$$

This theorem may be used to prove a more inclusive theorem:

Theorem 4. Let $ax + by + c = 0$ be the equation of a line l, and $P_1(x_1, y_1)$ any point in the plane (not necessarily on the line, therefore). Then the distance d of P_1 to l is

(3) $d = \dfrac{|ax_1 + by_1 + c|}{\sqrt{a^2 + b^2}}$

Proof: Note that if $(x_1, y_1) = (0,0)$, the result holds by Theorem 3. Also if (x_1, y_1) is on l, then $d = 0$, and so is the right side of (3), since $ax_1 + by_1 + c = 0$ in this case. Of course, $ax_1 + by_1 + c \neq 0$ if and only if $d \neq 0$.

   In the remaining cases, let l_1 be the line parallel to l passing through (x_1, y_1). An equation of l_1 is

(4) $ax + by + c_1 = 0$

where $c_1 = -(ax_1 + by_1)$ since (x_1, y_1) is on l_1 (Figure 14.11). If $c_1 = 0$ (so that $ax_1 + by_1 = 0$), l_1 passes through the origin. Formula (3) is seen to agree with Theorem 3 in this case.

   Otherwise we have two possibilities: (a) l and l_1 are on the same side of $O(0,0)$ or on opposite sides.

   Case (a): l and l_1 on the same side of O.

   In this case if h is the distance from O to l, and k the distance to l_1, then

(5) $d = |k - h| = \left| \dfrac{|c_1| - |c|}{\sqrt{a^2 + b^2}} \right|$

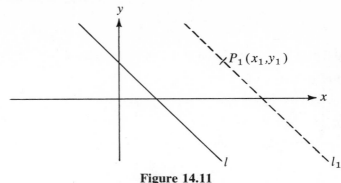

Figure 14.11

Now either a or b is distinct from 0; say $a \neq 0$. Then the x-intercept of l is $-\dfrac{c}{a}$ and of l_1 is $-\dfrac{c_1}{a}$. These are both positive or both negative in this case. Hence c and c_1 are both positive or both negative. Thus either

(i) $|c_1| = c_1$ and $|c| = c$

or

(ii) $|c_1| = -c_1$ and $|c| = -c$

If (i) holds,

$$|c_1| - |c| = c_1 - c = -ax_1 - by_1 - c$$
$$= -(ax_1 + by_1 + c)$$

If (ii) holds,

$$|c_1| - |c| = -c_1 + c = ax_1 + by_1 + c$$

Hence in either case, (5) yields

$$d = \frac{|ax_1 + by_1 + c|}{\sqrt{a^2 + b^2}}$$

If $b \neq 0$, the argument is similar.

Case (b): l and l_1 on the opposite side of O (cf. Exercise 27).

Example 26. Find the area of the triangle with vertices $(1,2)$, $(-2,1)$, and $(2,-2)$ (Figure 14.12).

Solution: One may use any base and corresponding altitude. Say we use the base BC and altitude from A. The length of the altitude is the distance from A to the line passing through B and C.

Thus we find the equation of this line. The slope is

$$\frac{1 - (-2)}{-2 - 2} = -\frac{3}{4}$$

Using this slope, and the point B, the equation of the line through B and C is

$$y - 1 = -\tfrac{3}{4}(x + 2)$$
$$3x + 4y + 2 = 0$$

By Theorem 4, the distance from A to this line is

$$\frac{|\,3(1) + 4(2) + 2\,|}{\sqrt{3^2 + 4^2}} = \frac{13}{5}$$

The length of BC is $\sqrt{9 + 16}$ or 5. The area is therefore $\tfrac{1}{2} \cdot 5 \cdot \tfrac{13}{5}$, or $\tfrac{13}{2}$.

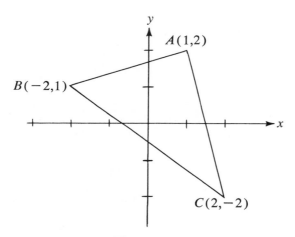

Figure 14.12

Exercises

21. In each of the following, find the distance of the given point to the given line.
   (a) $(3,2)$, $3x - 4y + 1 = 0$.   (d) $(0,0)$, $7x - 6x + 2 = 0$.
   (b) $(-2,0)$, $12x - 5y + 3 = 0$.   (e) $(2,-1)$, $2x + y - 3 = 0$.
   (c) $(3,4)$, $4x - 5 = 0$.

22. Find the lengths of the altitudes of the triangle whose sides are segments of the sides $5x - y - 10 = 0$, $3x - 4y + 11 = 0$, and $2x + 3y - 4 = 0$.

23. Suppose you were given the coordinates of the four points of a quadrilateral. Outline the method you would use to determine its area.

24. $3x - 2y + 5 = 0$ and $3x - 2y - 7 = 0$ are two parallel lines. Find the distance between them.

25. Find an equation of a line satisfying each of the following:
   (a) Having intercepts twice those of the line $x - 2y + 3 = 0$.
   (b) Slope 3 and having the same y-intercept as $2x - y + 1 = 0$.
   (c) x-intercept -2, y-intercept 5.

26. Is it possible for a line of slope -2 not passing through the origin to have an x-intercept which is twice its y-intercept? If so, give an example; if not, justify.

27. Carry out the proof of Theorem 4(b).

3. The Circle

We have classified the equations of lines, and now turn to the circle. A circle of radius r and center A is the set of all points in the plane at a distance r from A. We wish to find the necessary and sufficient condition on a point $P(x,y)$ in the plane that it be on the circle (Figure 14.13).

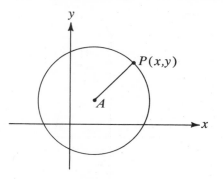

Figure 14.13

Let A have coordinates (h,k). Then $P(x,y)$ is on the circle if and only if its distance to A is r; that is, if and only if

(1) $\sqrt{(x-h)^2 + (y-k)^2} = r$

But squaring both sides of (1) yields

(2) $(x-h)^2 + (y-k)^2 = r^2$

Conversely if (2) holds, the positive square roots of both sides are equal. As $r > 0$, for the right side this is r, and (1) follows from (2). But (1) is the condition, by the distance formula, that the point $P(x,y)$ be at the distance r from the point $A(h,k)$.

Theorem 5. An equation of the circle with center $A(h,k)$ and radius r is given by (2).

Example 27. Find an equation of the circle with center $(2,-3)$ and radius 4.
Solution: By Theorem 5, an equation is

(3) $(x-2)^2 + (y+3)^2 = 16$

We can multiply out to obtain another form of this equation.

$$x^2 - 4x + 4 + y^2 + 6y + 9 = 16$$

(4) $x^2 + y^2 - 4x + 6y - 3 = 0$

Example 28. Find an equation of the circle with center $(-1,0)$ and radius 3.
Solution: (5) $(x + 1)^2 + y^2 = 9$
      (6) $x^2 + y^2 + 2x - 8 = 0$

Example 29. An equation of the circle with center at $O(0,0)$ and radius r is

    (7) $x^2 + y^2 = r^2$
    (8) $x^2 + y^2 - r^2 = 0$

In (2) of Section 1.1 we gave the most general equation of second degree in two variables. We repeat it here.

(9) $ax^2 + bxy + cy^2 + dx + ey + f = 0$

Now (4), (6), and (8) are special cases of (9). And it is not difficult to see that every circle has an equation of the form (9). Namely from (2), we obtain

$$x^2 - 2hx + h^2 + y^2 - 2ky + k^2 = r^2$$

(10) $x^2 + y^2 - 2hx - 2ky + h^2 + k^2 - r^2 = 0$

Comparing (10) and (9), we see that $a=1, b=0, c=1, d=-2h, e=-2k$, and $f = h^2 + k^2 - r^2$. Of course, multiplying (10) by a constant gives an equivalent equation, so that we shall consider equations of the following form:

(11) $ax^2 + ay^2 + dx + ey + f = 0$ $(a \neq 0)$

and ask when this represents a circle. We know every circle is included among such equations.

The idea is to start from an equation of the form (11), and try to put it into the form (2).

In Example 27 we had (4):

$$x^2 + y^2 - 4x + 6y - 3 = 0$$

Trying to work toward (2), one can group the x terms and y terms, and put the constant on the right.

$$(x^2 - 4x \quad) + (y^2 + 6y \quad) = 3$$

We left space to complete the square, and add the same numbers to the right.

$$(x^2 - 4x + 4) + (y^2 + 6y + 9) = 3 + 4 + 9$$
$$(x - 2)^2 + (y + 3)^2 = 16$$

We can then see that this is the equation of a circle with center $(2,-3)$, radius 4 by comparison with (2).

Example 30. What does the equation $4x^2 + 4y^2 - 4x + 16y + 1 = 0$ represent?

Solution: Multiply through by $\frac{1}{4}$:

$$x^2 + y^2 - x + 4y + \tfrac{1}{4} = 0$$
$$(x^2 - x + \tfrac{1}{4}) + (y^2 + 4y + 4) = -\tfrac{1}{4} + \tfrac{1}{4} + 4$$
$$(x - \tfrac{1}{2})^2 + (y + 2)^2 = 4$$

Hence the equation represents a circle with center $(\tfrac{1}{2}, -2)$ and radius 2.

Example 31. What does the equation $36x^2 + 36y^2 + 24x - 36y + 85 = 0$ represent?

Solution:

$$x^2 + y^2 + \tfrac{2}{3}x - y + \tfrac{85}{36} = 0$$
$$(x^2 + \tfrac{2}{3}x \quad) + (y^2 - y \quad) = -\tfrac{85}{36}$$
$$(x^2 + \tfrac{2}{3}x + \tfrac{1}{9}) + (y^2 - y + \tfrac{1}{4}) = -\tfrac{85}{36} + \tfrac{4}{36} + \tfrac{9}{36}$$
$$(x + \tfrac{1}{3})^2 + (y - \tfrac{1}{2})^2 = -2$$

This represents the empty set (cf. Examples 7 and 8).

Example 32. What does the equation $x^2 + y^2 - 2x + 4y + 5 = 0$ represent?

Solution:

$$(x^2 - 2x \quad) + (y^2 + 4y \quad) = -5$$
$$(x^2 - 2x + 1) + (y^2 + 4y + 4) = -5 + 1 + 4$$
$$(x - 1)^2 + (y + 2)^2 = 0$$

This represents the point $(1, -2)$ (cf. Examples 9, 10, and 11).

These examples seem to suggest that one can always pass from an equation of the form (11) to one of the form

$$(12) \quad (x - h)^2 + (y - k)^2 = \delta$$

If $\delta > 0$, we have a circle of center (h,k), radius $\sqrt{\delta}$; if $\delta = 0$, we have the point (h,k); if $\delta < 0$, we have the empty set.

Theorem 6. Equation (11) is equivalent with an equation of the form (12). Hence (11) represents a circle, a point, or the empty set depending upon, respectively, whether $\delta > 0$, $\delta = 0$, or $\delta < 0$.

Proof: Multiplying (11) by $\dfrac{1}{a}$ we obtain

$$x^2 + y^2 + \frac{d}{a}x + \frac{e}{a}y + \frac{f}{a} = 0$$

$$\left(x^2 + \frac{d}{a}x \quad\right) + \left(y^2 + \frac{e}{a}y \quad\right) = -\frac{f}{a}$$

$$\left(x^2 + \frac{d}{a}x + \frac{d^2}{4a^2}\right) + \left(y^2 + \frac{e}{a}y + \frac{e^2}{4a^2}\right) = -\frac{f}{a} + \frac{d^2}{4a^2} + \frac{e^2}{4a^2}$$

$$\left(x + \frac{d}{2a}\right)^2 + \left(y + \frac{e}{2a}\right)^2 = \frac{d^2 + e^2 - 4af}{4a^2}$$

Thus (11) is in the form (12), where $h=-\dfrac{d}{2a}$, $k=-\dfrac{e}{2a}$, and $\delta=\dfrac{d^2+e^2-4af}{4a^2}$.

Corollary. Equation (11) represents a circle if $d^2+e^2-4af>0$; a point if $d^2+e^2-4af=0$; the empty set if $d^2+e^2-4af<0$.

Equation (2) is called the *standard form* of the equation of a circle, (11) the *general form*. In Examples 27, 28, and 29 we see that (3), (5), and (7) are in standard form, (4), (6), and (8) are in general form.

If an equation is given in general form, one can determine the center and radius by bringing the equation into standard form. This is done by completing the square as above.

The question remains to classify the remaining second degree equations in (9). This is generally covered, today, in an introductory calculus course, although the calculus is not essential for this purpose.

Exercises

28. Find the equations of the following circles, first in standard form, and then in general form.
    (a) Center (2,−3), radius 2.
    (b) Center (0,1), radius 5.
    (c) Center (−1,−2), radius 1.
    (d) Center (−3,0), radius 2.
    (e) Center ($\sqrt{2},\sqrt{3}$), radius $\sqrt{2}$.
    (f) Center (h,2), radius $s+1$.
29. Convert the following equations to standard form [equation (12)] and tell what they represent.
    (a) $x^2+y^2-6x+2y+8=0$.
    (b) $x^2+y^2+2x+1=0$.
    (c) $x^2+y^2+4x-6y-3=0$.
    (d) $2x^2+2y^2+4x+8y+9=0$.
    (e) $x^2+y^2+6x+2y+7=0$.
    (f) $x^2+y^2-4x-8y+20=0$.
30. Find the equation of the line tangent to each of the following circles at the indicated point [cf. (27) of Section 2.7 of Chapter 13].
    (a) $x^2+y^2=25$ at (4,−3).
    (b) $x^2+y^2-6x+2y-64=0$ at (−2,6).
    (c) $x^2+y^2+2x+2y-167=0$ at (4,11).
31. Find equations of the circles satisfying the following:
    (a) Passing through the points (1,−3), (−5,5), and (2,4). [*Hint:* We indicate two methods. (1) Use (24) of Section 2.7 of Chapter 13. This shows that the perpendicular bisectors of any pair of points passes through the center. Use two of these to determine the center. (2) Every circle can be written in the form $x^2+y^2+dx+ey+f=0$. Substitute the coordinates of the given points in this equation to obtain three equations in d,e,f. Solve.]
    (b) Passing through the points (7,−2), (3,2), (−1,−2).
    (c) Having center (1,−2) and a tangent line $3x-4y+14=0$.
    (d) Having diameter with endpoints (−6,1) and (−2,−3).

4. Simultaneous Equations Continued

Example 33. Solve the simultaneous system of equations, where x and y are variables over R:

(a) $x^2 + y^2 = 25$
(b) $2x - 3y = 18$

Solution: The method is by substitution.
One obtains from (b) the equivalent equation:

(c) $y = \frac{2}{3}x - 6$

Substitute (c) in (a):

(d) $x^2 + (\frac{2}{3}x - 6)^2 = 25$

From (d) one obtains

$$x^2 + \tfrac{4}{9}x^2 - 8x + 36 = 25$$
$$9x^2 + 4x^2 - 72x + 99 = 0$$
$$13x^2 - 72x + 99 = 0$$

This factors into

(e) $(x - 3)(13x - 33) = 0$

Thus (b) and (e) are equivalent to (a) and (b).
However, if one does not wish to check that (b) and (e) are equivalent to (a) and (b), it is clear in any case that any solution of (a) and (b) is a solution of (e). Thus the x-coordinate of any solution must be either 3 or $\frac{33}{13}$. Substituting 3 in (b) yields $y = -4$; substituting $\frac{33}{13}$ in (b) yields $y = -\frac{56}{13}$. So we see that $(3,-4)$ and $(\frac{33}{13},-\frac{56}{13})$ are possible solutions of (a) and (b). Since they are solutions of (a), these constitute all the solutions.
Had we substituted 3 and $\frac{33}{13}$ for x in (a), we would have obtained the four possible solutions $(3,4)$, $(3,-4)$, $(\frac{33}{13},\frac{56}{13})$, $(\frac{33}{13},-\frac{56}{13})$. But checking in (b) would reveal $(3,4)$ and $(\frac{33}{13},\frac{56}{13})$ to be extraneous.
The situation graphically is as shown in Figure 14.14. Note that the line $x = \frac{33}{13}$ intersects the curve $x^2 + y^2 = 25$ in $(\frac{33}{13},-\frac{56}{13})$ and $(\frac{33}{13},\frac{56}{13})$. But it intersects $2x - 3y = 18$ only in $(\frac{33}{13},-\frac{56}{13})$. Similarly, $x = 3$ intersects $x^2 + y^2 = 25$ in both $(3,-4)$ and $(3,4)$, but intersects $2x - 3y = 18$ only in $(3,-4)$. In this example it would be difficult to determine geometrically that there are two points of intersection, a fact which the algebraic solution reveals quite clearly.

Example 34. Solve the simultaneous system
(a) $3x - 2y = 5$
(b) $2x^2 + 4y^2 = 6$
Solution: The same method yields

$$y = \tfrac{3}{2}x - \tfrac{5}{2} \qquad \text{from (a)}$$

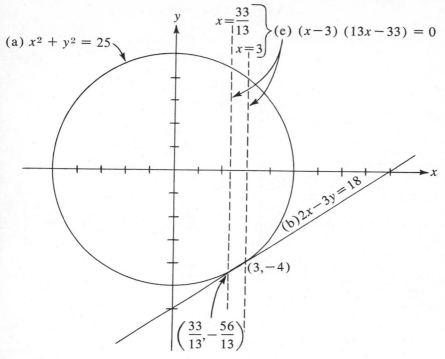

y

$x = \dfrac{33}{13}$

$x = 3$

(e) $(x-3)(13x-33) = 0$

(a) $x^2 + y^2 = 25$

(b) $2x - 3y = 18$

$(3, -4)$

$\left(\dfrac{33}{13}, -\dfrac{56}{13} \right)$

x

Figure 14.14

Substituting in (b) yields $11x^2 - 30x + 19 = 0$, or

$$(x - 1)(11x - 19) = 0$$

Thus $x = 1$ or $x = \frac{19}{11}$. Using (a) yields the solution set

$$\{(1,-1),(\tfrac{19}{11},\tfrac{1}{11})\}$$

As we have not studied equations of type (b) geometrically, one may obtain its graph by plotting sample points. The situation, graphically, is then seen to be as shown in Figure 14.15.

Example 35. Solve the simultaneous system
   (a) $3x^2 - 2y^2 = 10$
   (b) $x^2 + 5y^2 = 9$
Solution: We use the method of elimination as used in the linear case. Multiply (b) by -3 and add:

$$-17y^2 = -17$$
$$y^2 = 1$$

Thus the possible values of y are 1 and -1. Substituting in either (a) or (b) yields

$$(x - 1)(11x - 19) = 0$$

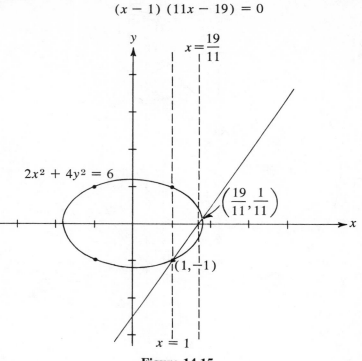

Figure 14.15

$$x^2 = 4$$

Thus the four possible solutions are $(2,1)$, $(2,-1)$, $(-2,1)$, and $(-2,-1)$. All of these are readily seen to be solutions, which means that in fact

$$x^2 = 4$$
$$y^2 = 1$$

is a system equivalent with (a) and (b). Graphically we have Figure 14.16.

Exercises

Solve the following systems of simultaneous equations, all variables being over R.

32. $x^2 + y^2 = 25$
           $x^2 - y^2 + 7 = 0$

33. $x^2 + y^2 = 25$
           $x^2 - y^2 + 7 = 0$
           $2x - 3y = 18$

34. $2x^2 - 4y^2 = 1$
           $6y - 5x - 8 = 0$

35. $2x^2 - 4y^2 = 1$
           $6y - 5x - 8 = 0$
           $x = -1$
           $y = \frac{1}{2}$

36. $x^3 - y^2 + xy = 20$
        $x^2 + x - 2y = 40xy + 1$
        $x = 0$
        $y = x$

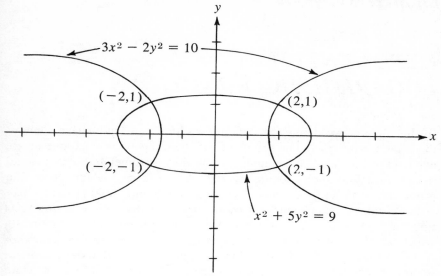

Figure 14.16

37. $x^2 - xy + x - 1 = 0$
$x + y = 0$

38. $\dfrac{x^2 - y^2}{x + y} = x - y$
$x + y = 0$

39. $3x^2 - 2y^2 = 10$
$2x^2 - 5y^2 = 3$

chapter xv

EXPONENTIAL AND LOGARITHMIC FUNCTIONS

In this chapter we define the exponential functions, and derive some of their basic properties. The proofs of the theorems on real exponents are deferred to the end of the chapter, where they are given in full. The logarithmic functions appear as the inverses of the exponential functions. The properties of these functions are applied to computational problems.

In Section 7.2 of Chapter 10 we defined a^α, where a is a *positive* real number and α *any* real number. We stated there that Theorem 30, which was proved for rational exponents, can be proved for real exponents. Although Theorem 32 followed Theorem 30 in that development, for real exponents the analogue of Theorem 32 is proved first. We state here four theorems which represent the basic results for real exponents. The proofs, although logically accessible to the interested reader, are possibly too technical for a first reading of this subject. We defer them, accordingly, to Section 7.

1. The Basic Theorems Stated

Theorem 1. Let $a \in P$ and $\alpha, \beta \in R$.

(I) If $a > 1$, then
   (1) $a^\alpha > a^\beta$ if and only if $\alpha > \beta$
   (2) $a^\alpha = a^\beta$ if and only if $\alpha = \beta$ [1]
   (3) $a^\alpha < a^\beta$ if and only if $\alpha < \beta$ [1]
(II) $1^\alpha = 1$
(III) If $a < 1$, then
   (1) $a^\alpha < a^\beta$ if and only if $\alpha > \beta$
   (2) $a^\alpha = a^\beta$ if and only if $\alpha = \beta$ [1]
   (3) $a^\alpha > a^\beta$ if and only if $\alpha < \beta$ [1]

Theorem 2. Let $c \in P$. Then if x is a variable over R, $a^x = c$ has a unique solution.

Theorem 3 (The Fundamental Theorem for Real Exponents). If $a, b \in P$ and $r, s \in R$, then

---

[1] (2) is an immediate consequence of (1), and (3) is the same as (1) (with α and β interchanged). We include these for emphasis.

416

(1) $a^r \cdot a^s = a^{r+s}$ (4) $(ab)^r = a^r b^r$

(2) $\dfrac{a^r}{a^s} = a^{r-s}$ (5) $\left(\dfrac{a}{b}\right)^r = \dfrac{a^r}{b^r}$

(3) $(a^r)^s = a^{rs}$

Theorem 4. Let $a,b \in P$ and $\alpha \in R$.

(1) If $\alpha > 0$, then $a^\alpha > b^\alpha$ if and only if $a > b$.
(2) If $\alpha = 0$, then $a^\alpha = b^\alpha$.
(3) If $\alpha < 0$, then $a^\alpha > b^\alpha$ if and only if $a < b$.

2. The Exponential Functions

We may now extend our study of functions to the exponential functions, one such function for every positive real number. Namely, for each $\ \epsilon P$, we consider the function

(1) $f(x) = a^x$

which may also be regarded as a relation between the variables x and y:

(2) $y = a^x$

The domain of this function is the set of all real numbers (cf. Definition 8, Chapter 10).

In Exercise 63 of Chapter 10 it was seen that $a^\alpha > 0$ for all $\alpha \in R$. Hence the range of this function is a subset of P. By Theorem 2, however, we see that the range of f is precisely P. This yields:

Theorem 5. Let $f(x)$ be the function defined by (1) with domain R. Then the range of f is precisely P.

Example 1. By plotting sample points, sketch the graph of $y = 2^x$.

Solution:

x	0	1	2	3	4	-1	-2	-3
2^x	1	2	4	8	16	$\frac{1}{2}$	$\frac{1}{4}$	$\frac{1}{8}$

(Figure 15.1)

Example 2. By plotting sample points, sketch the graph of $y = (\frac{1}{2})^x$.

Solution:

x	0	1	2	3	4	-1	-2	-3
$(\frac{1}{2})^x$	1	$\frac{1}{2}$	$\frac{1}{4}$	$\frac{1}{8}$	$\frac{1}{16}$	2	4	8

(Figure 15.2)

The difference between the graphs of Example 1, where $a = 2$, and Example 2, where $a = \frac{1}{2}$, is contained in Theorem 1. For all $a \in P$, $a^0 = 1$. Now Theorem 1 says that if $a > 1$, then as x gets larger so does y [cf. Theorem 1, I(1)]. Thus from $x = 0$ where $y = 1$, as x increases through the positive real numbers, y increases through numbers above 1. Furthermore [cf. Theorem 1, I(3)], as x decreases through negative real numbers, y decreases below 1. Since for all x, we have $a^x \in P$, the curve remains

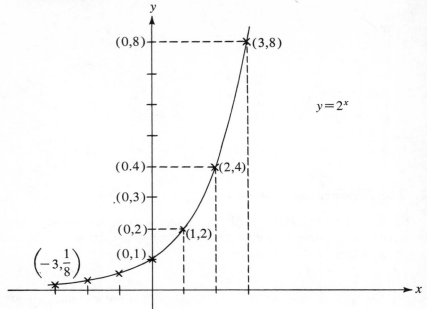

$y=2^x$

Figure 15.1

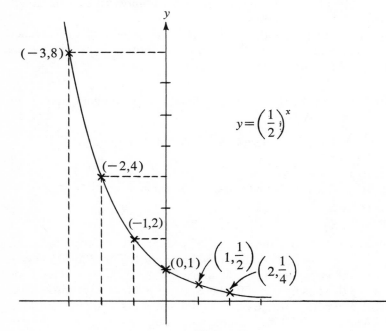

$y=\left(\dfrac{1}{2}\right)^x$

Figure 15.2

above the x-axis. By Theorem 5, it gets closer and closer to the x-axis as x moves to the left (i.e., decreases).

The same analysis applies for $a < 1$ (Example 2), but here one must apply Theorem 1, III(1, 3).

Theorem 1 indicates for a fixed a whether the graph rises or falls with increasing x. To distinguish the graphs for different values of a all greater (or all less) than 1, however, we use Theorem 4.

Example 3. Draw the graphs of $y = (\frac{3}{2})^x$, $y = (7.1)^x$, $y = 10^x$ on the same coordinate system. Also $y = (\frac{2}{3})^x$, $y = (7.1)^{-x}$ [i.e., $y = (\frac{1}{7.1})^x$], $y = 10^{-x}$.

Solution: We observe that the graphs will all be similar to those of Examples 1 and 2. But Theorem 4(1) says that to the right of the y-axis, the graph of $y = (7.1)^x$ is higher than that of $y = (\frac{3}{2})^x$, and similarly the graph of 10^x is higher than that of $y = (7.1)^x$.

On the other hand, the situation is reversed, according to Theorem 4(3) when we go to the left of the x-axis.

The same holds for $y = (\frac{2}{3})^x$, $y = (\frac{1}{7.1})^x$, $y = (\frac{1}{10})^x$. Since $\frac{2}{3} > \frac{1}{7.1} > \frac{1}{10}$ the graph of $y = (\frac{2}{3})^x$ is above that of $y = (7.1)^{-x}$, which is above that of $y = 10^{-x}$ when to the right of the x-axis; the roles are reversed to the left.

We shall not draw to scale, but only reflect the above analysis, in Figure 15.3. Dividing the functions $y = a^x$, where $a > 1$ and $a < 1$, is the function $y = 1^x$ which by Theorem (1,II) is $y = 1$ and is a horizontal line one unit above the x-axis.

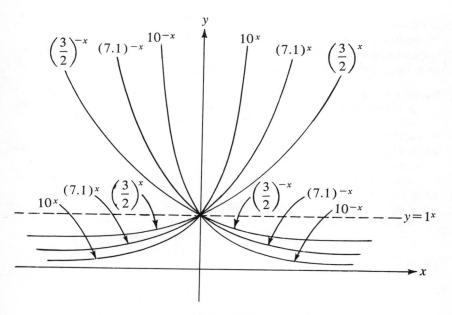

Figure 15.3

Exercises

1. Sketch the following, using at least four sample points.
   (a) $y = 3^{-x}$.   (e) $y = 5^{-x}$.
   (b) $y = (\frac{1}{3})^x$.   (f) $y = (\frac{1}{2})^x$.
   (c) $y = (\frac{1}{5})^{-x}$.   (g) $y = (\frac{3}{4})^{-x}$.
   (d) $y = 5^x$.   (h) $y = (\frac{4}{3})^x$.

2. (a) If $a \in P$, $a \neq 1$, prove that $y = a^x$ is a 1-1 function from R onto P. (*Hint:* Use Theorem 1.)
   (b) Draw the function $y = 2^x$ (which is from R onto P), and the inverse function (which is from P onto R).

3. If $f(x) = 2^{-x}$ and $g(x) = 3^x$, find the following:
   (a) $f(0) + g(0)$.   (d) $gf(1)$.
   (b) $f(1) \cdot g(1)$.   (e) $\dfrac{f(3)}{g(2)}$.
   (c) $fg(1)$.

3. The Logarithmic Functions

The functions $f(x) = a^x$, $a > 0$, $a \neq 1$, are 1-1 functions of R onto P (cf. Exercise 2), and hence have inverses from P onto R. Indeed the inverse function assigns to each $c \in P$ the unique solution (Theorem 2) of $a^x = c$. This solution is called the *logarithm* of c base a, written $\log_a c$, in accordance with the following:

Definition 1. The function $y = \log_a x$ from P to R is defined to be the inverse function of $y = a^x$ ($a \in P$, $a \neq 1$). That is, $y = \log_a x$ means $a^y = x$ (interchanging the variables in $a^x = y$). We call a the *base* of both the exponential function $y = a^x$, and the logarithmic function $y = \log_a x$.

Example 4. The function $y = \log_2 x$ is the inverse function of $y = 2^x$. According to Section 6.3 of Chapter 11, the graph of the inverse function (or more generally, relation) is obtained by reflection in the line $y = x$ (Figure 15.4).

Example 5. In Figure 15.5 we give the graphs of $y = (\frac{1}{2})^x$ and $y = \log_{1/2} x$.

Example 6. We give the graphs of $\log_{1/10} x$, $\log_{1/7} x$, $\log_{2/3} x$, $\log_{3/2} x$, $\log_7 x$, and $\log_{10} x$. As in Example 3 of exponential functions, we only indicate the relation of these functions and do not draw to scale (Figure 15.6).

Example 7. Find $\log_2 8$, $\log_3 27$, $\log_{1/2} 8$, $\log_{1/3} 27$, $\log_6 1$, and $\log_3 (-1)$.

Solution: $y = \log_a x$ means $a^x = y$. Thus $\log_2 8 = \alpha$ means $2^\alpha = 8$; i.e., $\alpha = 3$ or $\log_2 8 = 3$. Hence $(8,3)$ is an element of the graph of $y = \log_2 x$. It follows, of course, that $(3,8)$ is an element of the inverse function $y = 2^x$. Note that $\log_2 8$ *is the exponent* to which 2 must be raised to yield 8, namely 3.

$$\log_3 27 = 3 \qquad \text{since } 3^3 = 27$$
$$\log_{1/2} 8 = -3 \qquad \text{since } (\tfrac{1}{2})^{-3} = 8$$
$$\log_{1/3} 27 = -3 \qquad \text{since } (\tfrac{1}{3})^{-3} = 27$$
$$\log_6 1 = 0 \qquad \text{since } 6^0 = 1$$

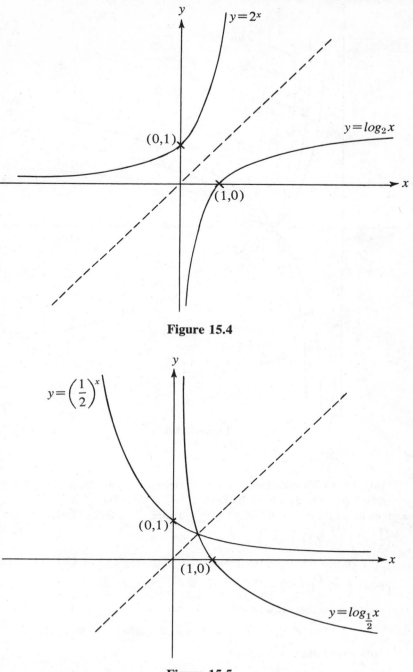

Figure 15.4

Figure 15.5

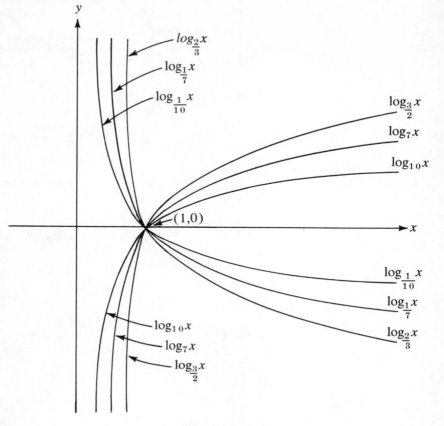

Figure 15.6

$\log_3(-1)$ is an undefined symbol, since $\log_3 x$ is a mapping with domain P, and $-1 \notin P$. The graphs of Example 3 reveal this clearly.

Example 8. (a) Points of the graph of $y = 2^x$ are $(0,1)$, $(1,2)$, $(2,4)$, $(3,8)$, $(4,16)$, $\left(\frac{1}{2}, \sqrt{2}\right)$, $\left(\frac{1}{3}, \sqrt[3]{2}\right)$, $\left(-2, \frac{1}{4}\right)$, $\left(-\frac{1}{2}, \frac{1}{\sqrt{2}}\right)$, etc.

(b) Hence points of the graph of $y = \log_2 x$ are $(1,0)$, $(2,1)$, $(4,2)$, $(8,3)$, $(16,4)$, $\left(\sqrt{2}, \frac{1}{2}\right)$, $\left(\sqrt[3]{2}, \frac{1}{3}\right)$, $\left(\frac{1}{4}, -2\right)$, $\left(\frac{1}{\sqrt{2}}, -\frac{1}{2}\right)$, etc.

(c) Rephrasing (a) we have

$$2^0 = 1,\ 2^1 = 2,\ 2^2 = 4,\ 2^3 = 8,\ 2^4 = 16,\ 2^{1/2} = \sqrt{2}, \ldots$$

(d) Rephrasing (b) we have

$$\log_2 1 = 0,\ \log_2 2 = 1,\ \log_2 4 = 2,\ \log_2 8 = 3,\ \log_2 16 = 4,\ \log_2 \sqrt{2} = \tfrac{1}{2}, \ldots$$

There are many uses of the exponential and logarithmic functions, but we shall only indicate their application to computations. It is customary to use the logarithmic function for this purpose, so we shall first develop a theorem summarizing often-used properties of logarithms.

Theorem 6. Let $a,b,M,N \in P$, and let $r \in R$, and assume $a,b \neq 1$. Then

(1) $\log_a MN = \log_a M + \log_a N$

(2) $\log_a \dfrac{M}{N} = \log_a M - \log_a N$

(3) $\log_a M^r = r \log_a M$

(4) $\log_a a = 1$

(5) $\log_a 1 = 0$

(6) $\log_a \dfrac{1}{N} = -\log_a N$

(7) $\log_a M = \dfrac{\log_b M}{\log_b a}$

(8) $a^{\log_a M} = M$

Proof: Let $\log_a M = \alpha$, $\log_a N = \beta$, so that $a^\alpha = M$, $a^\beta = N$. Hence by Theorem 3(1), $MN = a^\alpha a^\beta = a^{\alpha+\beta}$. But $MN = a^{\alpha+\beta}$ means $\log_a MN = \alpha + \beta$, that is, $\log_a MN = \log_a M + \log_a N$. This proves (1).

Similarly, one uses $\dfrac{a^\alpha}{a^\beta} = a^{\alpha-\beta}$ to prove (2).

Since $a^\alpha = M$, we have $(a^\alpha)^r = M^r$, or by Theorem 3(3), $a^{\alpha r} = M^r$, which means $\log_a M^r = r\alpha = r \log_a M$, and this proves (3).

(4) and (5) state $a^1 = a$ and $a^0 = 1$, which have already been observed.

(6) follows from (2) with $M = 1$, and from (5).

We now prove (7). We have $a^\alpha = M$. Hence

$$\log_b a^\alpha = \log_b M$$
$$\alpha \log_b a = \log_b M \qquad \text{by (3)}$$
$$\alpha = \frac{\log_b M}{\log_b a} \qquad \text{which is (7)}$$

We now prove (8). First proof: $\log_a M = \gamma$ means $a^\gamma = M$. Take $\gamma = \log_a M$. Equivalent proof: a^x and $\log_a x$ are inverse functions. Hence taking the composite in either order yields the identity function, one order yielding $I_R(x)$, the other $I_P(x)$:

(i) $R \to P \xrightarrow{\quad} R$ 　　(ii) $P \xrightarrow{\quad} R \to P$

$\quad \overset{\frown}{a^x \quad \log_a x}$ 　　　　$\quad \overset{\frown}{\log_a x \quad a^x}$

$\quad I_R(x) = \log_a a^x$ 　　　　$\quad I_P(x) = a^{\log_a x}$

From (i), we have $\log_a a^x = x$ for all $x \in R$, which also follows from (3) and (4).

From (ii) we have $a^{\log_a x} = x$ for all $x \in P$. This proves (8).

Exercises

4. If $f(x) = \log_3 x$, $g(x) = \log_2 x$, $h(x) = \log_{1/2} x$, find the following:
   (a) $f(1) + g(1) + h(1)$.   (e) $hg(4)$.
   (b) $f(9) + g(8) + h(4)$.   (f) $h(-3) + g(2)$.
   (c) $gf(1)$.   (g) $f(\frac{1}{9}) \cdot g(\frac{1}{16}) \cdot h(\frac{1}{8})$.
   (d) $gf(3) + g(2^c)$.

5. Sketch the following, using at least four sample points:
   (a) $y = \log_{1/3} x$.   (e) $y = \log_{2/3} x$.
   (b) $y = \log_3 x$.   (f) $y = \log_{3/2} x$.
   (c) $y = \log_2 x$.   (g) $y = \log_{3/4} x$.
   (d) $y = \log_{1/2} x$.   (h) $y = \log_{10} x$.

6. Solve the following equations, where x is a variable over P.
   (a) $\log_x x = 1$.
   (b) $\log_2 x = 0$.
   (c) $\log_2 2^x = x + 1$.
   (d) $\log_3 x^2 = \log_3 x$. (*Hint*: Conclude $x^2 = x$. Give reasoning!)
   (e) $2^{\log_2 x} = 3$.

7. Evaluate the following:
   (a) $\log_2 \sqrt[3]{2}$.   (f) $\log_{10} (.01)$.
   (b) $\log_{1/3} 9$.   (g) $\log_{10} (.0001)$.
   (c) $\log_{10} 100$.   (h) $\log_a a^4$.
   (d) $\log_{10} 1000$.   (i) $\log_a (\log_a a)$.
   (e) $\log_{10} (.1)$.   (j) $\log_3 (\log_a a^3)$.

8. Prove: $\log_a \dfrac{M_1 M_2 \cdots M_m}{N_1 N_2 \cdots N_n} = \log_a M_1 + \log_a M_2 + \cdots + \log_a M_m$
   $- \log_a N_1 - \log_a N_2 - \cdots - \log_a N_n$.

4. Further Theory of Logarithmic Functions

The analogues of Theorems 1 and 4 for logarithmic functions can be seen by inspection of the graphs given in Example 3. In this section we state and prove these theorems.

Theorem 7. Let $a, M, N \in P$, $a \neq 1$.

(I) If $a > 1$, then
   (1) $M > N$ if and only if $\log_a M > \log_a N$
   (2) $M = N$ if and only if $\log_a M = \log_a N$
   (3) $M < N$ if and only if $\log_a M < \log_a N$
(II) If $a < 1$, then
   (1) $M > N$ if and only if $\log_a M < \log_a N$
   (2) $M = N$ if and only if $\log_a M = \log_a N$
   (3) $M < N$ if and only if $\log_a M > \log_a N$

Proof: Let $\log_a M = \alpha$, $\log_a N = \beta$ so that $a^\alpha = M$, $a^\beta = N$. Apply Theorem 1. For example, if $a > 1$, then $a^\alpha > a^\beta$ if and only if $\alpha > \beta$; thus $M > N$ if and only if $\log_a M > \log_a N$. Etc.

Theorem 8. Let $a,b \in P$, where $a,b \neq 1$, and $M \in P$.

(I) If $a,b < 1$, then
　(1) If $M > 1$, $\log_a M > \log_b M$ if and only if $a < b$.
　[(2) If $M = 1$, $\log_a M = \log_b M = 0$.]
　(3) If $M < 1$, $\log_a M > \log_b M$ if and only if $a > b$.
(II) If $a,b > 1$, then
　(1) If $M > 1$, $\log_a M > \log_b M$ if and only if $a < b$.
　[(2) If $M = 1$, $\log_a M = \log_b M = 0$.]
　(3) If $M < 1$, $\log_a M > \log_b M$ if and only if $a > b$.

Proof: (I) Assume $a,b < 1$.
　(1) Assume $M > 1$. Let $\log_a M = \alpha$ and $\log_b M = \beta$. Then

$$a^\alpha = b^\beta = M$$

Since $M > 1, a^\alpha > a^0$ and $b^\beta > b^0$. By Theorem 1, $\alpha < 0$ and $\beta < 0$.
　(a) Suppose $a < b$. Then $a^\alpha > b^\alpha$ by Theorem 4(3). Since $a^\alpha = b^\beta$ this means $b^\beta > b^\alpha$. By Theorem 1, $\beta < \alpha$. Hence

$$\log_b M < \log_a M$$

　(b) If $\log_b M < \log_a M$, then the argument in (a) may be reversed to obtain $a < b$.
　(3) Cf. Exercise 9.
(II) Assume $a,b > 1$.
　(1) Assume $M > 1$. As in (I), let $\alpha = \log_a M$, $\beta = \log_b M$. Then

$$a^\alpha = b^\beta = M > 1$$

and $a^\alpha > a^0$, $b^\beta > b^0$. Now by Theorem 1, $\alpha > 0$, $\beta > 0$.
　(a) Suppose $a < b$. Then $a^\alpha < b^\alpha$ by Theorem 4(1). Since $a^\alpha = b^\beta$ this means $b^\beta < b^\alpha$. By Theorem 1, $\beta < \alpha$. Hence

$$\log_b M < \log_a M$$

　(b) Cf. (1b) in (I) above.
　(3) Cf. Exercise 9.

Exercises

9. Complete the proof of Theorem 8.
10. Which of the following is true? Justify your answer. (a) $\log_6 18 > \log_3 11$. (b) $\log_6 18 = \log_3 11$. (c) $\log_6 18 < \log_3 11$.
11. Show that if $1 < N < 10$, then $0 < \log_{10} N < 1$.

5. Applications to Computations

5.1 Introduction

The properties of the logarithmic or exponential functions can be used effectively in computations. Indeed, we shall see that we can reduce the problem of multiplication to one of addition, that of division to subtraction, and — most important — that of raising to a power to multiplication. However, we shall see that it is necessary (or at least easier) to have tables at hand; and second, the results obtained will be approximate.

The idea is as follows. Suppose we wish to find 53×672. By Theorem 2, $\exists \alpha \ni a^\alpha = 53$, and $\beta \ni a^\beta = 672$. If we had a table which listed x and a^x, we could look up 53 and 672 under a^x (Tables 15.1).

Tables 15.1

x	a^x	x	$\log_a x$
.	.	.	.
.	.	.	.
.	.	.	.
α	53	53	α
.	.	.	.
.	.	.	.
.	.	.	.
.	.	.	.
β	672	672	β
.	.	.	.
.	.	.	.
.	.	.	.
$\alpha + \beta$	35,616	35,616	$\alpha + \beta$

Then $(53)(672) = a^\alpha a^\beta = a^{\alpha+\beta}$. We now look up $\alpha + \beta$ under x, and next to it under a^x appears $a^{\alpha+\beta}$, or in this example 35,616.

If instead we use x and $\log_a x$, the columns of the first table are then reversed. For if $a^\alpha = 53$, then $\log_a 53 = \alpha$, etc.

In practice there are two bases which are most often used; one is 10, and one is an irrational number between 2 and 3, which occurs very often in mathematics and its applications. This latter number, after the eighteenth century Swiss mathematician Leonard Euler, is designated as 'e.' Its decimal expansion has been carried out to a large number of places, but we give here only the first twelve:

$$e = 2.718281828459 \ldots$$

In this section we shall work with base 10. We shall add further comments on other bases, and the number e, in Section 6. We use the logarithmic function rather than the exponential, as is traditional.

5.2 Tables

We shall work with positive numbers having three or less digits, preceded by or followed by any number of zeros. Examples of such numbers are 30,100, .0021, 2.32, 351, .00782, 806,000, 3, and .2. This is so that we can use smaller tables. The larger the number of digits, the more voluminous the tables needed.

Our first aim is to show that if we have a table for $\log_{10} 1.01, \log_{10} 1.02$, $\log_{10} 1.03$, and so forth for every increase of .01 up to $\log_{10} 1.99$, then we can compute $\log_{10} N$ for every positive number N (with the stipulation on N as above: three or less digits). When we say we have a table, we mean to a given number of decimal places, for the numbers involved are in general irrational.

We give part of such a table, where the logarithm of the number is given to the nearest fourth place:

x	5.70	5.71	5.72	5.73	5.74	5.75	5.76	$\cdots$
$\log x$	.7559	.7566	.7574	.7582	.7589	.7597	.7604	$\cdots$

Unless otherwise stated, $\log x$ shall mean $\log_{10} x$.

As seen in Exercise 10, since we are considering numbers x with $1 < x < 10$, it follows that $0 < \log x < 1$.

Example 9. Use the above table to find (to the nearest fourth place) the following:
(a) log 5710, (b) log .0057, (c) log .576, (d) log 573,000, (e) log 57.4, and (f) log .000572.

Solution: (a) $5710 = 5.71 \times 10^3$

$$\log 5710 = \log 5.71 + \log 10^3 \qquad \text{Th. 6(1)}$$
$$= .7566 + 3$$
$$= 3.7566^2$$

Note that we used the fact that $\log 10^3 = 3 \log 10 = 3$. In general $\log 10^n = n$.
(b) $\qquad .0057 = 5.70 \times 10^{-3}$

$$\log .0057 = \log 5.7 + \log 10^{-3}$$
$$= .7559 + (-3)$$
$$= -2.2441 \ (\textbf{NOT} \ -3.7559, \text{ which is } -.7559 - 3)$$

---

[2] Although we are using equals signs, it is understood that 'log 5710 = 3.7566' means log 5710 is *approximately* equal to 3.7566.

    (c) $.576 = 5.76 \times 10^{-1}$

$$\begin{aligned}
\log .576 &= \log 5.76 + \log 10^{-1} \\
&= .7604 + (-1) \\
&= -.2396 \text{ (NOT } -1.7604)
\end{aligned}$$

    (d) $573,000 = 5.73 \times 10^5$

$$\begin{aligned}
\log 573,000 &= \log 5.73 + \log 10^5 \\
&= .7582 + 5 \\
&= 5.7582
\end{aligned}$$

    (e) $57.4 = 5.74 \times 10$

$$\begin{aligned}
\log 57.4 &= \log 5.74 + \log 10 \\
&= .7589 + 1 \\
&= 1.7589
\end{aligned}$$

    (f) $.000572 = 5.72 \times 10^{-4}$

$$\begin{aligned}
\log .000572 &= \log 5.72 + \log 10^{-4} \\
&= .7574 + (-4) \\
&= -3.2426 \text{ (NOT } -4.7574)
\end{aligned}$$

The method is undoubtedly clear. Every positive number N can be written as

(1) $N = N_0 \cdot 10^n$

where $1 \leq N_0 < 10$. When N is written in the form (1), it is said to be written in *standard form*. We have seen in the above examples that (a) 5710 in standard form is 5.71×10^3, (b) $.0057 = 5.70 \times 10^{-3}$, (c) $.576 = 5.76 \times 10^{-1}$, etc.

From (1), we deduce

$$\log N = \log (N_0 \cdot 10^n)$$
$$\log N = \log N_0 + \log 10^n$$
(2) $\log N = \log N_0 + n$

Hence a knowledge of $\log N_0$ $(1 \leq N_0 < 10)$ yields a knowledge of $\log N$.

Definition 2. In (2) above, $\log N_0$ is called the *mantissa,* and n is called the *characteristic* of $\log N$.

In (a), the mantissa of $\log 5710$ is .7566, the characteristic is 3. In (b), the mantissa of $\log .0057$ is .7559, the characteristic is -3. In (c), the mantissa of $\log .576$ is .7604, the characteristic is -1. In (d), the mantissa of $\log 573,000$ is .7582, the characteristic is 5. In (e), the mantissa of $\log 57.4$ is .7589, the characteristic is 1. In (f), the mantissa of $\log .000572$ is .7574, the characteristic is -4. Thus the table gives the mantissas.

We have now seen how to find $\log N$ for any given N. We next consider the converse problem: Suppose $\log N$ is given; how do we find N? (We call N the *antilogarithm* of $\log N$.)

Example 10. Suppose $\log N = 3.7566$. What is N?
Solution: Write $3.7566 = \lambda + n$, where $0 \leq \lambda < 1$ and n is an integer. Here we have

$$3.7566 = .7566 + 3$$

Then 3 is the characteristic, and .7566 the mantissa.

Look up the table of mantissas, under log x. The corresponding x is N_0 in our earlier discussion, in this case 5.71. Hence $N = 5.71 \times 10^3$, since 3 is the characteristic, or

$$N = 5710 \text{ is the antilog of } 3.7566$$

Example 11. Suppose log $N = 1.7584$. What is N?

Solution: $1.7584 = .7584 + 1$. The mantissa is .7584, the characteristic is 1. The table of mantissas shows .7582 and .7589, but not .7584, which is in between. We take the closer one, .7582, as a suitable approximation. Thus $N_0 = 5.73$ and $N = 5.73 \times 10 = 57.3$.

Example 12. Suppose log $N = -3.2442$. Find N.

Solution: Note that $-3 > -3.2442 > -4$. Adding 4 to each number in this inequality yields

$$1 > -3.2442 + 4 > 0$$

Hence we write

$$
\begin{aligned}
-3.2442 &= -3.2442 + (4 - 4) \\
&= \underbrace{(-3.2442 + 4)}_{\substack{\text{between 0} \\ \text{and 1}}} + \underbrace{(-4)}_{\substack{\text{an} \\ \text{integer}}} \\
&= .7558 + (-4)
\end{aligned}
$$

The mantissa is .7558, the characteristic is -4. .7558 is closest to the listing of .7559 in the table, which yields $N_0 = 5.70$ so that

$$N = 5.70 \times 10^{-4} = .000570$$

CAUTION: When given log $N = -3.2442$, do **NOT** conclude that the mantissa is .2442 and the characteristic is -3.

This example shows that writing

$$\log .000570 = .7558 + (-4) \tag{$*$}$$

displays the mantissa and characteristic more immediately than by writing log $.000570 = -3.2442$. For computation problems, $(*)$ is the preferable form, as we shall see.

5.3   Reading the Tables [3]

If one looks up a table of logarithms for three digit numbers with the mantissas to the fourth place, he will see something like that shown in Table 15.2.[4]

---

[3] The methods one uses for constructing these tables are developed in one's further study of the calculus.

[4] A complete table is given in the Appendix, Table A-1.

Table 15.2

N	0	1	2	3	4	5	6	7	8	9
10	0000	0043	0086	0128	0170	0212	0253	0294	0334	0374
11	1414	0453	0492	0531	0569	0607	0645	0682	0719	0755
12	0792	0828	0864	0899	0934	0969	1004	1038	1072	1106
13	1139	1173	1206	1239	1271	1303	1335	1367	1399	1430
.										
.										
.										
57	7559	7566	7574	7582	7589	7597	7604	7612	7619	7627
.										
.										
.										
97	9868	9872	9877	9881	9886	9890	9894	9899	9903	9908
98	9912	9917	9921	9926	9930	9934	9939	9943	9948	9952
99	9956	9961	9965	9969	9974	9978	9983	9987	9991	9996

Although no decimal points appear, a decimal point is understood to be in front of every number appearing in the columns $0, 1, 2, \ldots, 9$. To find log 1.27, look up 12 (the first two digits) in the left column. Then to the right under 7 (the third digit) appears 1038. Hence log $1.27 = .1038$. This then is the mantissa of log 12.7, log 127, log .00127, and of course also the mantissa of log 1.27. The characteristics, respectively, are $1, 2, -3$, and 0.

For log 9.82, look up 98 in the left column, and to the right in the 2-column appears 9921 (so that $.9921 = $ log 9.82).

Similarly, log $5.76 = .7604$, log $1 = .0000$, log $1.3 = .1139$ and log 9.99 $= .9996$.

Exercises

12. Write the following numbers in standard form and find their logarithms by use of a table. Also state, in each case, the characteristic and mantissa of the logarithm.

   (a) 37,100.   (g) 83.2.
   (b) 4.   (h) .000832.
   (c) .0021.   (i) 7620.
   (d) 8.32.   (j) 5.31.
   (e) .9.   (k) .612.
   (f) .00007.   (l) 7.05.

13. Find the numbers of which the following are logarithms (that is, find the anti-logs of each of the following). Before using the table, state the characteristic and mantissa.

(a) .4082.
(b) 1.4082.
(c) 2.4082.
(d) 5.4082.
(e) .4082 − 1.
(f) 1.4082 − 2.
(g) −.5918.
(h) 7.4082 − 10.

(i) −2.5918.
(j) 14.4082 − 16.
(k) 17.4082 − 20.
(l) .5918.
(m) −1.4082.
(n) 7.9363 − 10.
(o) 26.990 − 30.
(p) −.8149.

5.4 Computations

Example 13. Find (approximately) $\dfrac{43.2 \times .0413}{.912}$.

Solution: If $N = \dfrac{43.2 \times .0413}{.912}$, then

$$
\begin{aligned}
\log N &= \log 43.2 + \log .0413 - \log .912 \text{ (cf. Exercise 8)} \\
&= (.6355 + 1) + (.6160 - 2) - (.9600 - 1) \\
&= .2915 + (1 - 2 + 1) \\
&= .2915
\end{aligned}
$$

To find N, we now find the antilog of .2915, which yields

$$N = 1.96$$

It is usually recommended that the above computation be worked out in the following form:

$$
\begin{aligned}
\log 43.2 &= .6355 + 1 \qquad \text{(here one can also use 1.6355)} \\
\log .0413 &= .6160 - 2 \\
\text{sum} &= 1.2515 - 1 \\
\log .912 &= .9600 - 1 \\
\log N = \text{difference} &= .2915 \\
N &= 1.96
\end{aligned}
$$

Example 14. Find $\dfrac{.321}{86 \times .00941}$.

Solution:

$$
\begin{aligned}
\log .321 &= .5065 - 1 \\
\log 86 &= .9345 + 1 \\
\text{difference} &= -.4280 - 2 \\
\log .00941 &= .9736 - 3 \\
\log N = \text{difference} &= -1.4016 + 1 \\
&= -.4016 \\
&= .5984 - 1 \\
N &= .397
\end{aligned}
$$

It is probably easier to avoid getting negative numbers such as $-.4280$ in the third line of the computation in Example 14, or -1.4016 and $-.4016$ in the fifth and sixth lines, since this necessitates line 7. One way of doing this is to write log .321 in the first line as $1.5065 - 2$, or if one wishes $2.5065 - 3$, etc. Actually, it is recommended in many books that one always write negative integers appearing as characteristics in multiples of -10 in computations with logarithms. Thus log .321 would be written $9.5065 - 10$ and log .00941 as $7.9736 - 10$. Under this recommended procedure, one can also use log .321 $= 19.5065 - 20$ or $29.5065 - 30$, etc. For the sake of consistency, we shall adopt this procedure here.

The solution to Example 14 would then look as follows:

$$\begin{aligned} \log .321 = \quad & 9.5065 - 10 \\ \log 86 = \quad & 1.9345 \\ \hline \text{difference} = \; & 17.5720 - 20 \end{aligned}$$

(we write $7.5720 - 10$ as $17.5720 - 20$ because of the next line)

$$\begin{aligned} \log .00941 = \quad & 7.9736 - 10 \\ \log N = \text{difference} = \quad & 9.5984 - 10 \\ N = \quad & .397 \end{aligned}$$

(characteristic is $9 - 10$, or -1)

Example 15. Find $\left(\dfrac{6.17 \times .0891}{48.6}\right)^{21}$.

Here the method of logarithmic computation dramatically shortens the work. If we let $M = \dfrac{6.17 \times .0891}{48.6}$, then $N = M^{21}$. By Theorem 6(3), $\log N = 21 \log M = 21 \, (\log 6.17 + \log .0891 - \log 48.6)$. The multiplication of 21 and log M can itself be done by logarithms on the side, or arithmetically if one prefers. In multiplying 21 by log M by the logarithmic method, one would have to round off log M to three digits if using the tables given here.

Solution:

$$\begin{aligned} \log 6.17 = \quad & .7903 \\ \log .0891 = \quad & 8.9499 - 10 \\ \hline \text{sum} = \quad & 9.7402 - 10 \\ \log 48.6 = \quad & 1.6866 \\ \hline \log M = \text{difference} = \quad & 8.0536 - 10 \\ \log N = 21 \log M = \quad & 169.1256 - 210 \\ N = \quad & 1.34 \times 10^{-41} \end{aligned}$$

(characteristic is $169 - 210 = -41$)

(Of course, whatever error of approximation is introduced in the computation of log M, the error is magnified 21 times in the computation of log N.)

Example 16. Find $\sqrt[6]{.0761}$.

Solution: Here $N = (.0761)^{1/6}$, and by Theorem 6(3), $\log N = \frac{1}{6} \log .0761$. We shall let $M = .0761$ below.

$$\log .0761 = 8.8814 - 10$$

Since we shall multiply by $\frac{1}{6}$, we change -10 to an integer divisible by 6.

$$\log .0761 = 4.8814 - 6$$
$$\log N = \tfrac{1}{6} \log M = .8136 - 1$$
$$N = .651$$

Exercises

14. Find (approximately) the following:

(a) $\dfrac{72.1}{.841}$.

(b) 40.1×2.79.

(c) $(.807)^3$.

(d) $(.807)^{1/3}$.

(e) $\dfrac{46.8 \times .791}{.012 \times 501}$.

(f) $69.1 \times .072 \times 8.46 \times 113$.

(g) $\left(\dfrac{7.68 \times .000732}{612} \right)^4$.

(h) $\sqrt[4]{\dfrac{7.68 \times .00732}{612}}$.

(i) $\sqrt{5.32}$.

(j) $(.0866)^{2/3}$.

(k) $\dfrac{(.732)^3 \sqrt[3]{871}}{\sqrt{10.9}}$.

(l) $\left(\dfrac{.218 \times 3.17 \times 8}{.00073 \times 87 \times 11.2} \right)^{3/4}$.

15. Given $\log 2 = .3010$ and $\log 3 = .4771$, find the following without using the tables:

(a) $\log 6$.

(b) $\log 4$.

(c) $\log .009$.

(d) $\log 8$.

(e) $\log 2.7$.

(f) $\log 5$.

(g) $\log 200$.

(h) $\log .72$.

6. Other Bases

Suppose one wished to find $\log_7 423$, and had only tables at hand for $\log_{10} x$. Then Theorem 6(7) provides a method. According to that formula,

$$\log_7 423 = \frac{\log_{10} 423}{\log_{10} 7}$$

As we have mentioned, a base which is frequently used is the base e. The reason for this is found in the calculus, and shall not be considered here. Logarithms to the base 10 are called *common logarithms;* those to the base e *natural logarithms.* In calculus texts, and in most of the mathematical literature, 'log x' refers to $\log_e x$ rather than $\log_{10} x$. Also used for $\log_e x$ is 'ln x.'

The number e can be defined to be the least upper bound of the set $\left\{ \left(1 + \dfrac{1}{n}\right)^n \in R \middle/ n \in N \right\}$. This set can be shown to be bounded above, so that the least upper bound exists. In fact, the numbers in this set,

$$(1 + 1)^1, (1 + \tfrac{1}{2})^2, (1 + \tfrac{1}{3})^3, \ldots$$

increase with increasing n (toward the number e).

Exercise

16. Find the following using a table of common logarithms. Use 2.72 as a rational approximation for e.

(a) $\log_e 32.1$.   (c) $\log_e .631$.   (e) $\log_e 10$.

(b) $\log_e 8.62$.   (d) $\log_e 1$.   (f) $\log_{10} e$.

* 7. Proofs of Theorems

We shall need the following results in the proof of Theorem 1.

(1) Let $a, d \in P$ with $a \neq 1$. Then $\exists r, s \in \bar{R} \ni$

$$1 - d < a^r < 1 < a^s < 1 + d$$

(2) Theorem 31 of Chapter 10 holds if α is assumed to be in R: Let $a \in P$ and $\alpha \in R$.

    (I) If $a > 1$, then
       (1) $a^\alpha > 1$ if and only if $\alpha > 0$.
       (2) $a^\alpha = 1$ if and only if $\alpha = 0$.
       (3) $a^\alpha < 1$ if and only if $\alpha < 0$.
   (II) If $a = 1$, then $a^\alpha = 1$.
  (III) If $a < 1$, then
       (1) $a^\alpha < 1$ if and only if $\alpha > 0$.
       (2) $a^\alpha = 1$ if and only if $\alpha = 0$.
       (3) $a^\alpha > 1$ if and only if $\alpha < 0$.

(3) If $a \in P$, $\alpha \in R$, then $a^\alpha \cdot a^{-\alpha} = 1$. [This is a special case of Theorem 3, but we shall need it in the proof of (4), which is used in the proof of Theorem 1.]

(4) If $a \in P$ and $\alpha, \beta \in R$, then $a^\alpha \cdot a^\beta = a^{\alpha+\beta}$. (This is Theorem 3(1).)

(5) If $a \in P$ and $\alpha, \beta \in R$, then $\dfrac{a^\alpha}{a^\beta} = a^{\alpha-\beta}$. (This is Theorem 3(2).)

Proof of (1): (a) We first show that if $b > 1$, then $b - 1 \leqq \dfrac{b^n - 1}{n}$ for all $n \in N$. For

$$b^n - 1 = (b - 1)(b^{n-1} + b^{n-2} + \cdots + 1) \qquad \text{by Th. 51, Chapter 8}$$
$$\geqq (b - 1)(1 + 1 + \cdots + 1)$$
$$= (b - 1)n$$

The result follows.

(b) Next we show that if $a > 1$, $\exists n \in N \ni 1 < a^{1/n} < 1 + d$. Namely, choose $n \in N \ni n > \dfrac{a-1}{d}$ (Theorem 2, Chapter 10). Then $\dfrac{a-1}{n} < d$.

Since $a > 1$, we have $a^{1/n} > 1$ [Theorem 31, I (1), Chapter 10]. Letting $b = a^{1/n}$ in part (a) yields

$$a^{1/n} - 1 \leqq \frac{a-1}{n} < d$$

Hence $1 < a^{1/n} < 1 + d$, and this proves part of (1) if we take $s = \dfrac{1}{n}$, i.e., $1 < a^s < 1 + d$.

(c) We show that if $a > 1$, $\exists r \in \bar{R} \ni 1 - d < a^r < 1$. Namely, choose n as in part (b). We shall first show $a^{-1/n} < 1$ and then show $1 - d < a^{-1/n}$. Combining these two with $r = -\dfrac{1}{n}$, we will then have

$$1 - d < a^r < 1$$

Since $1 < a^{1/n}$, we have $a^{-1/n} \cdot 1 < a^{-1/n} \cdot a^{1/n}$, or $a^{-1/n} < 1$. Hence $a^{-1/n}d < d$. In part (b) we saw that $a^{1/n} - 1 < d$. Hence

$$a^{-1/n}(a^{1/n} - 1) < a^{-1/n}d < d$$

$$1 - a^{-1/n} < d$$

$$1 - d < a^{-1/n}$$

(d) It remains to prove (1) for $a \in P$ with $a < 1$. Since $\dfrac{1}{a} > 1$, by (b) and (c), $\exists u,v \in \bar{R} \ni$

$$1 - d < \left(\frac{1}{a}\right)^u < 1 < \left(\frac{1}{a}\right)^v < 1 + d$$

$$1 - d < a^{-u} < 1 < a^{-v} < 1 + d$$

Take $r = -u$, $s = -v$. This completes the proof of (1).

Proof of (2):

(I) Suppose $a > 1$.

    (a) Consider the case $\alpha > 0$. Then $\exists r \in \bar{R} \ni 0 < r < \alpha$ (Theorem 3, Chapter 10). Then $a^r \leqq a^\alpha$ [Definition 8(1), Chapter 10]. But $r \in \bar{R}$ and $r > 0$ means $a^r > 1$ (Theorem 31, I(1), Chapter 10). Hence $a^\alpha > 1$.

    (b) If $\alpha = 0$, $a^\alpha = 1$, by definition.

    (c) If $\alpha < 0$, $\exists r \in \bar{R}$ with $\alpha < r < 0$. Then $a^r > a^s$ for every $s \in \bar{R}$

with $s \leqq \alpha$ (Theorem 32, I, Chapter 10). Hence $a^r \geqq a^\alpha$ [Definition 8(1), Chapter 10]. But $a^r < 1$. Hence $a^\alpha < 1$.

(II) Suppose $a = 1$. Then Definition 8(2) of Chapter 10 yields $a^\alpha = 1$.

(III) Suppose $a < 1$.

(a) $\alpha > 0$. Take $r \in \bar{R}$ with $0 < r < \alpha$. Then $a^r > a^s$ for all $s \in \bar{R}$ with $s \geqq \alpha$ (Theorem 32, III, Chapter 10). Hence $a^r \geqq a^\alpha$. But $r \in \bar{R}$ and $r > 0$ means $a^r < 1$. Hence $a^\alpha < 1$.

(b) If $\alpha = 0$, then $a^\alpha = 1$.

(c) If $\alpha < 0$, take $r \in \bar{R}$ with $\alpha < r < 0$. Then $a^r \leqq a^\alpha$ [Definition 8(3), Chapter 10]. Since $a^r > 1$, we have $a^\alpha > 1$.

Proof of (3): If $\alpha = 0$ the result is obvious.

(a) Assume $a > 1$. Let

$$S = \{a^x \in R/x \in \bar{R}, x \leqq \alpha\}$$
$$T = \{a^x \in R/x \in \bar{R}, x \leqq -\alpha\}$$

Then lub $ST = (\text{lub } S)(\text{lub } T) = a^\alpha a^{-\alpha}$ (Theorem 70, Chapter 10).

(i) We shall show that 1 is an upper bound of ST, from which it will follow that $a^\alpha \cdot a^{-\alpha} \leqq 1$. Every element of ST is of the form $a^r a^s$ where $a^r \in S$, $a^s \in T$, and $r, s \in \bar{R}$. But $a^r \cdot a^s = a^{r+s}$ (theory of rational exponents). Since $r \leqq \alpha$, $s \leqq -\alpha$, we have $r + s \leqq \alpha + (-\alpha) = 0$. Hence $a^r \cdot a^s = a^{r+s} \leqq a^0 = 1$. (We are using Theorem 32 of Chapter 10).

(ii) We next show $a^\alpha \cdot a^{-\alpha} = 1$. For suppose not. Then by (i), $a^\alpha \cdot a^{-\alpha} < 1$, and $1 - a^\alpha a^{-\alpha} = d$ is positive. By (1), $\exists\, p \in \bar{R} \ni 1 - d < a^p < 1$. p is negative by (2) (or also Chapter 10). Hence $-\alpha + \dfrac{p}{2} < -\alpha$ and $\alpha + \dfrac{p}{2} < \alpha$. Choose $u, v \in \bar{R}$ (Theorem 3 of Chapter 10) such that

$$-\alpha + \frac{p}{2} < u < -\alpha$$
$$\alpha + \frac{p}{2} < v < \alpha \qquad (*)$$

Then $a^u \leqq a^{-\alpha}$, $a^v \leqq a^\alpha$, so that $a^u a^v \leqq a^\alpha a^{-\alpha}$. But adding inequalities ($*$) we have $p < u + v < 0$, so that $a^p < a^u a^v$. Combining our results we have

$$a^\alpha a^{-\alpha} = 1 - d < a^p < a^u a^v \leqq a^\alpha a^{-\alpha}$$

This leads to the contradiction that $a^\alpha a^{-\alpha} < a^\alpha a^{-\alpha}$.

(b) Assume $a < 1$. Let

$$S = \{a^x \in R/x \in \bar{R}, x \geqq \alpha\}$$
$$T = \{a^x \in R/x \in \bar{R}, x \geqq -\alpha\}$$

If $r \geq \alpha$, $s \geq -\alpha$, then $r + s \geq 0$ and $a^r \cdot a^s = a^{r+s} \leq a^0 = 1$. The argument that $a^\alpha a^{-\alpha} \leq 1$ is then identical to the one given in part (a(i)) of this proof. So is the remainder of the proof, except that one uses $1 - d < a^p < 1$ (p is now positive); and

$$\left.\begin{array}{r} -\alpha < u < -\alpha + \dfrac{p}{2} \\[2mm] \alpha < v < \alpha + \dfrac{p}{2} \end{array}\right\} \quad \text{or} \quad \left\{\begin{array}{l} a^u \leq a^{-\alpha} \\[2mm] a^v \leq a^{\alpha} \end{array}\right.$$

Hence $a^u a^v \leq a^\alpha a^{-\alpha}$, $u + v < p$.

$$1 - d = a^\alpha a^{-\alpha} < a^p < a^{u+v} = a^u a^v \leq a^\alpha a^{-\alpha}$$

This yields the contradiction.

Proof of (4): (a) Assume $a > 1$. Let

$$S = \{a^x \in R / x \in \bar{R}, x \leq \alpha\}$$
$$T = \{a^x \in R / x \in \bar{R}, x \leq \beta\}$$

Then $a^\alpha a^\beta = \text{lub } ST$. We shall show that $a^{\alpha+\beta}$ is an upper bound of ST, from which it will follow that $a^\alpha a^\beta \leq a^{\alpha+\beta}$. Every element of ST is of the form $a^r a^s$, where $a^r \in S$, $a^s \in T$, and $r,s \in \bar{R}$. But $a^r a^s = a^{r+s}$. Since $r \leq \alpha$, $s \leq \beta$, we have $r + s \leq \alpha + \beta$. Hence $a^{r+s} \leq a^{\alpha+\beta}$ and $a^{\alpha+\beta}$ is an upper bound of ST. Thus we have shown that $a^\alpha a^\beta \leq a^{\alpha+\beta}$. Multiply through by $a^{-\beta}$ to obtain

(i) $a^\alpha a^\beta a^{-\beta} \leq a^{\alpha+\beta} a^{-\beta}$

Now since $a^\alpha a^\beta \leq a^{\alpha+\beta}$ for all $\alpha, \beta \in R$, we may apply this result to the exponents $\alpha + \beta$ and $-\beta$ to obtain $a^{\alpha+\beta} a^{-\beta} \leq a^{(\alpha+\beta)+(-\beta)} = a^\alpha$; i.e.,

(ii) $a^{\alpha+\beta} a^{-\beta} \leq a^\alpha$

Combining (i) and (ii) yields

$$a^\alpha a^\beta a^{-\beta} \leq a^{\alpha+\beta} a^{-\beta} \leq a^\alpha$$

Apply (3) to $a^\beta a^{-\beta}$ to obtain

$$a^\alpha \leq a^{\alpha+\beta} a^{-\beta} \leq a^\alpha$$

Hence $a^\alpha = a^{\alpha+\beta} a^{-\beta}$, and multiplying through by a^β yields

$$a^\alpha a^\beta = a^{\alpha+\beta}$$

(b) If $a < 1$, one defines S and T appropriately and then imitates the proof of part (a).

Proof of (5): $a^{\alpha-\beta} a^\beta = a^{(\alpha-\beta)+\beta} = a^\alpha$ by (4). Hence $a^{\alpha-\beta} = \dfrac{a^\alpha}{a^\beta}$.

Proof of Theorem 1:

(I) Suppose $a > 1$. If $a^\alpha > a^\beta$, then $\dfrac{a^\alpha}{a^\beta} > 1$, and by (5), $a^{\alpha-\beta} > 1$. By (2), $\alpha - \beta > 0$ and $\alpha > \beta$. The same argument applies if $a^\alpha = a^\beta$ or $a^\alpha < a^\beta$.

(II) As in (2), $1^\alpha = 1$.

(III) Suppose $a < 1$. If $a^\alpha > a^\beta$, then $\dfrac{a^\alpha}{a^\beta} > 1$, $a^{\alpha-\beta} > 1$ and by (2), $\alpha - \beta < 0$ or $\alpha < \beta$. Similarly, if $a^\alpha = a^\beta$ or $a^\alpha < a^\beta$.

We use the following in the proof of Theorem 2.

(6) Let $a, c \in P$. Let $A = \{r \in \bar{R} / a^r \leq c\}$, so that A is a subset of $\bar{R}$. Then:
   (i) if $a > 1$, A is bounded above.
   (ii) if $a < 1$, A is bounded below.

Proof: In part (a) of the proof of (1), we showed if $a > 1$,

$$a^n - 1 \geq (a - 1)n$$

Hence $a^n \geq (a - 1)n + 1$. Since $a - 1 > 0$, we may choose n so large, by Theorem 2 of Chapter 10, that $(a - 1)n > c$. Then for such an n, $a^n \geq (a - 1)n + 1 > c$. Hence n is an upper bound of A in (i), by Theorem 32, Chapter 10. If $a < 1$, then $\dfrac{1}{a} > 1$. Then $\exists n \in N$ by the above argument such that $\left(\dfrac{1}{a}\right)^n > c$. By the theory of exponents for integers, $\left(\dfrac{1}{a}\right)^n = a^{-n}$. Hence $a^{-n} > c$, and $-n$ is a lower bound of A.

Proof of Theorem 2:

We give the proof for the case $a > 1$. Let $A = \{r \in \bar{R} / a^r \leq c\}$. By (6), A is bounded above. Let $\alpha = \text{lub } A$.

(a) If $u \in \bar{R}$ and $u < \alpha$, then $u \in A$. For since u is not an upper bound of A, $\exists v \in A$ with $u < v$. But then $a^u < a^v \leq c$, and hence $u \in A$.

(b) $a^\alpha \leq c$. For suppose not. That is, suppose $a^\alpha > c$. Then $1 > \dfrac{c}{a^\alpha}$. By (1), $\exists u \in \bar{R} \ni 1 > a^u > \dfrac{c}{a^\alpha}$. Multiply through by a^α:

$$a^\alpha > a^{\alpha+u} > c \qquad \text{by (4)}$$

Hence by Theorem 1, $\alpha > \alpha + u$, and $\exists v \in \bar{R} \ni$

$$\alpha > v > \alpha + u$$

Then $a^\alpha > a^v > a^{\alpha+u} > c$ by Theorem 1. But since $v < \alpha$, $v \in A$ and hence $a^v \leq c$. This is a contradiction.

(c) $a^\alpha \geq c$. For suppose that $a^\alpha < c$. Then $1 < \dfrac{c}{a^\alpha}$ and as in (b) we obtain $1 < a^u < \dfrac{c}{a^\alpha}$, or $a^\alpha < a^{\alpha+u} < c$. Again as in (b),

$$a^\alpha < a^v < a^{\alpha+u} < c$$

or $a^v < c$. But then $v \in A$, so that $v \leq \alpha$ and $a^v \leq a^\alpha$. This is a contradiction.

(d) Parts (b) and (c) prove $a^\alpha = c$, and α is a solution of $a^x = c$.

(e) That the solution is unique is a corollary of Theorem 1.

(7) If $a \in P$ and $\alpha \in R$, then $\left(\dfrac{1}{a}\right)^\alpha = \dfrac{1}{a^\alpha} = a^{-\alpha}$.

Proof: $\dfrac{1}{a^\alpha} = a^{-\alpha}$ is a restatement of (3), and we include it here only for purposes of summary. It remains to prove $\left(\dfrac{1}{a}\right)^\alpha = \dfrac{1}{a^\alpha}$. The result is clear, of course, if $a = 1$.

(a) Suppose $a < 1$, so that $\dfrac{1}{a} > 1$.

(i) We show $\left(\dfrac{1}{a}\right)^\alpha \geq \dfrac{1}{a^\alpha}$. For suppose, to the contrary,

$$\left(\frac{1}{a}\right)^\alpha < \frac{1}{a^\alpha}$$

By Theorem 2, $\exists \beta \in R \ni \left(\dfrac{1}{a}\right)^\beta = \dfrac{1}{a^\alpha}$. Hence $\left(\dfrac{1}{a}\right)^\alpha < \left(\dfrac{1}{a}\right)^\beta$, or $\alpha < \beta$. Choose $u \in \bar{R} \ni \alpha < u < \beta$. Then

$$\left(\frac{1}{a}\right)^\alpha < \left(\frac{1}{a}\right)^u < \left(\frac{1}{a}\right)^\beta = \frac{1}{a^\alpha}$$

Hence $\dfrac{1}{a^u} < \dfrac{1}{a^\alpha}$ $\left[$since $\left(\dfrac{1}{a}\right)^u = \dfrac{1}{a^u}$ for rational exponents$\right]$. So $a^\alpha < a^u$. Since $a < 1$, it follows that $\alpha > u$, a contradiction.

(ii) We show $\left(\dfrac{1}{a}\right)^\alpha \leq \dfrac{1}{a^\alpha}$. Again, suppose to the contrary $\left(\dfrac{1}{a}\right)^\alpha > \dfrac{1}{a^\alpha}$. We let $\left(\dfrac{1}{a}\right)^\beta = \dfrac{1}{a^\alpha}$ as before, so that $\dfrac{1}{a^\alpha} = \left(\dfrac{1}{a}\right)^\beta < \left(\dfrac{1}{a}\right)^\alpha$ and $\beta < \alpha$. Choose $u \in \bar{R}$ with $\beta < u < \alpha$ to obtain

$$\frac{1}{a^\alpha} = \left(\frac{1}{a}\right)^\beta < \left(\frac{1}{a}\right)^u = \frac{1}{a^u} < \left(\frac{1}{a}\right)^\alpha$$

It follows that $\dfrac{1}{a^\alpha} < \dfrac{1}{a^u}$ or $a^u < a^\alpha$; hence $u > \alpha$, a contradiction.

(i) and (ii) prove $\left(\dfrac{1}{a}\right)^\alpha = \dfrac{1}{a^\alpha}$.

(b) Suppose $a > 1$. One may imitate the above proof. But also one may apply the result of (a) to $\dfrac{1}{a} < 1$. One obtains

$$\left[\dfrac{1}{(1/a)}\right]^\alpha = \dfrac{1}{(1/a)^\alpha}$$

$$a^\alpha = \dfrac{1}{(1/a)^\alpha}$$

$$\left(\dfrac{1}{a}\right)^\alpha = \dfrac{1}{a^\alpha}$$

(8) Let $\alpha,\beta,\gamma \in P$.
   (a) If $\alpha\beta < \gamma$, then $\exists u,v \in \bar{R}$ with $u > \alpha, v > \beta \ni \alpha\beta < uv < \gamma$.
   (b) If $\alpha\beta > \gamma$, then $\exists u,v \in \bar{R}$ with $u < \alpha, v < \beta \ni \gamma < uv < \alpha\beta$, and u,v positive.

Proof: (a) Suppose $\alpha\beta < \gamma$. Then $\alpha < \dfrac{\gamma}{\beta}$. Choose $u \in \bar{R} \ni$ $\alpha < u < \dfrac{\gamma}{\beta}$. Then $\alpha\beta < u\beta < \gamma$. Hence $\beta < \dfrac{\gamma}{u}$. Choose $v \in \bar{R} \ni \beta < v < \dfrac{\gamma}{u}$. Then $\alpha\beta < u\beta < uv < \gamma$.

(b) The case $\gamma < \alpha\beta$ is proved similarly. $\Big[$Or one may apply part (a) to $\dfrac{1}{\alpha}, \dfrac{1}{\beta}, \dfrac{1}{\gamma}.\Big]$ One sees that u and v are chosen as positive.

In (4) and (5) we have proved Theorem 3(1) and 3(2). We now prove Theorem 3(3).

(9) If $a \in P$ and $\alpha,\beta \in R$, then $(a^\alpha)^\beta = a^{\alpha\beta}$.
   (a) Assume $a > 1$, and $\alpha,\beta \in P$.

   (i) $(a^\alpha)^\beta \geq a^{\alpha\beta}$. For suppose, to the contrary, $(a^\alpha)^\beta < a^{\alpha\beta}$. By Theorem 2, $\exists \gamma \in R \ni a^\gamma = (a^\alpha)^\beta$. Since $a > 1$, $\alpha > 0$, we have $a^\alpha > 1$. Since $\beta > 0$, $(a^\alpha)^\beta > 1$. Thus $a^\gamma > 1$ and $\gamma > 0$. Since $a^\gamma < a^{\alpha\beta}$, we must have $\gamma < \alpha\beta$ by Theorem 1. Apply (8b). $\exists u,v \in \bar{R} \ni$

   $u < \alpha,\ v < \beta,\ \gamma < uv < \alpha\beta$, and u,v positive

Then $a^\gamma < a^{uv} < a^{\alpha\beta}$. Since $u < \alpha$, $a^u < a^\alpha$. Hence

$$(a^u)^v < (a^\alpha)^v$$

(Exercise 43, Chapter 10). Since $v < \beta$, $(a^\alpha)^v < (a^\alpha)^\beta$. Combining the last two steps yields

$$(a^u)^v < (a^\alpha)^v < (a^\alpha)^\beta$$
$$a^{uv} < (a^\alpha)^\beta = a^\gamma \qquad \text{(theory of exponents for } \bar{R})$$

This means $uv < \gamma$, a contradiction to the choice of u and v.
(ii) $(a^\alpha)^\beta \leq a^{\alpha\beta}$. For suppose to the contrary that $(a^\alpha)^\beta > a^{\alpha\beta}$. As before, choose $\gamma \in R \ni (a^\alpha)^\beta = a^\gamma$ so that $\gamma > \alpha\beta$. Choose $u,v \in \bar{R}$ with $\alpha < u$, $\beta < v$, $\alpha\beta < uv < \gamma$. Then $u > \alpha$ means $a^u > a^\alpha$, and as in part (i) we see that

$$(a^u)^v > (a^\alpha)^v > (a^\alpha)^\beta = a^\gamma$$

Hence $a^{uv} > a^\gamma$ and $uv > \gamma$, a contradiction.
From (i) and (ii) we conclude that $(a^\alpha)^\beta = a^{\alpha\beta}$.
(b) If $a = 1$, then $(a^\alpha)^\beta$ and $a^{\alpha\beta}$ are both 1.

(c) Assume $a < 1$, $\alpha,\beta \in P$. Then $\dfrac{1}{a} > 1$. Hence by part (a),

$$\left[\left(\frac{1}{a}\right)^\alpha\right]^\beta = \left(\frac{1}{a}\right)^{\alpha\beta}. \quad \text{But} \quad \left[\left(\frac{1}{a}\right)^\alpha\right]^\beta = \left(\frac{1}{a^\alpha}\right)^\beta = \frac{1}{(a^\alpha)^\beta}, \quad \text{applying (7)}$$

twice. Also $\left(\dfrac{1}{a}\right)^{\alpha\beta} = \dfrac{1}{a^{\alpha\beta}}$ by (7). Hence $\dfrac{1}{(a^\alpha)^\beta} = \dfrac{1}{a^{\alpha\beta}}$ and

$$(a^\alpha)^\beta = a^{\alpha\beta}$$

(d) If either $\alpha = 0$ or $\beta = 0$, the theorem is obvious.
(e) Assume $\alpha > 0, \beta < 0$. Then α and $-\beta$ are positive. $(a^\alpha)^{-\beta} = a^{\alpha(-\beta)}$.

by parts (a), (b), (c). $\dfrac{1}{(a^\alpha)^\beta} = \dfrac{1}{a^{\alpha\beta}}$ by (7). $(a^\alpha)^\beta = a^{\alpha\beta}$.
(f) Assume $\alpha < 0, \beta > 0$. Then $-\alpha$ and β are positive.

$$(a^{-\alpha})^\beta = a^{-\alpha\beta}$$
$$\left(\frac{1}{a^\alpha}\right)^\beta = \frac{1}{a^{\alpha\beta}}$$
$$\frac{1}{(a^\alpha)^\beta} = \frac{1}{a^{\alpha\beta}}$$
$$(a^\alpha)^\beta = a^{\alpha\beta}$$

(g) Assume $\alpha < 0, \beta < 0$. Then $\alpha < 0, -\beta > 0$. Apply (f).

$$(a^\alpha)^{-\beta} = a^{-\alpha\beta}. \text{ Etc.}$$

We next prove Theorem 3(4).

(10) If $a,b \in P$ and $\alpha \in R$, then $(ab)^\alpha = a^\alpha b^\alpha$.

Proof:

(1) Assume $a > 1$, $b > 1$ so that $ab > 1$. Let

$$S = \{a^x \in R / x \in \bar{R} \text{ and } x \leq \alpha\}$$
$$T = \{b^x \in R / x \in \bar{R} \text{ and } x \leq \alpha\}$$
$$U = \{(ab)^x \in R / x \in \bar{R} \text{ and } x \leq \alpha\}$$

(a) We show any upper bound of U is an upper bound of ST. For let $a^s b^t$ be any element of ST. Either $s \leq t$ or $t \leq s$; say $s \leq t$. Then $a^s \leq a^t$ and $a^s b^t \leq a^t b^t = (ab)^t \in U$, since s and t are in $\bar{R}$.

(b) We show any upper bound of ST is an upper bound of U. For suppose $(ab)^t \in U$. Then since $(ab)^t = a^t b^t$ (for $t \in \bar{R}$), $(ab)^t \in ST$. Hence $U \subseteq ST$.

(c) By (a) and (b), lub $ST = $ lub U.

(d) By definition, $a^\alpha = $ lub S, $b^\alpha = $ lub T, $(ab)^\alpha = $ lub U. But lub $ST = $ lub $S \cdot$ lub $T = a^\alpha b^\alpha$. Hence $a^\alpha b^\alpha = (ab)^\alpha$ according to (c).

(2) If either $a = 1$ or $b = 1$, the result is obvious.

(3) Assume $a > 1$, $b < 1$.

(a) Suppose $ab > 1$. Then $\left[(ab) \cdot \dfrac{1}{b}\right]^\alpha = (ab)^\alpha \left(\dfrac{1}{b}\right)^\alpha$ by part (1).

But the left side is a^α; the right $(ab)^\alpha \cdot \dfrac{1}{b^\alpha}$ by (7). Hence

$a^\alpha = \dfrac{(ab)^\alpha}{b^\alpha}$, or $a^\alpha b^\alpha = (ab)^\alpha$.

(b) Assume $ab = 1$. Then $a = \dfrac{1}{b}$, and we must show

$$\left(\frac{1}{b} \cdot b\right)^\alpha = \left(\frac{1}{b}\right)^\alpha \cdot b^\alpha$$

The left side is 1^α or 1; the right side is $\dfrac{1}{b^\alpha} \cdot b^\alpha$, which is also 1.

(c) Assume $ab < 1$. Then $\left(\dfrac{1}{ab} \cdot a\right)^\alpha = \left(\dfrac{1}{ab}\right)^\alpha \cdot a^\alpha$ by part (1).

$$\left(\frac{1}{b}\right)^\alpha = \frac{1}{(ab)^\alpha} \cdot a^\alpha$$
$$(ab)^\alpha = a^\alpha \cdot b^\alpha$$

(4) Assume $a < 1$, $b < 1$. Then $\dfrac{1}{a} > 1$, $\dfrac{1}{b} > 1$. Hence

$$\left(\frac{1}{a} \cdot \frac{1}{b}\right)^\alpha = \left(\frac{1}{a}\right)^\alpha \left(\frac{1}{b}\right)^\alpha$$

$$\frac{1}{(ab)^\alpha} = \frac{1}{a^\alpha} \cdot \frac{1}{b^\alpha}$$

$$a^\alpha b^\alpha = (ab)^\alpha$$

Finally, we prove Theorem 3(5).

(11) If $a,b \in P$ and $\alpha \in R$, then $\left(\frac{a}{b}\right)^\alpha = \frac{a^\alpha}{b^\alpha}$.

Proof: $\left(\frac{a}{b}\right)^\alpha = \left(a \cdot \frac{1}{b}\right)^\alpha$

$\qquad = a^\alpha \cdot \left(\frac{1}{b}\right)^\alpha \qquad$ by (10)

$\qquad = a^\alpha \cdot \frac{1}{b^\alpha} \qquad$ by (7)

$\qquad = \frac{a^\alpha}{b^\alpha}$

Proof of Theorem 4:

(a) Suppose $\alpha > 0$. Then if $a > b$, we have $\frac{a}{b} > 1$ and by (2), $\left(\frac{a}{b}\right)^\alpha > 1$.
By (11), $\frac{a^\alpha}{b^\alpha} > 1$ and $a^\alpha > b^\alpha$. Conversely if $a^\alpha > b^\alpha$, then $\frac{a^\alpha}{b^\alpha} > 1$,
$\left(\frac{a}{b}\right)^\alpha > 1$. But since $\left(\frac{a}{b}\right)^\alpha > 1$ we could not have $\frac{a}{b} = 1$ or $\frac{a}{b} < 1$,
since by (2) these would imply, respectively, $\left(\frac{a}{b}\right)^\alpha = 1$ or $\left(\frac{a}{b}\right)^\alpha < 1$,
which are contradictions. Hence $\frac{a}{b} > 1$ and $a > b$.

(b) If $\alpha = 0$, $a^\alpha = 1$, $b^\alpha = 1$.

(c) Suppose $\alpha < 0$. The argument then imitates the argument above in (a).

chapter xvi

TRIGONOMETRIC FUNCTIONS

We conclude our study of functions with the introduction of the trigonometric and inverse trigonometric functions. The trigonometric functions are defined in Section 2, the inverse trigonometric functions in
Section 11. We consider the graphs of these functions. We give the application of trigonometry to the "solution" of right triangles. On the basis of
the law of sines and the law of cosines, we also give the solution of arbitrary triangles. We develop 28 basic trigonometric identities, and use
these in deriving other identities and solving equations.

1. Numbers Associated with Rays from the Origin

We choose a coordinate system in the plane and label the axis of abscissas the u-axis, the axis of ordinates the v-axis, as in Figure 16.1. (We
wish to reserve 'x' and 'y' for the definitions of the functions we later
introduce in this chapter.)

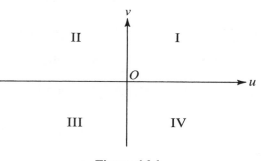

Figure 16.1

The axes divide the plane into four portions: (1) $u > 0$, $v > 0$;
(2) $u < 0$, $v > 0$; (3) $u < 0$, $v < 0$; (4) $u > 0$, $v < 0$. We shall refer to these
portions of the plane, respectively, as quadrant I, quadrant II, quadrant
III, and quadrant IV.

If l is any ray emanating from the origin, l falls either in one of the four
quadrants or else along an axis. Assume l is a ray from $O(0,0)$ not falling
along an axis, and let $P(a,b)$ be any point distinct from O on l. Let r be
the distance from P to O, so that r is the *positive* number $\sqrt{a^2 + b^2}$ (Figure 16.2).

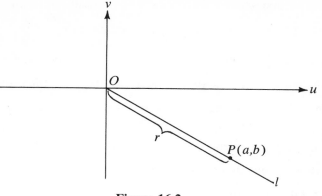

Figure 16.2

Consider the number $\dfrac{b}{r}\left(=\dfrac{b}{\sqrt{a^2+b^2}}\right)$. In the first and second quad-

rants, this number will be positive, since b is positive there (and of course $r > 0$). In the third and fourth quadrants it will be negative.

Thus for a fixed ray l, this number will always be positive or always

negative, no matter which point $P(a,b)$ was selected on l. Actually $\dfrac{b}{r}$ is

itself independent of the point on l which was selected. For if $P_1(a_1,b_1)$ is any other point distinct from O on l, we have similar triangles OAP and

OBP_1 (Figure 16.3) so that $\dfrac{AP}{OP} = \dfrac{BP_1}{OP_1}$ or $\dfrac{|b|}{r} = \dfrac{|b_1|}{r_1}$, where r_1 is the dis-

tance from P_1 to O. This is so no matter which quadrant l happened to fall in.

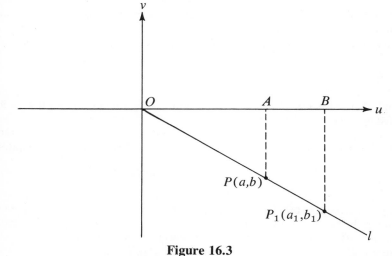

Figure 16.3

In the first and second quadrants, $|b|=b$ and $|b_1|=b_1$; in the third and fourth, $|b|=-b$ and $|b_1|=-b_1$. In either case $\dfrac{b}{r}=\dfrac{b_1}{r_1}$.

If l falls along one of the axes, $\dfrac{b}{r}$ again depends only on the ray l and not on the point P selected on l distinct from O. If l is the positive u-axis, this number $\dfrac{b}{r}$ is always 0; if on the positive v-axis, it is always 1 $(b=r)$; on the negative u-axis it is 0; on the negative v-axis it is -1 $(-b=r)$.

Thus if l is any ray from O and $P(a,b)$ any point on l distinct from O, the number $\dfrac{b}{r}$ depends only on l and not upon the particular point P selected on l distinct from O.

The same can be shown for the number $\dfrac{a}{r}$. Or again for $\dfrac{b}{a}$, when defined (i.e., when $a \neq 0$). Indeed we have the following:

Theorem 1. Let l be any ray emanating from the origin. Let $P(a,b)$ be any point on l distinct from $O(0,0)$. Then the following numbers depend only on l, and not on the particular point selected on l:

(1) $\dfrac{b}{r}$ (3) $\dfrac{b}{a}$ (5) $\dfrac{r}{a}$

(2) $\dfrac{a}{r}$ (4) $\dfrac{a}{b}$ (6) $\dfrac{r}{b}$

(This is to mean that if one of the above numbers is undefined for one point on l distinct from O, it is undefined for all such points.)

Example 1. Find the six numbers of Theorem 1 corresponding to the ray from O passing through $(-3,4)$.

Solution: Here $a=-3$, $b=4$, $r=\sqrt{(-3)^2+4^2}=5$. The numbers are therefore:

(1) $\tfrac{4}{5}$ (3) $-\tfrac{4}{3}$ (5) $-\tfrac{5}{3}$
(2) $-\tfrac{3}{5}$ (4) $-\tfrac{3}{4}$ (6) $\tfrac{5}{4}$

Example 2. Find the six numbers of Theorem 1 corresponding to the ray from O falling along the negative v-axis.

Solution: We may choose any point distinct from O on this ray. Let us choose $(0,-1)$. Then $a=0$, $b=-1$, $r=\sqrt{0^2+(-1)^2}=1$. The numbers are therefore:

(1) $-\tfrac{1}{1}=-1$ (3) $\tfrac{-1}{0}$ which is undefined   (5) $\tfrac{1}{0}$ undefined
(2) $\tfrac{0}{1}=0$ (4) $\tfrac{0}{-1}=0$ (6) $\tfrac{1}{-1}=-1$

Example 3. Consider the directed angle of $120°$ with vertex at O and initial side along the positive u-axis; and let the terminal side be l (falling in the second quadrant). Find the six numbers of Theorem 1 corresponding to l.

Solution (Figure 16.4): If P is on l, let A be the projection of P on the u-axis.

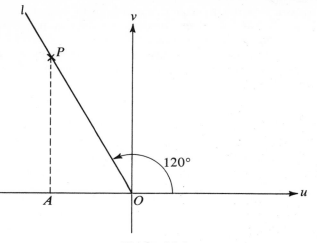

Figure 16.4

The triangle POA then has interior angles of 30° (at P), 60° (at O), and 90° (at A). We copy this triangle as Figure 16.5. If $OP = r$, then by Exercise 13 of Chapter 13, $AO = \dfrac{r}{2}$, and $AP = \dfrac{r}{2}\sqrt{3}$. It would therefore follow that the

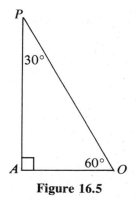

Figure 16.5

coordinates of P are $\left(-\dfrac{r}{2}, \dfrac{r}{2}\sqrt{3}\right)$. As we may choose any point on l distinct from O, we shall choose P to be 2 units on l from O (i.e., $r = 2$). Then the coordinates of P are $(-1, \sqrt{3})$.

We then have $a = -1$, $b = \sqrt{3}$, $r = 2$, and the six numbers of Theorem 1 are:

(1) $\dfrac{\sqrt{3}}{2}$ (3) $-\sqrt{3}$ (5) -2

(2) $-\frac{1}{2}$ (4) $-\dfrac{1}{\sqrt{3}}\left(\text{or} -\dfrac{\sqrt{3}}{3}\right)$ (6) $\dfrac{2}{\sqrt{3}}\left(\text{or} \dfrac{2}{3}\sqrt{3}\right)$

Remark: Had we said l was the terminal side of a directed angle of $480°$ (initial side as before), or $-240°$, etc., since l would be the same ray, the six numbers of Theorem 1 would remain unchanged.

Example 4. Let l be the terminal side of an angle of $-45°$ with vertex at O and initial side the positive u-axis. Find the six numbers of Theorem 1 corresponding to l (Figure 16.6).

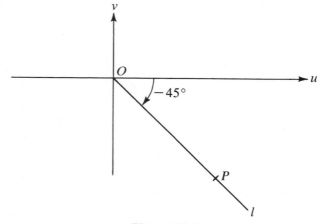

Figure 16.6

Solution: It is clear the point $P(1,-1)$ is on l. Hence $a = 1$, $b = -1$, $r = \sqrt{2}$. The six numbers of Theorem 1 are then:

(1) $-\dfrac{1}{\sqrt{2}}\left(\text{or } -\dfrac{\sqrt{2}}{2}\right)$ (3) -1 (5) $\sqrt{2}\left(\text{or } \dfrac{2}{\sqrt{2}}\right)$

(2) $\dfrac{1}{\sqrt{2}}\left(\text{or } \dfrac{\sqrt{2}}{2}\right)$ (4) -1 (6) $-\sqrt{2}\left(\text{or } -\dfrac{2}{\sqrt{2}}\right)$

Exercises

1. In each of the following let l be a ray emanating from O and passing through the given point. Find the six numbers of Theorem 1 associated with l.

(a) $(1,1)$.   (d) $(-3,2)$.   (g) $(0,6)$.   (j) $(5,-12)$.
(b) $(-2,-1)$.   (e) $(-6,4)$.   (h) $(0,-6)$.   (k) $(-3,0)$.
(c) $(4,0)$.   (f) $(-12,8)$.   (i) $(0,-30)$.   (l) $(-4,-5)$.

2. In each of the following, let l be the terminal side of the directed angle with vertex O and initial side the positive u-axis having the indicated measure. Find the six numbers of Theorem 1 associated with l.

(a) $30°$.
(b) $210°$.   (e) $\dfrac{3\pi}{4}$ radians.
(c) $330°$.
(d) $-120°$.   (f) $\dfrac{3\pi}{2}$ radians.

(g) $-\pi$ radians.

(h) $\dfrac{\pi}{3}$ radians.

(i) 450°.

(j) −720°.

(k) 2π radians.

(l) $-\dfrac{10\pi}{3}$ radians.

(m) $\dfrac{5\pi}{6}$ radians.

(n) −420°.

(o) 1440°.

(p) $-\dfrac{7\pi}{3}$ radians.

2. The Six Trigonometric Functions

We have studied polynomial, exponential, and logarithmic functions. In this section we introduce a new class of functions by means of Theorem 1.

We have seen that the measure of directed angles involves the entire real-number system. For convenience, we shall consider directed angles of the type considered in Exercise 2.

Definition 1. A *standard directed angle* is a directed angle with vertex at O, and having as initial side the positive u-axis. If the terminal side falls in quadrant I, the angle will be called a *first quadrant angle,* or an angle in the first quadrant. Similarly for second, third, and fourth quadrants.

An angle which is not a standard angle is called a first, second, third, or fourth quadrant angle if it is equal to a standard angle of that quadrant.

Example 5. Examples of first quadrant angles are (those of measure) 30°, −320°, $\dfrac{\pi}{6}$ radians, and $\dfrac{13\pi}{6}$ radians. Second quadrant angles are 170°, −210°, 460°, and $\dfrac{29\pi}{10}$ radians. Third quadrant angles are 240°, 600°, −100°, and $-\dfrac{3\pi}{4}$ radians. Fourth quadrant angles are −2°, 358°, $\dfrac{11\pi}{6}$ radians, and $-\dfrac{\pi}{24}$ radians.

Now we may define a function f with domain R as follows: If $t \in R$, consider a standard angle of measure t. Then associated with the terminal side of this angle is the number of Theorem 1 given in (1): $\dfrac{b}{r}$. Define $f(t)$ to be this number.

The question arises, however, as to *which measure* should be used. If we use degrees, we would get one value for $f(t)$; if radians another; if revolutions, still another. The fact is, different measures lead to different functions. We may take account of this as follows:

Let m, in a given measure, be the number assigned to an angle of 1 positive revolution. Thus $m = 360$ if the measure is in degrees, or 2π if in radians, or 1 if in revolutions. Then define the function f_m as follows, for $x \in R$:

$f_m(x)$ is the number $\dfrac{b}{r}$ of (1) in Theorem 1 assigned to the terminal side of a standard angle of measure x in the measuring system where m is used for an angle of one (positive) revolution.

This defines a set of functions, one for each positive number m. If the measure being used is understood, one usually calls this function "the sine of x" and writes sin x ('sin' is an abbreviation for 'sine'). At the outset, however, we shall write $\underset{m}{\text{sin}}\ x$ for $f_m(x)$.

Example 6. Let $g(x) = \underset{360}{\sin}\ x$. Find $g(30)$, $g(-330)$, $g(90)$, $g(-135)$.

Solution (Figure 16.7): (a) To find $\underset{360}{\sin}\ 30$, we consider the standard angle of 30°. We may take any point on the terminal side, say $(\sqrt{3},1)$, and we compute $\dfrac{b}{r}$. Here $b = 1$, $r = 2$, so that $\dfrac{b}{r} = \dfrac{1}{2}$. Hence $g(30) = \dfrac{1}{2}$.

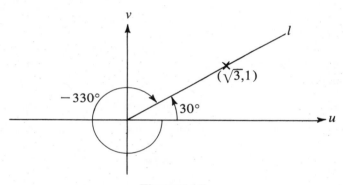

Figure 16.7

(b) To find $\underset{360}{\sin}\ (-330)$, we consider the standard angle of $-330°$. As can be seen in Figure 16.7, this standard angle has the same terminal side as the standard angle of 30°. Since the function $\underset{360}{\sin}\ x$ *depends only on the terminal side of the standard angle of measure x,* the answer here is the same as in (a): $g(-330) = \tfrac{1}{2}$.

(c) To find $\underset{360}{\sin}\ (90)$, we consider the standard angle of 90°. The terminal side is along the positive v-axis. Choose the point $(0,1)$ on this terminal side, so that $a = 0$, $b = 1$, $r = 1$. Then $\dfrac{b}{r} = 1$. Hence $\underset{360}{\sin}\ 90 = 1$.

(d) To find $\underset{360}{\sin}\ (-135)$, consider the standard angle of $-135°$. Choose the point $(-1,-1)$ on the terminal side so that $r = \sqrt{2}$. Then $\dfrac{b}{r} = \dfrac{-1}{\sqrt{2}} = -\dfrac{\sqrt{2}}{2}$.

Hence $\sin(-135) = -\dfrac{\sqrt{2}}{360} \ \ 2$ (Figure 16.8).

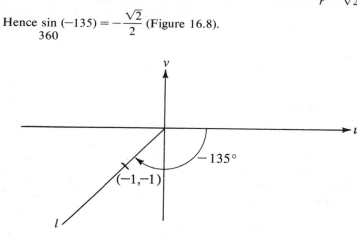

Figure 16.8

Example 7. Find $\sin \dfrac{\pi}{2\pi} 6$, $\sin\left(-\dfrac{11\pi}{2\pi} 6\right)$, $\sin \dfrac{\pi}{2\pi} 2$, and $\sin\left(-\dfrac{3\pi}{2\pi} 4\right)$.

Solution: As these involve the same angles (although different measures thereof) of parts (a), (b), (c), and (d), respectively, of Example 6, and hence the same

terminal sides, we have $\sin \dfrac{\pi}{2\pi} 6 = \dfrac{1}{2}$, $\sin\left(-\dfrac{11\pi}{2\pi} 6\right) = \dfrac{1}{2}$, $\sin \dfrac{\pi}{2\pi} 2 = 1$, and

$$\sin\left(-\dfrac{3\pi}{2\pi} 4\right) = -\dfrac{\sqrt{2}}{2}$$

We may use the other five numbers of Theorem 1 to define still other functions, and we include these and the above in the following:

Definition 2. Let $x \in R$, and let l be the terminal side of the standard angle of measure x in the measuring system where $m > 0$ in R corresponds to a standard angle of 1 counterclockwise revolution. Let $P(a,b)$ be any point on l distinct from $O(0,0)$, and let r be the length of OP. Then

(1) $\sin x = \dfrac{b}{m} \ \ r$ \qquad ($\sin$ = sine)

(2) $\cos x = \dfrac{a}{m} \ \ r$ \qquad ($\cos$ = cosine)

(3) $\tan x = \dfrac{b}{m} \ \ a$ \qquad ($\tan$ = tangent)

(4) $\cot x = \dfrac{a}{b}$ (cot = cotangent)

(5) $\sec x = \dfrac{r}{a}$ (sec = secant)

(6) $\csc x = \dfrac{r}{b}$ (csc = cosecant)

The domain of each of these functions is a subset of R. It is all of R in (1) and (2), since $\dfrac{b}{r}$ and $\dfrac{a}{r}$ are always defined. But it is undefined for those $x \in R$ which lead to $a = 0$ in (3) and (5), and $b = 0$ in (4) and (6).

Theorem 1 shows that Definition 2 does indeed define six functions.

In the mathematical literature, if one sees $y = \sin x$, the function probably being considered is $y = \underset{2\pi}{\sin} x$, although sometimes the reference may be to $y = \underset{360}{\sin} x$. The reason for the prevalence of radian measure may again be found — as was the case for the base e in logarithms — in the calculus.

As we are nearing the conclusion of our presentation in this book, we shall favor those who plan to favor themselves (by continuing their mathematical studies), and $y = \sin x$ shall mean throughout this chapter $y = \underset{2\pi}{\sin} x$. Similarly $\cos x$, $\tan x$, $\cot x$, $\sec x$, and $\csc x$ shall mean, respectively, $\underset{2\pi}{\cos} x$, $\underset{2\pi}{\tan} x$, $\underset{2\pi}{\cot} x$, $\underset{2\pi}{\sec} x$, and $\underset{2\pi}{\csc} x$. When we refer to *the* trigonometric functions, we shall mean those of Definition 2 for which $m = 2\pi$.

In this terminology, one sees that $\sin x$ and $\underset{m}{\sin} x$ are connected as follows:

$$\underset{m}{\sin} x = \sin\left(\frac{2\pi}{m} x\right)$$

Similarly for the other trigonometric functions.

Example 8. Find the trigonometric functions of $\dfrac{2\pi}{3}$ (Figure 16.9).

Solution: We choose $P(-1, \sqrt{3})$ on l. Then $a = -1$, $b = \sqrt{3}$, $r = 2$.

(1) $\sin \dfrac{2\pi}{3} = \dfrac{\sqrt{3}}{2}$ (4) $\cot \dfrac{2\pi}{3} = -\dfrac{\sqrt{3}}{3}$

(2) $\cos \dfrac{2\pi}{3} = -\dfrac{1}{2}$ (5) $\sec \dfrac{2\pi}{3} = -2$

(3) $\tan \dfrac{2\pi}{3} = -\sqrt{3}$ (6) $\csc \dfrac{2\pi}{3} = \dfrac{2}{3}\sqrt{3}$

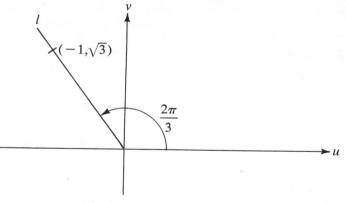

Figure 16.9

Now sometimes one sees, in the literature, sin 120° or cos 60° or tan 180°. We shall regard this as another way of writing sin 120, cos 60, $\frac{}{360}$ $\frac{}{360}$ tan 180. These are not the same as the trigonometric functions used in 360 Example 8.

Thus when we say "Find the trigonometric functions of 120°," we shall mean "Find sin 120°, cos 120°, tan 120°, cot 120°, sec 120°, and csc 120°," i.e., sin 120, cos 120, . . . , csc 120.
    360   360   360

But we wish to state that one does not find the sine, cosine, tangent, etc., of angles, degrees, or radians. One applies these functions to numbers. If one drops $\frac{\pi}{2}$ into the sin machine, out will come one answer; into the sin machine, out will come a different answer. *Hence these are dif-* 360 *ferent functions.* There often arises confusion because 90° and $\frac{\pi}{2}$ radians are measures of the same standard angle. But sin is not to be applied to 2π $\frac{\pi}{2}$ radians, but to $\frac{\pi}{2}$ or the *number* of radians; and sin is not applied to 90° 360 (even though the misleading, but practical, notation sin 90° is used for sin 90) but to 90 or to the *number* of degrees. 360

It is true that we have involved directed angles and their measures in defining these functions. But that is only one way to construct machines housing these functions. There are other ways which make no reference to angle. The approach we have taken is one which highlights the early applications one makes of these functions, but the reader will see these functions in varied colors in his further study. We may add that the same may be said of the exponential and logarithmic functions.

Example 9. Find the trigonometric functions of $-90°$.
Solution: We choose the point $(0,-1)$ on l. Thus $a = 0$, $b = -1$, $r = 1$.

$\sin(-90°) = -1$	$\cot(-90°) = 0$
$\cos(-90°) = 0$	$\sec(-90°)$ undefined
$\tan(-90°)$ undefined	$\csc(-90°) = -1$

Now that we have emphasized that one does not apply sin or cos, etc., to angles but only to numbers, we in fact will speak of $\underset{m}{\sin} A$, $\underset{m}{\cos} A$, etc., where A is an angle; or of the sin of an angle in the second quadrant, etc. This is conventional, and no confustion should arise. For what is always meant is the sin or cos, etc., of the measure of the angle involved.

For example, we can say that the sin of any first quadrant angle is positive $\left(\text{since } \dfrac{b}{r} \text{ is positive in quadrant I}\right)$; the sin of any second quadrant angle is positive; of any third quadrant angle is negative; and of any fourth quadrant angle is negative. What we mean, of course, is — for example — that $\sin x$ is negative if x is a measure (in the system m) of a third quadrant angle. We shall even speak of x being in the third quadrant in this case. In this terminology, we have:

Theorem 2.[1] (1) $\sin x$ and $\csc x$ are positive in quadrants I and II; negative in quadrants III and IV.
(2) $\cos x$ and $\sec x$ are positive in I and IV, negative in II and III.
(3) $\tan x$ and $\cot x$ are positive in I and III, negative in II and IV.

Proof: One observes that in quadrant I, a and b are positive; in II, $a < 0$, $b > 0$; in III, $a < 0$, $b < 0$; in IV, $a > 0$, $b < 0$. In all quadrants, $r > 0$.

Hence $\dfrac{b}{r}$ is positive in quadrants I and II, negative in III and IV. The same is true for $\dfrac{r}{b}$. By Definition 2(1) and 2(6), this proves (1).

Similarly, $\dfrac{a}{r}$ and $\dfrac{r}{a}$ are positive in I and IV, negative in II and III. By Definition 2(2) and 2(5), this proves (2).

The proof of (3) is similar.

We may summarize Theorem 2 by means of Table 16.1.

[1] All theorems in this chapter hold, with identical proofs, if $\sin x$, $\cos x$, ... are replaced by $\underset{m}{\sin} x$, $\underset{m}{\cos} x$, ... , and the measure of angles is taken to mean in the system m.

Table 16.1

	I	II	III	IV
sin x and csc x	+	+	−	−
cos x and sec x	+	−	−	+
tan x and cot x	+	−	+	−

Exercises

3. Find the trigonometric functions of the following:

(a) 0.   (e) $\frac{\pi}{2}$.   (i) π.   (m) $\frac{3\pi}{2}$.

(b) $\frac{\pi}{6}$.   (f) $\frac{2\pi}{3}$.   (j) $\frac{7\pi}{6}$.   (n) $\frac{5\pi}{3}$.

(c) $\frac{\pi}{4}$.   (g) $\frac{3\pi}{4}$.   (k) $\frac{5\pi}{4}$.   (o) $\frac{7\pi}{4}$.

(d) $\frac{\pi}{3}$.   (h) $\frac{5\pi}{6}$.   (l) $\frac{4\pi}{3}$.   (p) $\frac{11\pi}{6}$.

4. For each part of Exercise 3, give 4 positive and 4 negative numbers for which the trigonometric functions have the same values.

5. Let l be the terminal side of the standard angle of θ radians. Find the trigonometric functions of θ if l passes through the points indicated:

(a) (3,1).   (d) (4,3).   (g) $(-\sqrt{3},1)$.

(b) (−2,5).   (e) (6,2).   (h) (−2,0).

(c) (−4,−3).   (f) $(1,-\sqrt{2})$.

6. In Exercise 5, would your answers change if θ were the number of degrees, and the trigonometric functions were sin, cos, etc.?

$$\frac{360\ \ 360}{}$$

7. Find the trigonometric functions of the following:

(a) −30°.   (e) 360°.   (i) 750°.

(b) 225°.   (f) 315°.   (j) −750°.

(c) −540°.   (g) −45°.   (k) 270°.

(d) 390°.   (h) 210°.   (l) 135°.

3. Some Basic Formulas

In the next theorem we collect some basic formulas which will be used repeatedly, and which all follow from Definition 2.

Theorem 3. The following are identities in x over the subset of R for which the given functions are defined.

(1) $\sin x \csc x = 1$

(2) $\cos x \sec x = 1$

(3) $\tan x \cot x = 1$

(4) $\dfrac{\sin x}{\cos x} = \tan x$

(5) $\dfrac{\cos x}{\sin x} = \cot x$

(6) $\sin^2 x + \cos^2 x = 1$ [2]

(7) $\tan^2 x + 1 = \sec^2 x$

(8) $\cot^2 x + 1 = \csc^2 x$

Proof: (1) $\sin x = \dfrac{b}{r}$, $\csc x = \dfrac{r}{b}$. If $b = 0$, $\csc x$ is undefined (and $\sin x = 0$). Otherwise, $\sin x \csc x = \dfrac{b}{r} \cdot \dfrac{r}{b} = 1$.

(2) Exercise 8. (Observe that when $\cos x = 0$, $\csc x$ is undefined.)

(3) Exercise 9. (Observe that if $\tan x = 0$, $\cot x$ is undefined; and if $\cot x = 0$, $\tan x$ is undefined.)

(4) $\dfrac{\sin x}{\cos x} = \dfrac{\frac{b}{r}}{\frac{a}{r}} = \dfrac{b}{a} = \tan x$. Both sides of formula (4) are undefined if $\cos x = 0$ (i.e., if $a = 0$).

(5) Exercise 10. (Observe that both sides are undefined if $\sin x = 0$.)

(6) $\sin^2 x + \cos^2 x = \dfrac{b^2}{r^2} + \dfrac{a^2}{r^2} = \dfrac{b^2 + a^2}{r^2} = \dfrac{r^2}{r^2} = 1$.

(7) $\tan^2 x + 1 = \dfrac{b^2}{a^2} + 1 = \dfrac{b^2 + a^2}{a^2} = \dfrac{r^2}{a^2} = \sec^2 x$. $\tan x$ is undefined if and only if $\sec x$ is undefined.

(8) Exercise 11. (Observe $\cot x$ is undefined if and only if $\csc x$ is undefined.)

Example 10. Suppose $\tan x = \frac{4}{3}$ and x is in the third quadrant. Find the trigonometric functions of x.

Solution: By formula (7) of Theorem 3,

$$\tan^2 x + 1 = \sec^2 x$$
$$(\tfrac{4}{3})^2 + 1 = \sec^2 x$$
$$\sec^2 x = \tfrac{25}{9}$$
$$\sec x = \pm \tfrac{5}{3}$$

[2] '$\sin^2 x$' is used to mean $(\sin x)^2$. This convention is also used for $\log^2 x = (\log x)^2$. Also, $\sin^n x = (\sin x)^n$, etc.

Since x is in quadrant III, by Theorem 2 sec x is negative. Hence sec $x = -\frac{5}{3}$. By formula (2), cos $x = -\frac{3}{5}$. As tan $x = \frac{4}{3}$, and cos $x = -\frac{3}{5}$, by formula (4), sin $x = (-\frac{3}{5}) \cdot \frac{4}{3} = -\frac{4}{5}$. By formula (1), csc $x = -\frac{5}{4}$. Also since tan $x = \frac{4}{3}$, by formula (3), cot $x = \frac{3}{4}$.

sin $x = -\frac{4}{5}$	tan $x = \frac{4}{3}$	sec $x = -\frac{5}{3}$
cos $x = -\frac{3}{5}$	cot $x = \frac{3}{4}$	csc $x = -\frac{5}{4}$

With practice, one can use these formulas very quickly. An alternative method is a geometric argument:

Choose a point P in the third quadrant so that tan $x = \frac{4}{3}$ for any x measuring a standard angle with terminal side OP. All such P fall on the same ray (prove it!). For example, take $P(-3,-4)$. Then $a = -3$, $b = -4$, $r = 5$. One then easily computes the six trigonometric functions of x.

Exercises

8. Prove formula (2) of Theorem 3.
9. Prove formula (3).
10. Prove formula (5).
11. Prove formula (8).
12. In each of the following find the trigonometric functions of θ if:
    (a) sin $\theta = \frac{2}{3}$ and θ is in quadrant II.
    (b) cos $\theta = -\frac{2}{3}$ and θ is in quadrant II.
    (c) tan $\theta = -\frac{1}{3}$ and θ is in quadrant IV.
    (d) cot $\theta = 6$ and θ is in quadrant I.
    (e) sec $\theta = 2$ and θ is in quadrant IV.
    (f) csc $\theta = -\frac{13}{5}$ and θ is in quadrant III.

4. Graphs of Trigonometric Functions

4.1 Periodic Functions

The trigonometric functions are examples of what are generally called *periodic* functions.

Graphically speaking, a periodic function is one which is completely determined on some interval, say of length p, and the graph repeats on each preceding and succeeding interval of the same length.

Example 11 (Figure 16.10). This is a *periodic* function, having a *period* of $p = 2$. That is, if one starts anywhere, say at $x = 4$, and proceeds for 2 units (to $x = 6$), then the graph will look the same from 6 to 8, from 2 to 4, from 0 to 2, from −2 to 0, from −4 to −2, etc.

Or one may start at $x = 1$ and go to $x = 3$. The graph is then the same over $x = 3$ to $x = 5$, $x = 5$ to $x = 7$, $x = -1$ to $x = 1$, etc.

Or one may start at $x = -2.137$. And so on.

Example 12 (Figure 16.11). This is periodic, and has a period of $p = 2\pi$ (approx. 6.28).

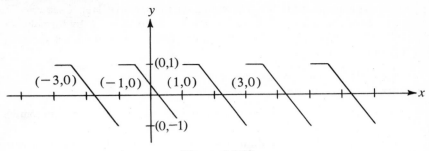

Figure 16.10

In Example 11 above, 4 is also a period of the function, since an interval of length 4 determines the function. So is 6, or 8, or 26, etc. But 2 is the *smallest* period.

Similarly in Example 2 above, 4π, 6π, 8π, etc., are periods of the function. But 2π is the *smallest* period.

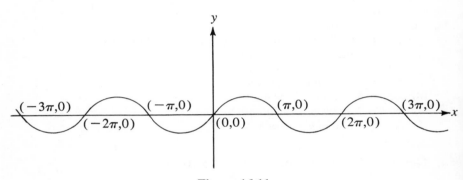

Figure 16.11

Example 13 (Figure 16.12). This function is periodic, and has a period π. The numbers $\frac{\pi}{2}$, $-\frac{\pi}{2}$, $\frac{3\pi}{2}$, $-\frac{3\pi}{2}$, ... are not in the domain of the function: the function is not defined on these points.

If x is in the domain, so is $x + \pi$; and conversely. Similarly if x is not in the domain, neither is $x + \pi$.

The function is completely determined on the (open) interval $\left(-\frac{\pi}{2}, \frac{\pi}{2}\right)$.[3]

Definition 3. Let f be a function with domain and range subsets of R. Then f is said to be *periodic* if $\exists p \in R$, $p \neq 0$, such that:

---

[3] By the open interval (a,b), where $a,b \in R$ and $a < b$, we mean $\{x \in R / a < x < b\}$. By the closed interval $[a,b]$, we mean $\{x \in R / a \leq x \leq b\}$.

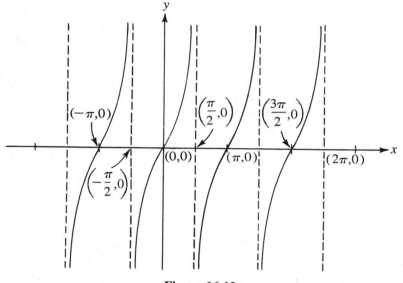

Figure 16.12

(a) x is in the domain of f if and only if $x + p$ is in the domain of f.
(b) $f(x + p) = f(x)$ for all x in the domain of f.

We call p a *period* of f. If f has a smallest positive period, we call this *the* period of f.

If f has period p then f also has period $-p$ (and conversely). For by Definition 2, $f(x - p) = f((x - p) + p) = f(x)$. So one may as well restrict himself to positive periods.

We say in Definition 3 that "*if*" f has a smallest positive period, we call this "*the*" period of f. To see that a periodic function need not have a smallest period, we consider the following:

Example 14. Let

$$f(x) = \begin{cases} 0 & \text{if } x \text{ is rational} \\ 1 & \text{if } x \text{ is irrational} \end{cases}$$

Every nonzero rational number is a period of this function.

For if p is any positive rational number, $x + p$ is rational or irrational depending upon whether x is. Hence $f(x + p) = f(x)$ for all $x \in R$.

A period of each of the six trigonometric functions is 2π. For a standard angle of measure x has the same terminal side as one of $x + 2\pi$. Thus the trigonometric functions are periodic.

We shall consider the graphs of the trigonometric functions on the interval $[0, 2\pi]$. The entire graph is then obtained by repeating this graph on all succeeding and preceding intervals of length 2π.

4.2   *Graph of y = sin x*

By definition, $\sin x = \dfrac{b}{r}$, where $P(a,b)$ is any point on the terminal side of a standard angle of measure x and r is the distance of P to the origin. If the point P is chosen always on the unit circle, then $r = 1$ and the v-coordinate of P (for this choice of P) is equal to $\sin x$. We now consider what happens to the v-coordinate of P — and hence to $\sin x$ — as x ranges from 0 to 2π.

Table 16.2

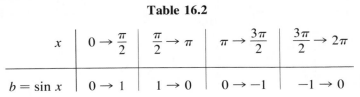

x	$0 \to \dfrac{\pi}{2}$	$\dfrac{\pi}{2} \to \pi$	$\pi \to \dfrac{3\pi}{2}$	$\dfrac{3\pi}{2} \to 2\pi$
$b = \sin x$	$0 \to 1$	$1 \to 0$	$0 \to -1$	$-1 \to 0$

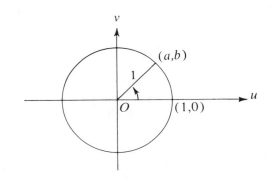

Figure 16.13

Table 16.2 and Figure 16.13 indicate the situation. We then obtain the graph of Figure 16.14.

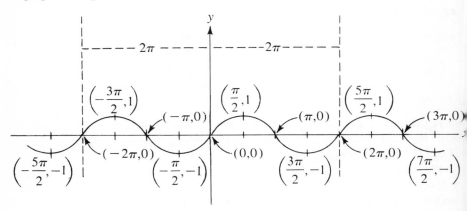

Figure 16.14

One sees from the graph that sin x has no smaller period than 2π, so that *the* period of sin x is 2π.

4.3   Graph of $y = \cos x$

We again choose $P(a,b)$ on the unit circle, and then cos x is the u-coordinate of P. One checks that Table 16.3 holds. We leave the drawing of

Table 16.3

x	$0 \to \dfrac{\pi}{2}$	$\dfrac{\pi}{2} \to \pi$	$\pi \to \dfrac{3\pi}{2}$	$\dfrac{3\pi}{2} \to 2\pi$
$a = \cos x$	$1 \to 0$	$0 \to -1$	$-1 \to 0$	$0 \to 1$

the graph to Exercise 13.

4.4   Graph of $y = \tan x$

By definition, $\tan x = \dfrac{b}{a}$. We use a similar device to graph this function as the previous ones. Namely, we wish to choose $P(a,b)$ on the terminal side of the standard angle whose measure is x in such a way that the denominator a of $\dfrac{b}{a}$ is 1. However, this is not always possible. The closest we can come to this is to choose P so that $a = 1$ in the first and fourth quadrants, and so that $a = -1$ in the second and third quadrants. (At $x = \dfrac{\pi}{2}$ and $\dfrac{3\pi}{2}$, $\tan x$ is of course undefined since $a = 0$.)

Now what happens as x ranges from 0 to $\dfrac{\pi}{2}$? In Figure 16.15, the point P on the terminal side of the standard angles of measure x rise higher and higher on the line $u = 1$. That is, the v-coordinate becomes arbitrarily large; it can be made as large as one pleases by choosing x suitably near $\dfrac{\pi}{2}$ (cf. Figure 16.16 where the graph of $y = \tan x$ from $x = 0$ to $x = \dfrac{\pi}{2}$ is given).

As x ranges from $\dfrac{\pi}{2}$ to π, the point P descends along the line $u = -1$. Hence the v-coordinate descends from arbitrarily large values to 0. Since a is -1, $\tan x$ goes from negative values of large absolute value to 0 (cf. Figure 16.17 where the graph of $y = \tan x$ from $x = \dfrac{\pi}{2}$ to $x = \pi$ is given).

As x goes from π to $\dfrac{3\pi}{2}$, the point P descends along the line $u = -1$, and its v-coordinate assumes negative values of larger and larger absolute value. But $a = -1$, making $\tan x$ positive (cf. Theorem 2). Hence we get a

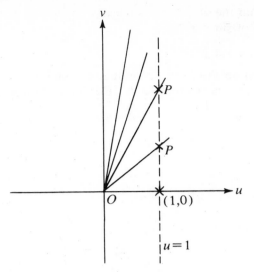

Figure 16.15

repetition of the first quadrant. Similarly, from $x = \dfrac{3\pi}{2}$ to 2π repeats

$x = \dfrac{\pi}{2}$ to π.

The graph is therefore as shown in Figure 16.18. One sees that *the period of tan x is π.*

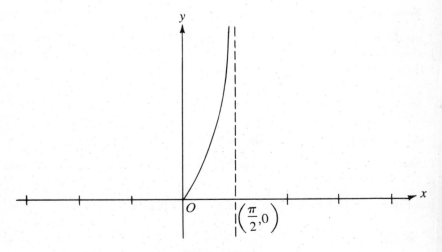

Figure 16.16

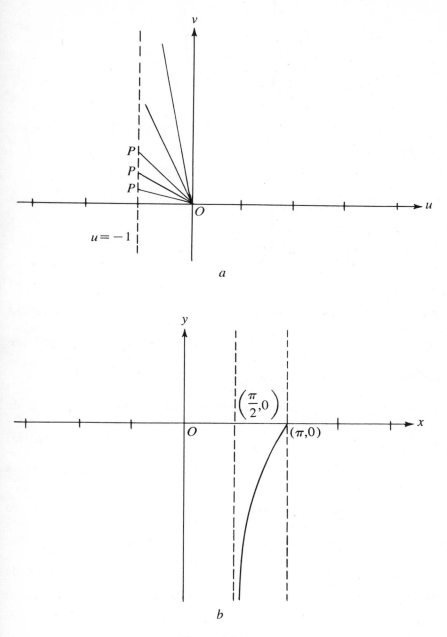

a

b

Figure 16.17

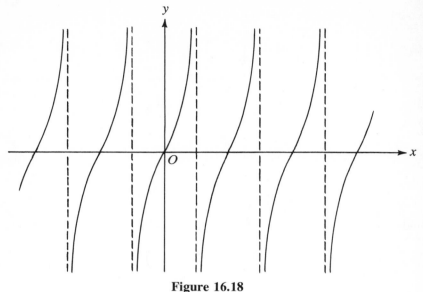

Figure 16.18

4.5 The Symbol '∞'

In computing $\tan \frac{\pi}{2}$, one takes a point $(0,b)$ on the positive y-axis, and obtains the undefined term $\frac{b}{0}$ $(b \neq 0)$. For example, $\frac{1}{0}, \frac{2}{0}, \frac{3}{0}, \frac{\sqrt{2}}{0}$, etc., are possible such terms. One frequently sees in the literature: "$\tan \frac{\pi}{2} = \infty$" and says, for this, that "$\tan \frac{\pi}{2}$ is infinity," rather than as we have said: $\tan \frac{\pi}{2}$ is undefined. One also says $\frac{1}{0} = \infty, \frac{2}{0} = \infty, \frac{3}{0} = \infty, \frac{b}{0} = \infty$ $(b \neq 0)$, etc. This notation and terminology is useful provided one understands its meaning.

Let us begin with $\frac{1}{0} = \infty$. This means that if in the expression $\frac{1}{x}$ you allow x to come nearer and nearer to 0, then $\frac{1}{x}$ will in absolute value become larger and larger; and that, in fact, $\frac{1}{x}$ can in absolute value be made as large as one pleases by choosing x sufficiently close to 0. *To say that* $\frac{1}{0} = \infty$ *expresses this behavior of* $\frac{1}{x}$ *in the vicinity of* $x = 0$.

It is in this sense that $\tan \frac{\pi}{2} = \infty$, namely, that as x nears $\frac{\pi}{2}$, $\tan x$ gets larger and larger, in fact arbitrarily large.

Sometimes one also sees "$\tan \frac{\pi}{2} = \pm\infty$." This is meant to indicate that tan x is positive on one side of $x = \frac{\pi}{2}$, and negative on the other. In fact, tan x assumes arbitrarily large positive values as x nears $\frac{\pi}{2}$ from the left, and negative values of arbitrarily large absolute value as x nears $\frac{\pi}{2}$ from the right. This can be seen clearly by inspection of the graph. For this reason one says that as x varies from 0 to $\frac{\pi}{2}$, tan x varies from 0 to $+\infty$; and when x varies from $\frac{\pi}{2}$ to π, tan x varies from $-\infty$ to 0 (Table 16.4).

Table 16.4

x	$0 \to \frac{\pi}{2}$	$\frac{\pi}{2} \to \pi$	$\pi \to \frac{3\pi}{2}$	$\frac{3\pi}{2} \to 2\pi$
tan x	$0 \to +\infty$	$-\infty \to 0$	$0 \to +\infty$	$-\infty \to 0$

4.6   The Graph of $y = cot \ x$

As cot $x = \frac{a}{b}$, we choose $P(a,b)$ on the terminal side of the standard angle of measure x so that $b = 1$ or $b = -1$ (except when $b = 0$ and cot x is undefined).

Thus, one chooses P on the line $v = 1$ in quadrants I and II, and on $v = -1$ in quadrants III and IV (Figure 16.19). Then cot x is the u-coordinate of P. We have Table 16.5. One sees that *the* period of cot x is π as shown in Figure 16.20, where the graph of $y = cot \ x$ is given.

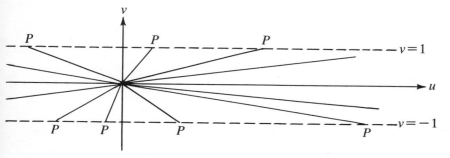

Figure 16.19

Table 16.5

x	$0 \to \dfrac{\pi}{2}$	$\dfrac{\pi}{2} \to \pi$	$\pi \to \dfrac{3\pi}{2}$	$\dfrac{3\pi}{2} \to 2\pi$
$\cot x$	$+\infty \to 0$	$0 \to -\infty$	$+\infty \to 0$	$0 \to -\infty$

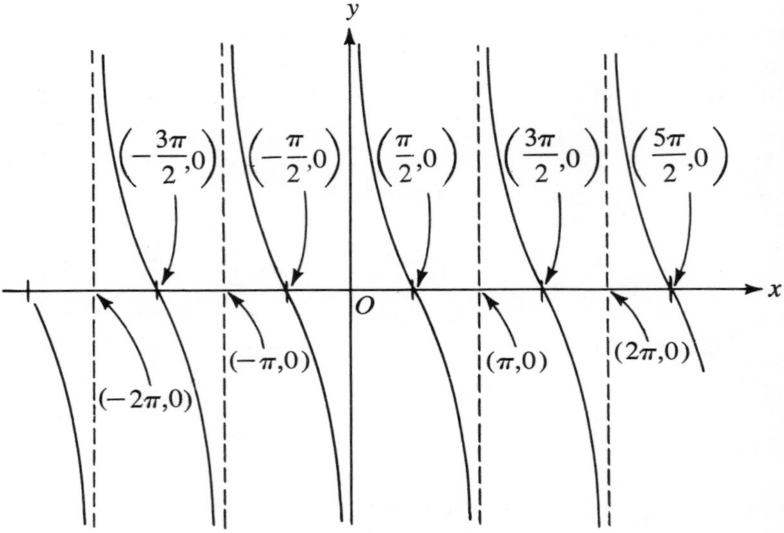

Figure 16.20

4.7 The Graph of $y = \sec x$

As $\sec x = \dfrac{r}{a}$, we again, as in Section 4.4, choose the point $P(a,b)$ on the line $u = 1$ in quadrants I and IV, and on $u = -1$ in quadrants II and III. One obtains Table 16.6. The period of $\sec x$ is 2π, as shown in Figure 16.21, where the graph of $y = \sec x$ is given.

Table 16.6

x	$0 \to \dfrac{\pi}{2}$	$\dfrac{\pi}{2} \to \pi$	$\pi \to \dfrac{3\pi}{2}$	$\dfrac{3\pi}{2} \to 2\pi$
$\sec x$	$1 \to +\infty$	$-\infty \to -1$	$-1 \to -\infty$	$+\infty \to 1$

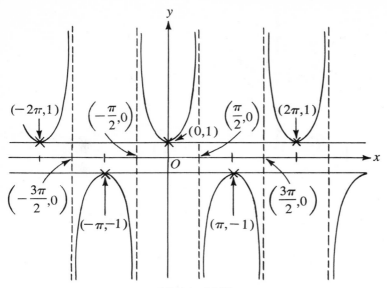

Figure 16.21

4.8   The Graph of $y = \csc x$

As $\csc x = \dfrac{r}{b}$, one chooses the point $P(a,b)$ on the line $v = 1$ in quadrants I and II and on the line $v = -1$ in quadrants III and IV. One obtains Table 16.7. The drawing of the graph is left to Exercise 14. The period of $\csc x$ is 2π.

Table 16.7

x	$0 \to \dfrac{\pi}{2}$	$\dfrac{\pi}{2} \to \pi$	$\pi \to \dfrac{3\pi}{2}$	$\dfrac{3\pi}{2} \to 2\pi$
$\csc x$	$+\infty \to 1$	$1 \to +\infty$	$-\infty \to -1$	$-1 \to -\infty$

4.9   Other Graphs

Example 15. Graph $y = \sin 2x$.
Solution: As x ranges from 0 to π, $2x$ ranges from 0 to 2π. The period is therefore π (since the period of $\sin x$ is 2π). The graph is as shown in Figure 16.22.
Example 16. Graph $y = \cos 3x$.
Solution: The period is $\dfrac{2\pi}{3}$ $\left(\text{i.e., } \dfrac{1}{3} \text{ of the period of } \cos x\right)$ and the graph is given in Figure 16.23.

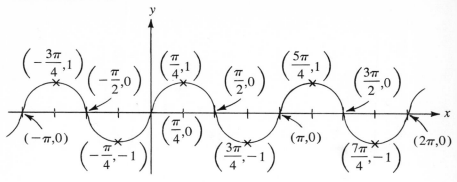

Figure 16.22

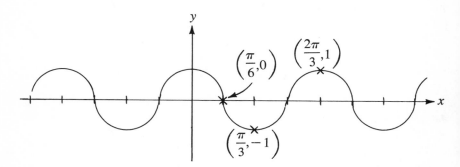

Figure 16.23

Exercises

13. Draw the graph of $y = \cos x$.

14. Draw the graph of $y = \csc x$.

15. Suppose $f(x) = x$ for $0 \leq x < 3$, and that f is periodic with period 3. Draw the graph of $y = f(x)$.

16. (a) What is the solution set of $\sin x = 5$ if $x \in R$? (*Hint:* Look at the graph of $y = \sin x$.)

(b) What is the solution set of $\sec x = 0$ if $x \in R$?

17. What is the precise domain and range of each of the trigonometric functions?

18. Tell the periods of each of the following, and draw the graphs:

(a) $y = \sin 3x$.   (e) $y = \cot 3x$.

(b) $y = \cos 2x$.   (f) $y = \sec 4x$.

(c) $y = \tan 2x$.   (g) $y = \sin \dfrac{x}{2}$.

(d) $y = \csc 2x$.

(h) $y = \cos \dfrac{x}{3}$.

5. Trigonometric Tables

We have seen how to determine particular points on the graphs of the trigonometric functions. For example, since $\sin \frac{\pi}{6} = \frac{1}{2}$, the point $\left(\frac{\pi}{6}, \frac{1}{2}\right)$ is on the graph of $y = \sin x$. But the values of x for which we have been able to evaluate the trigonometric functions have been restricted. As with the logarithmic function, tables have been constructed, and again the student will learn of the methods of constructing such tables in his further study of the calculus.

In this section we show that it is sufficient to construct such tables for values of x between 0 and $\frac{\pi}{4}$, or in degrees between 0 and 45.

Since all the trigonometric functions have a period of 2π (or in degrees, 360), it is clear that we need only construct a table between 0 and 2π.

Let α be the measure of any first quadrant angle (Figure 16.24). Consider the angles of measure $\pi - \alpha$ (quadrant II), $\pi + \alpha$ (quadrant III), and $2\pi - \alpha$ (quadrant IV). Let the terminal sides of α, $\pi - \alpha$, $\pi + \alpha$, $2\pi - \alpha$ be l_1, l_2, l_3, l_4, respectively. The rays l_1 and l_3 fall along the same straight line, as $(\pi + \alpha) - \alpha$ is π; similarly l_2 and l_4 fall along the same straight line. Indeed each ray forms a (Euclidean) angle equal to α with the u-axis: l_1 and l_4 with the positive u-axis, l_2 and l_3 with the negative u-axis.

Draw a circle of radius r, center at the origin, letting P_1, P_2, P_3, P_4 be the points in which it intersects l_1, l_2, l_3, l_4, respectively. The absolute values of the coordinates of each of these points are easily seen to be equal. It follows from Theorem 2 that knowing the trigonometric functions for α allows one to conclude the values for $\pi - \alpha$, $\pi + \alpha$, $2\pi - \alpha$ [or for α in degrees, $180 - \alpha$, $180 + \alpha$, $360 - \alpha$].

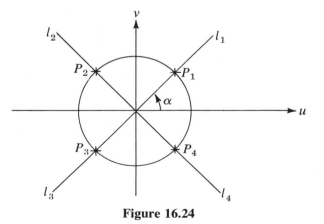

Figure 16.24

We show through examples how this discussion allows one to determine the trigonometric functions for all x from a knowledge of them on values of x between 0 and $\frac{\pi}{2}$ (or 0 and 90 in degrees).

Example 17. If $\cos \frac{3\pi}{20} = .891$ (approximately), find $\cos \frac{77\pi}{20}$.

Solution: Of course $\frac{3\pi}{20}$ is in the first quadrant. Now $\frac{77\pi}{20}$ is larger than 2π. Dividing $\frac{77\pi}{20}$ by 2π yields

$$\frac{77\pi}{20} = 1(2\pi) + \frac{37\pi}{20}$$

so that the trigonometric functions of $\frac{77\pi}{20}$ are the same as those for $\frac{37\pi}{20}$, which is in the fourth quadrant. Thus $\frac{37\pi}{20}$ can be written

$$\frac{37\pi}{20} = 2\pi - \alpha$$

where α is in the first quadrant. Solving for α yields

$$\alpha = \frac{3\pi}{20}$$

Hence the trigonometric functions of $\frac{3\pi}{20}$ are the same, *in absolute value*, as those of $\frac{37\pi}{20}$. But $\cos x$ is positive in the fourth quadrant, by Theorem 2. Hence $\cos \frac{37\pi}{20} = \cos \frac{3\pi}{20} = .891$, so that $\cos \frac{77\pi}{20} = .891$.

Example 18. If $\sec 81° = 6.392$ (approx.), find $\sec 261°$.
Solution: As $261°$ is in the third quadrant, write

$$261 = 180 + \alpha$$

for α in the first quadrant. Then $\alpha = 81$. Hence

$$|\sec 261°| = \sec 81°$$

But $\sec x$ is negative in the third quadrant (Theorem 2). Hence

$$\sec 81° = -6.392$$

Example 19. If $\tan 24° = .4452$ (approx.), find $\tan(-1284°)$.
Solution: $-1284 = (-4)(360) + 156$, and hence the trigonometric functions of $-1284°$ are the same as those for $156°$.

But $156°$ is in the second quadrant. Write

$$156 = 180 - \alpha$$

for α in the first quadrant. Then $\alpha = 24$. Then $|\tan 156| = \tan 24$. Hence $\tan 156 = -\tan 24 = -.4452$ by Theorem 2.

It remains to show how one can evaluate the trigonometric functions on values of x between $\frac{\pi}{4}$ and $\frac{\pi}{2}$ (45 and 90, if in degrees) if one knows them for values of x between 0 and $\frac{\pi}{4}$ (0 and 45, if in degrees).

The basic formulas used are the following:

$$\sin\left(\frac{\pi}{2} - x\right) = \cos x \qquad \left(\text{or } \sin\underset{360}{(90} - x) = \cos\underset{360}{x}\right)$$

$$\cos\left(\frac{\pi}{2} - x\right) = \sin x$$

$$\tan\left(\frac{\pi}{2} - x\right) = \cot x$$

$$\cot\left(\frac{\pi}{2} - x\right) = \tan x$$

$$\sec\left(\frac{\pi}{2} - x\right) = \csc x$$

$$\csc\left(\frac{\pi}{2} - x\right) = \sec x$$

We will show that these formulas hold for all x (for which the functions are defined) in Section 9.

For the case which concerns us (x in the first quadrant), the result is easily seen from Definition 2. Take l_1 to be the terminal side of x, and l_2 the terminal side of $\frac{\pi}{2} - x$ (Figure 16.25). The ray l_2 is obtained from l_1 by

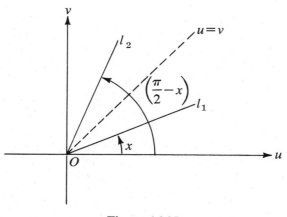

Figure 16.25

reflection in the line $u = v$. If $P_1(a,b)$ is on l_1, then $P_2(b,a)$ is on l_2 and the distance r of both P_1 and P_2 to O is the same. Hence $\sin x = \dfrac{b}{r}$, $\cos x = \dfrac{a}{r}$ (using P_1). Similarly, $\sin \left(\dfrac{\pi}{2} - x\right) = \dfrac{a}{r}$, $\cos \left(\dfrac{\pi}{2} - x\right) = \dfrac{b}{r}$ (using P_2). This yields the first two of the above formulas. The rest are proved similarly.

Example 20. If $\tan 24° = .4452$ (approx.), find $\cot 294°$.
Solution: $294°$ is in the fourth quadrant. $294 = 360 - \alpha$, where $\alpha = 66$. Hence $|\cot 294°| = \cot 66°$, and so $\cot 294° = -\cot 66°$. But

$$\cot 66° = \tan (90 - 66)° = \tan 24°$$

Thus $\cot 294° = -.4452$.

We shall consider trigonometric tables given in degrees. For radians one can either convert to degrees, or look up a table given in radians. Some tables list the values for the trigonometric functions for each degree. Some divide each degree into 60 equal parts, each part being called a *minute*. Thus 28 degrees and 32 minutes is written $28°32'$ and means $28 + \frac{32}{60}$ degrees. Some tables divide each minute into 60 equal parts, each part being called a *second*. Thus $28°32'46''$ means $28 + \frac{32}{60} + \frac{46}{3600}$ degrees.

A table given in degrees, with values approximated to the fourth place, would look as shown in Table 16.8. The complete table is given in the Appendix in Table A-2. To find the trigonometric functions of x between $0°$ and $45°$, one uses the left column, where the number of degrees is listed, and then to the right *under* the appropriate function listed at the top.

To find the trigonometric functions of x between $45°$ and $90°$, one uses the right column for the appropriate number of degrees, and then to the left *above* the appropriate function listed at the bottom.

If $\alpha°$ appears in the left column, then $(90 - \alpha)°$ appears on the same line in the right column. Since $\sin \alpha° = \cos (90 - \alpha)°$, the column used for $\sin x$ for the left column is the same as that used for $\cos x$ in the right column.

Thus $\sin 3°$ and $\cos 87°$ are both found in the same place, and are equal to $.0523$. Similarly $\tan 3° = \cot 87° = .0524$, $\cot 3° = \tan 87° = 19.08$, $\sec 3° = \csc 87° = 1.001$, etc.

Conversely, if one is given $\sin \theta° = .0352$, one looks under the sin column or above the sin column until one reaches an entry as close to $.0352$ as possible. In this case, the closest entry is $.0349$, corresponding to $2°$. One cannot conclude, however, that $\theta = 2$ without further information. For example, if θ were in the second quadrant, we would have $\theta = 178$ (approximately).

Example 21. If $\tan \theta° = 21.03$, and $\csc \theta° < 0$, find θ if θ is between 0 and 360.
Solution: Since $\tan \theta°$ is positive, θ is in the first or third quadrant. But since $\csc \theta°$ is negative, θ must be in the third quadrant.

Table 16.8

	sin	cos	tan	cot	sec	csc	
0°	.0000	1.0000	.0000	· · ·	1.000	· · ·	90°
1°	.0175	.9998	.0175	57.29	1.000	57.30	89°
2°	.0349	.9994	.0349	28.64	1.001	28.65	88°
3°	.0523	.9986	.0524	19.08	1.001	19.11	87°
.	.	.	.	.	.	.	.
.	.	.	.	.	.	.	.
.	.	.	.	.	.	.	.
44°	.6947	.7193	.9657	1.036	1.390	1.440	46°
45°	.7071	.7071	1.0000	1.000	1.414	1.414	45°
	cos	sin	cot	tan	csc	sec	

We look up 21.03 under tan or above tan in the tables. It is closest to 19.08 above tan. This corresponds to 87° found in the right column. But θ is in the third quadrant. Hence $\theta = 180 + 87$, or $\theta = 267$.

Exercises

19. Find the following (approx.) by using a table.

(a) sin 40°.
(b) cos 211°.
(c) tan 162°.
(d) cot (−32°).
(e) sec (−187°).
(f) csc 1281°.
(g) sin 687°.
(h) cos (−943°).
(i) tan 458°.
(j) cot (−458°).
(k) sec 1356°.
(l) csc (−1356°).

20. In each of the following, θ is between 0 and 360 and is the measure of a directed angle in degrees satisfying the given conditions. Find θ by use of the trigonometric tables.

(a) sin $\theta° = -.4216$ and cos $\theta° < 0$.
(b) cos $\theta° = .3172$ and tan $\theta° < 0$.
(c) tan $\theta° = 6.271$ and csc $\theta° < 0$.
(d) cot $\theta° = -2.765$ and sin $\theta° > 0$.
(e) sec $\theta° = 2.612$ and cot $\theta° > 0$.
(f) csc $\theta° = -3.105$ and sec $\theta° > 0$.

6. Applications to Solutions of Right Triangles

The general problem we solve in this section is the following: Given a right triangle, and given (a) the length of one of its sides and the measure of one of its (acute) angles, or (b) the length of two of its sides, to determine the remaining parts of the triangle. Determining the length of each of the sides of a triangle, and the measures of each of its interior angles, is called *solving the triangle*.

Let A, B, C be the vertices of any right triangle with right angle at C (Figure 16.26). If we have a given coordinate system, where the u-axis is

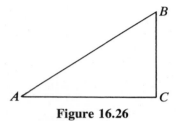

Figure 16.26

the axis of abscissas and the v-axis the axis of ordinates, we may, by a rigid motion through space, place the triangle ABC so that A is at the origin, C is on the positive u-axis, and B is in the first quadrant (Figure 16.27). Then the u-coordinate of B is the length of AC, and the v-co-

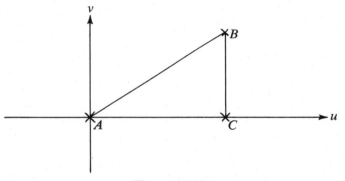

Figure 16.27

ordinate the length of BC. It follows that

$$\sin A = \frac{BC}{AB} \qquad \cot A = \frac{AC}{BC}$$

$$\cos A = \frac{AC}{AB} \qquad \sec A = \frac{AB}{AC}$$

$$\tan A = \frac{BC}{AC} \qquad \csc A = \frac{AB}{BC}$$

In terms of any right triangle, without regard to notation used, we may say:

> The sine of an acute angle of a right triangle is the opposite side divided by the hypotenuse; the cosine of an acute angle of a right triangle is the adjacent side divided by the hypotenuse; etc.

Using opp, adj, and hyp as abbreviations for (the length of) the opposite side, the adjacent side, and the hypotenuse, respectively, we have:

Theorem 4. Let θ be an acute angle of a right triangle.

Then: (1) $\sin \theta = \dfrac{\text{opp}}{\text{hyp}}$ (4) $\cot \theta = \dfrac{\text{adj}}{\text{opp}}$

(2) $\cos \theta = \dfrac{\text{adj}}{\text{hyp}}$ (5) $\sec \theta = \dfrac{\text{hyp}}{\text{adj}}$

(3) $\tan \theta = \dfrac{\text{opp}}{\text{adj}}$ (6) $\csc \theta = \dfrac{\text{hyp}}{\text{opp}}$

We now show how to solve the problem posed at the beginning of this section by means of several examples. In each of these examples, ABC is a right triangle with right angle at C, and a, b, c the sides opposite A, B, C, respectively. We also call A, B, C the angles of the triangle.

Example 22. Let $A = 37°$, $b = 41$. Solve the triangle (Figure 16.28).

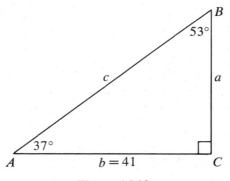

Figure 16.28

Solution: It is clear that $B = 53°$. To find a, if we work with angle A, we use that trigonometric function in Theorem 4 which places a in the numerator, and b (which we know) in the denominator. (This is because it is usually easier to multiply two numbers than it is to divide two numbers.) Thus

$$\tan 37° = \frac{a}{41} \quad \text{Th. 4(3)}$$
$$a = 41 \tan 37°$$

In the tables we find tan $37° = .7536$. Hence

$$a = 41(.7536)$$
$$= 30.9 \quad \text{(to the nearest tenth)}$$

To find c, we use Theorem 4(5).

$$\sec 37° = \frac{c}{41}$$
$$c = 41(1.252)$$
$$= 51.3$$

Example 23. If $a = 27$, $c = 49$, solve the triangle (Figure 16.29).

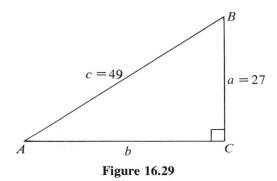

Figure 16.29

Solution: Of course we can find b by the Pythagorean theorem, but we shall instead use the trigonometric method. We may use either Theorem 4(1) or 4(6).

$$\sin A = \tfrac{27}{49} = .5510$$

Looking up the table under sin for the angle listed whose sine is closest to .5510, we find $A = 33°$ (approx.). Using this angle and either $a = 27$ or $c = 49$, we may find b. By Theorem 4(4), $\cot 33° = \dfrac{b}{27}$.

$$b = 27(1.540) = 41.6$$

(Of course, B is the complement of A.)

Exercise

21. Let A, B, C, a, b, c have the same meaning as in the examples of this section. Solve each of the following right triangles.

(a) $a = 30$, $B = 62°$.
(b) $a = 9$, $A = 38°$.
(c) $a = 21$, $b = 32$.
(d) $a = 11$, $c = 16$.
(e) $b = 9$, $c = 20$.
(f) $b = 6$, $A = 8°$.
(g) $b = 97$, $B = 71°$.

7. Solution of Arbitrary Triangles

The problem considered in Section 6 is a special case of the following problem:

Given any three parts of a triangle,[4] to solve the triangle; or where there is more than one triangle satisfying the given conditions, to solve all such triangles.

The parts one is given may be divided into cases as follows:

(a) Three sides (*s.s.s.*)
(b) Two sides and the included angle (*s.a.s.*)
(c) Two sides and a nonincluded angle (*a.s.s.*)
(d) Two angles and the included side (*a.s.a.*)
(e) Two angles and a nonincluded side (*s.a.a.*)

According to the theorems on congruence in Euclidean geometry, all parts of the triangle are uniquely determined in each of the above cases except (c). Accordingly, (c) is called *the ambiguous case*.

In Section 6, given a side and an angle of a right triangle (hence given another angle — of 90°) may be placed under (d) and (e). Given two sides of a right triangle is included in (b) and (c).

To solve the general triangle, two basic theorems are used.

Theorem 5 (The Law of Sines). Let A, B, C be the vertices of any triangle and a, b, c the corresponding (i.e., opposite) sides. Then

$$\frac{a}{\sin A} = \frac{b}{\sin B} = \frac{c}{\sin C}$$

Theorem 6 (The Law of Cosines). Let a triangle be given as in Theorem 5. Then

(1) $a^2 = b^2 + c^2 - 2bc \cos A$
(2) $b^2 = a^2 + c^2 - 2ac \cos B$
(3) $c^2 = a^2 + b^2 - 2ab \cos C$

[We need state only one of the above, since, for example, in (1), a can be any side, and b and c the two others. The angle appearing is the one opposite to the side appearing on the left of the formula.]

We shall prove both these formulas in the next section. In this section we show how they are used in the solution of the triangle. Note that if, say, $C = 90°$, Theorem 6(3) reduces to the Pythagorean theorem, and Theorem 5 reduces to Theorem 4(1).

We now give methods for solving each case.

Case (a): Given sides a, b, c. To find the angles.

---

[4] As two angles of a triangle determine the third, we count three given angles as being given two parts as regards the statement of this problem.

Solution: Use the law of cosines, say, Theorem 6(1), to find $\cos A$, Theorem 6(2) to find $\cos B$. If $\cos A$ is positive, A is acute; if $\cos A$ is negative, A is obtuse. Of course, if $\cos A = 0$, A is a right angle. The same for $\cos B$.

Case (b): Given two sides and the included angle, say, a, b, C.

Solution: Use the law of cosines to find side c [Theorem 6(3)]. Then use the law of cosines again [either Theorem 6(1) or 6(2)] to find A or B. (One could also use the law of sines, but finding $\sin A$ or $\sin B$ does not distinguish whether A is in the first or second quadrant, since $\sin x$ is positive in both these quadrants. Of course, if C is obtuse, then A and B would be known to be acute angles, and the law of sines can effectively be used.)

Case (c) (The Ambiguous Case): Given two sides and a nonincluded angle, say, A, a, b.

Solution: We must consider the case A is acute or A is obtuse separately.
(α) Assume A is acute. Draw angle A where one of the sides is b, given, and the other c to be determined (Figure 16.30). From C, drop a perpendicular meeting the opposite side at D. Then CD is the altitude of the triangle, and since $\sin A = \dfrac{CD}{b}$, we have $CD = b \sin A$.

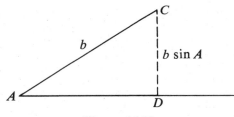

Figure 16.30

Draw a circle from C having radius a. Where this circle intersects the side through A and D determines the possibilities for the point B for which $CB = a$.
    (i) If $a < CD$, there is no point of intersection, and hence no triangle with the given conditions. Since $CD = b \sin A$, this is the case $a < b \sin A$.
    (ii) If $a = b \sin A$, then $D = B$, and we obtain a uniquely determined right triangle. It is then clear how to solve this triangle.
    (iii) $b \sin A < a < b$. In this case, there are two possible points B, and hence two triangles satisfying the given conditions (Figure 16.31). In one case B is an obtuse angle, in

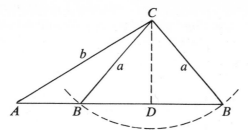

Figure 16.31

the other B is an acute angle. To solve these two triangles, use the law of sines (Theorem 4)

$$\frac{a}{\sin A} = \frac{b}{\sin B}$$

and solve for $\sin B$. Choosing B in quadrant I will give the acute angle for one of the triangles, in quadrant II will give the obtuse angle for the other triangle. Having A and B yields C. Use the law of sines again (in each case separately),

$$\frac{a}{\sin A} = \frac{c}{\sin C}$$

to determine c. [*Caution:* Determine B (two possibilities) first, not C.]

(iv) If $a = b$, the circle of center C and radius a intersects the opposite side in two points as in the previous case, but one of the points is A which does not lead to a triangle. Hence we obtain one triangle in this case, which is isosceles. This means $B = A$, and hence C is determined. It remains only to find c. Use $\dfrac{c}{\sin C} = \dfrac{a}{\sin A}$.

(v) If $a > b$, then one obtains one triangle, as in case (iv).

(β) Assume A is obtuse (Figure 16.32). Here it is clear there is no

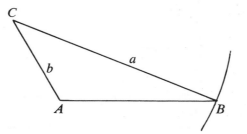

Figure 16.32

solution if $a \leq b$. If $a > b$, then drawing a circle of radius a from C will uniquely determine the point B on the opposite side.

To solve the triangle in this case, use the law of sines:

$$\frac{a}{\sin A} = \frac{b}{\sin B}$$

to determine $\sin B$. But since A is obtuse, B is acute and is hence uniquely determined. Then C is determined. Then use

$$\frac{a}{\sin A} = \frac{c}{\sin C}$$

to determine c.

Case (d): Given two angles and the included side, say B, C, a.

Solution: Knowing B and C determines A. Use the law of sines twice:

$$\frac{a}{\sin A} = \frac{b}{\sin B} \qquad \text{to determine } b$$
$$\frac{a}{\sin A} = \frac{c}{\sin C} \qquad \text{to determine } c$$

Case (e): Given two angles and a nonincluded side.

Solution: Same as case (d).

Summary: (a) *s.s.s.*: Use law of cosines twice.

(b) *s.a.s.*: Use law of cosines twice and if the angle given is obtuse, one may also use the law of cosines followed by the law of sines.

(c) *a.s.s.*, given A, a, b.

(α) A acute:

(i) $a < b \sin A$: no solution.

(ii) $a = b \sin A$: one solution; right triangle.

(iii) $b \sin A < a < b$: two solutions; use law of sines twice.

(iv) $a = b$: one solution, an isosceles triangle; use law of sines.

(v) $a > b$: one solution; use same method as in (iv).

(β) A obtuse:

(i) $a \leq b$: no solution.

(ii) $a > b$: one solution; use law of sines twice.

(d) *a.s.a.*: Use law of sines twice.

(e) *s.a.a.*: Use law of sines twice.

The solution is uniquely determined, except in the ambiguous case (c). In the ambiguous case, we used the letters A, a, b but, of course, it also applies for B, b, c; or A, a, c; or C, c, b; etc.

We remark there are other obvious situations where there is no solution. In (a), the sum of two given sides cannot be less than or equal to the third. And in (d) and (e), the sum of the two given angles must be less than 180°.

Example 24. Given $a = 8$, $c = 11$, $B = 52°$. Solve the triangle (Figure 16.33).

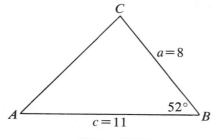

Figure 16.33

Solution: This is the case *s.a.s.* Use Theorem 6(2):

$$b^2 = a^2 + c^2 - 2ac \cos B$$
$$= 64 + 121 - 176 \cos 52°$$
$$= 185 - 176 \cos 52°$$

Now here, one can either find cos 52° and multiply by 176, or one can use logarithms. For this purpose, we point out that the logarithms of the trigonometric functions have been tabulated. Thus one can look up cos 52° in one table and the log of the result in another, or one can look up log cos 52° directly. One finds log cos $52° = 9.7893 - 10$. (In most tables, the '−10' is omitted, but understood. The characteristic must be −1, since cos 52° is between 0 and 1.)

Thus if $N = 176 \cos 52°$, log $N = \log 176 + \log \cos 52°$.

$$\log 176 = 2.2455$$
$$\underline{\log \cos 52° = 9.7893 - 10}$$
$$\text{sum} = \log N = 12.0348 - 10$$
$$N = 108 \text{ (approx.)}$$

Hence $b^2 = 185 - 108 = 77$. Hence $b = \sqrt{77}$.[5]

Example 25. Given $b = 6$, $c = 8$, $B = 28°$.

Solution: This is *a.s.s.*, where the given angle is acute. The side b is opposite the given angle. We have $b < c$, and we must now check how b compares with $c \sin B$. But sin $B = .4695$, so that $c \sin B = 3.7560$. Hence we have

$$c \sin B < b < c$$

and we are in (αiii) of the ambiguous case. There are two solutions (Figure 16.34).

Using the law of sines $\dfrac{b}{\sin B} = \dfrac{c}{\sin C}$, so that $\sin C = \dfrac{c \sin B}{b}$, we may

---

[5] One may now use the formula $a^2 = b^2 + c^2 - 2bc \cos A$ to determine A, since a, b, c are all known.

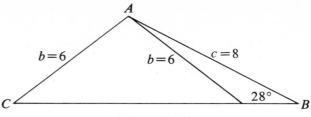

Figure 16.34

determine sin C. (In this example, the numbers are such that it does not pay to use logarithms. But the law of sines is well suited for using logarithmic computation. One would have log sin $C = \log c + \log \sin B - \log b$. One would then compute log sin C, and determine C directly from a log sin table.)

$$\sin C = \frac{3.7560}{6} = .6260$$

The angle in the table corresponding to .6260 is 39°. Hence the two possibilities for us are 39° and 141°.

Triangle 1: $b = 6$, $c = 8$, $B = 28°$, $C = 39°$, $A = 113°$.

$$\frac{b}{\sin B} = \frac{a}{\sin A} \quad \text{or} \quad a = \frac{b \sin A}{\sin B} = \frac{6 \sin 113°}{\sin 28°} = \frac{6 \sin 67°}{\sin 28°}$$

$\log a = \log 6 + \log \sin 67° - \log \sin 28°$. One then determines a.

Triangle 2: $b = 6$, $c = 8$, $B = 28°$, $C = 141°$, $A = 11°$.

$$a = \frac{b \sin A}{\sin B} = \frac{6 \sin 11°}{\sin 28°}$$

and one can determine a.

Exercise

22. Solve the following triangles:
    (a) $a = 11$, $B = 63°$, $C = 48°$.   (f) $a = 13$, $b = 9$, $B = 81°$.
    (b) $b = 17$, $A = 113°$, $B = 22°$.   (g) $b = 11$, $c = 15$, $C = 122°$.
    (c) $c = 27$, $A = 72°$, $B = 33°$.   (h) $a = 16$, $c = 12$, $C = 27°$.
    (d) $a = 3$, $b = 4$, $c = 5$.   (i) $a = 17$, $b = 12$, $C = 72°$.
    (e) $a = 4$, $b = 5$, $c = 6$.   (j) $a = 10$, $c = 20$, $B = 141°$.

8. Proofs of Law of Sines and Law of Cosines

8.1 The Law of Sines

We now prove Theorem 5. There are three cases: (1) all the angles are acute; (2) one of the angles is a right angle; (3) one of the angles is an obtuse angle.

Case (1): All angles are acute (Figure 16.35). Drop a perpendicular from C meeting the opposite side AB at D. Then $CD = b \sin A$ using the right triangle ACD, and also $CD = a \sin B$, using the right triangle CDB. Hence $b \sin A = a \sin B$ and $\dfrac{a}{\sin A} = \dfrac{b}{\sin B}$. The same proof shows $\dfrac{a}{\sin A} = \dfrac{c}{\sin C}$.

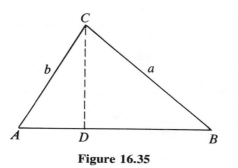

Figure 16.35

Case (2): A is a right angle (Figure 16.36). Then $\sin B = \dfrac{b}{a}$, $\sin C = \dfrac{c}{a}$. Hence $a = \dfrac{b}{\sin B} = \dfrac{c}{\sin C}$. But $\sin A = 1$. So we have

$$\frac{a}{\sin A} = \frac{b}{\sin B} = \frac{c}{\sin C}$$

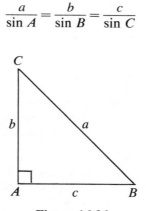

Figure 16.36

Case (3): A is an obtuse angle, B and C acute angles (Figure 16.37). Drop a perpendicular from C meeting the opposite side extended at D. As sin is positive in the first and second quadrants, $\sin A = \sin \alpha$, where $\alpha = \measuredangle DAC$.

Using the right triangle CDA, $\sin A = \sin \alpha = \dfrac{CD}{b}$; using the right tri-

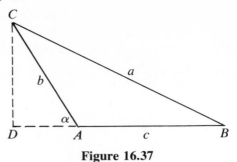

Figure 16.37

angle CDB, $\sin B = \dfrac{CD}{a}$. Hence $CD = a \sin B = b \sin A$ and

$\dfrac{a}{\sin A} = \dfrac{b}{\sin B}$. Similarly, $\dfrac{a}{\sin A} = \dfrac{c}{\sin C}$.[6]

8.2 The Generalized Law of Cosines

The law of cosines is a special case of the *generalized law of cosines:* Let l_1 and l_2 be any two rays in the plane, both emanating from the point A. Let θ be the measure of any directed angle having either of the rays as initial side, and the other as terminal side. Let B be any point distinct from A on l_1, and C any point on l_2 distinct from A. Then

(1) $\overline{BC}^2 = \overline{AB}^2 + \overline{AC}^2 - 2(AB)(AC) \cos \theta.$

Or if we let $AB = c$, $AC = b$, $BC = a$,

(2) $a^2 = b^2 + c^2 - 2bc \cos \theta.$

The difference between this theorem and Theorem 6 is that here we let θ be the measure of any of the directed angles with sides l_1 and l_2, whereas in Theorem 6 we take θ to be a particular such measure — namely that of the (Euclidean) interior angle at A of triangle ABC.

Proof: As interchanging b and c in formula (2) does not change the formula, it does not matter which ray we assume to be the initial side in proving (2). Hence we shall assume l_1 is the initial side, and l_2 the terminal side.

Choose the positive u-axis to coincide with the ray l_1 (Figure 16.38). Let the coordinates of C be (r,s). Now $\sin \theta$ and $\cos \theta$ depend only on the terminal side of a standard angle, and may be computed by using any point other than the origin on this terminal side. Using $C(r,s)$ on l_2 we have: $\sin \theta = \dfrac{s}{b}$, $\cos \theta = \dfrac{r}{b}$, or

$$r = b \cos \theta$$
$$s = b \sin \theta$$

[6] Namely, one drops a perpendicular from B on the side AC extended at E.

Hence the coordinates of C may be written $(b \cos \theta, b \sin \theta)$.
Apply the distance formula to $B(c,0)$ and $C(b \cos \theta, b \sin \theta)$.

$$
\begin{aligned}
\overline{BC}^2 = a^2 &= (b \cos \theta - c)^2 + (b \sin \theta - 0)^2 \\
&= b^2 \cos^2 \theta - 2bc \cos \theta + c^2 + b^2 \sin^2 \theta \\
&= b^2(\sin^2 \theta + \cos^2 \theta) + c^2 - 2bc \cos \theta \\
&= b^2 + c^2 - 2bc \cos \theta \qquad\qquad\qquad \text{[Th. 3(6)]}
\end{aligned}
$$

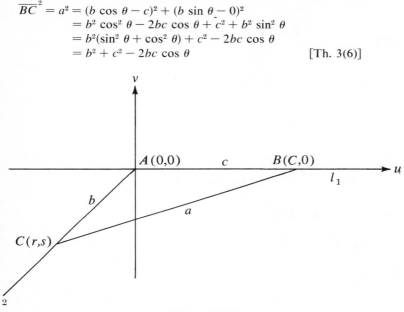

Figure 16.38

Corollary. $\cos(-\theta) = \cos \theta$ for all $\theta \in R$.

Proof: For θ and $-\theta$ may be regarded as measures of directed angles having the same sides, but with initial and terminal sides interchanged.

9. Development of Further Trigonometric Formulas

Theorem 7. For all $\alpha, \beta \in R$,

(9) $\cos(\alpha - \beta) = \cos \alpha \cos \beta + \sin \alpha \sin \beta$

[We list this as formula (9), the first eight appearing in Theorem 3.]

Proof: Let l_1 be the terminal side of a standard angle of measure α, and l_2 be the terminal side of a standard angle of measure β (Figure 16.39). Let the unit circle, center at O, intersect l_1 and l_2 at P and Q, respectively. (Hence $OP = OQ = 1$.) Now α is the measure of the length of arc traversed along the unit circle, starting at the u-axis, to P. (It is positive if counterclockwise, negative if clockwise.) The same for β to Q. It follows that $\beta - \alpha$ is the length of arc traversed from P to Q (with appropriately many revolutions). But this is precisely the radian measure of a directed angle with initial side l_1 and terminal side l_2.

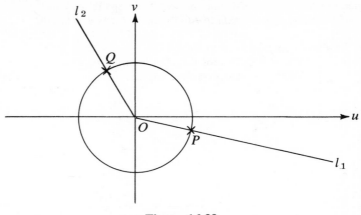

Figure 16.39

By the generalized law of cosines,

$$\overline{PQ}^2 = \overline{OP}^2 + \overline{OQ}^2 - 2(OP)(OQ) \cos (\alpha - \beta)\,^7$$
$$\overline{PQ}^2 = 1 + 1 - 2 \cos (\alpha - \beta)$$
(a) $\overline{PQ}^2 = 2 - 2 \cos (\alpha - \beta)$

Now P has coordinates $(\cos \alpha, \sin \alpha)$ and Q coordinates $(\cos \beta, \sin \beta)$. By the distance formula,

$$\overline{PQ}^2 = (\cos \alpha - \cos \beta)^2 + (\sin \alpha - \sin \beta)^2$$
$$\overline{PQ}^2 = \cos^2 \alpha - 2 \cos \alpha \cos \beta + \cos^2 \beta + \sin^2 \alpha - 2 \sin \alpha \sin \beta + \sin^2 \beta$$
$$\overline{PQ}^2 = (\sin^2 \alpha + \cos^2 \alpha) + (\sin^2 \beta + \cos^2 \beta) -$$
$$2(\cos \alpha \cos \beta + \sin \alpha \sin \beta)$$
(b) $\overline{PQ}^2 = 2 - 2(\cos \alpha \cos \beta + \sin \alpha \sin \beta)$ [Th. 3(6)]

Comparing (a) and (b) yields

$$2 - 2 \cos (\alpha - \beta) = 2 - 2(\cos \alpha \cos \beta + \sin \alpha \sin \beta)$$
$$\cos (\alpha - \beta) = \cos \alpha \cos \beta + \sin \alpha \sin \beta$$

Corollary. For all $\theta \in R$,

(10) $\cos \left(\dfrac{\pi}{2} - \theta\right) = \sin \theta$

(11) $\sin \left(\dfrac{\pi}{2} - \theta\right) = \cos \theta$

(12) $\cos (-\theta) = \cos \theta$

(13) $\sin (-\theta) = - \sin \theta$

---

[7] $\cos (\alpha - \beta) = \cos (\beta - \alpha)$ since $\cos \theta = \cos (-\theta)$.

Proof: In (9), take $\alpha = \dfrac{\pi}{2}$, $\beta = \theta$.

$$\cos\left(\frac{\pi}{2} - \theta\right) = \cos\frac{\pi}{2}\cos\theta + \sin\frac{\pi}{2}\sin\theta$$

$$= \sin\theta$$

This proves (10).

Now in (10), use $\dfrac{\pi}{2} - \theta$ for θ [since (10) holds for all elements of R].

$$\cos\left(\frac{\pi}{2} - \left(\frac{\pi}{2} - \theta\right)\right) = \sin\left(\frac{\pi}{2} - \theta\right)$$

$$\cos\theta = \sin\left(\frac{\pi}{2} - \theta\right) \qquad \text{which is (11)}$$

Formula (12) has already been proved as a corollary of the generalized law of cosines. Alternatively, one may take $\alpha = 0$ and $\beta = \theta$ in (9).

We now prove (13).

$$\cos\left(\frac{\pi}{2} + \theta\right) = \cos\left(\frac{\pi}{2} - (-\theta)\right)$$

$$= \cos\frac{\pi}{2}\cos(-\theta) + \sin\frac{\pi}{2}\sin(-\theta) \qquad \text{by (9)}$$

(a) $\qquad = \sin(-\theta)$

$$\cos\left(\frac{\pi}{2} + \theta\right) = \cos\left(\left(-\frac{\pi}{2}\right) - \theta\right) \qquad \text{by (12)}$$

$$= \cos\left(-\frac{\pi}{2}\right)\cos\theta + \sin\left(-\frac{\pi}{2}\right)\sin\theta \qquad \text{by (9)}$$

(b) $\qquad = -\sin\theta$

Comparison of (a) and (b) yields $\sin(-\theta) = -\sin\theta$.

Theorem 8. For all $\alpha, \beta \in R$,

(14) $\cos(\alpha + \beta) = \cos\alpha\cos\beta - \sin\alpha\sin\beta$
(15) $\sin(\alpha + \beta) = \sin\alpha\cos\beta + \cos\alpha\sin\beta$
(16) $\sin(\alpha - \beta) = \sin\alpha\cos\beta - \cos\alpha\sin\beta$

Proof: (14) $\cos(\alpha + \beta) = \cos(\alpha - (-\beta))$

$$= \cos\alpha\cos(-\beta) + \sin\alpha\sin(-\beta) \qquad \text{by (9)}$$

$$= \cos\alpha\cos\beta - \sin\alpha\sin\beta \qquad \text{by (12), (13)}$$

(15) $\sin(\alpha + \beta) = \cos\left(\frac{\pi}{2} - (\alpha + \beta)\right) \qquad \text{by (10)}$

$$= \cos\left(\left(\frac{\pi}{2} - \alpha\right) - \beta\right)$$

$$= \cos\left(\frac{\pi}{2} - \alpha\right)\cos\beta + \sin\left(\frac{\pi}{2} - \alpha\right)\sin\beta \qquad \text{by (9)}$$

$$= \sin\alpha\cos\beta + \cos\alpha\sin\beta \qquad \text{by (10), (11)}$$

(16) $\sin(\alpha - \beta) = \sin(\alpha + (-\beta))$

$= \sin \alpha \cos(-\beta) + \cos \alpha \sin(-\beta)$ by (15)

$= \sin \alpha \cos \beta - \cos \alpha \sin \beta$ by (12), (13)

Corollary. For all $\alpha, \beta \in R$ for which both sides are defined,

(17) $\tan(\alpha + \beta) = \dfrac{\tan \alpha + \tan \beta}{1 - \tan \alpha \tan \beta}$

(18) $\tan(\alpha - \beta) = \dfrac{\tan \alpha - \tan \beta}{1 + \tan \alpha \tan \beta}$

Proof: (17) $\tan(\alpha + \beta) = \dfrac{\sin(\alpha + \beta)}{\cos(\alpha + \beta)}$ by (4)

$= \dfrac{\sin \alpha \cos \beta + \cos \alpha \sin \beta}{\cos \alpha \cos \beta - \sin \alpha \sin \beta}$ by (15), (14)

$$= \dfrac{\dfrac{\sin \alpha \cos \beta}{\cos \alpha \cos \beta} + \dfrac{\cos \alpha \sin \beta}{\cos \alpha \cos \beta}}{\dfrac{\cos \alpha \cos \beta}{\cos \alpha \cos \beta} - \dfrac{\sin \alpha \sin \beta}{\cos \alpha \cos \beta}}$$

$= \dfrac{\tan \alpha + \tan \beta}{1 - \tan \alpha \tan \beta}$ by (4)

The proof of (18) is left to Exercise 24.

Formulas (9), (14), (15), (16), (17), and (18) are known as the addition formulas. These formulas can be used to find the trigonometric functions of $\alpha + \beta$ or $\alpha - \beta$ when they are known for α and β.

Example 26. Find sin 15° without using the tables.
Solution: $\sin 15° = \sin(45 - 30)°$

$= \sin 45° \cos 30° - \cos 45° \sin 30°$

$= \dfrac{\sqrt{2}}{2} \cdot \dfrac{\sqrt{3}}{2} - \dfrac{\sqrt{2}}{2} \cdot \dfrac{1}{2}$

$= \dfrac{1}{4}(\sqrt{6} - \sqrt{2})$

Example 27. Find sec 75° without using the tables.
Solution: $\cos 75° = \cos(45 + 30)°$

$= \cos 45° \cos 30° - \sin 45° \sin 30°$

$= \dfrac{\sqrt{6} - \sqrt{2}}{4}$

Hence $\sec 75° = \dfrac{4}{\sqrt{6} - \sqrt{2}} = \dfrac{4(\sqrt{6} + \sqrt{2})}{6 - 2} = \sqrt{6} + \sqrt{2}$.

Example 28. Find tan 105° without using the tables.
Solution: We may observe $\tan 105° = -\tan 75°$ and proceed as in Example 2, or as follows:

$$\tan 105° = \tan (60 + 45)°$$

$$= \frac{\tan 60° + \tan 45°}{1 - \tan 60° \tan 45°} \qquad \text{by (17)}$$

$$= \frac{\sqrt{3} + 1}{1 - \sqrt{3} \cdot 1}$$

$$= \frac{(1 + \sqrt{3})^2}{1 - 3}$$

$$= -\frac{1}{2}(1 + 2\sqrt{3} + 3)$$

$$= -(2 + \sqrt{3})$$

Theorem 9 (Double Angle Formulas). For all $\theta \in R$ where both sides are defined:

(19) $\sin 2\theta = 2 \sin \theta \cos \theta$
(20a) $\cos 2\theta = \cos^2 \theta - \sin^2 \theta$
(20b) $\cos 2\theta = 1 - 2 \sin^2 \theta$
(20c) $\cos 2\theta = 2 \cos^2 \theta - 1$

(21) $\tan 2\theta = \dfrac{2 \tan \theta}{1 - \tan^2 \theta}$

Formulas (19), (20a), and (21) are proved by taking $\alpha = \beta = \theta$ in (15), (14), and (17), respectively. Then (20b) and (20c) follow from (20a) by applying (6). We leave the details to the exercises.

Theorem 10 (Half-Angle Formulas). For all $\alpha \in R$ for which both sides are defined,

(22) $\sin \dfrac{\alpha}{2} = \pm\sqrt{\dfrac{1 - \cos \alpha}{2}}$

(23) $\cos \dfrac{\alpha}{2} = \pm\sqrt{\dfrac{1 + \cos \alpha}{2}}$

(24) $\tan \dfrac{\alpha}{2} = \dfrac{1 - \cos \alpha}{\sin \alpha} = \dfrac{\sin \alpha}{1 + \cos \alpha}$

Proof: Take $\theta = \dfrac{\alpha}{2}$ in (20b):

$$\cos\left(2 \cdot \frac{\alpha}{2}\right) = 1 - 2 \sin^2 \frac{\alpha}{2}$$

$$2 \sin^2 \frac{\alpha}{2} = 1 - \cos \alpha$$

$$\sin \frac{\alpha}{2} = \pm\sqrt{\frac{1 - \cos \alpha}{2}} \qquad \text{which is (22)}$$

The + or − is chosen depending on the quadrant of $\frac{\alpha}{2}$.

To prove (23), take $\theta = \frac{\alpha}{2}$ in (20c). This is left as an exercise.

To prove (24), divide (22) by (23):

$$\tan \frac{\alpha}{2} = \frac{\sin \frac{\alpha}{2}}{\cos \frac{\alpha}{2}}$$

$$= \pm \sqrt{\frac{1 - \cos \alpha}{1 + \cos \alpha}}$$

$$= \pm \sqrt{\frac{(1 - \cos \alpha)(1 - \cos \alpha)}{(1 + \cos \alpha)(1 - \cos \alpha)}}$$

$$= \pm \sqrt{\frac{(1 - \cos \alpha)^2}{\sin^2 \alpha}}$$

or

$$\tan \frac{\alpha}{2} = \frac{1 - \cos \alpha}{\pm \sin \alpha}$$

Now $1 - \cos \alpha$ is always positive or zero. If we can prove $\tan \frac{\alpha}{2}$ and $\sin \alpha$ always are *both* positive or *both* negative, then we may drop the '±.' But

$\tan \frac{\alpha}{2} = \frac{\sin \frac{\alpha}{2}}{\cos \frac{\alpha}{2}}$ and $\sin \alpha = 2 \sin \frac{\alpha}{2} \cos \frac{\alpha}{2}$ by (19). Multiplying yields

$$\tan \frac{\alpha}{2} \cdot \sin \alpha = \frac{\sin \frac{\alpha}{2}}{\cos \frac{\alpha}{2}} \cdot 2 \sin \frac{\alpha}{2} \cos \frac{\alpha}{2}$$

$$= 2 \sin^2 \frac{\alpha}{2}$$

which is always positive or zero. Hence

$$\tan \frac{\alpha}{2} = \frac{1 - \cos \alpha}{\sin \alpha}$$

Similarly, we could have written

$$\sqrt{\frac{1 - \cos \alpha}{1 + \cos \alpha}} = \sqrt{\frac{(1 - \cos \alpha)(1 + \cos \alpha)}{(1 + \cos \alpha)(1 + \cos \alpha)}}$$

and this would have led to $\tan \frac{\alpha}{2} = \frac{\sin \alpha}{1 + \cos \alpha}$. We leave the details to the exercises.

Finally we have:

Theorem 11. For all $A, B \in R$,

$$(25) \quad \sin A + \sin B = 2 \sin \frac{A+B}{2} \cos \frac{A-B}{2}$$

$$(26) \quad \sin A - \sin B = 2 \cos \frac{A+B}{2} \sin \frac{A-B}{2}$$

$$(27) \quad \cos A + \cos B = 2 \cos \frac{A+B}{2} \cos \frac{A-B}{2}$$

$$(28) \quad \cos A - \cos B = -2 \sin \frac{A+B}{2} \sin \frac{A-B}{2}$$

Proof: Add (15) and (16) to obtain

$$\sin(\alpha + \beta) + \sin(\alpha - \beta) = 2 \sin \alpha \cos \beta$$

Let $\alpha = \dfrac{A+B}{2}$, $\beta = \dfrac{A-B}{2}$ so that $\alpha + \beta = A$, $\alpha - \beta = B$.

$$\sin A + \sin B = 2 \sin \frac{A+B}{2} \cos \frac{A-B}{2}$$

We leave the proofs of the remaining formulas to the exercises.

Exercises

23. Prove $\tan(-\theta) = -\tan \theta$.

24. Use Exercise 23 to prove formula (18) from (17).

25. Prove $\cot(-\theta) = -\cot \theta$, $\sec(-\theta) = \sec \theta$, $\csc(-\theta) = -\csc \theta$.

26. Prove the formulas of Theorem 9.

27. Prove the second part of (24): $\tan \dfrac{\alpha}{2} = \dfrac{\sin \alpha}{1 + \cos \alpha}$.

28. Prove (26), (27), and (28).

29. Without using tables, find the following:

(a) $\tan \dfrac{\pi}{12}$.

(b) $\tan \dfrac{\pi}{24}$.

(c) $\cos 195°$.

(d) $\cos(-195°)$.

(e) $\sec \dfrac{\pi}{8}$.

(f) $\cot \dfrac{3\pi}{8}$.

(g) $\sin \dfrac{11\pi}{12}$.

(h) $\csc\left(-\dfrac{11\pi}{12}\right)$.

30. If $\sin \alpha = \dfrac{3}{4}$, $\cos \beta = -\dfrac{3}{5}$, and if $\dfrac{\pi}{2} < \alpha, \beta < \pi$, find $\sin(\alpha + \beta)$.

31. If $\sin \alpha = -\dfrac{3}{5}$, and $\pi < \alpha < \dfrac{3\pi}{2}$, find:

(a) $\sin 2\alpha$. (d) $\sin \dfrac{\alpha}{2}$.

(b) $\cos 2\alpha$.

(c) $\tan 2\alpha$. (e) $\sec \dfrac{\alpha}{2}$.

  (f) $\cot \dfrac{\alpha}{2}$.

10. Identities and Equations

10.1 *Identities*

The trigonometric formulas which we have numbered from 1 to 28 are examples of (trigonometric) identities. For example, formula (6):

$$\sin^2 x + \cos^2 x = 1$$

is an identity in the variable x over R. Or formula (9):

$$\cos (x - y) = \cos x \cos y + \sin x \sin y$$

is an identity in the two variables x and y over R. Of course whether we use 'x' and 'y' for variables, or other letters, is immaterial.

As we have seen, identities are useful in both deriving other identities, and in solving equations. We follow our previous convention of calling, for example,

$$\tan^2 x + 1 = \sec^2 x$$

an identity in the variable x over R, although strictly speaking one has to limit x to those elements of R for which both sides are defined.

We consider examples of proving identities on the basis of the 28 identities we have established above.

Example 29. Show that $\dfrac{1}{2} \sin 2x = \tan x - \dfrac{\sin^3 x}{\cos x}$.

Solution:
$$
\begin{aligned}
\tan x - \frac{\sin^3 x}{\cos x} &= \tan x - \sin^2 x \cdot \frac{\sin x}{\cos x} \\
&= \tan x - \sin^2 x \tan x & (4) \\
&= \tan x(1 - \sin^2 x) \\
&= \tan x \cos^2 x & (6) \\
&= \frac{\sin x}{\cos x} \cos^2 x & (4) \\
&= \sin x \cos x \\
&= \frac{1}{2} \sin 2x & (19)
\end{aligned}
$$

Of course, there are many ways of proving the above identity. For example, another is to begin with $\frac{1}{2} \sin 2x$ and show it can be reduced to $\tan x - \dfrac{\sin^3 x}{\cos x}$. We give another argument.

$$\tan x - \frac{\sin^3 x}{\cos x} = \frac{\sin x}{\cos x} - \frac{\sin^3 x}{\cos x} \qquad (4)$$

$$= \frac{\sin x(1 - \sin^2 x)}{\cos x}$$

$$= \frac{\sin x \cos^2 x}{\cos x} \qquad (6)$$

$$= \sin x \cos x$$

$$= \frac{1}{2} \sin 2x \qquad (19)$$

Example 30. Show that $\cos 3\theta = 4 \cos^3 \theta - 3 \cos \theta$.

Solution: $\cos 3\theta = \cos (2\theta + \theta)$

$$
\begin{aligned}
&= \cos 2\theta \cos \theta - \sin 2\theta \sin \theta && (14) \\
&= (\cos^2 \theta - \sin^2 \theta) \cos \theta - 2 \sin \theta \cos \theta \sin \theta && (19), (20a) \\
&= \cos^3 \theta - \sin^2 \theta \cos \theta - 2 \sin^2 \theta \cos \theta \\
&= \cos^3 \theta - 3 \sin^2 \theta \cos \theta \\
&= \cos^3 \theta - 3(1 - \cos^2 \theta) \cos \theta && (6) \\
&= 4 \cos^3 \theta - 3 \cos \theta
\end{aligned}
$$

10.2   Equations over R

We now consider the more general question of solving (trigonometric) equations. We shall restrict ourselves to equations in a single variable over R.

Example 31. Solve: $\sin x = 0$.

Solution: We first determine those solutions x with $0 \leq x < 2\pi$. These solutions are 0 and π. Hence all the solutions are given by adding all integral multiples (positive and negative) of 2π, since the period of $\sin x$ is 2π. The solution set is, therefore,

$$\{0, 2\pi, -2\pi, 4\pi, -4\pi, \ldots; \pi, -\pi, 3\pi, -3\pi, 5\pi, -5\pi, \ldots\}$$

One usually abbreviates this as follows:

$$\{2k\pi, \pi + 2k\pi\}_{k=0, \pm 1, \pm 2, \ldots}$$

[Also one may write $\{\pm 2k\pi, \pi \pm 2k\pi\}_{k=0,1,2,\ldots}$]

One may check that this solution set may also be written

$$\{n\pi\}_{n=0, \pm 1, \pm 2, \ldots}$$

Example 32. Solve $\sin 2x = 0$.

Solution: The period of $\sin 2x$ is π.

(a) $\sin 2x = 0$ when $2x = 0$ and $2x = \pi$, i.e., when $x = 0$ and $x = \dfrac{\pi}{2}$. The solution set is, therefore,

$$\left\{k\pi, \frac{\pi}{2} + k\pi\right\}_{k=0, \pm 1, \pm 2, \ldots}$$

(b) $\sin 2x = 2 \sin x \cos x$. Hence an equivalent equation is

$$2 \sin x \cos x = 0$$

The solution set is the union of the solution sets of $\sin x = 0$ and $\cos x = 0$. This yields the answer given in (a). The solution set may also be written

$$\left\{ n \cdot \frac{\pi}{2} \right\}_{n=0,\pm1,\pm2,\ldots}$$

Example 33. Solve $\cos 2x - \cos x = 0$.
Solution: $\cos 2x = 2 \cos^2 x - 1$ (by 20c)
Hence an equivalent equation is

$$2 \cos^2 x - 1 - \cos x = 0$$
$$2 \cos^2 x - \cos x - 1 = 0$$
$$(2 \cos x + 1)(\cos x - 1) = 0$$

The solution set is therefore the union of the solution sets of

(a) $2 \cos x + 1 = 0$
(b) $\cos x - 1 = 0$

From (a) we obtain $\cos x = -\frac{1}{2}$. In the first quadrant, $\cos \frac{\pi}{3} = \frac{1}{2}$. Hence the

two solutions between 0 and 2π of $\cos x = -\frac{1}{2}$ (one in the second quadrant,

one in the third) are:

$$\pi - \frac{\pi}{3} \qquad \text{and} \qquad \pi + \frac{\pi}{3}$$

i.e., $\frac{2\pi}{3}, \frac{4\pi}{3}$.

From (b) we have $\cos x = 1$, the solution being 0 for $0 \le x < 2\pi$. Hence the solution set is

$$\left\{ 2k\pi, \frac{2\pi}{3} + 2k\pi, \frac{4\pi}{3} + 2k\pi \right\}_{k=0,\pm1,\pm2,\ldots}$$

Exercises

32. Prove that the following are identities:

(a) $\dfrac{\sec x - \tan x}{2(1 + \sin x)} = \dfrac{1 - \sin x}{2 \cos x + \sin 2x}$.

(b) $\sin 4\theta = 4 \sin \theta \cos \theta (1 - 2 \sin^2 \theta)$.

(c) $1 - \dfrac{(1 + \cos \alpha) \tan \dfrac{\alpha}{2}}{\csc \alpha} = \cos^2 \alpha$.

(d) $\tan^2 \dfrac{x}{2} = \dfrac{\sec x - 1}{\sec x + 1}$.

(e) $\sin 7x + \sin x = \sin 6x \cos x + 2 \sin x \cos^2 3x$.

(f) $2 \sin^2 \dfrac{x}{2} = \dfrac{\sin x}{\csc x + \cot x}$.

(g) $\sin 2(x+y) - \sin 2(x-y) = \dfrac{\sin 4x \sin 2y}{\sin 2x}$.

(h) $\dfrac{1}{1 + \sec x} - \dfrac{1}{1 - \sec x} = \sin 2x \csc^3 x$.

33. Solve the following equations over R:

(a) $\sin \dfrac{x}{2} = \dfrac{1}{2}$.

(b) $(\sec x + 2)(\tan x - 1) = 0$.

(c) $(\sin x + 3)(2 \cos x - \sqrt{3}) = 0$.

(d) $\sin^2 x \sec x = 0$.

(e) $\cos^2 x = 1$.

(f) $\tan^4 x + \tan^2 x + x^2 = -3$.

34. Solve the following equations over R:

(a) $\sin 2x - \cos x = 0$.

(b) $\tan 3x = -1$.

(c) $2 \cos^2 x + \sin x - 1 = 0$.

(d) $2 \cos^2 2x + \sin 2x - 1 = 0$.

(e) $2 \cos^2 \dfrac{x}{2} + \sin \dfrac{x}{2} - 1 = 0$.

(f) $(\tan 3x - 1)e^x = 0$.

35. Solve for values of x where $0 \le x \le 2\pi$.

(a) $\left(2 \sin \dfrac{x}{3} + \sqrt{3}\right)(e^x + e^{-x}) = 0$.

(b) $(x^2 - x - 6) \cot 4x = 0$.

(c) $\sin^2 x - \sin x - 6 = 0$.

(d) $\cos 7x - \cos 5x = 0$.

(e) $\sin 5x + \sin 3x = 0$.

11. Inverse Trigonometric Relations and Functions

We now consider the inverse relation of each of the six trigonometric functions. The inverse relation of $y = \sin x$ may be written

(a) $x = \sin y$.

Its graph, as usual, is obtained by reflecting $y = \sin x$ in the line $y = x$ (Figure 16.40). This relation has infinitely many branch functions.

The inverse relation of $y = a^x$, namely $x = a^y$, was written $y = \log_a x$. This turned out to be a function. The inverse relation of $y = \sin x$, given by (a), is not a function. But very often one works with a branch function of (a), namely that branch which includes the measures of acute angles $\left(0 \text{ to } \dfrac{\pi}{2}\right)$, as this is the one occurring most often in practice. This is called the *principal branch function* of (a), and is written

(b) $y = \sin^{-1} x$ or $y = \arcsin x$.

One refers to this function either as the *inverse sine* (of x) or the *arc sine* (of x). Its domain is $\{x \in R / -1 \le x \le 1\}$, and its range

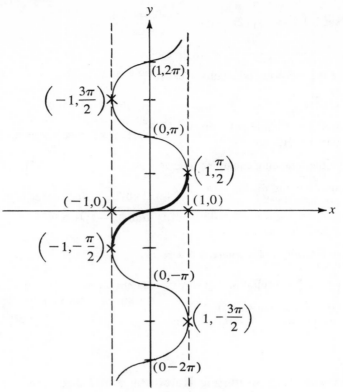

Figure 16.40

$$\left\{ y \in R \left/ -\frac{\pi}{2} \leq y \leq \frac{\pi}{2} \right. \right\}$$

Thus $y = \sin^{-1} x$ means $x = \sin y$ and $-\frac{\pi}{2} \leq y \leq \frac{\pi}{2}$. [One can work, if one wishes, with other branches of (a). For a branch other than the principal one, one writes, for example:

$$y = \sin^{-1} x \qquad \frac{\pi}{2} \leq y \leq \frac{3\pi}{2}$$

That is, one displays the range of the function. If no such range is displayed, the principal branch is assumed.]

Example 34. (a) $\sin^{-1} \frac{1}{2} = \frac{\pi}{6}$, since $\frac{\pi}{6}$ is the unique value of y with $-\frac{\pi}{2} \leq y \leq \frac{\pi}{2}$ for which $\sin y = \frac{1}{2}$.

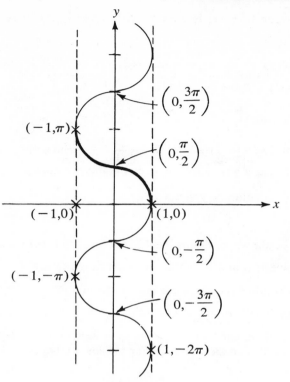

$\left(0, \dfrac{3\pi}{2}\right)$

$(-1, \pi)$

$\left(0, \dfrac{\pi}{2}\right)$

$(-1, 0)$ $(1, 0)$

$\left(0, -\dfrac{\pi}{2}\right)$

$(-1, -\pi)$

$\left(0, -\dfrac{3\pi}{2}\right)$

$(1, -2\pi)$

Figure 16.41

(b) $\sin^{-1}\left(-\dfrac{1}{2}\right) = -\dfrac{\pi}{6}$ $\left(not\ \dfrac{7\pi}{6}\ or\ \dfrac{11\pi}{6},\ etc.\right)$, since $-\dfrac{\pi}{6}$ is the unique

value of y with $-\dfrac{\pi}{2} \le y \le \dfrac{\pi}{2}$ for which $\sin y = -\dfrac{1}{2}$.

(c) $\sin^{-1} 1 = \dfrac{\pi}{2}$.

(d) $\sin^{-1}(-1) = -\dfrac{\pi}{2}$.

(e)[8] $\sin \sin^{-1}\left(-\dfrac{3}{4}\right) = -\dfrac{3}{4}$. For if $\sin^{-1}\left(-\dfrac{3}{4}\right) = \alpha$, this means $\sin \alpha = -\dfrac{3}{4}$, which is what we have stated.

The inverse relation of $y = \cos x$ is

(c) $\cos y = x$.

Its graph is as shown in Figure 16.41. The branch function including the

---

[8] By $\sin \sin^{-1} x$ we mean $\sin(\sin^{-1} x)$. Similarly $\cos \tan^{-1} x = \cos(\tan^{-1} x)$,

$$\sin^{-1} \cos x = \sin^{-1}(\cos x),\ \text{etc.}$$

y-values between 0 and $\frac{\pi}{2}$ is the one with range $\{y \in R/0 \leq y \leq \pi\}$. We write this function

(d) $y = \cos^{-1} x$ or $y = \arccos x$.

Its domain is $\{x \in R/-1 \leq x \leq 1\}$.

Example 35. (a) $\cos^{-1} \frac{1}{2} = \frac{\pi}{3}$; i.e., $\cos \frac{\pi}{3} = \frac{1}{2}$ and $0 \leq \frac{\pi}{3} \leq \pi$.

(b) $\cos^{-1} \left(-\frac{1}{2}\right) = \frac{2\pi}{3}$; i.e., $\cos \frac{2\pi}{3} = -\frac{1}{2}$ and $0 \leq \frac{2\pi}{3} \leq \pi$.

(c) $\cos^{-1} 2$ is undefined, as 2 is not in the domain of $\cos^{-1} x$.

The inverse relation of $y = \tan x$ is

(e) $\tan y = x$.

Its graph is as shown in Figure 16.42. The branch function including the y-values between 0 and $\frac{\pi}{2}$ is the one with range $\left\{y \in R \middle/ -\frac{\pi}{2} < y < \frac{\pi}{2}\right\}$. The domain is all of R. We write this function

(f) $y = \tan^{-1} x$ or $y = \arctan x$.

Example 36. (a) Find $\tan^{-1} 4.832$. The table, in degrees, shows $\tan 78° = 4.705$. To find the corresponding radians, we have

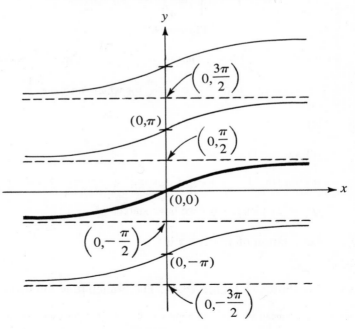

Figure 16.42

$$\frac{78}{180} = \frac{n}{\pi}$$

where n is the number of radians. Thus $n = \dfrac{13\pi}{30}$. Hence

$$\tan^{-1} 4.832 = \frac{13\pi}{30} \text{ (approx.).}$$

(b) $\tan^{-1} (-4.832) = -\dfrac{13\pi}{30}$.

(c) $\tan^{-1} 0 = 0$.

(d) $\tan \tan^{-1} 8.321 = 8.321$.

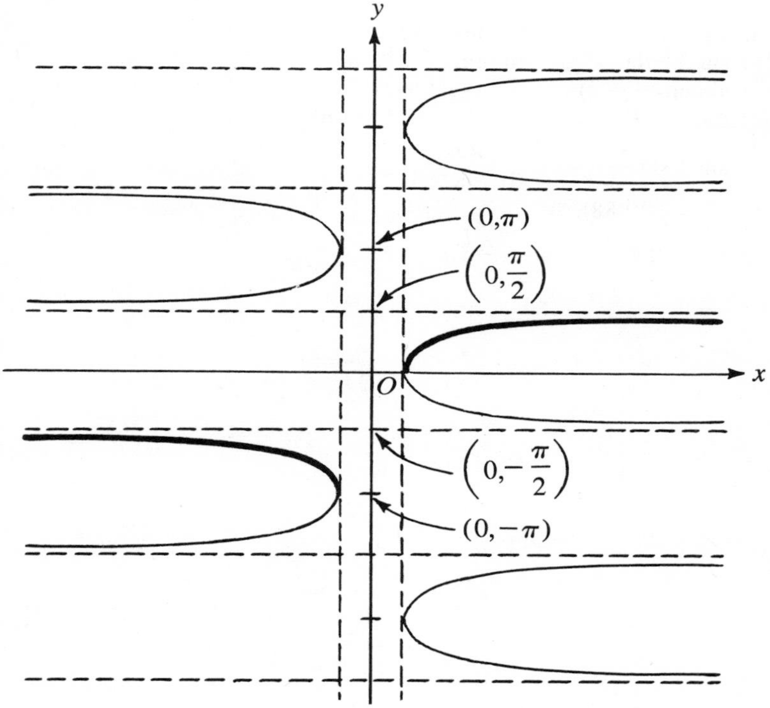

Figure 16.43

The graph of the inverse relation of $y = \cot x$, namely $x = \cot y$, will be left as an exercise. The domain of $y = \cot^{-1} x$ is again all of R, the range is $\{y \in R / 0 < y < \pi\}$.

The graph of the inverse relation of $y = \sec x$, namely $x = \sec y$, is as shown in Figure 16.43. The domain of $y = \sec^{-1} x$ is $\{x \in R / x \leqq -1$ or $x \geqq 1\}$; the range [9] is $\left\{y \in R \Big/ 0 \leqq y < \dfrac{\pi}{2} \text{ or } -\pi \leqq y < -\dfrac{\pi}{2}\right\}$.

---

[9] There appears to be a more natural way of choosing the principal branch functions of $x = \sec y$ and $x = \csc y$, and writers do differ on this. The choice we have made, however, is more convenient for use in the calculus, and is one of the standard choices in current practice.

The graph of the inverse relation of $y = \csc x$, namely $x = \csc y$, will be left as an exercise. The domain of $y = \csc^{-1} x$ is $\{x \in R / x \leq -1$ or $x \geq 1\}$; the range is $\left\{ y \in R \middle/ -\pi < y \leq -\dfrac{\pi}{2} \text{ or } 0 < y \leq \dfrac{\pi}{2} \right\}$.

Exercises

36. Draw the graph of $x = \cot y$, and mark off on it the graph of $y = \cot^{-1} x$.

37. Draw the graph of $x = \csc y$, and mark off on it the graph of $y = \csc^{-1} x$.

38. Find the following:

(a) $\sin^{-1} 1$.

(b) $\sin^{-1} (-1)$.

(c) $\sin \cos^{-1} (-\tfrac{1}{2})$.

(d) $\tan^{-1} (-1)$.

(e) $\sin^{-1} \sin \dfrac{3\pi}{2}$.

(f) $\sin \sin^{-1} (.88)$.

(g) $\tan^{-1} \sin 3\pi$.

(h) $\sec^{-1} \sqrt{2}$.

(i) $\csc^{-1} (-2)$.

(j) $\sec \sec^{-1} (-3.6)$.

(k) $\cos^{-1} 6$.

(l) $\sec^{-1} \tfrac{1}{2}$.

39. Find $\tan (\tan^{-1} \tfrac{1}{3} - \tan^{-1} (-\tfrac{3}{4}))$.

Appendix

Table A-1
Common Logarithms

N	0	1	2	3	4	5	6	7	8	9
10	0000	0043	0086	0128	0170	0212	0253	0294	0334	0374
11	0414	0453	0492	0531	0569	0607	0645	0682	0719	0755
12	0792	0828	0864	0899	0934	0969	1004	1038	1072	1106
13	1139	1173	1206	1239	1271	1303	1335	1367	1399	1430
14	1461	1492	1523	1553	1584	1614	1644	1673	1703	1732
15	1761	1790	1818	1847	1875	1903	1931	1959	1987	2014
16	2041	2068	2095	2122	2148	2175	2201	2227	2253	2279
17	2304	2330	2355	2380	2405	2430	2455	2480	2504	2529
18	2553	2577	2601	2625	2648	2672	2695	2718	2742	2765
19	2788	2810	2833	2856	2878	2900	2923	2945	2967	2989
20	3010	3032	3054	3075	3096	3118	3139	3160	3181	3201
21	3222	3243	3263	3284	3304	3324	3345	3365	3385	3404
22	3424	3444	3464	3483	3502	3522	3541	3560	3579	3598
23	3617	3636	3655	3674	3692	3711	3729	3747	3766	3784
24	3802	3820	3838	3856	3874	3892	3909	3927	3945	3962
25	3979	3997	4014	4031	4048	4065	4082	4099	4116	4133
26	4150	4166	4183	4200	4216	4232	4249	4265	4281	4298
27	4314	4330	4346	4362	4378	4393	4409	4425	4440	4456
28	4472	4487	4502	4518	4533	4548	4564	4579	4594	4609
29	4624	4639	4654	4669	4683	4698	4713	4728	4742	4757
30	4771	4786	4800	4814	4829	4843	4857	4871	4886	4900
31	4914	4928	4942	4955	4969	4983	4997	5011	5024	5038
32	5051	5065	5079	5092	5105	5119	5132	5145	5159	5172
33	5185	5198	5211	5224	5237	5250	5263	5276	5289	5302
34	5315	5328	5340	5353	5366	5378	5391	5403	5416	5428
35	5441	5453	5465	5478	5490	5502	5514	5527	5539	5551
36	5563	5575	5587	5599	5611	5623	5635	5647	5658	5670
37	5682	5694	5705	5717	5729	5740	5752	5763	5775	5786
38	5798	5809	5821	5832	5843	5855	5866	5877	5888	5899
39	5911	5922	5933	5944	5955	5966	5977	5988	5999	6010
40	6021	6031	6042	6053	6064	6075	6085	6096	6107	6117
41	6128	6138	6149	6160	6170	6180	6191	6201	6212	6222
42	6232	6243	6253	6263	6274	6284	6294	6304	6314	6325
43	6335	6345	6355	6365	6375	6385	6395	6405	6415	6425
44	6435	6444	6454	6464	6474	6484	6493	6503	6513	6522
45	6532	6542	6551	6561	6571	6580	6590	6599	6609	6618
46	6628	6637	6646	6656	6665	6675	6684	6693	6702	6712
47	6721	6730	6739	6749	6758	6767	6776	6785	6794	6803
48	6812	6821	6830	6839	6848	6857	6866	6875	6884	6893
49	6902	6911	6920	6928	6937	6946	6955	6964	6972	6981
50	6990	6998	7007	7016	7024	7033	7042	7050	7059	7067
51	7076	7084	7093	7101	7110	7118	7126	7135	7143	7152
52	7160	7168	7177	7185	7193	7202	7210	7218	7226	7235
53	7243	7251	7259	7267	7275	7284	7292	7300	7308	7316
54	7324	7332	7340	7348	7356	7364	7372	7380	7388	7396
N	0	1	2	3	4	5	6	7	8	9

N	0	1	2	3	4	5	6	7	8	9
55	7404	7412	7419	7427	7435	7443	7451	7459	7466	7474
56	7482	7490	7497	7505	7513	7520	7528	7536	7543	7551
57	7559	7566	7574	7582	7589	7597	7604	7612	7619	7627
58	7634	7642	7649	7657	7664	7672	7679	7686	7694	7701
59	7709	7716	7723	7731	7738	7745	7752	7760	7767	7774
60	7782	7789	7796	7803	7810	7818	7825	7832	7839	7846
61	7853	7860	7868	7875	7882	7889	7896	7903	7910	7917
62	7924	7931	7938	7945	7952	7959	7966	7973	7980	7987
63	7993	8000	8007	8014	8021	8028	8035	8041	8048	8055
64	8062	8069	8075	8082	8089	8096	8102	8109	8116	8122
65	8129	8136	8142	8149	8156	8162	8169	8176	8182	8189
66	8195	8202	8209	8215	8222	8228	8235	8241	8248	8254
67	8261	8267	8274	8280	8287	8293	8299	8306	8312	8319
68	8325	8331	8338	8344	8351	8357	8363	8370	8376	8382
69	8388	8395	8401	8407	8414	8420	8426	8432	8439	8445
70	8451	8457	8463	8470	8476	8482	8488	8494	8500	8506
71	8513	8519	8525	8531	8537	8543	8549	8555	8561	8567
72	8573	8579	8585	8591	8597	8603	8609	8615	8621	8627
73	8633	8639	8645	8651	8657	8663	8669	8675	8681	8686
74	8692	8698	8704	8710	8716	8722	8727	8733	8739	8745
75	8751	8756	8762	8768	8774	8779	8785	8791	8797	8802
76	8808	8814	8820	8825	8831	8837	8842	8848	8854	8859
77	8865	8871	8876	8882	8887	8893	8899	8904	8910	8915
78	8921	8927	8932	8938	8943	8949	8954	8960	8965	8971
79	8976	8982	8987	8993	8998	9004	9009	9015	9020	9025
80	9031	9036	9042	9047	9053	9058	9063	9069	9074	9079
81	9085	9090	9096	9101	9106	9112	9117	9122	9128	9133
82	9138	9143	9149	9154	9159	9165	9170	9175	9180	9186
83	9191	9196	9201	9206	9212	9217	9222	9227	9232	9238
84	9243	9248	9253	9258	9263	9269	9274	9279	9284	9289
85	9294	9299	9304	9309	9315	9320	9325	9330	9335	9340
86	9345	9350	9355	9360	9365	9370	9375	9380	9385	9390
87	9395	9400	9405	9410	9415	9420	9425	9430	9435	9440
88	9445	9450	9455	9460	9465	9469	9474	9479	9484	9489
89	9494	9499	9504	9509	9513	9518	9523	9528	9533	9538
90	9542	9547	9552	9557	9562	9566	9571	9576	9581	9586
91	9590	9595	9600	9605	9609	9614	9619	9624	9628	9633
92	9638	9643	9647	9652	9657	9661	9666	9671	9675	9680
93	9685	9689	9694	9699	9703	9708	9713	9717	9722	9727
94	9731	9736	9741	9745	9750	9754	9759	9763	9768	9773
95	9777	9782	9786	9791	9795	9800	9805	9809	9814	9818
96	9823	9827	9832	9836	9841	9845	9850	9854	9859	9863
97	9868	9872	9877	9881	9886	9890	9894	9899	9903	9908
98	9912	9917	9921	9926	9930	9934	9939	9943	9948	9952
99	9956	9961	9965	9969	9974	9978	9983	9987	9991	9996
N	0	1	2	3	4	5	6	7	8	9

Table A-2
Trigonometric Functions

↱	sin	cos	tan	cot	sec	csc	
0°	.0000	1.0000	.0000	· · · ·	1.000	· · · ·	90°
1°	.0175	.9998	.0175	57.29	1.000	57.30	89°
2°	.0349	.9994	.0349	28.64	1.001	28.65	88°
3°	.0523	.9986	.0524	19.08	1.001	19.11	87°
4°	.0698	.9976	.0699	14.30	1.002	14.34	86°
5°	.0872	.9962	.0875	11.43	1.004	11.47	85°
6°	.1045	.9945	.1051	9.514	1.006	9.567	84°
7°	.1219	.9925	.1228	8.144	1.008	8.206	83°
8°	.1392	.9903	.1405	7.115	1.010	7.185	82°
9°	.1564	.9877	.1584	6.314	1.012	6.392	81°
10°	.1736	.9848	.1763	5.671	1.015	5.759	80°
11°	.1908	.9816	.1944	5.145	1.019	5.241	79°
12°	.2079	.9781	.2126	4.705	1.022	4.810	78°
13°	.2250	.9744	.2309	4.331	1.026	4.445	77°
14°	.2419	.9703	.2493	4.011	1.031	4.134	76°
15°	.2588	.9659	.2679	3.732	1.035	3.864	75°
16°	.2756	.9613	.2867	3.487	1.040	3.628	74°
17°	.2924	.9563	.3057	3.271	1.046	3.420	73°
18°	.3090	.9511	.3249	3.078	1.051	3.236	72°
19°	.3256	.9455	.3443	2.904	1.058	3.072	71°
20°	.3420	.9397	.3640	2.747	1.064	2.924	70°
21°	.3584	.9336	.3839	2.605	1.071	2.790	69°
22°	.3746	.9272	.4040	2.475	1.079	2.669	68°
23°	.3907	.9205	.4245	2.356	1.086	2.559	67°
24°	.4067	.9135	.4452	2.246	1.095	2.459	66°
25°	.4226	.9063	.4663	2.145	1.103	2.366	65°
26°	.4384	.8988	.4877	2.050	1.113	2.281	64°
27°	.4540	.8910	.5095	1.963	1.122	2.203	63°
28°	.4695	.8829	.5317	1.881	1.133	2.130	62°
29°	.4848	.8746	.5543	1.804	1.143	2.063	61°
30°	.5000	.8660	.5774	1.732	1.155	2.000	60°
31°	.5150	.8572	.6009	1.664	1.167	1.942	59°
32°	.5299	.8480	.6249	1.600	1.179	1.887	58°
33°	.5446	.8387	.6494	1.540	1.192	1.836	57°
34°	.5592	.8290	.6745	1.483	1.206	1.788	56°
35°	.5736	.8192	.7002	1.428	1.221	1.743	55°
36°	.5878	.8090	.7265	1.376	1.236	1.701	54°
37°	.6018	.7986	.7536	1.327	1.252	1.662	53°
38°	.6157	.7880	.7813	1.280	1.269	1.624	52°
39°	.6293	.7771	.8098	1.235	1.287	1.589	51°
40°	.6428	.7660	.8391	1.192	1.305	1.556	50°
41°	.6561	.7547	.8693	1.150	1.325	1.524	49°
42°	.6691	.7431	.9004	1.111	1.346	1.494	48°
43°	.6820	.7314	.9325	1.072	1.367	1.466	47°
44°	.6947	.7193	.9657	1.036	1.390	1.440	46°
45°	.7071	.7071	1.0000	1.000	1.414	1.414	45°
	cos	sin	cot	tan	csc	sec	↵

504

selected answers and solutions to exercises

CHAPTER 1

1. (a) Yes; (b) Yes; (c) $\varnothing$; (d) {2,4}, $\varnothing$.
3. (a) {1,2,3}, {1,2,4}, {1,3,4}, {2,3,4}, {1,2,3,4}.
   (b) {1,2}, {1,3}, {1,4}, {2,3}, {2,4}, {3,4}.
   (c) Those in (b) and {1}, {2}, {3}, {4}, $\varnothing$.
   (d) No.
   (e) No.
   (f) Yes.
   (g) Yes.
5. (a) {Mr. Cole, Mrs. Herz}, {Mr. Cole, Miss Smith}, {Mr. Cole, Mr. Gauss}, {Mr. Cole, Mr. Bach}, {Mrs. Herz, Miss Smith}, {Mrs. Herz, Mr. Gauss}, {Mrs. Herz, Mr. Bach}, {Miss Smith, Mr. Gauss}, {Miss Smith, Mr. Bach}, {Mr. Gauss, Mr. Bach}.
   (b) 16.
   (c) 32.
   (d) 26.
7. $\varnothing$, {4}, {8}, {4,8} are all the subsets of F. All but {4,8} are proper subsets.
9. (b), (c), (e), (h), (i), (j), (l) are true; the others false.
11. Since $A \subset B$, we have $A \subseteq B$ by Def. 2. But we are given that $B \subseteq C$. We may therefore conclude that $A \subseteq C$. (This follows from (4) of the text, Sec. 3.3.) To show that $A \subset C$, it remains to show $A \neq C$. But suppose $A = C$. Then since $A \subseteq B$ we would have $C \subseteq B$. This together with the fact that $B \subseteq C$ would yield $B = C$ by (3) of Sec. 3.3, and hence that $B = A$. This is impossible since we are given $A \subset B$. So $A = C$ leads to a contradiction, and we conclude $A \neq C$.
13. Since $A \subseteq B$ and $B \subseteq C$, we conclude from (4) that $A \subseteq C$. But now $A \subseteq C$ and $C \subseteq D$ yields, again by (4), that $A \subseteq D$.
15. Let A, B, C, D be sets.
   (a) If $A \subset B$, $B \subset C$, $C \subseteq D$, then $A \subset D$.
   (b) If $A \subseteq B$, $B \subseteq C$, $C \subset D$, then $A \subset D$.
   We shall prove (a). Since $A \subset B$, $B \subset C$ it follows by Ex. 12 that $A \subset C$. Now since $A \subset C$, $C \subseteq D$ we conclude from Ex. 11 that $A \subset D$.
17. (a) False. Let $A = \{1\}$, $B = \{1,2\}$, $C = \{1,3\}$.
   (b) True. Since $A \subset F$, it follows that $A \subseteq F$. Hence $a \in A$ implies $a \in F$.
   (c) False. Let $D = G = E = \varnothing$, or any other specific set.
   (d) False. Let $S = \{1,3\}$, $T = \{2\}$. Then $S \neq T$ but $S \not\subset T$.
   (e) False. Let $A = \{1\}$, $B = \{2\}$, $C = \{1,2\}$.
21. Converse of (6): (Let A and B be sets.) If $A \neq B$, then $A \subset B$.
23. (a) $\in$; (b) $\subset$; (c) $\supset$; (d) $\subset$.
25. $\{\varnothing, \{\lambda\}, \{\rho\}, \{\sigma\}, \{\lambda,\rho\}, \{\lambda,\sigma\}, \{\rho,\sigma\}, \{\lambda,\rho,\sigma\}\}$.
27. (a) $\{\varnothing\}$; (b) $\{\varnothing, \{\varnothing\}\}$; (c) same as (b); (d) $\{\varnothing, \{\varnothing\}, \{\{a\}\}, \{\varnothing, \{a\}\}\}$.
29. (a) Suppose $A \subseteq B$. If $F \in [A]$, then $F \subseteq A$; since $A \subseteq B$, we conclude $F \subseteq B$ or equivalently $F \in [B]$. Thus $F \in [A]$ implies $F \in [B]$ so that $[A] \subseteq [B]$.
   (b) Conversely suppose $[A] \subseteq [B]$. Suppose $x \in A$. Then $\{x\} \in [A]$; hence $\{x\} \in [B]$. This yields $\{x\} \subseteq B$ so that $x \in B$. This shows every element of A is an element of B; hence that $A \subseteq B$.

505

31. (a)

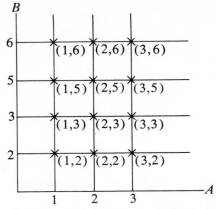

(b) {(1,2), (1,3), (1,5), (2,3), (2,5)}, {(2,2), (2,3), (3,2), (3,3), (3,5)}.

33. *mnr* elements.

CHAPTER 2

1. (a) No; yes; (b) no; yes; (c) no; (d) 16; (e) yes; (f) 2; 1; 1; 1.

3.

÷	1	2	3	4	5	6	7
1	1	$\frac{1}{2}$	$\frac{1}{3}$	$\frac{1}{4}$	$\frac{1}{5}$	$\frac{1}{6}$	$\frac{1}{7}$
2	2	1	$\frac{2}{3}$	$\frac{1}{2}$	$\frac{2}{5}$	$\frac{1}{3}$	$\frac{2}{7}$
3	3	$\frac{3}{2}$	1	$\frac{3}{4}$	$\frac{3}{5}$	$\frac{1}{2}$	$\frac{3}{7}$
4	4	2	$\frac{4}{3}$	1	$\frac{4}{5}$	$\frac{2}{3}$	$\frac{4}{7}$
5	5	$\frac{5}{2}$	$\frac{5}{3}$	$\frac{5}{4}$	1	$\frac{5}{6}$	$\frac{5}{7}$
6	6	3	2	$\frac{3}{2}$	$\frac{6}{5}$	1	$\frac{6}{7}$
7	7	$\frac{7}{2}$	$\frac{7}{3}$	$\frac{7}{4}$	$\frac{7}{5}$	$\frac{7}{6}$	1

5. (a)

○	1	2	3
1	5	5	5
2	5	5	5
3	5	5	5

(b)

○	1	2	3
1	2	3	4
2	3	4	5
3	4	5	6

(c)

○	1	2	3
1	1	2	3
2	2	2	3
3	3	3	3

7.

○	0	1	2	3
0	0	1	2	3
1	1	2	3	0
2	2	3	0	1
3	3	0	1	2

9. (a), (b), (d), (e) are false; the others are true.

11. (a) $[S] = \{\varnothing, \{1\}, \{2\}, \{1,2\}\}$.

(b)

∪	∅	{1}	{2}	S
∅	∅	{1}	{2}	S
{1}	{1}	{1}	S	S
{2}	{2}	S	{2}	S
S	S	S	S	S

(c)

∩	∅	{1}	{2}	S
∅	∅	∅	∅	∅
{1}	∅	{1}	∅	{1}
{2}	∅	∅	{2}	{2}
S	∅	{1}	{2}	S

13. (a) $Y \times Y = \{(2.2), (2,3), (3,2), (3,3)\}$.

(b)

(c)

	(2,2)	(2,3)	(3,2)	(3,3)
(2,2)	(4,4)	(6,4)	(4,6)	(6,6)
(2,3)	(4,6)	(6,6)	(4,9)	(6,9)
(3,2)	(6,4)	(9,4)	(6,6)	(9,6)
(3,3)	(6,6)	(9,6)	(6,9)	(9,9)

15. (a) Three; 1, 2, and 3.
  (b) One; 2.
  (c) Two; $A = \{1,2\}$, $B = \{2,3\}$.

17. $\{a,c,d,e\}$.

CHAPTER 3

1. (a) 11; (b) 11; (c) 1; (d) 5.
3. (a) 2; (b) 3; (c) 3.
5. (a) b; a; a; a.
  (b) d.
  (c) c.
7. (a) {2}; conditional.
  (b) N; identity.
  (c) {8}; conditional.
  (d) {3}; conditional.
  (e) {99}; conditional.
  (f) $\varnothing$; conditional.
  (g) $\varnothing$; conditional.

9. (a) $\{2\}$; conditional.
(b) $\{2,4,6, \ldots\}$; identity.
(c) $\{8\}$; conditional.
(d) $\varnothing$; conditional.
(e) $\varnothing$; conditional.
(f) $\varnothing$; conditional.
(g) $\varnothing$; conditional.

11. (a) $\{\{d\}, \{c,d\}, \{b,d\}, \{a,d\}, \{b,c,d\}, \{a,c,d\}, \{a,b,d\}, \{a,b,c,d\}\}$.
(b) $\{\{a,b\}\}$.
(c) $\{\varnothing, \{c\}, \{d\}, \{c,d\}\}$.
(d) $\{\{c\}, \{a,c\}, \{b,c\}, \{a,b,c\}\}$.
(e) $\{\{c\}, \{a,c\}, \{b,c\}, \{a,b,c\}\}$.
(f) $\{\{b,c\}, \{b,c,d\}\}$.

13. (a) $\varnothing$; (b) $\{(0,1), (1,0)\}$; (c) $\{(1,2), (2,1)\}$.

15. (a) $\{b\}$.
(b) $\{(b,a), (b,b), (b,c)\}$.
(c) $\{(b,a,a), (b,a,b), (b,a,c), (b,b,a), (b,b,b), (b,b,c), (b,c,a), (b,c,b)(b,c,c)\}$.

CHAPTER 4

1. (a) Replacing q by a,b,c, and d in turn in the equation $q \circ q = a \circ q$, we obtain respectively:
(i) $a \circ a = a \circ a$; (ii) $b \circ b = a \circ b$, or $a = b$; (iii) $c \circ c = a \circ c$, or $a = c$; (iv) $d \circ d = a \circ d$, or $a = d$. It follows that the solution set is $\{a\}$.
(b) We use the two identities observed in Sec. 1.1:
$(\alpha)\ x \circ x = a$; $(\beta)\ a \circ x = x$.
Then $q \circ q = a \circ q$ is equivalent with $a = a \circ q$ by (α), which in turn is equivalent to $a = q$ by (β). Hence the solution set is $\{a\}$.
(c) We must replace (x,y) in the equation $x \circ a = y$ by each of 16 ordered pairs: (a,a), (a,b), (a,c), (a,d), (b,a), (b,b), (b,c), (b,d), (c,a), (c,b), (c,c), (c,d), (d,a), (d,b), (d,c), (d,d). The ordered pair (a,a) yields $a \circ a = a$ which is correct. Hence (a,a) is a solution. The ordered pair (a,b) yields $a \circ a = b$ which is incorrect. Continuing this procedure yields the solution set $\{(a,a), (b,b), (c,c), (d,d)\}$.
(d) We use the fact that $x \circ a = x$ is an identity. Hence $x \circ a = y$ is equivalent with $x = y$. It therefore follows that $\{(a,a), (b,b), (c,c), (d,d)\}$ is the solution set.
(e) The equation $x \circ a = y$ is equivalent with $x = y$. Hence the solution set is $\{y\}$.
(f) As $d \circ b = e$, the right side of the equation may be replaced by $t \circ e$. But then replacing t by a,b,c, or d yields undefined expressions. The solution set is $\varnothing$.

3. (a) $x \circ (c \circ x) = (b \circ x) \circ c$.

$x \circ (x \circ c) = (x \circ b) \circ c$.	Rule 2
$(x \circ x) \circ c = x \circ (b \circ c)$.	Rule 3
$a \circ c = x \circ (b \circ c)$.	Rule 1
$c = x \circ d$.	Arithmetic
Solution set: $\{b\}$.	Arithmetic

Substituting b for x in the original equation yields $b \circ (c \circ b) = (b \circ b) \circ c$. Using the table, the left side $b \circ (c \circ b) = b \circ d = c$; the right side $(b \circ b) \circ c = a \circ c = c$. Hence the statement is correct and b is a solution.
(b) $\{(b,a), (b,b), (b,c), (b,d)\}$.

5. (a).

7. (a) No; (b) no; (c) yes; (d) inverse of a is a; b has no inverse.
9. (a) $d, e,$ or f.
 (b) $d, e,$ or f.
 (c) f.
11. (a) Yes; (b) yes; (c) yes; (d) the identity is 1, and is the only element having an inverse (namely, 1).
13. (a) No; (b) none.
15. (a) Yes; (b) yes; (c) yes; (d) there is none; (e) no element has an inverse.
17. (a) Yes; (b) yes; (c) yes; (d) $\varnothing$; (e) the inverse of $\varnothing$ is $\varnothing$; no other element has an inverse.
19. The table is:

$\circ$	a	b	c
a	b	c	a
b	c	a	b
c	a	b	c

The third row and third column arise from the fact that c is an identity; and given $a \circ a = b, b \circ a = c$ we may complete the first column. Since $b \circ a = c$ and $\circ$ is commutative, we obtain $a \circ b = c$; this completes the first row. It remains to determine $b \circ b$. From the associative law, we must have $(b \circ a) \circ a = b \circ (b \circ a)$, or $(b \circ b) \circ a = b$. But the table shows that a is the only element satisfying $x \circ a = b$. Hence $b \circ b = a$.

CHAPTER 5

1. Since the entries in both tables are all from S, it follows that $+$ and $\cdot$ are closed.

To test associativity of addition and multiplication, one must test the associativity on the eight ordered triples: $(0,0,0), (0,1,0), (0,0,1), (0,1,1), (1,0,0), (1,1,0), (1,0,1)$, and $(1,1,1)$. For example, testing the associativity of addition on $(1,0,1)$ we see that $(1+0)+1=1+1$ and $1+(0+1)=1+1$ so that $(1+0)+1=1+(0+1)$. Similarly for the other seven cases, and for all eight under multiplication.

$0+1=1$ and $1+0=1$ so that $0+1=1+0$; of course $0+0=0+0$ and $1+1=1+1$. Hence $+$ is commutative. Similarly $0 \cdot 1 = 0$ and $1 \cdot 0 = 0$ so that $\cdot$ is commutative.

Since $0+0=0$ and $0+1=1=1+0$, the additive identity is 0; since $1 \cdot 0 = 0 = 0 \cdot 1$ and $1 \cdot 1 = 1$, the multiplicative identity is 1. The additive inverse of 0 is 0 and of 1 is 1. The only non-zero element is 1, and its multiplicative inverse is 1.

Finally, to check the distributive law, it is sufficient to check the *left* distributive law on each of the ordered triples considered in proving the associative law. For example, testing the left distributive law on $(1,0,1)$ we see that $1 \cdot (0+1) = 1 \cdot 1 = 1$ and $1 \cdot 0 + 1 \cdot 1 = 0 + 1 = 1$ so that $1 \cdot (0+1) = 1 \cdot 0 + 1 \cdot 1$. Similarly for the other seven cases.

3. The tables are uniquely determined and are those given in Exercise 1. To see that $0+1=1$, we observe from the table that $1+0=1$ and apply $A3$. Thus 0 is seen to be the additive identity. As 1 must have an additive inverse, it follows that $1+1=0$. From the multiplication table we see that $1 \cdot 0 = 0$. This yields, applying $A3, 0 \cdot 1 = 0$. Finally $0(1+1) = 0 \cdot 1 + 0 \cdot 1 = 0 + 0 = 0$; but also $0(1+1) = 0 \cdot 0$. It follows that $0 \cdot 0 = 0$.

7. (a) (α) We first prove that if $a,b,c \in R$ and $a + b = c + a$, then $b = c$.

      (1) $a + b = c + a$ (1) Hyp.

      (2) $a + b = a + c$ (2) A3

      (3) $b = c$ (3) Th. 5

   (β) Conversely we show that if $a,b,c \in R$ and $b = c$, then $a + b = c + a$.

      (1) $b = c$ (1) Hyp.

      (2) $a + b = a + c$ (2) Th. 5 (or $+$ is a binary operation)

      (3) $a + b = c + a$ (3) A3

11. (1) $b + a = b$ (1) Hyp.

    (2) $b + a = b + 0$ (2) A4

    (3) $a = 0$ (3) Th. 5

13. (a) 0; (b) 1.

18. (1) A4; (2) Def. 1; (3) steps 1, 2; (4) Th. 5.

22. (1) $0 - a = 0 + (-a)$ (1) Def. 2

    (2) $= -a$ (2) A4

24. (a)

$-$	0	1	2
0	0	2	1
1	1	0	2
2	2	1	0

27. (1) $a - (-b) = a + (-(-b))$ (1) Def. 2

    (2) $= a + b$ (2) Th. 17

32. (b) (1) $a + b + c = b + a + c$ (1) Ex. 32(a)

    (2) $= b + (a + c)$ (2) Def. 3

    (3) $= (a + c) + b$ (3) A3

    (4) $= a + c + b$ (4) Def. 3

36. As in Sec. 2.1 of Ch. 4 we proceed from the given equation to equivalent equations, specifying to the right of each equation the reason it is equivalent to the preceding one.

   (a) $u + j + k = 0$

      $u + (j + k) = 0$ Def. 3

      Solution set is $\{-(j + k)\}$ Ex. 35(a)

   (b) $jk - l + u = k$

      $jk + (-l) + u = k$ Def. 3

      $(jk + (-l)) + u = k$ Def. 3

      $(jk - l) + u = k$ Def. 2

      Solution set is $\{k - (jk - l)\}$ Th. 34

39. (b) We use the same procedure as in Ex. 36.

      $b - (t - c) = d + a$

             $= d - (-a)$ Ex. 27

      $b + (-a) = (t - c) + d$ Th. 37

           $= (t + (-c)) + d$ Def. 2

           $= t + ((-c) + d)$ A2

           $= t + (d + (-c))$ A3

      $b - a = t + (d - c)$ Def. 2

      Solution set is $\{(b - a) - (d - c)\}$ Th. 34

43. (α) We first prove: If $a,b,c \in R$, $a \neq 0$, and $b = c$, then $ab = ac$.

    (1) $b = c$ (1) Hyp.

    (2) $ab = ac$ (2) $\cdot$ is a binary operation

   (β) We prove if $a,b,c \in R$, $a \neq 0$, and $ab = ac$, then $b = c$.

    (1) $a \neq 0$ (1) Hyp.

    (2) There exists $d \in R$ (2) M5 (and step 1)
       such that $da = 1$
    (3) $ab = ac$ (3) Hyp.
    (4) $d(ab) = d(ac)$ (4) $\cdot$ is a binary operation
    (5) $(da)b = (da)c$ (5) M2
    (6) $1 \cdot b = 1 \cdot c$ (6) Step 2 (applied to step 5)
    (7) $b = c$ (7) M4

51. (a) (1) $a \neq 0$ (1) Hyp.
    (2) $aa^{-1} = 1$ (2) Def. 5 (and step 1)
    (3) Either $a^{-1} = 0$ or $a^{-1} \neq 0$ (3) Listing of alternatives for a proof by contradiction
    (4) Suppose $a^{-1} = 0$ (4) Assumption to lead to a contradiction
    (5) $aa^{-1} = a \cdot 0$ (5) Ex. 43
    (6) $= 0$ (6) Th. 50
    (7) $1 = 0$ (7) Steps 2, 6
    (8) $a^{-1} = 0$ leads to a   (8) Step 7 contradicts B
       contradiction
    (9) $a^{-1} \neq 0$ (9) Steps 3, 8

53. (1) $b \neq 0$ (1) Hyp.
    (2) $b^{-1} \in R$ (2) Def. 5 (and step 1)
    (3) $ab^{-1} \in R$ (3) M1
    (4) $\dfrac{a}{b} \in R$ (4) Step 1, Def. 6 (and step 3)

59. (α) We prove if $abc = 0$, then $a = 0$, $b = 0$, or $c = 0$.
    (1) $abc = 0$ (1) Hyp.
    (2) $a(bc) = 0$ (2) Def. 7
    (3) $a = 0$; or $bc = 0$ (3) Th. 50
    (4) $a = 0$; or $b = 0$ or $c = 0$ (4) Th. 50

  (β) We prove if $a = 0$, then $abc = 0$. The cases $b = 0$, $c = 0$ are proved similarly.
    (1) $a = 0$ (1) Hyp.
    (2) $abc = 0bc$ (2) Step 1
    (3) $= (0b)c$ (3) Def. 7
    (4) $= 0 \cdot c$ (4) Th. 50
    (5) $= 0$ (5) Th. 50

66. (α) We prove 0 is a solution.
    (1) $a \neq 0$ (1) Hyp.
    (2) $\dfrac{0}{a} = 0 \cdot a^{-1}$ (2) Def. 7 (and step 1)
    (3) $= 0$ (3) Th. 50

  (β) We prove that if c is a solution $\left(\text{i.e. if } \dfrac{c}{a} = 0\right)$, then $c = 0$.
    (1) $a \neq 0$ (1) Hyp.
    (2) $a^{-1} \neq 0$ (2) Ex. 51(a)
    (3) $\dfrac{c}{a} = 0$ (3) Hyp.
    (4) $ca^{-1} = 0$ (4) Def. 6,
    (5) $c = 0$ (5) Th. 50, step 2

67. (c) s is a solution of $(ax + b)(cx + d) = 0$ if and only if $as + b = 0$ or $cs + d = 0$ by

Th. 50. It is easy to provide the reasoning that this is so if and only if $s = \dfrac{-b}{a}$ or

$s = \dfrac{-d}{c}$. Hence the solution set is $\left\{\dfrac{-b}{a}, \dfrac{-d}{c}\right\}$.

This informal argument brings out how one discovers the solution set (cf. Sec. 4 for a discussion of "informal proofs"). For a formal argument that $\left\{\dfrac{-b}{a},\dfrac{-d}{c}\right\}$ is the solution set, one may proceed as in the proof of Th. 63.

73. $-(a + b)$ is the additive inverse of $a + b$. If we can show that $-a - b$ is also the additive inverse of $a + b$, the result will follow. But

$$(a + b) + (-a - b) = (a + b) + ((-a) + (-b))$$
$$= (a + (-a)) + (b + (-b)) \qquad \text{by Def. 4 and Ex. 33}$$
$$= 0$$

80. $\dfrac{a}{b} \cdot \dfrac{c}{d} = (ab^{-1})(cd^{-1})$

$$= (ac)(b^{-1}d^{-1})$$

$$= (ac)\left(\dfrac{1}{b} \cdot \dfrac{1}{d}\right) \qquad \text{by Ex. 55}$$

$$= (ac)\dfrac{1}{bd} \qquad \text{by Th. 70}$$

$$= \dfrac{ac}{bd} \qquad \text{by Ex. 77}$$

87. $\dfrac{a}{b}\Big/\dfrac{c}{d} = \dfrac{a}{b} \cdot bd \Big/ \dfrac{c}{d} \cdot bd$

$$= \left(\dfrac{a}{b} \cdot b\right) d \Big/ \left(\dfrac{c}{d} \cdot d\right) b$$

$$= \dfrac{ad}{bc} \qquad \text{by Ex. 79}$$

95. (a) $(a + b)(c + d) = a(c + d) + b(c + d) \qquad \text{by D}$
$$= (ac + ad) + (bc + bd) \qquad \text{by D}$$
$$= ac + ad + bc + bd$$

102. If $a \neq 0$, then $-a \neq 0$ by Th. 40. Hence $-a$ has a multiplicative inverse which, by Def. 5, we have denoted by '$(-a)^{-1}$.' Since the multiplicative inverse of $-a$ is uniquely determined, it remains to show that $-(a^{-1})$ is also the multiplicative inverse of $-a$. But
$$[-(a^{-1})](-a) = a^{-1} \cdot a \qquad \text{by Th. 72}$$
$$= 1$$

CHAPTER 6

1. 0 by (5,21).
3. 0 by (5,50).
5. -9 by (5,22).
7. $-7 + (-3) = -7 - 3$
$$= -(7 + 3) \qquad \text{by (5,73)}$$
$$= -10 \qquad \text{by AN}$$
9. 0 by (5,50).
11. $(-8)(3) = -(8 \cdot 3) \qquad \text{by (5,71a)}$
$$= -24 \qquad \text{by MN}$$
13. (a) $5 + 9 - 12 = 5 + 9 + (-12) = (5 + 9) + (-12)$
$$= 14 - 12 \qquad\qquad\qquad \text{by AN}$$
$$12 + 2 = 14 \qquad\qquad\qquad\qquad \text{by AN}$$
$$14 - 12 = 2 \qquad\qquad\qquad\qquad \text{by (5,34)}$$
  (b) $5 + 9 - 12 = (2 + 3) + 9 - 12 \qquad \text{by AN}$
$$= 2 + (3 + 9) + (-12)$$
$$= 2 + 12 + (-12)$$
$$= 0$$

15. Two in N, four in J: 2, 3, 5, 7, 11, 13, 17, 19.

17. (b) $2^3 \cdot 3^3$; (d) $(-1)5^4$.

19. (a) 72; (c) 1; (f) 432.

21. (a) If a,b,c are nonzero integers, then an integer d is called a highest common factor of a, b, and c if (1) d is a common factor of a, b, and c, and (2) any common factor of a, b, and c is a factor of d.

23. For $a,b \in N$, $(a,b) = [a,b]$ if and only if $a = b$.

25. $\dfrac{1}{3} + \dfrac{2}{3} = \dfrac{1+2}{3}$ (5,97)

$\qquad\qquad = 1$ (5,56)

27. $\dfrac{2}{5} \cdot \dfrac{-1}{3} \cdot \dfrac{1}{2} = \left(\dfrac{2}{5} \cdot \dfrac{1}{2}\right)\left(\dfrac{-1}{3}\right)$

$\qquad = \dfrac{2 \cdot 1}{5 \cdot 2} \cdot \dfrac{-1}{3}$

$\qquad = \left(\dfrac{1}{5} \cdot \dfrac{2}{2}\right) \cdot \dfrac{-1}{3}$

$\qquad = \dfrac{1}{5} \cdot \dfrac{-1}{3}$

$\qquad = \dfrac{-1}{15}$

(In the above, several reasons may be needed to proceed from one line to the next, but the reasoning involved should be clear.)

29. $\dfrac{\frac{2}{3} \cdot \frac{1}{3}}{\frac{2}{3} \cdot 5} = \dfrac{\frac{2}{3} \cdot \frac{1}{3} \cdot 30}{\frac{2}{3} \cdot 5 \cdot 30} = \frac{4}{225}$

38. $x^2 + 2x + 1$.

40. $2x^2 + 5x + 3$.

44. $\dfrac{y + x}{y - x}$.

50. $(x + 1)(x + 2)$.

54. $t(s + u + t^2)$.

58. $(x - 2)^3$.

61. $(a + b + c^2)(a + b - c^2)$.

64. $(x - 2)(x - 3)(x + 3)$.

68. 1.

72. $(x + 2)(x - 2)$.

75. $\dfrac{4}{(x + 1)(x - 2)}$; $0, -1, 2$ are excluded.

78. $\dfrac{2x + y}{2x - y}$; solutions of $x + y = 0$, $x - y = 0$, and $2x - y = 0$ are excluded.

81. $x - 7 = 3x + 2$

$(x - 7) + (-x - 2) = (3x + 2) + (-x - 2)$ (5,5)

$\qquad\qquad -9 = 2x$

$\qquad\qquad \frac{1}{2}(-9) = \frac{1}{2}(2x)$ (5,43), valid for all $x \in R$

$\qquad\qquad -\frac{9}{2} = x$

Solution set in R: $\{-\frac{9}{2}\}$; in J: $\varnothing$.

87. $\dfrac{x}{3 - x} + \dfrac{7}{x} = \dfrac{-9}{x^2 - 3x}$

$\dfrac{-x}{x - 3} + \dfrac{7}{x} = \dfrac{-9}{x(x - 3)}$

$\left(\dfrac{-x}{x - 3} + \dfrac{7}{x}\right) x(x - 3) = \left(\dfrac{-9}{x(x - 3)}\right) x(x - 3)$ (5,43); $x \neq 0,3$.

$-x^2 + 7x - 21 = -9$

$-x^2 + 7(x - 3) = -9$

$0 = x^2 - 7x + 12$ by an application of (5,5)

$0 = (x - 4)(x - 3)$

Solution set in R and in J is $\{4\}$ by (5,50).

(Note 3 is not a solution since $x \neq 3$.)

92. Solution set in R is $\{b\}$; in J it is $\{b\}$ if $b \in J$, and $\emptyset$ if $b \notin J$.

95. Solution set is $\{-3\}$ in R and in J.

99. $3y - 4x = 12 - xy$

$xy + 3y - 4x - 12 = 0$ (5,5)

$(x + 3)(y - 4) = 0$

Solution set: $\{(-3,b)/b \in R\} \cup \{(a,4)/a \in R\}$ in $R \times R$, or $\{(-3,b)/b \in J\} \cup \{(a,4)/a \in J\}$ in $J \times J$.

CHAPTER 7

3. (d) If $a,b \in -P$, then $-a,-b \in P$ by Th. 1. Hence $(-a)(-b) \in P$. By (5,72), $(-a)(-b) = ab$. Thus $ab \in P$.

7. In Ex. (5,1), $1 + 1 = 0$. But according to Th. 4, 1 is positive. Hence by $(\mathcal{O}_1)$ it would follow that $1 + 1$ is positive. But by $(\mathcal{O}_3)$, $1 + 1$ cannot be both positive and zero. Similar reasoning would yield $(1 + 1) + 1$ is positive. But in Ex. (5,2), $(1 + 1) + 1 = 0$.

10. (a) By (5,20), $a = a - 0$. But $a > 0$ if and only if $a - 0$ is positive (cf. Def. 2). Hence $a > 0$ if and only if a is positive.

12. (a) $a - b < 0$ if and only if $0 - (a - b)$ is positive (cf. Def. 2), i.e. if and only if $b - a$ is positive. But by Def. 2, $b - a$ is positive if and only if $b > a$.

(b) Since $a \in P$, $-b \in P$, we conclude $a + (-b) \in P$; i.e. $a - b \in P$. But then $a > b$ by Def. 2.

17. (a) Since $0 < a$, then a and hence a^2 are positive. Thus $0 < a^2$. Also since $a < 1$, $1 - a \in P$. But $1 + a \in P$. Hence $(1 - a)(1 + a) \in P$; i.e. $1 - a^2 \in P$. This proves $a^2 < 1$.

19. We have already proved that $a + c > b + c$ if and only if $a > b$, and $a + c = b + c$ if and only if $a = b$ (cf. (5,5) and Th. 13).

22. If $a = b$, then $a \leq b$ and $b \leq a$ by Def. 3. Conversely suppose $a \leq b$ and $b \leq a$. If we should have $a \neq b$, then it would follow that $a < b$ and $b < a$. By Ex. 21(a) we could then conclude, since $a < b < a$, that $a < a$. This contradicts Th. 9, as $a = a$.

25. Since $a > b$, Th. 13 shows that $a + c > b + c$. Since $c > d$, Th. 13 shows that $b + c > b + d$. Thus we have $a + c > b + c > b + d$, and we may apply Ex. 21(a). (To show that $a \geq b$ and $c \geq d$ imply $a + c \geq b + d$, a similar argument involving Ex. 19 and Ex. 21(b) may be used.)

29. Since $a,b \in P$, it follows from Ex. 5 that $a^{-1},b^{-1} \in P$ so that $a^{-1}b^{-1} \in P$. By Th. 14(a), we may multiply both sides of $a < b$ by $a^{-1}b^{-1}$ to obtain $a^{-1}b^{-1}a < a^{-1}b^{-1}b$; i.e. $b^{-1} < a^{-1}$.

31. $\{x \in R/x > \frac{1}{2}\}$.

33. $\{x \in R/x < -\frac{5}{2}\}$.

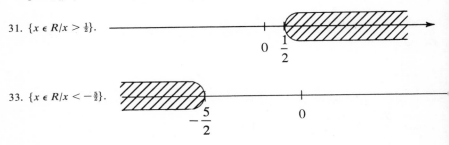

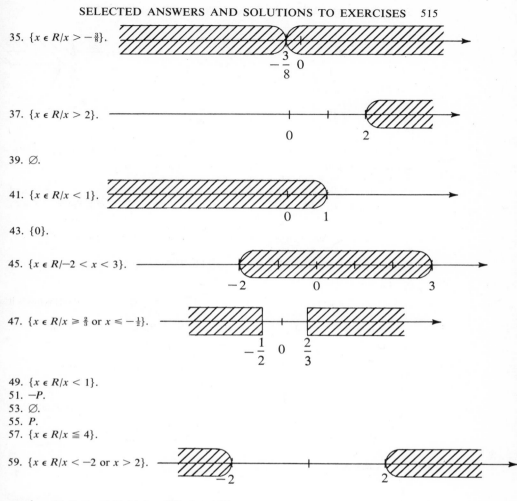

35. $\{x \in R/x > -\frac{3}{8}\}$.

37. $\{x \in R/x > 2\}$.

39. $\varnothing$.

41. $\{x \in R/x < 1\}$.

43. $\{0\}$.

45. $\{x \in R/-2 < x < 3\}$.

47. $\{x \in R/x \geq \frac{2}{3} \text{ or } x \leq -\frac{1}{2}\}$.

49. $\{x \in R/x < 1\}$.
51. $-P$.
53. $\varnothing$.
55. P.
57. $\{x \in R/x \leq 4\}$.

59. $\{x \in R/x < -2 \text{ or } x > 2\}$.

61. $\{x \in R/-2 \leq x \leq 1\} \cup \{x \in R/3 \leq x \leq 7\}$.

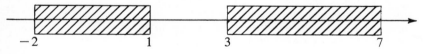

63. $\{x \in R/-1 < x < 1 \text{ or } x > 1\}$.

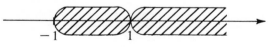

65. R.
67. $\{\frac{3}{2}\}$.
69. $\{x \in R/x < 1\}$.
71. P.
73. $\{x \in R/x > 1\}$.
75. $\varnothing$.

77. *R.*

79. $\{x \epsilon R/x < -2 \text{ or } 1 < x < 3\}$.

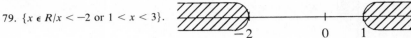

81. $\{x \epsilon R/x < -1 \text{ or } 1 < x < \frac{7}{3}\}$.
83. $\{x \epsilon R/x < -1\}$.
85. $\{x \epsilon R/0 < x < 1\}$.
87. $\{x \epsilon R/-10 < x < -1 \text{ or } x \geq -4\}$.
89. $\{x \epsilon R/x < -1\}$.
94. Suppose $|a| \leq b$. By Ex. 93, $a \leq |a|$ and $-a \leq |a|$. By Ex. 21(b), $a \leq b$ and $-a \leq b$. Conversely, suppose $a \leq b$ and $-a \leq b$. Since by Def. 5, $|a| = a$ or $|a| = -a$ (both in the case $a = 0$), it follows in either case that $|a| \leq b$.
97. The result is clear if $a = 0$. If $a \neq 0$, then $|a|, |b| \epsilon P$. By Ex. 28(a), $|a| < |b|$ if and only if $|a|^2 < |b|^2$. But by Ex. 92(b), $|a|^2 = |a^2|$ and $|b|^2 = |b^2|$. Since $a^2, b^2 \epsilon P$, it follows that $|a^2| = a^2$, $|b^2| = b^2$. Hence $|a| < |b|$ if and only if $a^2 < b^2$.

101. (a) The result is clear if either a or b is 0. Otherwise $|a| = |b|$ if and only if $\left|\dfrac{a}{b}\right| = 1$.

But $\left|\dfrac{a}{b}\right| = 1$ if and only if $\dfrac{a}{b} = 1$ or $\dfrac{a}{b} = -1$ by Def. 5, which in turn holds if and only if $a = b$ or $a = -b$.

(b) $|a| < |b|$ if and only if $\dfrac{|a|}{|b|} < 1$; i.e. if and only if $\left|\dfrac{a}{b}\right| < 1$. By Ex. 94, this holds if and only if $\dfrac{a}{b} < 1$ and $-\dfrac{a}{b} < 1$, which in turn holds if and only if $\dfrac{a}{b} < 1$ and $\dfrac{a}{b} > -1$; i.e. if and only if $-1 < \dfrac{a}{b} < 1$.

103. (a) $\{a, -a\}$ providing $a \geq 0$; $\varnothing$ otherwise.
    (b) $\{b - a, b + a\}$ providing $a \geq 0$; $\varnothing$ otherwise.
    (c) No solutions if $a < 0$; one solution if $a = 0$.
    (d) $\{x \epsilon R/b - a < x < b + a\}$.
    (e) (i) R; (ii) $P \cup -P$; (iii) $\{x \epsilon R/x < -a \text{ or } a < x\}$.
    (f) (i) R, if $a \leq 0$; (ii) $\{x \epsilon R/x \leq b - a \text{ or } b + a \leq x\}$, if $a > 0$.
    (g) $\{-5, -\frac{1}{3}\}$.
105. (b) $\{x \epsilon R/x \leq \frac{1}{2}\}$.
    (d) $\{x \epsilon R/x > 4\}$.
    (f) R.
    (h) $\{x \epsilon R/x \leq \frac{1}{3} \text{ or } x \geq 5\}$.
109. (a) S is bounded above by 3 (or also 4, or $8\sqrt{2}$).
    (b) Yes; 3 is such an upper bound.
    (c) S is bounded below by -1 (or also $\frac{3}{2}$, or $-\sqrt{3}$, or 0).
    (d) Yes; 2 is such a lower bound.
    (e) No.
    (f) Yes.
    (g) Yes.

    (h)

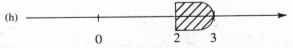

114. (a) Yes; 1,002 is an upper bound.
    (b) Yes; 1 is such an upper bound.
    (c) No.
    (d) $-$.

(e) Yes.

(f) −.

(g) No.

(h)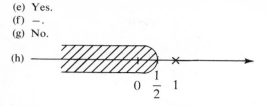

$$0 \quad \frac{1}{2} \quad 1$$

118. We are given a is an upper bound of S. To prove a is the lub of S, it remains to show that $a \leq b$ for all upper bounds b of S. But if b is an upper bound of S, $a \leq b$ since $a \in S$.

121. An element $a \in R$ is both a lower and upper bound of a subset S of R if and only if $S = \{a\}$.

CHAPTER 8

7. (a) 15; (b) 20; (c) 35.

10. We use induction on n. Since $a' = a$ by Def. 3(a), the result is correct for $n = 1$. Assume the result true for $n = k$, so that $a^k \in P$. Then $a^k \cdot a \in P$ by ($\mathscr{O}_2$), so that $a^{k+1} \in P$ by Def. 3(b). The result for $n = k$ implies the result for $n = k + 1$. Hence $a^n \in P$ for all $n \in N$.

13. (a) If $a \in P$, then either $0 < a < 1$, $a = 1$, or $1 < a$. If $a = 1$, then $a^k = 1$ by Ex. 3, contrary to hypothesis. If $1 < a$, then $1 < a^k$ by Ex. 12, contrary to hypothesis. Hence $0 < a < 1$.

   (b) If either $a = 1$ or $a < 1$, we may apply Ex. 3 and Ex. 11 to see that $a^k = 1$ or $a^k < 1$, respectively. These being contrary to hypothesis, we conclude $a > 1$.

   (c) If either $a < 1$ or $a > 1$, then $a^k < 1$ or $a^k > 1$ respectively, a contradiction. So $a = 1$.

20. (a) Suppose $m < n$. Then by Th. 18, $\exists\, r \in N \ni m + r = n$. Since $1 \leq r$ by Th. 3, $m + 1 \leq m + r = n$. Hence $m \leq n - 1$. Conversely, suppose $m \leq n - 1$. Then $m + 1 \leq n$, and since $m < m + 1$, we conclude $m < n$.

    (b) Since $m + 1 \leq n$ if and only if $(m + 1) + (-1) \leq n + (-1)$, the result follows.

25. We use induction on r, for $r \geq 4$. Since $2^4 = 16$ and $4! = 12$, we have $2^4 < 4!$ so that $P(4)$ is a theorem. By inductive hypothesis, for $n \geq 4$, we have $2^n < n!$ Since $2 < n + 1$, we conclude $2^n \cdot 2 < (n + 1)n!$; i.e. $2^{n+1} < (n + 1)!$ Hence $2^n < n!$ for all $n \in N$ with $n \geq 4$.

30. (a) $P(1)$: $1^2 = \dfrac{1(1 + 1)(2(1) + 1)}{6}$

    $P(2)$: $1^2 + 2^2 = \dfrac{2(2 + 1)(2(2) + 1)}{6}$

    $P(3)$: $1^2 + 2^2 + 3^2 = \dfrac{3(3 + 1)(2(3) + 1)}{6}$

    $P(4)$: $1^2 + 2^2 + 3^2 + 4^2 = \dfrac{4(4 + 1)(2(4) + 1)}{6}$

    $P(5)$: $1^2 + 2^2 + 3^2 + 4^2 + 5^2 = \dfrac{5(5 + 1)(2(5) + 1)}{6}$

    (b) The left side of $P(1)$ is 1, the right side $\dfrac{1 \cdot 2 \cdot 3}{6}$ or also 1. Similarly, assuming AN and MN, one checks that the left and right sides of $P(2)$ are 5, of $P(3)$ are 14, of $P(4)$ are 30, of $P(5)$ are 55.

    (c) $P(1)$ has been established in (b). Thus assume

    $$1^2 + 2^2 + \cdots + r^2 = \frac{r(r + 1)(2r + 1)}{6}.$$

Adding $(r + 1)^2$ to both sides yields:

$$1^2 + 2^2 + \cdots + r^2 + (r + 1)^2 = \frac{r(r + 1)(2r + 1)}{6} + (r + 1)^2$$
$$= \frac{r(r + 1)(2r + 1) + 6(r + 1)^2}{6}$$
$$= \frac{(r + 1)[r(2r + 1) + 6(r + 1)]}{6}$$
$$= \frac{(r + 1)(2r^2 + r + 6r + 6)}{6}$$
$$= \frac{(r + 1)(r + 2)(2r + 3)}{6}$$
$$= \frac{(r + 1)[(r + 1) + 1][2(r + 1) + 1]}{6}$$

But this is precisely the statement of $P(r + 1)$.

33. (a) Use induction on n. $P(1)$ is trivially correct since it states that if a_1 is negative then a_1 is negative. Now suppose $a_1, a_2, \ldots, a_n, a_{n+1}$ are negative real numbers. By inductive hypothesis $a_1 + \cdots + a_n$ is negative. By (7,2), it follows that $(a_1 + \cdots + a_n) + a_{n+1}$ is negative.

36. $d_1 = 0$; $d_2 = -1$, $d_3 = d_1 \cdot d_2 + d_1 = 0$, $d_4 = d_2 \cdot d_3 + d_2 = -1$, $d_5 = d_3 \cdot d_4 + d_3 = 0$.

46. By Th. 43, $C(n,r) = \dfrac{n!}{r!(n - r)!}$ and $C(n,n - r) = \dfrac{n!}{(n - r)!(n - (n - r))!} = \dfrac{n!}{(n - r)!r!}$. Thus $C(n,r) = C(n,n - r)$.

48. 635,013,559,600.

54. $(x - 1)(x^4 + x^3 + x^2 + x + 1)$.

56. (a) $C(10,2) = 45$; $C(10,7) = C(10,3) = 120$.
   (b) $C(50,48) = C(50,2) = 1225$.
   (c) No. The coefficient of $a^{42}b^{10} = C(42,10)$.
   But $C(42,10) > \frac{42}{4} \cdot \frac{41}{2} \cdot \frac{40}{3} \cdot \frac{39}{4} > (40)(20)(10)9 = 72000 > 42130$.

61. Of course $0 < a^n$ by Ex. 10. It remains to prove $a^n < a$. Since $n > 1$, so that $n - 1 \in N$ by Th. 16, it follows from Ex. 10 that $a^{n-1} < 1$. Hence by (8,14(a)), $a \cdot a^{n-1} < a \cdot 1$; i.e., $a^n < a$.

63. (a) By Th. 18, $m > n$ if and only if $\exists\, r \in N \ni m = n + r$. Since $a > 1$, it follows from Ex. 12 that $a^r > 1$. From Ex. 9 it also follows that $a^n \neq 0$. By (8,14(a)), $a^r > 1$ if and only if $a^n \cdot a^r > a^n \cdot 1$, i.e. if and only if $a^m > a^n$.

63. (b) Since $0 < a < 1$, it follows that $1 < \dfrac{1}{a}$. Hence $\left(\dfrac{1}{a}\right)^m < \left(\dfrac{1}{a}\right)^n$ if and only if $m < n$ by part (a). But $\left(\dfrac{1}{a}\right)^m < \left(\dfrac{1}{a}\right)^n \left(\text{i.e. } \dfrac{1}{a^m} < \dfrac{1}{a^n}\right)$ holds if and only if $a^m > a^n$.

65. Since $0 < a < b$, we conclude $0 < \dfrac{a}{b} < 1$. By Ex. 11, $0 < \left(\dfrac{a}{b}\right)^n < 1$; i.e. $\dfrac{a^n}{b^n} < 1$. Since $b^n \in P$ by Ex. 10, it follows that $a^n < b^n$. Of course if $a = b$, then $a^n = b^n$; and if $a > b$ then thinking of this as $0 < b < a$ we conclude $b^n < a^n$ from our first argument. (It now follows that $a^n < b^n$ implies $a < b$; for $a = b$ and $a > b$ lead to $a^n = b^n$ and $a^n > b^n$ respectively, which are contradictions.)

CHAPTER 9

1. $n = 2$; $a_2 = 3$, $a_1 = 8$, $a_0 = 0$.
3. $n = 0$; $a_0 = 6$.
5. $n = 1$; $a_1 = 1$, $a_0 = 0$.

7. $n = 4$; $a_4 = 1$, $a_3 = a_2 = a_1 = a_0 = 0$.

9. $n = 6$; $a_6 = 7$, $a_5 = 4$, $a_4 = 0$, $a_3 = 0$, $a_2 = 2$, $a_1 = 9$, $a_0 = 3$.

11. $99 + 999 = (9 \cdot 10 + 9) + (9 \cdot 10^2 + 9 \cdot 10 + 9)$

$$\begin{aligned}
&= 9 \cdot 10^2 + (9 + 9)10 + (9 + 9) \\
&= 9 \cdot 10^2 + 18 \cdot 10 + 18 \\
&= 9 \cdot 10^2 + (1 \cdot 10 + 8)10 + (1 \cdot 10 + 8) \\
&= 9 \cdot 10^2 + (1 \cdot 10^2 + 8 \cdot 10 + 1 \cdot 10 + 8 \\
&= (9 + 1)10^2 + (8 + 1)10 + 8 \\
&= 10 \cdot 10^2 + 9 \cdot 10 + 8 \\
&= 10^3 + 9 \cdot 10 + 8 \\
&= 1098
\end{aligned}$$

13. $732 + 89 + 8634 + 98$

$= (7 \cdot 10^2 + 3 \cdot 10 + 2) + (8 \cdot 10 + 9) + (8 \cdot 10^3 + 6 \cdot 10^2 + 3 \cdot 10 + 4) + (9 \cdot 10 + 8)$

$= 8 \cdot 10^3 + (7 + 6)10^2 + (3 + 8 + 3 + 9)10 + (2 + 9 + 4 + 8)$

(Now $7 + 6 = 13$ from the table; $3 + 8 = 11$,

$11 + 3 = 1 \cdot 10 + 1 + 3 = 1 \cdot 10 + 4 = 14$;

$14 + 9 = 1 \cdot 10 + 4 + 9 = 1 \cdot 10 + 13 = 1 \cdot 10 + 1 \cdot 10 + 3$

$$= (1 + 1)10 + 3 = 2 \cdot 10 + 3 = 23.$$

Thus $3 + 8 + 3 + 9 = 23$. Similarly $2 + 9 + 4 + 8 = 23$.)

$= 8 \cdot 10^3 + 13 \cdot 10^2 + 23 \cdot 10 + 23$

$= 8 \cdot 10^3 + (1 \cdot 10 + 3)10^2 + (2 \cdot 10 + 3)10 + 2 \cdot 10 + 3$

$= 8 \cdot 10^3 + 1 \cdot 10^3 + 3 \cdot 10^2 + 2 \cdot 10^2 + 3 \cdot 10 + 2 \cdot 10 + 3$

$= (8 + 1)10^3 + (3 + 2)10^2 + (3 + 2)10 + 3$

$= 9 \cdot 10^3 + 5 \cdot 10^2 + 5 \cdot 10 + 3$

$= 9553$

15. $2 + 2 = 2 + (1 + 1)$ Def. 1

$\quad\quad\;\; = (2 + 1) + 1$

$\quad\quad\;\; = 3 + 1$ Def. 1

$\quad\quad\;\; = 4$ Def. 1

17. $1 + 7 = 7 + 1$ A_3

$\quad\quad\;\; = 8$ Def. 1

20. (a)

	1	2	3
1	2	3	10
2	3	10	11
3	10	11	12

$(10232)_4 + (3133)_4 = (20031)_4$

$(10232)_4 = 4^4 + 2 \cdot 4^2 + 3 \cdot 4 + 2 = 256 + 32 + 12 + 2 = 302$

$(3133)_4 = 3 \cdot 4^3 + 4^2 + 3 \cdot 4 + 3 = 192 + 16 + 12 + 3 = 223$

$(20031)_4 = 2 \cdot 4^4 + 3 \cdot 4 + 1 = 512 + 12 + 1 = 525$

Hence we should have $302 + 223 = 525$, and this, in fact, is the case.

(b) $(2031)_4 + (333)_4 + (1003)_4 = (10033)_4$

$(2031)_4 = 141$; $(333)_4 = 63$; $(1003)_4 = 67$; $(10033)_4 = 271$.

Hence we should have $141 + 63 + 67 = 271$, which is correct.

(c) $(32)_4 + (22)_4 + (10)_4 + (300)_4 + (21)_4 + 2 = (1113)_4$

$(32)_4 = 14$; $(22)_4 = 10$; $(10)_4 = 4$; $(300)_4 = 48$; $(21)_4 = 9$;

$(2)_4 = 2$; $(1113)_4 = 87$.

Hence we should have $14 + 10 + 4 + 48 + 9 + 2 = 87$, which is correct.

24. $80012 - 9643$.

$= (8 \cdot 10^4 + 1 \cdot 10 + 2) - (9 \cdot 10^3 + 6 \cdot 10^2 + 4 \cdot 10 + 3)$

$$= 8 \cdot 10^4 + (0 - 9)10^3 + (0 - 6)10^2 + (1 - 4)10 + (2 - 3)$$
$$= 8 \cdot 10^4 + (0 - 9)10^3 + (0 - 6)10^2 + (1 - 4 - 1)10 + (12 - 3)$$
$$= 8 \cdot 10^4 + (0 - 9)10^3 + (0 - 6)10^2 + (1 - 5)10 + 9$$
$$= 8 \cdot 10^4 + (0 - 9)10^3 + (0 - 6 - 1)10^2 + (11 - 5)10 + 9$$
$$= 8 \cdot 10^4 + (0 - 9)10^3 + (0 - 7)10^2 + 6 \cdot 10 + 9$$
$$= 8 \cdot 10^4 + (0 - 9 - 1)10^3 + (10 - 7)10^2 + 6 \cdot 10 + 9$$
$$= 8 \cdot 10^4 + (0 - 10)10^3 + 3 \cdot 10^2 + 6 \cdot 10 + 9$$
$$= (8 - 1)10^4 + (10 - 10)10^3 + 3 \cdot 10^2 + 6 \cdot 10 + 9$$
$$= 7 \cdot 10^4 + 3 \cdot 10^2 + 6 \cdot 10 + 9$$
$$= 70369$$

29. $(1100010)_2 - (11001)_2 = (1001001)_2$
$(1100010)_2 = 64 + 32 + 2 = 98$; $(11001)_2 = 16 + 8 + 1 = 25$;
$(1001001)_2 = 64 + 8 + 1 = 73$.
Hence we should have $98 - 25 = 73$, which is correct.

32. $(924)_{11} - (835)_{11} = (9u)_{11}$
$(924)_{11} = 9 \cdot 11^2 + 2 \cdot 11 + 4 = 1089 + 22 + 4 = 1115$;
$(835)_{11} = 968 + 33 + 5 = 1006$;
$(9u)_{11} = 9 \cdot 11 + 10 = 109$.
Hence we should have $1115 - 1006 = 109$, which is correct.

35. $(9uv)_{12}(u6)_{12} = (88076)_{12}$
$(9uv)_{12} = 1427$; $(u6)_{12} = 126$; $(88076)_{12} = 179802$.
Hence we should have $(1427)(126) = 179802$, which is correct.

37. $(2500)_6 \cdot (103)_6 = (302300)_6$
$(2500)_6 = 612$; $(103)_6 = 39$; $(302300)_6 = 23868$.
Hence we should have $(612)(39) = 23868$, which is correct.

39. $q = (115)_9$, $r = (25)_9$.
$(7286)_9 = 5343$; $(62)_9 = 56$; $(115)_9 = 95$; $(25)_9 = 23$.
Hence dividing 5343 by 56 should yield a quotient of 95 and remainder of 23, which it does.

41. $q = (20042)_5$, $r = (20)_5$.
$(4124201)_5 = 67426$; $(203)_5 = 53$; $(20042)_5 = 1272$; $(20)_5 = 10$.
Hence dividing 67426 by 53 should yield a quotient of 1272 and remainder of 10, which it does.

43. (a) 4976; (c) 297; (e) 22400.

44. (a) $762 = (1,011,111,010)_2 = (1,001,020)_3 = (11,022)_5 = (1372)_8$
$= (633)_{11} = (536)_{12}$.
(c) $3000 = (101,110,111,000)_2 = (11,010,010)_3 = (44,000)_5$
$= (5670)_8 = (2288)_{11} = (18u0)_{12}$.
(e) $6 = (110)_2 = (20)_3 = (11)_5 = (6)_8 = (6)_{11} = (6)_{12}$.

45. (c) *Method 1:* We first convert the digits 6, 1, 2, 0, 0 in base seven to numbers in base two; and also the base (seven) is converted to a number in base 2.
$(6)_7 = (110)_2$, $(1)_7 = (1)_2$, $(2)_7 = (10)_2$, and $7 = (111)_2$.
Then $(61200)_7 = (110)_2(111)_2^4 + (1)_7(111)_2^3 + (10)_2(111)_2 = (11,100,111,111,111)_2$.
Similarly, $(61200)_7 = (6)_{12}(7)_{12}^4 + (1)_{12}(7)_{12}^3 + (2)_{12}(7)_{12}^2 = (8713)_{12}$.
Method 2: We use repeated division by $(2)_7$:
$(61200)_7$ divided by $(2)_7$ yields quotient $(30433)_7$ and remainder $(1)_7$
$(30433)_7$ divided by $(2)_7$ yields quotient $(13551)_7$ and remainder $(1)_7$
$(13551)_7$ divided by $(2)_7$ yields quotient $(5260)_7$ and remainder $(1)_7$
$(5260)_7$ divided by $(2)_7$ yields quotient $(2463)_7$ and remainder $(1)_7$
$(2463)_7$ divided by $(2)_7$ yields quotient $(1231)_7$ and remainder $(1)_7$
$(1231)_7$ divided by $(2)_7$ yields quotient $(450)_7$ and remainder $(1)_7$
$(450)_7$ divided by $(2)_7$ yields quotient $(223)_7$ and remainder $(1)_7$
$(223)_7$ divided by $(2)_7$ yields quotient $(111)_7$ and remainder $(1)_7$

$(111)_7$ divided by $(2)_7$ yields quotient $(40)_7$ and remainder $(1)_7$
$(40)_7$ divided by $(2)_7$ yields quotient $(20)_7$ and remainder $(0)_7$
$(20)_7$ divided by $(2)_7$ yields quotient $(10)_7$ and remainder $(0)_7$
$(10)_7$ divided by $(2)_7$ yields quotient $(3)_7$ and remainder $(1)_7$
$(3)_7$ divided by $(2)_7$ yields quotient $(1)_7$ and remainder $(1)_7$
$(1)_7$ divided by $(2)_7$ yields quotient $(0)_7$ and remainder $(1)_7$.

The remainders—written in base 2—then give the answer. Reading from top to bottom above corresponds to reading from right to left below:

$$(11,100,111,111,111)_2$$

Similarly the remainders obtained by dividing by twelve, i.e. by $(15)_7$, are: $(3)_7$, $(1)_7$, $(10)_7$, and $(11)_7$. In base twelve these would be, respectively, $(3)_{12}$, $(1)_{12}$, $(7)_{12}$, $(8)_{12}$. Hence the answer is $(8713)_{12}$.

Method 3: In this method everything is referred to base ten. Thus $(61200)_7$ in base ten is $6 \cdot 7^4 + 1 \cdot 7^3 + 2 \cdot 7^2$. Thus $(61200)_7 = 14847$. Now to convert (the designation of) 14847 to base two, we divide—as in Method 2—by 2. But our work is all in base ten. The successive quotients and remainders are then, respectively, as follows:

7423 and 1; 3711 and 1; 1855 and 1; 927 and 1; 463 and 1; 231 and 1; 115 and 1; 57 and 1; 28 and 1; 14 and 0; 7 and 0; 3 and 1; 1 and 1; 0 and 1.
Hence $(61200)_7 = 14847 = (11,100,111,111,111)_2$.

Similarly to convert 14847 to base 12, we divide—again as in Method 2—by 12. Again our work is all in base ten, and our successive quotients and remainders are, respectively, as follows:
1237 and 3; 103 and 1; 8 and 7; 0 and 8.
Hence $(61200)_7 = 14847 = (8713)_{12}$.

(Remark: If one of the remainders had been 10 or 11, this would become u or v, respectively, when writing the number in base twelve.)

46. (a) $3x^2 - \frac{5}{3}x + \frac{3}{2}$.
   (c) $(a + 2)x^2 + (b - 1)x + c + 1$.

47. (a) $3x^2 - \frac{5}{3}x + \frac{3}{2}$.
   (c) $x^4 + 3x^3 - 5x^2 + 7x + 2$.
   (e) $(a + 2)x^2 + (b - 1)x + c + 1$.

48. (a) $-4x^3 + \frac{35}{18}x^2 - \frac{17}{6}x + 1$.
   (c) $2ax^4 + (2b - a)x^3 + (2c - b + a)x^2 + (b - c)x + c$.

49. (a) Quotient: $-\frac{9}{4}x - \frac{19}{32}$; Remainder: $\frac{147}{64}$.
   (c) Quotient: $x^2 + x$; Remainder: 0.
   (e) Quotient: $-x^2 - x$; Remainder: $2x + 1$.
   (g) Quotient: $\frac{7}{2}x^3 + \frac{7}{4}x^2 - \frac{7}{8}x - \frac{5}{16}$; Remainder: $\frac{9}{16}x + \frac{5}{16}$.
   (i) Quotient: $-3x^3 + 5x$; Remainder: $-4x - 1$.

50. (a) Quotient: $3x + \frac{8}{3}$; Remainder: $\frac{14}{3}$.
   (c) Quotient: $x + 2$; Remainder: 0.
   (e) Quotient: $x + 1$; Remainder: 4.
   (g) Quotient: $x^2 - 2x - 1$; Remainder: 0.
   (i) Quotient: $2x^3 + 2x^2 + x + 3$; Remainder: 3.

51. 101, 103, 107, 109, 113, 127, 131, 137, 139, 149.

CHAPTER 10

7. If $\alpha \in R$ and $\alpha \neq 0$, then $\alpha^3 = \alpha \cdot \alpha^2$ is positive if α is positive, 0 if α is 0, and negative if α is negative. Thus if $\alpha^3 = 2$, it follows that α is positive. Hence any solution of $x^3 = 2$ in R must be an element of P.

9. (a) (i) We first show every integer is even or odd, and in (ii) we show that an integer cannot be both even and odd. If $n \in N$, then dividing n by 2 according to Th. 1 of Ch. 9 shows $n = 2n' + 0$ or $n = 2n' + 1$. (That is, $n = 2n' + r$ where $n', r \in J$, $n' \geq 0$, and $0 \leq r < 2$.) Thus n is even or odd in this case. Also n is even if $n = 0$, since $0 = 2 \cdot 0$. Now suppose n is a negative integer. Then $-n \in N$ and we have $-n = 2m + 0$ or $-n = 2m + 1$. If $-n = 2m + 0$, then $n = 2n'$ where $n' = -m$ and n is even in this case. If $-n = 2m + 1$, then $n = 2(-m) - 1 = 2(-m - 1) + 1 = 2n' + 1$ where $n' = -m - 1$, and n is odd in this case.

(ii) Suppose n is odd and even. Thus $n = 2r = 2s + 1$ where $r, s \in J$. Then since $2r = 2s + 1$, we obtain $2(r - s) = 1$ and $r - s = \frac{1}{2}$. But $r - s \in J$, whereas $\frac{1}{2} \notin J$. This is a contradiction, so that n cannot be both even and odd.

(c) Let $n = 2n'$ where $n' \in N$. If $\alpha \in R$ and $\alpha \neq 0$, then $\alpha^2 \in P$. Hence $(\alpha^2)^{n'} \in P$ by (8,10). But $(\alpha^2)^{n'} = \alpha^{2n'}$ by the theory of exponents (cf. (8,58)), and since $2n' = n$ we see that $\alpha^n \in P$. Hence $x^n = a$ where a is negative can have no solution in R.

11. (a) 32; (c) $\frac{2}{3}$; (e) $\frac{1}{4}$; (g) 64; (i) 3281; (k) $\frac{1}{2}$.

13. Let $r = \dfrac{m}{n}$, where m and n are positive integers. Then $a^r = (a^{1/n})^m$. But by Def. 1 (which includes Th. 5), $a^{1/n}$ is the unique *positive* solution of $x^n = a$. Thus $a^{1/n} \in P$ and hence by (8,10), $(a^{1/n})^m \in P$.

16. $(8^{1/5})^3$ and $(8^{1/3})^5$ are both equal to $8^{5/3}$ by part (3) of Th. 14.

18. $\sqrt{cd} = (cd)^{1/2} = c^{1/2}d^{1/2}$ by part (4) of Th. 14.
$$= \sqrt{c}\sqrt{d}$$

21. $16^{1/3} = (2^3 \cdot 2)^{1/3}$
$\qquad = (2^3)^{1/3} \cdot 2^{1/3}$ Part (4) of Th. 14.
$\qquad = (2^{1/3})^3 \cdot 2^{1/3}$ Ex. 17
$\qquad = 2\sqrt[3]{2}$ Def. 1 (since $2^{1/3}$ is defined to be the unique element of P for which $(2^{1/3})^3 = 2$)

25. If α is positive, then $1^\alpha = 1$ by Ex. 12.
If α is 0, then $1^\alpha = 1$ by Def. 3.
If α is negative, then $1^\alpha = \dfrac{1}{(1)^{-\alpha}}$ by Th. 24, and $(1)^{-\alpha} = 1$ by the above since $-\alpha$ is positive. Hence $1^\alpha = 1$ in this case also.

27. (a) $\frac{1}{32}$; (c) $\frac{3}{2}$; (e) 4; (g) $\frac{1}{3}$; (i) $\dfrac{1}{d}$.

33. (a) $(\sqrt{2})^2 = 2$ and $1^2 = 1$. Thus $(\sqrt{2})^2 > 1^2$. By (8,65), $\sqrt{2} > 1$.

(c) $(5^{-7/4})^4 = \dfrac{1}{(5)^7}$, which is clearly less than $(1)^4$. By (8,65), $5^{-7/4} < 1$.

(e) $\frac{1}{2} > \frac{1}{3}$. Hence by Th. 32(III), $(\frac{1}{2})^{1/2} < (\frac{1}{2})^{1/3}$; i.e. $\sqrt{\frac{1}{2}} < \sqrt[3]{\frac{1}{2}}$.

(g) $(\frac{3}{2})^2 > (\sqrt{2})^2$. Hence $\frac{3}{2} > \sqrt{2}$ by (8,65).

(i) $(\sqrt[6]{5})^6 = 5$ and $(\sqrt{2})^6 = (2^{1/2})^6 = 2^3 = 8$. Thus $(\sqrt[6]{5})^6 < (\sqrt{2})^6$, and by (8,65) we conclude $\sqrt[6]{5} < \sqrt{2}$.

(k) $5^2 = 25$ and $(3^{3/2})^2 = 27$. Thus $5^2 < (3^{3/2})^2$, and by (8,65), $5 < 3^{3/2}$. Now $(\frac{21}{4})^2 = \frac{441}{16} > \frac{432}{16} = 27$. Hence $(3^{3/2})^2 < (\frac{21}{4})^2$ so that $3^{3/2} < \frac{21}{4}$.

35. If a is a real number, then $a^2 \geq 0$. It follows that $|a^2| = a^2$. Thus $|1 - \sqrt{2}| < \frac{1}{2}$ if and only if $(1 - \sqrt{2})^2 < \frac{1}{4}$; i.e. if and only if $3 - 2\sqrt{2} < \frac{1}{4}$ or $\frac{11}{8} < \sqrt{2}$. But $(\frac{11}{8})^2 < (\sqrt{2})^2$ so that $\frac{11}{8} < \sqrt{2}$ and hence $|1 - \sqrt{2}| < \frac{1}{2}$.

An alternative argument is to observe that $\sqrt{2} > 1$ so that $|1 - \sqrt{2}| = \sqrt{2} - 1$. But $\sqrt{2} < \frac{3}{2}$ so that $\sqrt{2} - 1 < \frac{3}{2} - 1 = \frac{1}{2}$. Hence $|1 - \sqrt{2}| < \frac{1}{2}$.

40. That 3 is a solution of $2^x = 8$ is clear by computation. But if $\alpha \in \bar{R}$ and $\alpha > 3$, then $2^\alpha > 2^3$ by Th. 32(I), and similarly if $\alpha < 3$, then $2^\alpha < 2^3$.

42. Let α be any rational number greater than $\sqrt{2}$. Then if $r \in \bar{R}$ and $r \leq \sqrt{2}$, we have $r < \alpha$. By Th. 32, $a^r < a^\alpha$. Thus a^α is an upper bound of S. For example, a^2 is an upper bound of S. Hence S is bounded above.

48. (a) rational; (c) irrational; (e) irrational; (g) irrational; (i) irrational.

50. $\sqrt{2} < \frac{3}{2} < \sqrt{3}$; $\sqrt{2} < \dfrac{\sqrt{2} + \sqrt{3}}{2} < \sqrt{3}$.

52. (a) $2\sqrt{3}$; (c) $4\sqrt{15}$; (e) $2\sqrt[6]{3}$; (h) $3\sqrt[3]{3}$; (j) $27\sqrt{3}$.

53. (a) $\frac{1}{3}\sqrt{3}$; (c) $2 + \sqrt{3}$; (e) $-1 - \sqrt[3]{2} - \sqrt[3]{4}$; (g) $2\sqrt{3} - 2\sqrt{2}$.

54. (b) 0; (d) 2; (f) 0.

55. (a) 1; (c) $\dfrac{b^4}{a^3}$; (e) $-\dfrac{3}{2}\dfrac{(a^3 + b^3)^2}{(a^2 + b^2)(a - b)a^2b^2}$; (g) $a^3b + c$.

56. (b) $\varnothing$; (d) $\{-8\}$; (f) $\{2\}$; (h) R; (j) $\varnothing$; (l) $\{-9,9\}$.

57. (a) $\{x \in R/3 \leq x < 7\}$; (c) R.

59. By Th. 2, $\exists\, n \in N \ni n > \alpha$. Then if $\beta \in R$ and $\beta \leq \alpha$, we have $\beta < n$. By Th. 32, $a^\beta < a^n$. Hence a^n is an upper bound of S and S is bounded above.

63. By Ex. 26, $a^\beta > 0$ for all rational numbers β. By parts (1) and (3) of Def. 8, a^α is the least upper bound of a set of positive numbers if $a \neq 1$. Hence a^α is positive if $a \neq 1$. But by (2) of Def. 8, a^α is also positive if $a = 1$.

65. (b) .6; (d) 3.666. . . .

66. (a) $\frac{2}{11} = (.0232202322\ldots)_4$; $\frac{3}{5} = (.212121\ldots)_4$; $\frac{4}{5} = (.1301301301\ldots)_4$; $\frac{11}{3} = (3.222\ldots)_4$.

(b) $\frac{2}{11} = (.2)_{11}$; $\frac{3}{5} = (.6666\ldots)_{11}$; $\frac{4}{5} = (.498612498612498612\ldots)_{11}$; $\frac{11}{3} = (3.737373\ldots)_{11}$.

67. (a) $n = 2$; $a_2 = 7$, $a_1 = 3$, $a_0 = 2$, $a_{-1} = 0$, $a_{-r} = 2$ if $r = 2,4,6,\ldots$, $a_{-s} = 1$ if $s = 3,5,7,\ldots$.

(c) $n = -2$, $a_{-2} = 7$, $a_{-r} = 3$ if $r = 3,9,15,21,\ldots$, $a_{-r} = 2$ if $r = 4,10,16,22,\ldots$, $a_{-r} = 1$ if $r = 5,11,17,23,\ldots$, $a_{-r} = 0$ if $r = 6,12,18,24,\ldots$, $a_{-r} = 2$ if $r = 7,13,19,25,\ldots$, $a_{-r} = 1$ if $r = 8,14,20,26,\ldots$.

(e) $n = -1$; $a_{-1} = 4$, $a_{-2} = 7$, $a_{-3} = 8$, $a_{-4} = 6$, $a_{-5} = 1$.

LABORATORY EXERCISE

1. $(x + i)(x - i) = x^2 - i^2 = x^2 - (-1) = x^2 + 1$.

3. If $a + bi = c + di$, then $a - c = (d - b)i$. Squaring both sides yields the result, where $i^2 = -1$.

5. (a) $(a + bi) + (c + di) = a + bi + c + di = a + c + bi + di = (a+c)+(bi + di)=(a+c)+ (b + d)i$.

   The reasons may be supplied from Ch. 5, where the results apply to any field.

7. By Def. 1, $\oplus$ and $\otimes$ are closed, since $+$, $-$, and $\cdot$ are closed binary operations defined on R.

$[(a,b) \oplus (c,d)] \oplus (e,f) = (a + c,b + d) \oplus (e,f)$

$\qquad\qquad = ((a + c) + e, (b + d) +f)$ Def. 1

$\qquad\qquad = (a + (c + e), b + (d +f))$ $+$ is associative in R

$\qquad\qquad = (a,b) \oplus (c + e,d +f)$ Def. 1

$\qquad\qquad = (a,b) \oplus [(c,d) \oplus (e,f)]$ Def. 1

This proves A_2 for $\oplus$ as defined on C.

$(a,b) \oplus (c,d) = (a + c,b + d)$ Def. 1

$\qquad\qquad = (c + a,d + b)$ $+$ is commutative in R.

$\qquad\qquad = (c,d) \oplus (a,b)$ Def. 1

This proves A_3 for $\oplus$.

One checks that $(0,0)$ is the additive identity, and that the additive inverse of (a,b) is $(-a,-b)$.

To check M_2 for $\otimes$, we compute $[(a,b) \otimes (c,d)] \otimes (e,f)$ and $(a,b) \otimes [(c,d) \otimes (e,f)]$ and observe that the results are equal.

$$[(a,b) \otimes (c,d)] \otimes (e,f) = (ac - bd, ad + bc) \otimes (e,f)$$
Def. 1

$$= ((ac - bd)e - (ad + bc)f, (ac - bd)f + (ad + bc)e)$$
Def. 1

$$= (ace - bde - adf - bcf, acf - bdf + ade + bce)$$
By rules which hold in R.

$$(a,b) \otimes [(c,d) \otimes (e,f)] = (a,b) \otimes (ce - df, cf + de)$$

$$= (a(ce - df) - b(cf + de), a(cf + de) + b(ce - df)$$

$$= (ace - adf - bcf - bde, acf + ade + bce - bdf)$$

One easily sees that M_2 holds for $\otimes$, that the multiplicative identity is $(1,0)$, and that the multiplicative inverse of (a,b) — assuming $(a,b) \neq (0,0)$ — is $\left(\dfrac{a}{a^2 + b^2}, \dfrac{-b}{a^2 + b^2}\right)$.

Finally $(0,0) \neq (1,0)$, and one checks that the distributive law holds.

9. $a^* \oplus [b^* \otimes i] = (a,0) \oplus [(b,0) \otimes (0,1)]$
$$= (a,0) \oplus (0,b)$$
$$= (a,b).$$

10. $i \otimes i = (0,1) \otimes (0,1) = (-1,0).$

12. $\{i,-i\}$ is solution set.

14. (b) $\dfrac{1}{3} - \dfrac{\sqrt{2}}{3} i$; (d) $-i$; (f) $\dfrac{3}{13} + \dfrac{2}{13} i$.

16. (a) $2 + i, \sqrt{5}$; (c) $-i,1$; (e) $0,0$; (g) $\dfrac{1-i}{2}, \dfrac{\sqrt{2}}{2}$.

18. (a) Use induction on n. For $n = 1$, the result is obvious.
$$\overline{z_1 + \cdots + z_{n-1} + z_n} = \overline{(z_1 + \cdots + z_{n-1}) + z_n}$$
$$= \overline{(z_1 + \cdots + z_{n-1})} + \overline{z_n} \qquad \text{Ex. 17(a)}$$
$$= (\bar{z}_1 + \cdots + \bar{z}_{n-1}) + \bar{z}_n \qquad \text{Inductive hypothesis}$$
$$= \bar{z}_1 + \cdots + \bar{z}_{n-1} + \bar{z}_n$$

20. Assume $a_0 z^n + a_1 z^{n-1} + \cdots + a_n = 0.$
$$\overline{a_0 z^n + a_1 z^{n-1} + \cdots + a_n} = \overline{0}$$
$$\overline{a_0 z^n} + \overline{a_1 z^{n-1}} + \cdots + \overline{a_n} = 0 \qquad \text{Ex. 18(a)}$$
$$\bar{a}_0 \bar{z}^n + \bar{a}_1 \bar{z}^{n-1} + \cdots + \bar{a}_n = 0 \qquad \text{Ex. 17(b)}$$
$$a_0 \bar{z}^n + a_1 \bar{z}^{n-1} + \cdots + a_n = 0 \qquad \text{Ex. 19}$$

22. Let $z = a + bi$. Then $z + \bar{z} = (a + bi) + (a - bi) = 2a \in R$.

24. Let $w = a + bi$, $z = c + di$, so that $wz = (ac - bd) + (ad + bc)i$.
$$|wz| = \sqrt{(ac - bd)^2 + (ad + bc)^2}$$
$$= \sqrt{a^2 c^2 - 2abcd + b^2 d^2 + a^2 d^2 + 2abcd + b^2 c^2}$$
$$= \sqrt{a^2(c^2 + d^2) + b^2(c^2 + d^2)}$$
$$= \sqrt{(a^2 + b^2)(c^2 + d^2)}$$
$$= |w||z|.$$

CHAPTER 11

1. $f(2) = 1; f(\sqrt{2}) = 2\sqrt{2} - 3.$

2. $\{8\}$.

4. $\{-1,2\}$.

6. $I_J(3) = 3; I_J(-3) = -3; I_N(-3)$ is undefined; $I_R(\sqrt{2}) = \sqrt{2}.$

7. (a) Domain of f is N; range of f is the set of positive even integers.
    (b) $\{1\}; \varnothing; \varnothing; \varnothing; \{1\}$.

9. Domain of f is A; range of f is $\{2,4,6,8,10,12\}$.

(a)

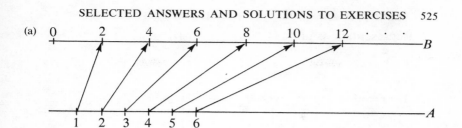

(b)

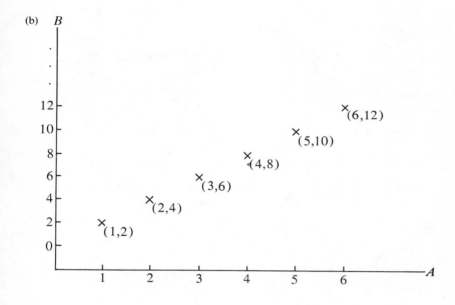

11. There are four functions: f: $1 \to 1$, $2 \to 1$; g: $1 \to 1$, $2 \to 2$; h: $1 \to 2$, $2 \to 1$; k: $1 \to 2$, $2 \to 2$.

The domain of f, g, h, and k is A. The range of f is $\{1\}$; of g is A; of h is A; of k is $\{2\}$.

Representations of f:

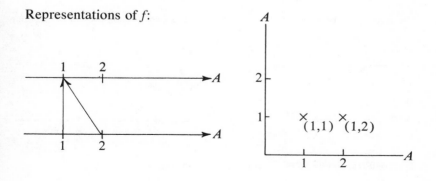

Representations of g:

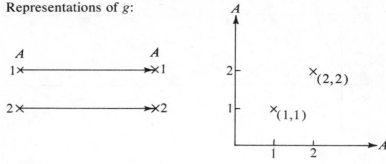

13. Three functions from A to $[A]$ are f, g, h as defined below:

$f: 1 \to \varnothing, 2 \to \varnothing.$

$g: 1 \to \varnothing, 2 \to \{1\}$

$h: 1 \to A, 2 \to \{2\}$

The domain in each case is A; the range of f is $\{\varnothing\}$, of g is $\{\varnothing, \{1\}\}$, of h is $\{\{2\}, A\}$.

The function g:

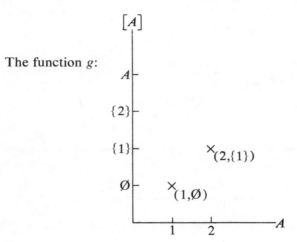

16. The domain and range are both R. The following is only an indication of the function:

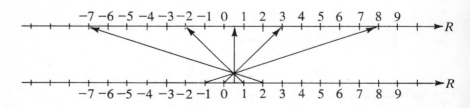

A second representation of the graph is the following:

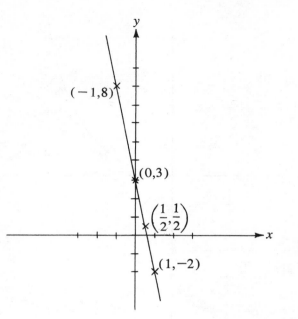

19. Domain is R, range is $\{x \in R/x \leqq 0\}$.

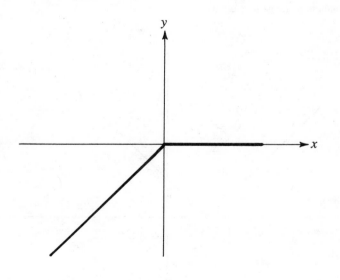

21. Domain is R, range is $P \cup \{-2\}$.

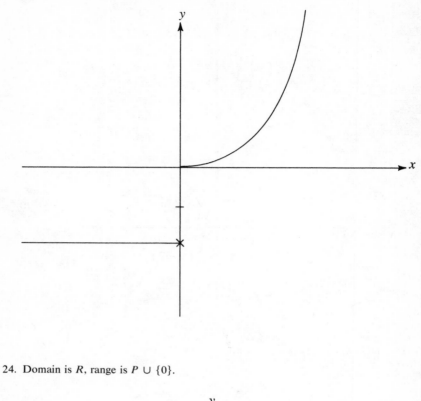

24. Domain is R, range is $P \cup \{0\}$.

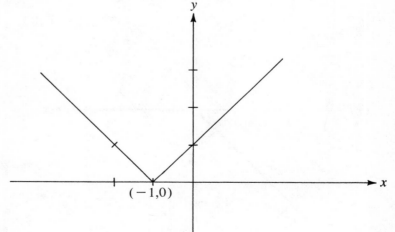

27. Domain is R, range is R.

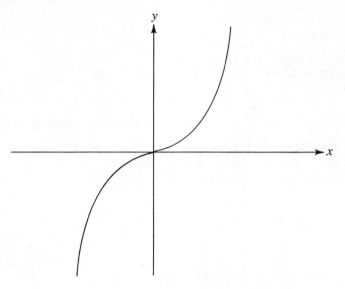

30. Domain is A, range is A.

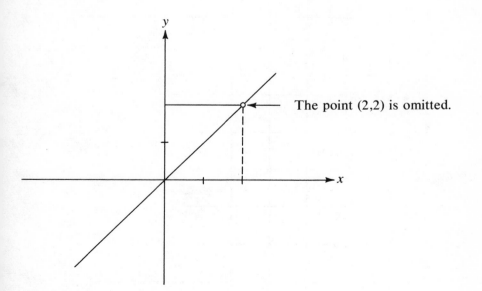

The point (2,2) is omitted.

32. (a) $gf(n) = n$.
   (c) fg is not defined.
34. (a) $gf(x) = x^6$.
   (c) fg is defined.
   (d) $fg = gf$.
36. $f = gh$ where $h(x) = x + 1$, $g(x) = x^{50}$.
38. $f = qp$ where $p(x) = x - x^2$, $q(x) = |x|$.
40. $f = st$ where $t(x) = x^3$, $s(x) = x - 3$.
42. Case (d). The inverse function g^{-1} from B to A is given by: $g^{-1}(a) = 1$, $g^{-1}(b) = 0$.
44. Case (a).
46. Case (d). The inverse function f^{-1} from R to R is given by $f^{-1}(x) = \frac{1}{2}x - \frac{1}{2}$.
48. Case (b).
50. Case (d). The inverse function f^{-1} from $\{2,4,6, \ldots\}$ to N is $f^{-1}(x) = \frac{1}{2}x$.
52. Case (d). The inverse function f^{-1} from P to P is $f^{-1}(x) = x^2$.
54. (a) Domain of T is $\{a,c\}$, range of T is B.

(b)

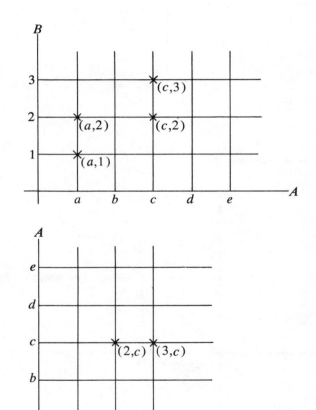

(c)

(d) No. T assigns 1 and 2 to a.

(e) $\{(a,1),(c,2)\} = T_1$ and $\{(a,2),(c,3)\} = T_2$ may be taken as branch functions. In this case, T_1 and T_2 both have domain $\{a,c\}$. The range of T_1 is $\{1,2\}$ and of T_2 is $\{2,3\}$.

CHAPTER 12

1. (a) -3; (c) $-\frac{87}{32}$.
2. (a) Yes; (c) Yes; (e) No.
3. (b) $\frac{53}{9}$; (d) 33.
4. (b) $2x - \frac{1}{3}$; (d) $x^3 - 2x^2 + 7x - 16$.
5. (a) No; (c) $(2x + 1)(x - 1)$; (e) No.
7. (b) x^{40} and x.
   (d) $x(x + 1)$ and $x(x + 1)^2$.
   (f) $(x + i)(x - i)$ and $(x + i)^3(x - i)^2$.
   (h) $(x - 1)(x - 2)(x + 1)$ and $(x - 1)^2(x - 2)(x + 1)$.
   (j) $(x - \sqrt{2})(x - 1)$ and $(x - \sqrt{2})^4(x - 1)^3$.
8. (a) $3(x^3 - \frac{1}{3}x^2 + 2x - \frac{1}{3})$.
   (c) $\frac{1}{4}(x^2 - 8x)$.
   (e) $(-1)(x^4 - 5x^2)$.
9. (a) $x^3 - x^2 + 1$.
   (c) 1. $\{a + b\sqrt{2}/a,b \in \bar{R}\}$ is the smallest subfield of C containing the coefficients.
   (e) $x^4 + x^3 + x^2 + x + 1$.
12. (a) $x^3 - x^2 + 1 = [\frac{1}{2}](x^5 - x^4 + x^3 + 1) + [(-\frac{1}{2})(x + 1)](x^4 - 2x^3 + x^2 + x - 1)$.
    Here $s(x) = \frac{1}{2}$, $t(x) = (-\frac{1}{2})(x + 1)$.
    (c) $1 = \left[\dfrac{1}{3 + 4\sqrt{2}}\right] (\sqrt{2}x^2 - x + 1) + \left[\dfrac{-\sqrt{2}x + 2\sqrt{2} + 1}{3 + 4\sqrt{2}}\right] (x + 2)$.
    Here $s(x) = \dfrac{1}{3 + 4\sqrt{2}}$, $t(x) = \dfrac{-\sqrt{2}x + 2\sqrt{2} + 1}{3 + 4\sqrt{2}}$.
    (e) $x^4 + x^3 + x^2 + x + 1 = 0 \cdot (2x^5 - 2) + 1 \cdot (x^4 + x^3 + x^2 + x + 1)$.
14. (a) Since $m(x) = a_1(x)b_1(x)d(x)$ where $a_1(x)d(x) = a(x)$ and $b_1(x)d(x) = b(x)$, we have $m(x) = a(x)b_1(x) = b(x)a_1(x)$. Hence $m(x)$ is a multiple of $a(x)$ and $b(x)$.
    (b) Note that since $d(x) = (a(x),b(x))$, we must have $a_1(x)$ and $b_1(x)$ relatively prime. For if $a_1(x)$ and $b_1(x)$ had a common factor $h(x)$ of positive degree, then $h(x)d(x)$ would divide $a(x)$ and $b(x)$ but would not divide $d(x)$. By Th. 11, $\exists\, s(x),t(x) \in \mathscr{P} \ni s(x)a_1(x) +$ $t(x)b_1(x) = 1$. Multiply through by $l(x)$, obtaining $s(x)a_1(x)l(x) + t(x)b_1(x)l(x) = l(x)$. Now $l(x) = u(x)a(x) = v(x)b(x)$. Thus
    $l(x) = s(x)a_1(x)l(x) + t(x)b_1(x)l(x)$
    $\quad = s(x)a_1(x)b(x)v(x) + t(x)b_1(x)a(x)u(x)$
    $\quad = s(x)a_1(x)b_1(x)d(x)v(x) + t(x)b_1(x)a_1(x)d(x)u(x)$
    $\quad = m(x)[s(x)v(x) + t(x)u(x)]$
    Hence $m(x)$ divides $l(x)$.
15. (a) $(x^3 - x^2 + 1)(x^2 + 1)(x - 1)$.
    (c) $\left(x^2 - \dfrac{\sqrt{2}}{2} x + \dfrac{\sqrt{2}}{2}\right) (x + 2)$.
    (e) $x^5 - 1$.
16. (a) 1; (c) 0; (e) 0.
17. (b) 2; (d) 5; (f) 1.
18. (a) $x^2(x - 1)$; (c) $(x - \sqrt{2})(x - i + 2)$.

19. (a) Sum is 0; product is 1.

(c) Sum is 0; product is $\dfrac{3i - 2}{3}$.

(e) Sum is $\frac{5}{2}$; product is $-\frac{7}{2}$.

22. By Corollary 1 of Th. 17, if all roots of $f(x)$ were imaginary, $f(x)$ would have to be of even degree.

23. (a) (i) $x^2 - 2x - 3 = 0$

$x^2 - 2x + 1 = 4$

$(x - 1)^2 = 4$

$x - 1 = \pm 2$

$x = 1 \pm 2$

Solution set is $\{-1,3\}$.

(ii) Here $a = 1$, $b = -2$, $c = -3$. Hence the solution set is

$$\left\{ \frac{2 \pm \sqrt{16}}{2} \right\} = \{-1,3\}.$$

(iii) $x^2 - 2x - 3 = 0$

$(x + 1)(x - 3) = 0$

Solution set is $\{-1,3\}$.

(d) (i) $3x^2 - x + 6 = 0$

$x^2 - \frac{1}{3}x + \frac{1}{36} = -2 + \frac{1}{36}$

$(x - \frac{1}{6})^2 = -\frac{71}{36}$

$x = \dfrac{1}{6} \pm \dfrac{i}{6} \sqrt{71}$

Solution set is $\{\frac{1}{6}(1 - i\sqrt{71}),\ \frac{1}{6}(1 + i\sqrt{71})\}$.

(ii) Here $a = 3$, $b = -1$, $c = 6$. Hence the solution set is

$$\left\{ \frac{1 \pm \sqrt{-71}}{6} \right\} = \left\{ \frac{1 - i\sqrt{71}}{6},\ \frac{1 + i\sqrt{71}}{6} \right\}.$$

24. (b) Discriminant is 0. Hence the roots are real and equal.

(d) Discriminant is 1. Hence the roots are real and unequal.

(f) Discriminant is $2 - 8\sqrt{3}$. Hence the roots are imaginary.

25. (a) Roots are -1 and 3, leading coefficient is 1. Hence $x^2 - 2x - 3 = (x + 1)(x - 3)$.

(d) Roots are $\dfrac{1 - i\sqrt{71}}{6}$ and $\dfrac{1 + i\sqrt{71}}{6}$, leading coefficient is 3. Hence

$$3x^2 - x + 6 = 3 \left(x - \frac{1 - i\sqrt{71}}{6} \right) \left(x - \frac{1 + i\sqrt{71}}{6} \right).$$

26. (b) Sum is $\frac{4}{3}\sqrt{3}$; product is $\frac{4}{3}$.

(d) Sum is 5; product is 6.

(f) Sum is $-\dfrac{\sqrt{2}}{2}$; product is $\dfrac{\sqrt{3}}{2}$.

27. (a) $\{\frac{1}{2}\}$; (c) $\{-1,0,\frac{3}{8}\}$; (e) $\varnothing$; (g) $\{0,1\}$; (i) $\{0\}$.

28. (a) $\{2,i,-i\}$; (c) $\left\{-2,-1,\dfrac{1}{2},3\right\}$; (e) $\left\{0,\dfrac{1 + i\sqrt{3}}{4},\dfrac{1 - i\sqrt{3}}{4},\dfrac{1 + i\sqrt{7}}{2},\dfrac{1 - i\sqrt{7}}{2}\right\}$.

30. (a) Real; unequal and rational.

(c) Real; equal and rational.

(e) Real; unequal and irrational.

31. (a) $f(-1) = -9$; $f(0) = 1$; $f(1) = -1$; $f(6) = 19$.

(b) By the intermediate value theorem, $f(x)$ has a real root between -1 and 0, a real root between 0 and 1, and a real root between 1 and 6. Thus $f(x)$ has at least 3 roots in R. But by Th. 15, $f(x)$ has at most 3 roots in C, so that all of the roots must b real.

35. (a) $-\frac{1}{8}$; (b) $-\frac{7}{8}$.

38. 10 and 10.

40. The side parallel to the partition should be 48 ft., the other side 72 ft.

41. The side parallel to the partitions should be 36 ft., the other side 72 ft.

42. Width is $\dfrac{P}{6}$ ft., length is $\dfrac{P}{4}$ ft.

43. Width is $\dfrac{P}{8}$ ft., length is $\dfrac{P}{4}$ ft.

44. Width is $\dfrac{P}{2(n+2)}$ ft., length is $\dfrac{P}{4}$ ft.

CHAPTER 13

1. (a) (i) 420°, 780°, 1500°; −300°, −660°, −1020°.
   (ii) 300°, 660°, 1020°; −60°, −420°, −780°.
   (c) (i) $\dfrac{\pi}{2}, \dfrac{5\pi}{2}, \dfrac{9\pi}{2}$ radians; $-\dfrac{7\pi}{2}, -\dfrac{11\pi}{2}, -\dfrac{15\pi}{2}$ radians.
   (ii) $\dfrac{3\pi}{2}, \dfrac{7\pi}{2}, \dfrac{11\pi}{2}$ radians; $-\dfrac{\pi}{2}, -\dfrac{5\pi}{2}, -\dfrac{9\pi}{2}$ radians.
   (f) (i) $\sqrt{2}-1$, $\sqrt{2}+1$, $\sqrt{2}+2$ revolutions; $\sqrt{2}-2$, $\sqrt{2}-3$, $\sqrt{2}-4$ revolutions.
   (ii) $2-\sqrt{2}$, $3-\sqrt{2}$, $4-\sqrt{2}$ revolutions; $1-\sqrt{2}$, $-\sqrt{2}$, $-1-\sqrt{2}$ revolutions.

4. (a) $\dfrac{\pi}{8}$; (b) $\dfrac{\pi}{4}$; (c) $\dfrac{3\pi}{8}$; (d) $\dfrac{\pi a}{8}$.

6. (a) 30; (b) 150; (c) 60; (d) $2\sqrt{3}$; (e) $\sqrt{3}$.

8. The triangles are congruent by *a.s.a.* = *a.s.a.* This follows from the fact that $\measuredangle ADB = \measuredangle DBC$ and $\measuredangle ABD = \measuredangle BDC$ by (13c), and BC is a side common to both triangles. It follows that the sides opposite the equal angles are equal, and this yields the result.

9. The statement of the converse is the following: A quadrilateral whose opposite sides are equal is a parallelogram.

11. Let the length of each arm be x. Then by the Pythagorean theorem, $x^2 + x^2 = a^2$. Thus $x^2 = \dfrac{a^2}{2}$ or $x = \dfrac{a}{2}\sqrt{2}$.

14. By (13d), $\measuredangle CAB = \measuredangle FDE$; and $\measuredangle ABC = \measuredangle DEF$ since by hypothesis they are right angles. By (18), the triangles are similar.

17. (a) 4; (c) 24; (e) 24.

18. These lengths are in contradiction to (14).

20. 36.

22. (a) 3; 3. (c) −3; 3. (e) $\pi - 1$; $\pi - 1$. (g) 1; 1. (i) $t - s$; $|t - s|$. (k) $-|s|$; $|s|$.
    (m) $t_7 - t_5$; $|t_7 - t_5|$.

23. (a) 2; positive. (c) π; negative. (e) $\sqrt{2}$; negative. (g) $\sqrt{2} - 1$; negative.

25. (a) −1, 3, −1; (b) $\tfrac{7}{2}$; (c) they are equal.

27. (a) $[-3,-1]$, $\sqrt{10}$; (c) $[x_1 - x_2, y_1 - y_2]$, $\sqrt{(x_1 - x_2)^2 + (y_1 - y_2)^2}$; (e) $[-3,7]$, $\sqrt{58}$.

29. Show that $d(A,C) = d(B,C) = \sqrt{58}$ by Th. 2.

32. Let $A(3,1)$, $B(1,-3)$, $C(7,-1)$. By Th. 2, $|AB| = \sqrt{20}$, $|AC| = \sqrt{20}$, $|BC| = \sqrt{40}$. Hence $|BC|^2 = |AB|^2 + |AC|^2$. By (16) of Sec. 2.7, A, B, and C are the vertices of a right triangle.

33. The points of (a) and (d) lie on a line; those in (b) and (c) do not.

35. (a) $(-\tfrac{1}{4}, \tfrac{9}{4})$; (c) $(1, \tfrac{8}{3})$; (e) $(\tfrac{5}{4}, \tfrac{11}{4})$.

37. $B(7,9)$.

39. (a) $[-1,6]$; (b) $[1,-6]$, $[2,-12]$; (c) $[-k,6k]$, where k is any nonzero real number; (d) −6;
    (e) $(3,-7)$ and $(4,-13)$.

41. Slope of perpendicular bisector of BC and altitude from A is $-\frac{5}{17}$; slope of perpendicular bisector of AC and altitude from B is $-\frac{3}{7}$; slope of perpendicular bisector of AB and altitude from C is $-\frac{1}{5}$.

43. The midpoint of OB is $\left(\frac{a}{2}, \frac{a}{2}\right)$, and that of AC is also $\left(\frac{a}{2}, \frac{a}{2}\right)$. Hence the diagonals bisect each other. The slope of OB is 1 and that of AC is -1. As the product of these slopes is -1, the diagonals meet at right angles according to Th. 6.

45. Let A, B, C, D be the vertices of the quadrilateral, and let the coordinate system be so chosen that $A(0,0)$, $B(2a,0)$, $C(2b,2c)$, $D(2d,2e)$. The midpoint E of AB is $(a,0)$, F of BC is $(a + b,c)$, G of CD is $(b + d,c + e)$, H of DA is (d,e). We must show EG and FH bisect each other. The midpoint of EG is $\left(\dfrac{a + b + d}{2}, \dfrac{c + e}{2}\right)$, as is that of FH, the result thereby being proved.

47. Choose the coordinate system so that the vertices A, B, C of the right triangle are $A(0,0)$, $B(2a,0)$, and $C(0,2b)$. Then the midpoint M of the hypotenuse BC is (a,b). By the distance formula, the lengths of MA, MB, and MC are all $\sqrt{a^2 + b^2}$.

49. We choose the coordinate system so that the vertices of the parallelogram $OABC$ are $O(0,0)$, $A(a,0)$, $B(a + b,c)$, $C(b,c)$ as was done in Fig. 13.70. We are given that $OB = AC$. By the distance formula, this means $\sqrt{(a + b)^2 + c^2} = \sqrt{(a - b)^2 + c^2}$. This yields $a^2 + 2ab + b^2 + c^2 = a^2 - 2ab + b^2 + c^2$, or that $ab = 0$. We cannot have $a = 0$ since O is distinct from A. Hence $b = 0$ and the vertices become $O(0,0)$, $A(a,0)$, $B(a,c)$, $C(0,c)$, which are the vertices of a rectangle.

CHAPTER 14

1. (a) $y + 2 = 0$; (c) $y + 2 = 0$; (e) $x - 1 = 0$; (g) $y - 2 = 0$; (i) $x - \alpha = 0$.
2. (a) $(x - 1)^2 + (y + 2)^2 = 0$; (c) $|x - 2| + |y - 2| = 0$; (e) $x^2 + y^2 = 0$;
   (g) $[(x - 3)^2 + (y + 1)^2][(x - 1)^2 + (y + 3)^2]y = 0$.
4. (a) $2x - y - 7 = 0$; (c) $3x - y = 0$; (e) $x - 3y + 7 = 0$; (g) $y - 3 = 0$.
5. (a) $7x - 3y + 13 = 0$; (c) $3x - y - 5 = 0$; (e) $x + y = 0$ and $8x - y - 19 = 0$;
   (g) $3x - y - 4 = 0$, $9x + y - 32 = 0$, $x + 2y + 4 = 0$, $2x + y - 1 = 0$.
7. (a) $(1,0)$, $-\frac{2}{3}$; (c) $(0,2)$,3.
9. (a) $y = mx + \beta$.
10. (a) $\{(4,1)\}$; (b) $\{(0,3)\}$; (c) $\varnothing$; (d) $R \times R$; (e) $\varnothing$; (f) $\{(1,0,-1)\}$.
11. (a) Solving $2x - y - 4 = 0$ and $x + 3y + 5 = 0$ simultaneously yields $(1,-2)$ as the unique solution. But $(1,-2)$ also satisfies $3x - 2y - 7 = 0$. Hence the three lines pass through a point.
13. (a) (i) Assume the lines have the same slope. They are both horizontal if and only if $a_1 = a_2 = 0$, and both vertical if and only if $b_1 = b_2 = 0$. In the remaining cases, a_1, a_2, b_1, b_2 are all distinct from 0. The slopes of the two lines are then $-\dfrac{a_1}{b_1}$ and $-\dfrac{a_2}{b_2}$ by Th. 2. Assuming equality, we have $\dfrac{a_1}{b_1} = \dfrac{a_2}{b_2}$ or $\dfrac{a_1}{a_2} = \dfrac{b_1}{b_2}$. This yields $a_1 b_2 - a_2 b_1 = 0$, which also holds in the cases $a_1 = a_2 = 0$, $b_1 = b_2 = 0$.
    (ii) Conversely, suppose $a_1 b_2 - a_2 b_1 = 0$. If $a_1 = 0$, then $a_2 = 0$ (since we cannot have a_1 and b_1 equal to 0 if $a_1 x + b_1 y + c_1 = 0$ represents a line); similarly if $b_1 = 0$, then $b_2 = 0$. In these cases, the lines have the same slopes (where we are regarding vertical lines as having the same slopes, although technically they do not have slopes). In the remaining cases, $\dfrac{a_1}{a_2} = \dfrac{b_1}{b_2}$, or also $-\dfrac{a_1}{b_1} = -\dfrac{a_2}{b_2}$, and the slopes are therefore equal.

(b) (i) Assume the given equations equivalent. That means each has the same solution set, and hence they represent the same line. If $a_1 = a_2 = 0$, we have $b_1y + c_1 = 0$ and $b_2y + c_2 = 0$ as the equations, or $y = -\dfrac{c_1}{b_1}$ and $y = -\dfrac{c_2}{b_2}$. Since these represent the same line, $\dfrac{c_1}{b_1} = \dfrac{c_2}{b_2}$. Thus $c_1 = 0$ if and only if $c_2 = 0$. If c_1 and c_2 are not 0, we have $\dfrac{b_1}{b_2} = \dfrac{c_1}{c_2}$. One checks that in each of the foregoing cases, $b_1c_2 - b_2c_1 = 0$, and $a_1c_2 - a_2c_1 = 0$. We already know from (a) that $a_1b_2 - a_2b_1 = 0$. A similar analysis may be given if $b_1 = b_2 = 0$. The remaining case is a_1,a_2,b_1,b_2 all distinct from 0. Then $\dfrac{a_1}{a_2} = \dfrac{b_1}{b_2}$ by (a). Let $k = \dfrac{a_1}{a_2} = \dfrac{b_1}{b_2}$. Then $a_1 = ka_2$, $b_1 = kb_2$, and $k \neq 0$. Now $a_2x + b_2y + c_2$ is equivalent to $ka_2x + kb_2y + kc_2 = 0$, which in turn may be written $a_1x + b_1y + kc_2 = 0$. If this is to represent the same line as $a_1x + b_1y + c_1 = 0$, we must have $c_1 = kc_2$. (Why?) Thus either $c_1 = c_2 = 0$, or $\dfrac{c_1}{c_2} = k = \dfrac{a_1}{a_2} = \dfrac{b_1}{b_2}$. Again one may check that $b_1c_2 - b_2c_1 = 0$, and $a_1c_2 - a_2c_1 = 0$.

(ii) Conversely, suppose $a_1b_2 - a_2b_1 = 0$, $b_1c_2 - b_2c_1 = 0$, and $a_1c_2 - a_2c_1 = 0$. Then $a_1 = 0$ if and only if $a_2 = 0$, and $b_1 = 0$ if and only if $b_2 = 0$. Say $a_1 = a_2 = 0$. Then b_1 and b_2 are not 0, and we have $\dfrac{c_1}{b_1} = \dfrac{c_2}{b_2}$. The given equations become $y = -\dfrac{c_1}{b_1}$ and $y = -\dfrac{c_2}{b_2}$, which are the same equations. Note $c_1 = 0$ if and only if $c_2 = 0$. If c_1 and c_2 are not 0, we have $\dfrac{b_1}{b_2} = \dfrac{c_1}{c_2}$. A similar analysis may be given if $a_1 = a_2 = 0$. Thus it remains to consider the case $a_1,a_2,b_1,b_2 \neq 0$, so that $\dfrac{a_1}{a_2} = \dfrac{b_1}{b_2} = k$. One sees that $c_1 = 0$ if and only if $c_2 = 0$. In this case the equations become $ka_2x + kb_2y = 0$ and $a_2x + b_2y = 0$, which are clearly equivalent. If c_1 and c_2 are not 0, then from $b_1c_2 - b_2c_1 = 0$, we conclude $\dfrac{b_1}{b_2} = \dfrac{c_1}{c_2}$. Hence we have $a_1 = ka_2$, $b_1 = kb_2$, $c_1 = kc_2$ and the equations become $ka_2x + kb_2y + kc_2 = 0$ and $a_2x + b_2y + c_2 = 0$. Again these are clearly equivalent.

15. (a) One; (b) none; (c) infinitely many; (d) one.

17. Referring to Fig. 13.69, we see that the equation of the line passing through O and C is $cx - by = 0$, this being valid even if $b = 0$ (certainly $c \neq 0$). The equation of the line passing through A and E is $cx - (3a + b)y + 2ac = 0$. Solving these two equations simultaneously yields the point $\left(\dfrac{2b}{3}, \dfrac{2c}{3}\right)$. This point satisfies the equation of the line passing through B and D, namely the equation $cx - (b - 3a)y - 2ac = 0$.

19. The slope of the line through (a) and (b) is $\dfrac{\dfrac{c}{3} - \dfrac{ab + c^2}{2c}}{\dfrac{a+b}{3} - \dfrac{a+b}{2}}$ or $\dfrac{c^2 + 3ab}{ac + bc}$. The slope of the line through (b) and (c) is $\dfrac{-\dfrac{ab}{c} - \dfrac{c}{3}}{-\dfrac{a+b}{3}}$, or also $\dfrac{c^2 + 3ab}{ac + bc}$.

21. (a) $\frac{2}{5}$; (c) $\frac{7}{4}$; (e) 0.

23. Say the vertices of the quadrilateral are A, B, C, and D. Draw the diagonal AC. Then the problem is reduced to finding the areas of triangles ABC and ADC. Their sum will then

be the area of the quadrilateral. To find the area of triangle ABC, for example, we apply
(20) of Sec. 2.7, Ch. 13. Thus we find the length b of AC by the distance formula, and
the length h of the altitude from B to AC by Th. 4. The area of triangle ABC is then
$\frac{1}{2} bh$.

25. (a) $x - 2y + 6 = 0$.
26. If the line crosses the y-axis at $(0,\beta)$, then it would have to cross the x-axis at $(2\beta,0)$. It
would follow that the slope is $\frac{0 - \beta}{2\beta - 0}$, or $-\frac{1}{2}$, so that a slope of -2 is certainly impossible.
28. (a) $(x - 2)^2 + (y + 3)^2 = 4$; $x^2 + y^2 - 4x + 6y + 9 = 0$.
    (c) $(x + 1)^2 + (y + 2)^2 = 1$; $x^2 + y^2 + 2x + 4y + 4 = 0$.
    (e) $(x - \sqrt{2})^2 + (y - \sqrt{3})^2 = 2$; $x^2 + y^2 - 2\sqrt{2}x - 2\sqrt{3}y + 3 = 0$.
29. (a) $(x - 3)^2 + (y + 1)^2 = 2$; circle with center $(3,-1)$ and radius $\sqrt{2}$.
    (c) $(x + 2)^2 + (y - 3)^2 = 16$; circle with center $(-2,3)$ and radius 4.
    (f) $(x - 2)^2 + (y - 4)^2 = 0$; the point $(2,4)$.
30. (a) $4x - 3y - 25 = 0$; (c) $5x + 12y - 152 = 0$.
31. (b) The points are rather special in this problem. For example, the line through $(-1,-2)$
    and $(7,-2)$ is horizontal. Hence the perpendicular bisector is $x = 3$, and the center
    lies on this line. But $(3,2)$ is on this line, and one may see by inspection that $(3,-2)$ is
    at a distance 4 from each of the given points of this exercise. Hence this is a circle
    with center $(3,-2)$ and radius 4. The equation is $(x - 3)^2 + (y + 2)^2 = 16$, or
    $x^2 + y^2 - 6x + 4y - 3 = 0$. Alternatively, one may substitute the coordinates of the
    points $(7,-2)$, $(3,2)$, and $(-1,-2)$ in the equation $x^2 + y^2 + dx + ey + f = 0$ to obtain
    three linear equations in d, e, and f:
    $7d - 2e + f + 53 = 0$
    $3d + 2e + f + 13 = 0$
    $-d - 2e + f + 5 = 0$.
    Solving simultaneously yields the solution set $\{(-6,4,-3)\}$.
    (d) $x^2 + y^2 + 8x + 2y + 9 = 0$.
32. $\{(3,4), (3,-4), (-3,4), (-3,-4)\}$.
34. $\{(-\frac{73}{7}, -\frac{103}{14}), (-1,\frac{1}{2})\}$.
36. $\varnothing$.
38. $\varnothing$.

CHAPTER 15

2. (a) That $f(x) = a^x$ is a function from R into P follows from Ex. 63 of Ch. 10. That f is
   onto is a consequence of Theorem 2. Finally, suppose $a^\alpha = a^\beta$. Then by Th. 1, we
   must have $\alpha = \beta$, so that f is $1 - 1$.
   (b) Cf. Fig. 15.4.
3. (a) 2; (c) $\frac{1}{8}$; (e) $\frac{1}{72}$.
4. (a) 0; (c) undefined; (e) -1; (g) 24.
6. (a) P; (c) $\varnothing$; (e) $\{3\}$.
7. (a) $\frac{1}{3}$; (c) 2; (e) -1; (g) -4; (i) 0.
8. We first prove $\log_a (M_1 M_2 \ldots M_m) = \log_a M_1 + \log_a M_2 + \cdots + \log_a M_m$ by induction
   on m. If $m = 1$, there is nothing to prove. Thus assume $m > 1$. Then
   $\log_a (M_1 M_2 \ldots M_m) = \log_a [(M_1 M_2 \ldots M_{m-1})M_m]$
   $\qquad = \log_a (M_1 M_2 \ldots M_{m-1}) + \log_a M_m$ Th. 6(1)
   $\qquad = \log_a M_1 + \log_a M_2 + \cdots + \log_a M_{m-1} + \log_a M_m$
   $\qquad\qquad$ by inductive hypothesis

This proves the result. It then also follows that

$$\log_a (N_1 N_2 \ldots N_n) = \log_a N_1 + \log_a N_2 + \cdots + \log_a N_n.$$

Hence

$$\log_a \frac{M_1 M_2 \ldots M_m}{N_1 N_2 \ldots N_n} = \log_a (M_1 M_2 \ldots M_m) - \log_a (N_1 N_2 \ldots N_n) \qquad \text{Th. } 6(2)$$

$$= (\log_a M_1 + \log_a M_2 + \cdots + \log_a M_m)$$
$$- (\log_a N_1 + \log_a N_2 + \cdots + \log_a N_n),$$

from which our result follows.

10. $\log_6 6 < \log_6 18 < \log_6 36$ by Th. 7. Hence $1 < \log_6 18 < 2$. Similarly, $\log_3 9 < \log_3 11$, so that $2 < \log_3 11$. Hence (c) is true, and (a) and (b) false.

12. (a) 3.71×10^4; log $37100 = 4.5694$; characteristic is 4, mantissa .5694.
    (c) 2.1×10^{-3}; log $.0021 = .3222 - 3$; characteristic is -3, mantissa .3222.
    (e) 9.0×10^{-1}; log $.9 = .9542 - 1$; characteristic is -1, mantissa .9542.
    (g) 8.32×10; log $83.2 = 1.9201$; characteristic is 1, mantissa .9201.
    (i) 7.62×10^3; log $7620 = 3.8820$; characteristic is 3, mantissa .8820.
    (k) 6.12×10^{-1}; log $.612 = .7868 - 1$; characteristic is -1, mantissa .7868.

13. (a) Characteristic is 0, mantissa .4082. Antilog .4082 = 2.56.
    (c) Characteristic is 2, mantissa .4082. Antilog 2.4082 = 256.
    (e) Characteristic is -1, mantissa .4082. Antilog $(.4082 - 1) = .256$.
    (g) Characteristic is -1, mantissa .4082. Antilog $(-.5918) = .256$.
    (i) Characteristic is -3, mantissa .4082. Antilog $(-2.5918) = .00256$.
    (k) Characteristic is -3, mantissa .4082. Antilog $(17.4082 - 20) = .00256$.
    (m) Characteristic is -2, mantissa .5918. Antilog $(-1.4082) = .0391$.
    (o) Characteristic is -4, mantissa .9900. Antilog $(26.990 - 30) = .000977$.

14. (a) 85.7; (c) .526; (e) 6.16; (g) 7.12×10^{-21}; (i) 2.31; (k) 1.13.

15. (a) $\log 6 = \log 2 \cdot 3 = \log 2 + \log 3 = .3010 + .4771 = .7781$.
    (c) $\log .009 = \log (3^2 \cdot 10^{-3}) = \log 3^2 + \log 10^{-3} = 2 \log 3 + \log 10^{-3} = 2(.4771) - 3 = .9542 - 3$.
    (e) $\log 2.7 = \log 3^3 \cdot 10^{-1} = 3 \log 3 + \log 10^{-1} = 1.4313 - 1 = .4313$.
    (g) $\log 200 = \log 2 \cdot 10^2 = \log 2 + \log 10^2 = 2.3010$.

16. (a) 3.47; (c) $-.460$; (e) 2.30.

CHAPTER 16

1. (a) $\dfrac{\sqrt{2}}{2}, \dfrac{\sqrt{2}}{2}, 1, 1, \sqrt{2}, \sqrt{2}$.
   (c) 0, 1, 0, undefined, 1, undefined.
   (e) $\dfrac{2}{\sqrt{13}}, -\dfrac{3}{\sqrt{13}}, -\dfrac{2}{3}, -\dfrac{3}{2}, -\dfrac{\sqrt{13}}{3}, \dfrac{\sqrt{13}}{2}$.
   (g) 1, 0, undefined, 0, undefined, 1.
   (i) -1, 0, undefined, 0, undefined, -1.
   (k) 0, -1, 0, undefined, -1, undefined.

2. (a) $\dfrac{1}{2}, \dfrac{\sqrt{3}}{2}, \dfrac{1}{\sqrt{3}}, \sqrt{3}, \dfrac{2}{\sqrt{3}}, 2$.
   (d) $-\dfrac{\sqrt{3}}{2}, -\dfrac{1}{2}, \sqrt{3}, \dfrac{\sqrt{3}}{3}, -2, -\dfrac{2}{3}\sqrt{3}$.
   (g) 0, -1, 0, undefined, -1, undefined.
   (j) 0, 1, 0, undefined, 1, undefined.

(m) $\dfrac{1}{2}, -\dfrac{\sqrt{3}}{2}, -\dfrac{1}{\sqrt{3}}, -\sqrt{3}, -\dfrac{2}{\sqrt{3}}, 2.$

(p) $-\dfrac{\sqrt{3}}{2}, \dfrac{1}{2}, -\sqrt{3}, -\dfrac{\sqrt{3}}{3}, 2, -\dfrac{2}{3}\sqrt{3}.$

3. (a) 0, 1, 0, undefined, 1, undefined.

(d) $\dfrac{\sqrt{3}}{2}, \dfrac{1}{2}, \sqrt{3}, \dfrac{1}{\sqrt{3}}, 2, \dfrac{2}{\sqrt{3}}.$

(g) $\dfrac{\sqrt{2}}{2}, -\dfrac{\sqrt{2}}{2}, -1, -1, -\sqrt{2}, \sqrt{2}.$

(j) $-\dfrac{1}{2}, -\dfrac{\sqrt{3}}{2}, \dfrac{1}{\sqrt{3}}, \sqrt{3}, -\dfrac{2}{\sqrt{3}}, -2.$

(m) -1, 0, undefined, 0, undefined, -1.

(p) $-\dfrac{1}{2}, \dfrac{\sqrt{3}}{2}, -\dfrac{\sqrt{3}}{3}, -\sqrt{3}, \dfrac{2\sqrt{3}}{3}, -2.$

4. (a) $2\pi, 4\pi, 6\pi, 8\pi; -2\pi, -4\pi, -6\pi, -8\pi.$

(g) $\dfrac{11\pi}{4}, \dfrac{19\pi}{4}, \dfrac{27\pi}{4}, \dfrac{35\pi}{4}; -\dfrac{5\pi}{4}, -\dfrac{13\pi}{4}, -\dfrac{21\pi}{4}, -\dfrac{29\pi}{4}.$

(m) $\dfrac{7\pi}{2}, \dfrac{11\pi}{2}, \dfrac{15\pi}{2}, \dfrac{19\pi}{2}; -\dfrac{\pi}{2}, -\dfrac{5\pi}{2}, -\dfrac{9\pi}{2}, -\dfrac{13\pi}{2}.$

5. (a) $\dfrac{1}{\sqrt{10}}, \dfrac{3}{\sqrt{10}}, \dfrac{1}{3}, 3, \dfrac{\sqrt{10}}{3}, \sqrt{10}.$

(d) $\dfrac{3}{5}, \dfrac{4}{5}, \dfrac{3}{4}, \dfrac{4}{3}, \dfrac{5}{4}, \dfrac{5}{3}.$

(g) $\dfrac{1}{2}, -\dfrac{\sqrt{3}}{2}, -\dfrac{1}{\sqrt{3}}, -\sqrt{3}, -\dfrac{2}{\sqrt{3}}, 2.$

6. No.

7. (a) Same as Exercise 3(p).

(d) $\dfrac{1}{2}, \dfrac{\sqrt{3}}{2}, \dfrac{1}{\sqrt{3}}, \sqrt{3}, \dfrac{2}{\sqrt{3}}, 2.$

(g) $-\dfrac{1}{\sqrt{2}}, \dfrac{1}{\sqrt{2}}, -1, -1, \sqrt{2}, -\sqrt{2}.$

(j) Same as (a).

12. (a) $\dfrac{2}{3}, -\dfrac{\sqrt{5}}{3}, -\dfrac{2}{\sqrt{5}}, -\dfrac{\sqrt{5}}{2}, -\dfrac{3}{\sqrt{5}}, \dfrac{3}{2}.$

(c) $-\dfrac{1}{\sqrt{10}}, \dfrac{3}{\sqrt{10}}, -\dfrac{1}{3}, -3, \dfrac{\sqrt{10}}{3}, -\sqrt{10}.$

(e) $-\dfrac{\sqrt{3}}{2}, \dfrac{1}{2}, -\sqrt{3}, -\dfrac{1}{\sqrt{3}}, 2, -\dfrac{2}{\sqrt{3}}.$

16. (a) $\varnothing$; (b) $\varnothing$.

17. Domain of $\sin x$ is R; range is $[-1,1]$, i.e. $\{y \in R/-1 \leqq y \leqq 1\}$. Domain of $\tan x$ is $\left\{x \in R/x \neq \dfrac{\pi}{2}, -\dfrac{\pi}{2}, \dfrac{3\pi}{2}, -\dfrac{3\pi}{2}, \dfrac{5\pi}{2}, -\dfrac{5\pi}{2}, \ldots\right\}$; range is R.

Domain of $\sec x$ is same as that of $\tan x$; range is $\{y \in R/y \geqq 1 \text{ or } y \leqq -1\}$.

19. (a) .6428; (c) $-.3249$; (e) -1.008; (g) $-.5446$; (j) .1405; (l) 1.006.

20. (a) 205; (c) 261; (e) 67.

21. (a) $a = 30, b = 56.4, c = 63.9, A = 28°, B = 62°, C = 90°.$

(d) $a = 11, b = 11.4, c = 16, A = 44°, B = 46°, C = 90°.$

(g) $a = 33.4, b = 97, c = 102.6, A = 19°, B = 71°, C = 90°.$

22. (a) $a = 11, b = 10.5, c = 8.8, A = 69°, B = 63°, C = 48°.$

(d) $a = 3, b = 4, c = 5, A = 37°, B = 53°, C = 90°.$

(g) The unique solution is $a = 6.0, b = 11, c = 15, A = 20°, B = 38°, C = 122°.$

(j) $a = 10, b = 28.5, c = 20, A = 13°, B = 141°, C = 26°.$

29. (a) $2 - \sqrt{3}$; (c) $-\dfrac{1}{2}\sqrt{2+\sqrt{3}}$; (e) $\dfrac{2}{\sqrt{2+\sqrt{2}}}$; (g) $\dfrac{1}{2}\sqrt{2-\sqrt{3}}$.

31. (a) $\frac{24}{25}$; (c) $\frac{24}{7}$; (e) $-\sqrt{10}$.

32. (a) $\dfrac{1-\sin x}{2\cos x + \sin 2x}$

$\quad = \dfrac{1-\sin x}{2\cos x + 2\sin x \cos x}$ \qquad (19)

$\quad = \dfrac{1-\sin x}{2\cos x(1+\sin x)}$

$\quad = \dfrac{\sec x(1-\sin x)}{2(1+\sin x)}$ \qquad (2)

$\quad = \dfrac{\sec x - \dfrac{1}{\cos x}\cdot \sin x}{2(1+\sin x)}$ \qquad (2)

$\quad = \dfrac{\sec x - \tan x}{2(1+\sin x)}$ \qquad (4)

(d) $\tan^2 \dfrac{x}{2}$

$\quad = \dfrac{\sin^2 \dfrac{x}{2}}{\cos^2 \dfrac{x}{2}}$ \qquad (4)

$\quad = \dfrac{1-\cos x}{1+\cos x}$ \qquad (22) and (23)

$\quad = \dfrac{(1-\cos x)\cdot \dfrac{1}{\cos x}}{(1+\cos x)\cdot \dfrac{1}{\cos x}}$

$\quad = \dfrac{\sec x - 1}{\sec x + 1}$ \qquad (2)

(h) $\dfrac{1}{1+\sec x} - \dfrac{1}{1-\sec x}$

$\quad = \dfrac{1-\sec x - 1 - \sec x}{1 - \sec^2 x}$

$\quad = \dfrac{-2\sec x}{-\tan^2 x}$ \qquad (7)

$\quad = \dfrac{2\cos x}{\sin^2 x}$ \qquad (2) and (4)

$\quad = \dfrac{2\sin x \cos x}{\sin^3 x}$

$\quad = \sin 2x \, \csc^3 x$ \qquad (19) and (1)

33. (a) $\left\{\dfrac{\pi}{3} \pm 4k\pi, \dfrac{5\pi}{3} \pm 4k\pi\right\}_{k=0,1,2,\ldots}$

(c) $\left\{\dfrac{\pi}{6} \pm 2k\pi, \dfrac{11\pi}{6} \pm 2k\pi\right\}_{k=0,1,2,\ldots}$

(e) $\{\pm k\pi\}_{k=0,1,2,\ldots}$

34. (a) $\left\{\dfrac{\pi}{2} \pm k\pi, \dfrac{\pi}{6} \pm 2k\pi, \dfrac{5\pi}{6} \pm 2k\pi\right\}_{k=0,1,2,\ldots}$

(c) $\left\{\dfrac{\pi}{2} \pm 2k\pi, \dfrac{7\pi}{6} \pm 2k\pi, \dfrac{11\pi}{6} \pm 2k\pi\right\}_{k=0,1,2,\ldots}$

(f) $\left\{\dfrac{\pi}{12} \pm \dfrac{2k\pi}{3}, \dfrac{5\pi}{12} \pm \dfrac{2k\pi}{3}\right\}_{k=0,1,2,\ldots}$

35. (b) $\left\{3, \dfrac{\pi}{8}, \dfrac{3\pi}{8}, \dfrac{5\pi}{8}, \dfrac{7\pi}{8}, \dfrac{9\pi}{8}, \dfrac{11\pi}{8}, \dfrac{13\pi}{8}, \dfrac{15\pi}{8}\right\}.$

(d) $\left\{0, \dfrac{\pi}{6}, \dfrac{\pi}{3}, \dfrac{\pi}{2}, \dfrac{2\pi}{3}, \dfrac{5\pi}{6}, \pi, \dfrac{7\pi}{6}, \dfrac{4\pi}{3}, \dfrac{3\pi}{2}, \dfrac{5\pi}{3}, \dfrac{11\pi}{6}, 2\pi\right\}.$

38. (a) $\dfrac{\pi}{2}$; (c) $\dfrac{\sqrt{3}}{2}$; (e) $-\dfrac{\pi}{2}$; (g) 0; (i) $-\dfrac{5\pi}{6}$; (k) undefined.

39. $\frac{13}{9}$.

index